New Concise Maths 5

George Humphrey

Gill & Macmillan

In memory of my grandmother,
Jane Montgomery

Gill & Macmillan
Hume Avenue
Park West
Dublin 12
with associated companies throughout the world
www.gillmacmillan.ie

© George Humphrey 2004

ISBN-13: 978 07171 3344 4

The paper used in this book is made from the wood pulp of managed forests. For every tree felled, at least one tree is planted, thereby renewing natural resources.

CONTENTS

Revision Exercises

Each revision exercise concentrates on a particular question on the examination paper and is divided into three parts: Part A's, RA, Part B's, RB and Part C's, RC.

PREFACE

New Concise Maths 5 is the second of two volumes covering Leaving Certificate Mathematics, Higher Level.

Full analysis of the pattern and level of difficulty of the examination questions was taken into account. The book reflects the author's experience that students learn better from worked examples than from abstract discussion of principles. The emphasis is on clear and concise presentation of the material. Long explanations are avoided, on the principle that these are best left to the teacher. A comprehensive range of worked examples, with helpful comments highlighted in colour, is included. The author has very carefully graded the exercises through testing them in class. Concepts are built up in a logical manner. Each chapter is broken down into short, manageable sections. A numbered, step-by-step approach, highlighted in colour, is used to help with problem solving. Key terms are defined simply, and highlighted. This has been found to save valuable class time, otherwise spent copying notes from the board. The proofs required are in their own separate chapter.

The last part of the book is a 'revision book' within the book. This provides a comprehensive range of graded questions. Each revision exercise contains an extensive selection of 'part a', 'part b' and 'part c' type questions similar in standard to the Leaving Certificate questions. Tackling these exercises is an excellent form of revision.

I would especially like to thank my colleague, Geoffrey Reeves, St Andrew's College, Booterstown, who helped when mathematical clarification was required. I would also like to thank Brendan Guildea, Skerries Community College, Skerries; Patricia Wrynn, Coláiste Chiaráin, Leixlip; Margaret Klotz, Alexandra College, Milltown; Gary Ryan, St Munchin's College, Limerick and Pat Butler, Coláiste na Trócaire, Rathkeale, Limerick, for making many constructive suggestions, which are included in the final text. Thanks must also go to Geraldine Finucane, School of Mathematics, Trinity College, Dublin, who took on the task of checking my answers and making many valuable contributions.

Finally, I wish to express my thanks to the staff of Gill & Macmillan and to Patrick Roberts in particular, for their advice, guidance and untiring assistance.

George Humphrey
St Andrew's College
Dublin

COORDINATE GEOMETRY OF THE CIRCLE

Equation of a Circle, Centre (0, 0) and Radius r

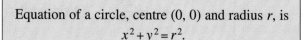

A circle is a set of points (a locus) which are equidistant from a fixed point called the '**centre**'.
The distance from the centre to any point on the circle is called the '**radius**'.
On the right is a circle with centre (0, 0), radius r and (x, y) any point on the circle.
Distance between (0, 0) and (x, y) equals the radius, r.

$$\therefore \quad \sqrt{(x-0)^2 + (y-0)^2} = r \qquad \text{(distance formula)}$$

$$\sqrt{x^2 + y^2} = r$$

$$x^2 + y^2 = r^2 \qquad \text{(square both sides)}$$

Hence, $x^2 + y^2 = r^2$ is said to be the equation of the circle.

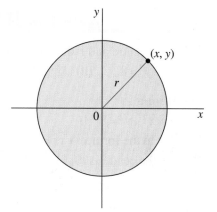

> Equation of a circle, centre (0, 0) and radius r, is
> $$x^2 + y^2 = r^2.$$

Two quantities are needed to find the equation of a circle:

> **1.** Centre   **2.** Radius
> If the centre is (0, 0), the equation of the circle will be of the form $x^2 + y^2 = r^2$.

Example ▼

Find the equations of the following circles, each of centre (0, 0):
(i) K_1, which has radius $\sqrt{13}$ **(ii)** K_2, which contains the point $(4, -1)$.

Solution:

(i) Centre is (0, 0), therefore K_1 is of the form $x^2 + y^2 = r^2$.

$$x^2 + y^2 = r^2$$
$$x^2 + y^2 = (\sqrt{13})^2 \qquad \text{(put in } \sqrt{13} \text{ for } r)$$
$$x^2 + y^2 = 13$$

Thus, the equation of the circle K_1 is $x^2 + y^2 = 13$.

(ii) Centre is $(0, 0)$, therefore K_2 is of the form $x^2 + y^2 = r^2$.

$$x^2 + y^2 = r^2$$
$$(4)^2 + (-1)^2 = r^2 \qquad \text{(put in 4 for } x \text{ and } -1 \text{ for } y)$$
$$16 + 1 = r^2$$
$$17 = r^2$$

Thus, the equation of the circle K_2 is $x^2 + y^2 = 17$.

Alternatively, the radius is the distance from $(0, 0)$ to $(4, -1)$.
Using the distance formula, the radius

$$= \sqrt{(4-0)^2 + (-1-0)^2} = \sqrt{16+1} = \sqrt{17}.$$

Thus, the equation of the circle K_2 is $x^2 + y^2 = 17$. $\qquad ((\sqrt{17})^2 = 17)$

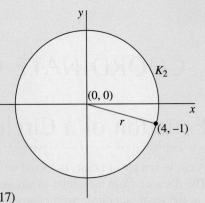

Example ▼

Find the centre and radius of each of the following circles:

(i) $x^2 + y^2 = 8$ **(ii)** $4x^2 + 4y^2 = 25$.

Solution:

(i) $x^2 + y^2 = 8$

In the form $x^2 + y^2 = r^2$

∴ the centre is $(0, 0)$

$$r^2 = 8$$
$$r = \sqrt{8} = 2\sqrt{2}$$

∴ the radius is $\sqrt{8}$ or $2\sqrt{2}$.

(ii) $4x^2 + 4y^2 = 25$

$$x^2 + y^2 = \frac{25}{4} \qquad \text{(divide each side by 4)}$$

In the form $x^2 + y^2 = r^2$

∴ the centre is $(0, 0)$

$$r^2 = \frac{25}{4}$$

$$r^2 = \sqrt{\frac{25}{4}} = \frac{\sqrt{25}}{\sqrt{4}} = \frac{5}{2}$$

∴ the radius is $\dfrac{5}{2}$.

Example ▼

In the diagram, the line L: $3x + y - 10 = 0$ is
a tangent to the circle C.
Find the equation of the circle C.

Solution:

As the centre of the circle C is $(0, 0)$, its equation
is of the form $x^2 + y^2 = r^2$.
We need to find the value of r.
The radius, $r =$ perpendicular distance from the
centre $(0, 0)$ to the line $3x + y - 10 = 0$.
Using the formula for the perpendicular distance
from a point to a line:

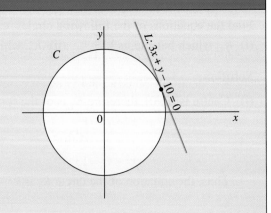

$$d = \frac{|ax_1 + by_1 + c|}{\sqrt{a^2 + b^2}}$$

$$r = \frac{|3(0) + 1(0) - 10|}{\sqrt{3^2 + 1^2}} \qquad (a = 3,\ b = 1,\ c = -10,\ x_1 = 0,\ y_1 = 0)$$

$$r = \frac{|-10|}{\sqrt{10}} = \frac{10}{\sqrt{10}} = \sqrt{10}$$

Thus, the equation of the circle C is $x^2 + y^2 = 10$. $\qquad ((\sqrt{10})^2 = 10)$

Exercise 1.1 ▼

In Q1 to Q14, find the equation of each of the following circles of centre $(0, 0)$ and:

1. radius 2   **2.** radius 4   **3.** radius 5   **4.** radius $\sqrt{13}$

5. radius $\sqrt{2}$ **6.** radius $2\sqrt{3}$ **7.** radius $\dfrac{1}{2}$ **8.** radius $\dfrac{\sqrt{10}}{2}$

9. containing the point $(3, 4)$ **10.** containing the point $(-5, 12)$

11. containing the point $(-1, -5)$ **12.** containing the point $(0, -3)$

13. containing the point $(-1, 1)$ **14.** containing the point $(2, -5)$

Write down the radius length of each of the following circles:

15. $x^2 + y^2 = 16$ **16.** $x^2 + y^2 = 100$ **17.** $x^2 + y^2 = 1$

18. $x^2 + y^2 = 13$ **19.** $x^2 + y^2 = 5$ **20.** $x^2 + y^2 = 29$

21. $4x^2 + 4y^2 = 9$ **22.** $9x^2 + 9y^2 = 25$ **23.** $16x^2 + 16y^2 = 1$

24. Find the equation of the circle which has the line segment joining $(3, -4)$ to $(-3, 4)$ as diameter.

25. $a(6, 1)$ and $b(-6, -1)$ are two points. Find the equation of the circle with $[ab]$ as diameter.

26. $(6, -3)$ is an extremity of a diameter of the circle $x^2 + y^2 = 45$. What are the coordinates of the other extremity of the same diameter?

27. What is the area of the circle $x^2 + y^2 = 40$? Leave your answer in terms of π.

Find the equation of each of the following circles, centre $(0, 0)$ and having as a tangent the line:

28. $2x + y + 5 = 0$ **29.** $4x + y - 17 = 0$ **30.** $x + 3y + 10 = 0$

31. $5x - y - 26 = 0$ **32.** $x - y - 4 = 0$ **33.** $x + 2y - 10 = 0$

Equation of a Circle, Centre (h, k) and Radius r

On the right is a circle with centre (h, k) and radius r, and (x, y) is any point on the circle.

Distance between (h, k) and (x, y) equals the radius, r.

$\therefore \sqrt{(x-h)^2 + (y-k)^2} = r$ (distance formula)

$(x-h)^2 + (y-k)^2 = r^2$ (square both sides)

Hence, $(x-h)^2 + (y-k)^2 = r^2$ is said to be the equation of the circle.

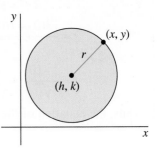

> The equation of a circle, centre (h, k) and radius r, is
> $$(x-h)^2 + (y-k)^2 = r^2.$$

Two quantities are needed to find the equation of a circle:

> **1.** Centre, (h, k) **2.** Radius, r
>
> Then use the formula $(x-h)^2 + (y-k)^2 = r^2$.

Note: If $(h, k) = (0, 0)$, the equation $(x-h)^2 + (y-k)^2 = r^2$ reduces to $x^2 + y^2 = r^2$.

Example ▼

(i) Find the centre and radius of the circle $(x-2)^2 + (y+5)^2 = 9$.

(ii) Find the equation of the circle, centre $(1, -4)$ and radius $\sqrt{13}$.

Solution:

(i) $(x-2)^2 + (y+5)^2 = 9$

Compare exactly to:

$(x-h)^2 + (y-k)^2 = r^2$

$\downarrow$ $\downarrow$ $\downarrow$

$(x-2)^2 + (y+5)^2 = 9$

$\therefore h = 2, \quad k = -5, \quad r = 3$

Thus, centre $= (2, -5)$ and radius $= 3$.

(ii) Centre $= (1, -4)$, radius $= \sqrt{13}$

$h = 1, \quad k = -4, \quad r = \sqrt{13}$

$(x-h)^2 + (y-k)^2 = r^2$

$(x-1)^2 + (y+4)^2 = (\sqrt{13})^2$

$(x-1)^2 + (y+4)^2 = 13$

Example ▼

Find the equation of the circle which has the line segment from $a(-4, 3)$ to $b(2, 1)$ as diameter.

Solution:

The **centre** and **radius** are needed.

The diagram on the right illustrates the situation.

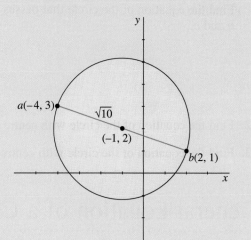

Centre:

The centre is the midpoint of $[ab]$.

$$\text{Centre} = \left(\frac{-4+2}{2}, \frac{3+1}{2}\right) = \left(\frac{-2}{2}, \frac{4}{2}\right) = (-1, 2).$$

Radius:

The radius, r, is the distance from the centre $(-1, 2)$ to $(-4, 3)$ or $(2, 1)$.

Distance from $(-1, 2)$ to $(-4, 3)$

$$r = \sqrt{(-4+1)^2 + (3-2)^2} = \sqrt{(-3)^2 + (1)^2} = \sqrt{9+1} = \sqrt{10}$$

$$h = -1, \qquad k = 2, \qquad r = 10$$

Equation:　　$(x-h)^2 + (y-k)^2 = r^2$

$$(x+1)^2 + (y-2)^2 = (\sqrt{10})^2$$

$$(x+1)^2 + (y-2)^2 = 10$$

Exercise 1.2 ▼

Find the equation of each of the following circles, with given centre and radius:

1. Centre $(2, 3)$ and radius 4

2. Centre $(-2, -4)$ and radius 5

3. Centre $(-3, 2)$ and radius $\sqrt{10}$

4. Centre $(-3, 0)$ and radius $\sqrt{13}$

5. Centre $(0, 2)$ and radius $\frac{3}{2}$

6. Centre $(-1, 7)$ and radius $\frac{5}{2}$

Find the equation of the circle with:

7. centre $(1, 2)$ and containing the point $(2, 5)$

8. centre $(2, -1)$ and containing the point $(6, 4)$

9. centre $(-1, 3)$ and containing the point $(0, 5)$

10. centre $(-1, -3)$ and containing the point $(3, 0)$

11. centre $(-2, -5)$ and containing the point $(1, 1)$

12. centre $(4, -2)$ and containing the point $(0, 0)$

Find the coordinates of the centre and the length of the radius of each of the following circles:

13. $(x-2)^2 + (y-3)^2 = 25$

14. $(x+1)^2 + (y-2)^2 = 9$

15. $(x-5)^2 + (y+7)^2 = 1$

16. $(x+5)^2 + (y+7)^2 = 4$

17. $x^2 + (y-5)^2 = 10$

18. $(x-4)^2 + y^2 = 13$

19. $a(5, 2)$ and $b(1, 4)$ are two points. Find the equation of the circle with $[ab]$ as diameter.

20. The end points of a diameter of a circle are $p(2, 4)$ and $q(-4, 0)$. Find the equation of the circle.

21. $a(-1, 5)$, $b(5, 13)$ and $c(-2, 12)$ are the vertices of triangle abc.
Show that the triangle is right angled at c.
Find the equation of the circle that passes through the coordinates a, b and c.

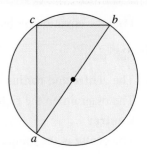

22. Find the equation of the circle with centre $(1, 3)$ and having the line $3x + 4y + 10 = 0$ as a tangent.

23. Find the equation of the circle with centre $(-6, 1)$ and having the line $x + y + 1 = 0$ as a tangent.

General Equation of a Circle

The general equation of a circle is written as:

$$x^2 + y^2 + 2gx + 2fy + c = 0$$

When the equation of a circle is given in this form, we use the following method to find its centre and radius.

---

1. Make sure every term is on the left-hand side and the coefficients of x^2 and y^2 are equal to 1.

2. Centre $= (-g, -f) = (-\frac{1}{2}$ coefficient of x, $-\frac{1}{2}$ coefficient of $y)$

3. Radius $= \sqrt{g^2 + f^2 - c}$ (provided $g^2 + f^2 - c > 0$)

Notes: 1. The equation is of the second degree (highest power is 2).
2. The coefficients of x^2 and y^2 are equal.
3. There is no xy term.

Example ▼

Find the centre and radius of each of the circles:

(i) $x^2 + y^2 - 4x + 2y - 11 = 0$ **(ii)** $x^2 + y^2 - 8y + 3 = 0$.

Solution:

(i) $x^2 + y^2 - 4x + 2y - 11 = 0$

Centre $= (2, -1)$

Radius $= \sqrt{(2)^2 + (-1)^2 + 11}$

$= \sqrt{4 + 1 + 11} = \sqrt{16} = 4$

(ii) $x^2 + y^2 + 0x - 8y + 3 = 0$ (put in $0x$)

Centre $= (0, 4)$

Radius $= \sqrt{(0)^2 + (4)^2 - 3}$

$= \sqrt{0 + 16 - 3} = \sqrt{13}$

Example ▼

The equation of a circle with radius 5 is $x^2 + y^2 - 6x + 4ky + 20 = 0$, $\quad k \in \mathbf{Z}$.

(i) Find the centre of the circle and the radius length in terms of k.

(ii) Find the values of k.

Solution:

(i) $x^2 + y^2 - 6x + 4ky + 20 = 0$

Centre $= (3, -2k)$

Radius $= \sqrt{(3)^2 + (-2k)^2 - 20}$

$\qquad = \sqrt{9 + 4k^2 - 20}$

$\qquad = \sqrt{4k^2 - 11}$

(ii) Given: Radius $= 5$

$\therefore \quad \sqrt{4k^2 - 11} = 5$

$4k^2 - 11 = 25$

$4k^2 = 36$

$k^2 = 9$

$k = \pm\sqrt{9} = \pm 3$

Points inside, on or outside a circle

Method 1:

To find whether a point is inside, on or outside a circle, calculate the distance from the centre to the point and compare this distance with the radius. Three cases arise:

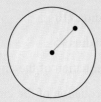

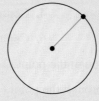

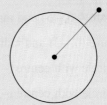

Inside	**On**	**Outside**
1. Distance from the centre, to the point is **less** than the radius	**2.** Distance from the centre to the point is **equal** to the radius	**3.** Distance from the centre to the point is **greater** than the radius
$\therefore$ point inside the circle.	$\therefore$ point on the circle.	$\therefore$ point outside the circle.

Method 2:

The equation of a circle can be of the form:
$$x^2 + y^2 = r^2$$
$$(x - h)^2 + (y - k)^2 = r^2$$
$$x^2 + y^2 + 2gx + 2fy + c = 0$$

If the coordinates of a point satisfy the equation of a circle, then the point is **on** the circle. Otherwise, the point is either **inside** or **outside** the circle. By substituting the coordinates into the equation of the circle, one of the following situations can arise:

1. LHS < RHS: the point is **inside** the circle.

2. LHS = RHS: the point is **on** the circle.

3. LHS > RHS: the point is **outside** the circle.

Determine whether the points $(-3, -2)$, $(5, -1)$, and $(-2, 1)$ are inside, on or outside the circle $x^2 + y^2 - 2x + 8y - 8 = 0$.

Solution: (using Method 2)

$$x^2 + y^2 - 2x + 8y - 8 = 0$$

substitute $(-3, -2)$: $(-3)^2 + (-2)^2 - 2(-3) + 8(-2) - 8 = 9 + 4 + 6 - 16 - 8 = -5 < 0$

∴ $(-3, -2)$ is **inside** the circle.

substitute $(5, -1)$: $(5)^2 + (-1)^2 - 2(5) + 8(-1) - 8 = 25 + 1 - 10 - 8 - 8 = 0$

∴ $(5, -1)$ is **on** the circle.

substitute $(-2, 1)$: $(-2)^2 + (1)^2 - 2(-2) + 8(1) - 8 = 4 + 1 + 4 + 8 - 8 = 9 > 0$

∴ $(-2, 1)$ is **outside** the circle.

Exercise 1.3 ▼

Find the equation of each of the following circles with given centre and radius, writing your answers in the form $x^2 + y^2 + 2gx + 2fy + c = 0$:

1. Centre $(1, 2)$ and radius 3

2. Centre $(-2, 3)$ radius 5

3. Centre $(-3, -5)$ and radius $\sqrt{17}$

4. Centre $(2, 0)$ and radius $\sqrt{10}$

5. Centre $(0, -3)$ and radius $2\sqrt{2}$

6. Centre $(\frac{1}{2}, -\frac{1}{2})$ and radius $\sqrt{5}$

7. A circle with centre $(-1, 3)$ passes through the point $(1, -1)$. Find the equation of the circle.

8. A circle with centre $(-3, -2)$ passes through the point $(1, 1)$. Find the equation of the circle.

Find the centre and radius length of each of the following circles:

9. $x^2 + y^2 - 6x - 8y - 11 = 0$

10. $x^2 + y^2 - 4x - 6y - 3 = 0$

11. $x^2 + y^2 - 2x + 4y - 4 = 0$

12. $x^2 + y^2 - 10x + 2y + 6 = 0$

13. $x^2 + y^2 + 8x - 6y = 0$

14. $x^2 + y^2 + 2x - 10y - 10 = 0$

15. $x^2 + y^2 + 6x - 7 = 0$

16. $x^2 + y^2 = 4y + 4$

17. $2x^2 + 2y^2 - 2x - 6y - 13 = 0$

18. $9x^2 + 9y^2 - 6x + 54y + 46 = 0$

19. $(x - 2)(x + 4) + (y - 1)(y - 5) = 3$

20. $(x - 3)(x + 3) + (y + 2)(y + 6) = 0$

In each of the following, determine whether the given point is inside, on or outside the given circle:

21. $(3, -2)$; $x^2 + y^2 = 13$

22. $(5, 3)$; $(x - 3)^2 + (y - 2)^2 = 20$

23. $(4, -1)$; $x^2 + y^2 + 6x - 4y - 3 = 0$

24. $(-1, 5)$; $x^2 + y^2 + 4x - 6y - 25 = 0$

25. $(4, 3)$; $x^2 + y^2 - 4x + 2y - 15 = 0$

26. $(-1, 4)$; $x^2 + y^2 + 10x - 6y + 21 = 0$

27. The circle C has the equation $x^2 + y^2 + 2x + 2y - 32 = 0$.
The point $(-4, k)$ lies on C. Find the two real values of k.

28. The circle S has the equation $(x-4)^2+(y-2)^2=13$.
The point $(p, 0)$ lies on S. Find the two real values of p.

29. The equation of a circle with radius length 4 is $x^2+y^2-6x+2y+k=0, \quad k \in \mathbf{Z}$.
Find the value of k.

30. The equation of a circle with radius length 6 is $x^2+y^2-2kx+4y-7=0, \quad k \in \mathbf{Z}$.
(i) Find the centre of the circle and the radius length in terms of k.
(ii) Find the values of k.

31. The equation of a circle with radius length 5 is $x^2+y^2+2x-4ky+12=0, \quad k \in \mathbf{Z}$.
Find the values of k.

32. $a(k, 1)$ and $b(-7, -k)$ are end points of a diameter of circle C.
If the centre of C is $(2, -5)$, find the value of k, and the radius length of C.

33. $a(-2, 0)$ and $b(6, 2)$ are points of a circle of centre $c(2k, k)$.
(i) Express in terms of k: **(a)** $|ac|^2$ **(b)** $|bc|^2$.
(ii) Find the value of k and the equation of the circle.

Proving that a Locus is a Circle

If the locus of a set of points is of the form $x^2+y^2+2gx+2fy+c=0$, then the locus is a circle and we can find its centre and radius.

| *Example* ▼ |

$p(1, 2)$, $q(1, -1)$ and $r(x, y)$ are points such that $2|qr|=|pr|$.
Show that $r(x, y)$ is on a circle. Find the centre and the length of the radius of the circle.

Solution:

$p(1, 2)$, $q(1, -1)$, $r(x, y)$

$|qr|=\sqrt{(x-1)^2+(y+1)^2}=\sqrt{x^2-2x+1+y^2+2y+1}=\sqrt{x^2+y^2-2x+2y+2}$

$|pr|=\sqrt{(x-1)^2+(y-2)^2}=\sqrt{x^2-2x+1+y^2-4y+4}=\sqrt{x^2+y^2-2x-4y+5}$

Given: $\qquad\qquad 2|qr|=|pr|$

$2\sqrt{x^2+y^2-2x+2y+2}=\sqrt{x^2+y^2-2x-4y+5}$

$(2\sqrt{x^2+y^2-2x+2y+2})^2=(\sqrt{x^2+y^2-2x-4y+5})^2$ $\qquad$ (square both sides)

$4(x^2+y^2-2x+2y+2)=(x^2+y^2-2x-4y+5)$

$4x^2+4y^2-8x+8y+8=x^2+y^2-2x-4y+5$

$3x^2+3y^2-6x+12y+3=0$

$x^2+y^2-2x+4y+1=0$ $\qquad$ (divide both sides by 3)

This is the equation of a circle, as it is written in the form $x^2+y^2+2gx+2fy+c=0$.

$x^2+y^2-2x+4y+1=0$

Centre $=(1, -2)$ $\qquad$ Radius $=\sqrt{(1)^2+(-2)^2-1}=\sqrt{1+4-1}=\sqrt{4}=2$

1. $p(1, 5)$, $q(-5, -3)$ and $r(x, y)$ are three points such that $pr \perp rq$.
      (i) Find, in terms of x and y, the slope of: **(a)** pr **(b)** rq.
      (ii) Hence, or otherwise, find the equation of the circle that passes through p, q and r.

2. $p(1, 0)$, $q(4, 0)$ and $r(x, y)$ are points such that $2|qr| = |pr|$.
      Show that $r(x, y)$ is on a circle. Find the centre and the radius length of the circle.

3. $a(0, -1)$, $b(6, -1)$ and $c(x, y)$ are points such that $2|ac| = |bc|$.
      Show that the locus of c is a circle. Find the centre and radius length of the circle.

4. $a(2, -1)$, $b(10, 15)$ are two points. A point $c(x, y)$ moves such that $9|ac|^2 + 288 = |bc|^2$.
      Show that the locus of c is a circle. Find the centre and radius length of the circle.

Parametric Equations of a Circle

A circle may be defined by a pair of parametric equations. On our course we shall meet two types of parametric equation.

1. Trigonometric Parametric Equations

$$x = h \pm r \cos \theta, \qquad y = k \pm r \sin \theta$$
are the parametric equations of the circle
$$(x - h)^2 + (y - k)^2 = r^2.$$

We use the fact that $\cos^2 \theta + \sin^2 \theta = 1$.

Example ▼

The parametric equations of a circle are $x = -2 + \sqrt{3} \cos \theta$, $y = 1 + \sqrt{3} \sin \theta$.
Find its Cartesian equation. Find its centre and radius length.

Solution:

$$x = -2 + \sqrt{3} \cos \theta \qquad\qquad y = 1 + \sqrt{3} \sin \theta$$
$$x + 2 = \sqrt{3} \cos \theta \qquad\qquad y - 1 = \sqrt{3} \sin \theta$$
$$\frac{x+2}{\sqrt{3}} = \cos \theta \qquad\qquad \frac{y-1}{\sqrt{3}} = \sin \theta$$

Thus, $\left(\dfrac{x+2}{\sqrt{3}}\right)^2 + \left(\dfrac{y-1}{\sqrt{3}}\right)^2 = \cos^2 \theta + \sin^2 \theta$

$\dfrac{(x+2)^2}{3} + \dfrac{(y-1)^2}{3} = 1$ $(\cos^2 \theta + \sin^2 \theta = 1)$

$(x+2)^2 + (y-1)^2 = 3$ (multiply both sides by 3)

This is the Cartesian equation of the circle, as it is in the form $(x - h)^2 + (y - k)^2 = r^2$.
The centre is $(-2, 1)$ and the radius is $\sqrt{3}$.

2. Algebraic Parametric Equations

We can also represent the equation of a circle with x and y written as algebraic functions of the parameter t. For example:

$$x = \frac{6t}{1+t^2}, \quad y = \frac{3(1-t^2)}{1+t^2}$$

Example ▼

The parametric equations of a circle are $\quad x = \dfrac{1-t^2}{1+t^2}, \quad y = \dfrac{2t}{1+t^2}.$

Find its Cartesian equation. Write your answer in the form $x^2 + y^2 = r^2$.

Solution:

$$x^2 + y^2 = \left(\frac{1-t^2}{1+t^2}\right)^2 + \left(\frac{2t}{1+t^2}\right)^2$$

$$= \frac{1 - 2t^2 + t^4}{1 + 2t^2 + t^4} + \frac{4t^2}{1 + 2t^2 + t^4}$$

$$= \frac{1 + 2t^2 + t^4}{1 + 2t^2 + t^4} \qquad \text{(same base)}$$

$$= 1$$

Thus, the Cartesian equation is $x^2 + y^2 = 1$.

Exercise 1.5 ▼

Find the Cartesian equation of each of the following circles:

1. $x = 2 \cos \theta$, $y = 2 \sin \theta$ **2.** $x = \sqrt{3} \cos \theta$, $y = \sqrt{3} \sin \theta$

3. $x = 1 + \cos \theta$, $y = 2 + \sin \theta$ **4.** $x = -3 + \cos \theta$, $y = 4 + \sin \theta$

5. $x = 3 + 2 \cos \theta$, $y = 5 + 2 \sin \theta$ **6.** $x = -2 + 3 \cos \theta$, $y = -5 + 3 \sin \theta$

7. $x = 1 + 4 \cos \theta$, $y = -2 + 4 \sin \theta$ **8.** $x = -5 + 5 \cos \theta$, $y = 3 + 5 \sin \theta$

9. $x = 3 + \sqrt{2} \cos \theta$, $y = -5 + \sqrt{2} \sin \theta$ **10.** $x = -2 + \sqrt{8} \cos \theta$, $y = 1 + \sqrt{8} \sin \theta$

11. $x = -3 + \frac{1}{2} \cos \theta$, $y = -1 + \frac{1}{2} \sin \theta$ **12.** $x = 3 + \frac{\sqrt{3}}{2} \cos \theta$, $y = -2 + \frac{\sqrt{3}}{2} \sin \theta$

Find the Cartesian equation of each of the following circles, writing your answers in the form $x^2 + y^2 = k$. Find the radius in each case.

13. $x = t, \quad y = \pm \sqrt{9 - t^2}$ **14.** $x = t - 1, \quad y = \pm \sqrt{3 + 2t - t^2}$

15. $x = 2t, \quad y = \pm \sqrt{16 - 4t^2}$ **16.** $x = \dfrac{2(1 - t^2)}{1 + t^2}, \quad y = \dfrac{4t}{1 + t^2}$

17. $x = \dfrac{t^2 - 4}{t^2 + 4}, \quad y = \dfrac{4t}{t^2 + 4}$ **18.** $x = \dfrac{6t}{t^2 + 1}, \quad y = \dfrac{3(t^2 - 1)}{t^2 + 1}$

19. The parametric equations of a circle are $\quad x = a + 3a \cos\theta, \quad y = -2a + 3a \sin\theta, \quad a \in \mathbf{R}$.
Find its Cartesian equation. Find, in terms of a, its centre and radius length.

20. The parametric equations of a circle are $\quad x = \dfrac{a(1-t^2)}{1+t^2}, \quad y = \dfrac{2at}{1+t^2}, \quad a \in \mathbf{R}$.

Find its Cartesian equation and its radius length.

Sometimes we have to deal with algebraic parametric equations where the centre of the circle is not $(0, 0)$. Consider the next example:

Example ▼

Show that the parametric equations $\quad x = \dfrac{2t}{1+t^2}, \quad y = \dfrac{3+t^2}{1+t^2}, \quad t \in \mathbf{R}$, represent a circle, and find its centre and its radius length.

Solution:

$$x = \frac{2t}{1+t^2} \qquad\qquad y = \frac{3+t^2}{1+t^2},$$

(Begin with y as it contains t^2, but not t)

$$y = \frac{3+t^2}{1+t^2}, \qquad\qquad x = \frac{2t}{1+t^2}$$

$$y + t^2 y = 3 + t^2 \qquad\qquad x^2 = \frac{4t^2}{(1+t^2)^2} \qquad\qquad \left(\begin{array}{c}\text{square} \\ \text{both sides}\end{array}\right)$$

$$t^2 y - t^2 = 3 - y \qquad\qquad x^2 = \frac{4\left(\dfrac{3-y}{y-1}\right)}{\left(1 + \dfrac{3-y}{y-1}\right)^2} \qquad\qquad \left(\begin{array}{c}\text{put in} \\ t^2 = \dfrac{3-y}{y-1}\end{array}\right)$$

$$t^2(y-1) = 3 - y \qquad\qquad x^2 = \frac{4\left(\dfrac{3-y}{y-1}\right)}{\left(\dfrac{y-1+3-y}{y-1}\right)^2}$$

$$t^2 = \frac{3-y}{y-1} \qquad\qquad x^2 = \frac{4\left(\dfrac{3-y}{y-1}\right)}{\left(\dfrac{2}{y-1}\right)^2}$$

$$x^2 = \frac{4\left(\dfrac{3-y}{y-1}\right)}{\dfrac{4}{(y-1)^2}}$$

$$x^2 = 4\left(\frac{3-y}{y-1}\right) \cdot \frac{(y-1)^2}{4}$$

$$x^2 = (3-y)(y-1)$$
$$x^2 = 3y - 3 - y^2 + y$$
$$x^2 + y^2 - 4y + 3 = 0$$

This is the equation of a circle, as it is in the form $x^2 + y^2 + 2gx + 2fy + c = 0$.

Its centre is $(0, 2)$ and its radius length $= \sqrt{0^2 + 2^2 - 3} = \sqrt{4-3} = \sqrt{1} = 1$.

Find the Cartesian equation of each of the following circles. Find its centre and radius length in each case:

21. $x = \dfrac{3+t^2}{1+t^2}$, $y = \dfrac{2t}{1+t^2}$

22. $x = \dfrac{1}{1+4t^2}$, $y = \dfrac{2t}{1+4t^2}$

Intersection of a Line and a Circle

To find the points where a line and a circle meet, the '**method of substitution**' between their equations is used.

The method involves the following three steps:

1. Get x or y on its own from the equation of the line.
   (Look carefully and select the variable which will make the working easier.)
2. Substitute for this same variable into the equation of the circle and solve the resultant quadratic equation.
3. Substitute **separately** the value(s) obtained in step 2 into the linear equation in step 1 to find the corresponding value(s) of the other variable.

Note: If there is only **one point of intersection** between a line and a circle, then the line is a **tangent** to the circle.

Example ▼

The equation of a circle is $x^2 + y^2 + 4x - 2y - 5 = 0$.

The line $x - 2y - 1 = 0$ intersects the circle at the points p and q.
Find the coordinates of p and the coordinates of q.

Solution:

1. Get x or y on its own from the line:
   $$x - 2y - 1 = 0$$
   $$x = (2y + 1) \qquad\qquad [x \text{ on its own}]$$

2. Substitute $(2y+1)$ for x into the equation of the circle:
$$x^2 + y^2 + 4x - 2y - 5 = 0$$

$$(2y+1)^2 + y^2 + 4(2y+1) - 2y - 5 = 0 \qquad \text{[put in } (2y+1) \text{ for } x\text{]}$$
$$4y^2 + 4y + 1 + y^2 + 8y + 4 - 2y - 5 = 0$$
$$5y^2 + 10y = 0$$
$$y^2 + 2y = 0 \qquad \text{[divide both sides by 5]}$$
$$y(y+2) = 0$$
$$\therefore \quad y = 0 \quad \text{or} \quad y = -2$$

3. Substitute, separately, $y = 0$ and $y = -2$ into the equation of the line in step 1 to find the x coordinates:

$y = 0$	$y = -2$
$x = 2y + 1$	$x = 2y + 1$
$x = 2(0) + 1$	$x = 2(-2) + 1$
$x = 1$	$x = -4 + 1 = -3$
point is $(1, 0)$	point is $(-3, -2)$

Thus, the coordinates of the points of intersection are
$p(-3, -2)$ and $q(1, 0)$.
The diagram on the right illustrates the situation.

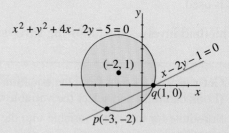

| *Example* ▼ |

L: $3x - y + 8 = 0$ is a line and C: $x^2 + y^2 - 4x - 8y + 10 = 0$ is a circle.
Verify that L is a tangent to C and find the point of contact.

Solution:

As we need the point of contact, we use an algebraic approach.

1. Get x or y on its own from the line:
$$3x - y + 8 = 0$$
$$-y = -3x - 8$$
$$y = (3x + 8) \qquad \text{[} y \text{ on its own]}$$

2. Substitute $(3x + 8)$ for y into the equation of the circle:
$$x^2 + y^2 - 4x - 8y + 10 = 0$$

$$x^2 + (3x+8)^2 - 4x - 8(3x+8) + 10 = 0 \qquad \text{[put in } (3x+8) \text{ for } y\text{]}$$

$$x^2 + 9x^2 + 48x + 64 - 4x - 24x - 64 + 10 = 0$$
$$10x^2 + 20x + 10 = 0$$
$$x^2 + 2x + 1 = 0$$
$$(x + 1)(x + 1) = 0$$
$$\therefore \quad x = -1 \quad \text{or} \quad x = -1$$

3. Substitute $x = -1$ into the equation of the line in step 1 to find the y coordinate:

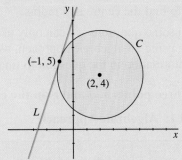

$x = -1$
$y = 3x + 8$
$y = 3(-1) + 8$
$y = -3 + 8$
$y = 5$
point of contact $(-1, 5)$

Since there is only **one point of contact**, $(-1, 5)$, between L and C, the line L is a tangent to the circle C.
The diagram on the right illustrates the situation.

Note: To show that a given line is a tangent to a circle, it is sufficient to show that the perpendicular distance from the centre of the circle to the line is equal to the radius. However, to find the point of contact an algebraic method (as shown above) is required.

Exercise 1.6 ▼

Find the coordinates of the point, or points, of intersection of the given line and circle. State whether or not the line is a tangent to the circle.

1. $x - 3y = 0; \quad x^2 + y^2 = 10$

2. $x + 2y - 5 = 0; \quad x^2 + y^2 = 10$

3. $x + 3y - 5 = 0; \quad x^2 + y^2 = 5$

4. $4x - y - 17 = 0; \quad x^2 + y^2 = 17$

5. $x - y - 1 = 0; \quad x^2 + y^2 - 2x - 2y + 1 = 0$

6. $x - 2y - 1 = 0; \quad x^2 + y^2 + 2x - 8y - 8 = 0$

7. $2x - y + 8 = 0; \quad x^2 + y^2 + 4x + 2y = 0$

8. $x - 3y + 5 = 0; \quad x^2 + y^2 - 6x - 2y - 15 = 0$

9. $x + 2y - 7 = 0; \quad x^2 + y^2 - 2x + 4y - 15 = 0$

10. $x - 4y - 6 = 0; \quad x^2 + y^2 + 6x - 4y - 4 = 0$

11. $5x - 3y - 17 = 0; \quad x^2 + y^2 = 17$

12. $3x + 2y - 20 = 0; \quad x^2 + y^2 - 6x + 2y - 3 = 0$

13. The line $x - 2y - 3 = 0$ intersects the circle $(x - 2)^2 + (y + 3)^2 = 25$ at p and q. Calculate $|pq|$.

14. The equation of a circle is $(x - 2)^2 + (y - 1)^2 = 10$.
The line $x - 3y + 1 = 0$ intersects the circle at points a and b.
(i) Find the coordinates of a and the coordinates of b.
(ii) Investigate whether $[ab]$ is a diameter of the circle.

Finding the Equation of a Circle

If the centre and radius are given, or can be found, then using the formula
$$(x-h)^2+(y-k)^2=r^2$$
is the preferred method for finding the equation of a circle.

However, for many questions it is difficult to find the centre and radius.

In these questions we have to use an algebraic approach, or rely on our knowledge of the geometry of a circle to find the centre and radius.

Note: In some questions we can only use an algebraic approach.
In using an algebraic approach, we let the circle be $x^2+y^2+2gx+2fy+c=0$ and use the information in the question to find g, f and c.

Given three points p, q and r on the circle

Method 1: Algebraic Approach

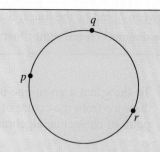

Let the equation of the circle be $x^2+y^2+2gx+2fy+c=0$.
1. Substitute each point into this equation.
2. This gives three equations in three unknowns: g, f and c.
3. Solve these equations for g, f and c.
4. Put these values back into the equation.

Method 2: Geometric Approach

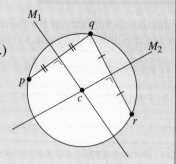

1. Find the equations of the perpendicular bisectors M_1 and M_2 of the chords $[pq]$ and $[qr]$, respectively.
   (The perpendicular bisector of a chord passes through the centre.)
2. The centre of the circle is $c = M_1 \cap M_2$.
   (Solve the equations of M_1 and M_2 simultaneously.)
3. The radius is the distance from c to p, q or r.
4. Use the formula: $(x-h)^2+(y-k)^2=r^2$.
   Note: There is only one circle that contains the points p, q and r.

Example ▼

Points $p(-4, 2)$, $q(-2, 6)$ and $r(4, 8)$ are on a circle S. Find the equation of S.

Solution:

Method 1: Algebraic approach
We are given three points on the circumference of the circle.
Let the equation of the circle be $x^2+y^2+2gx+2fy+c=0$.

We need the values of g, f and c.

(−4, 2) on the circle: $(-4)^2+(2)^2+2g(-4)+2f(2)+c=0 \Rightarrow 8g-4f-c=20$ ①

(−2, 6) on the circle: $(-2)^2+(6)^2+2g(-2)+2f(6)+c=0 \Rightarrow 4g-12f-c=40$ ②

(4, 8) on the circle: $(4)^2+(8)^2+2g(4)+2f(8)+c=0 \Rightarrow 8g+16f+c=-80$ ③

We now solve between the simultaneous equations ①, ② and ③.

Eliminate c from two different pairs of equations:

$$8g-4f-c = 20 \quad ①$$
$$\underline{8g+16f+c=-80 \quad ③}$$
$$16g+12f \quad =-60 \quad \text{(add)}$$
$$4g+3f \quad =-15 \quad ④$$

$$4g-12f-c=40 \quad ②$$
$$\underline{8g+16f+c=-80 \quad ③}$$
$$12g+4f \quad =-40 \quad \text{(add)}$$
$$3g+f \quad =-10 \quad ⑤$$

Now solve between ④ and ⑤ to find the values of g and f.

$$4g+3f=-15 \quad ④$$
$$\underline{-9g-3f=30 \quad ⑤\times-3}$$
$$-5g=15$$
$$5g=-15$$
$$g=-3$$

$$3g+f=-10 \quad ⑤$$
$$3(-3)+f=-10$$
$$-9+f=-10$$
$$f=-1$$

Put $g=-3$ into ④ or ⑤.

Put $g=-3$ and $f=-1$ into ①, ② or ③ to find the value of c.

$$8g-4f-c=20 \quad ①$$
$$8(-3)-4(-1)-c=20$$
$$-24+4-c=20$$
$$-20-c=20$$
$$-c=40$$
$$c=-40$$

The equation of the circle S is:

$$x^2+y^2+2gx+2fy+c=0$$
$$x^2+y^2+2(-3)x+2(-1)y-40=0$$

(put in $g=-3$, $f=-1$ and $c=-40$)

$$x^2+y^2-6x-2y-40=0$$

Method 2: Geometric approach

The diagram on the right represents the situation.

We find the equation of M_1, the perpendicular bisector of $[pq]$, and then the equation of M_2, the perpendicular bisector of $[qr]$. The centre, c, is the point of intersection of M_1 and M_2. The radius is $|pc|$, $|qc|$ or $|rc|$.

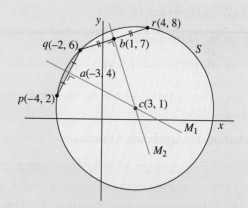

Slope of $pq = \dfrac{6-2}{-2+4} = \dfrac{4}{2} = 2$

$\therefore$ Slope of $M_1 = -\dfrac{1}{2}$

Slope of $qr = \dfrac{8-6}{4+2} = \dfrac{2}{6} = \dfrac{1}{3}$

$\therefore$ Slope of $M_2 = -3$

$$\text{Midpoint of } [pq] = a\left(\frac{-4-2}{2}, \frac{2+6}{2}\right)$$

$$= a(-3, 4)$$

Equation of M_1 [slope $= -\frac{1}{2}$, point $= (-3, 4)$]:

$$(y - y_1) = m(x - x_1)$$

$$(y - 4) = -\tfrac{1}{2}(x + 3)$$

$$2y - 8 = -x - 3$$

$$M_1: x + 2y - 5 = 0$$

$$\text{Midpoint of } [qr] = b\left(\frac{-2+4}{2}, \frac{6+8}{2}\right)$$

$$= b(1, 7)$$

Equation of M_2 [slope $= -3$, point $= (1, 7)$]:

$$(y - y_1) = m(x - x_1)$$

$$(y - 7) = -3(x - 1)$$

$$y - 7 = -3x + 3$$

$$M_2: 3x + y - 10 = 0$$

Solving the simultaneous equations M_1 and M_2 gives the centre of the circle $c(3, 1)$.
The radius of S is $|pc|$ or $|qc|$ or $|rc|$.
$p(-4, 2)$, $c(3, 1)$.

$$|pc| = \sqrt{(x_2 - x_1)^2 + (y_2 - y_1)^2} = \sqrt{(3+4)^2 + (1-2)^2} = \sqrt{(7)^2 + (-1)^2} = \sqrt{49 + 1} = \sqrt{50}$$

Thus, the centre of S is $(3, 1)$ and the radius length is $\sqrt{50}$.

Equation of S:

$$(x - h)^2 + (y - k)^2 = r^2$$

$$(x - 3)^2 + (y - 1)^2 = (\sqrt{50})^2$$

$$(x - 3)^2 + (y - 1)^2 = 50$$

or

$$x^2 + y^2 - 6x - 2y - 40 = 0$$

Exercise 1.7 ▼

Find the equation of the circle which contains the points:

1. $(2, 2)$, $(6, 4)$ and $(4, 8)$

2. $(-3, -4)$, $(-5, 2)$ and $(1, 8)$

3. $(0, 0)$, $(4, 0)$ and $(6, -2)$

4. $(10, -2)$, $(-2, 4)$ and $(2, -2)$

5. $(4, 1)$, $(-2, 1)$ and $(2, 3)$

6. $(-2, -1)$, $(0, -5)$ and $(1, -2)$

Given two points p and q on the circle and the equation of a line, L, containing the centre $c(-g, -f)$

Method 1: Algebraic Approach

Let the equation of the circle be $x^2 + y^2 + 2gx + 2fy + c = 0$.
1. Substitute each point into this equation.
2. Substitute $(-g, -f)$ into the equation of the given line.
3. This gives three equations in three unknowns: g, f and c.
4. Solve these equations for g, f and c.
5. Put these values back into the equation.

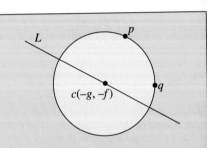

Method 2: Geometric Approach

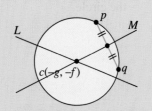

1. Find the equation of M, the perpendicular bisector of $[pq]$.
2. Solve the simultaneous equations L and M to find the centre.
3. Find the radius r, the distance from the centre c to p or q.
4. Use the formula $(x-h)^2+(y-k)^2=r^2$.

Example ▼

Find the equation of the circle that contains the points $(-4, 1)$, and $(0, 3)$ and whose centre lies on the line $x-2y+11=0$.

Solution:

Method 1: Algebraic approach

We are given two points on the circumference and the equation of a line containing the centre.

Let the equation of the circle be $x^2+y^2+2gx+2fy+c=0$.

$(-4, 1)$ on the circle: $(-4)^2+(1)^2+2g(-4)+2f(1)+c=0 \Rightarrow 8g-2f-c=17$ ①

$(0, 3)$ on the circle: $(0)^2+(3)^2+2g(0)+2f(3)+c=0 \Rightarrow \qquad 6f+c=-9$ ②

The centre $(-g, -f)$ is on the line $x-2y+11=0$.

Thus, $(-g)-2(-f)+11=0 \Rightarrow g-2f=11$ ③

Eliminate c from ① and ②:

$$\begin{array}{l} 8g-2f-c=17 \quad ① \\ \underline{\quad\ \ 6f+c=-9 \quad ②} \\ \quad 8g+4f=8 \quad \text{(add)} \\ \quad 2g+f=2 \quad ④ \end{array}$$

Now solve between ③ and ④ to find the values of g and f:

$$\begin{array}{l} \quad g-2f=11 \quad ③ \\ \underline{4g+2f=4 \quad ④\times 2} \\ \quad 5g=15 \\ \quad\ \ g=3 \end{array} \qquad\qquad \begin{array}{l} 2g+f=2 \quad ④ \\ 2(3)+f=2 \\ 6+f=2 \\ f=-4 \end{array}$$

Put $g=3$ into ③ or ④.

Put $g=3$ and $f=-4$ into ① or ② to find the value of c.

$$\begin{array}{l} \quad 6f+c=-9 \quad ② \\ 6(-4)+c=-9 \\ -24+c=-9 \\ \quad\ \ c=15 \end{array} \qquad \begin{array}{l} \text{The equation of the circle is:} \\ \qquad x^2+y^2+2gx+2fy+c=0 \\ x^2+y^2+2(3)x+2(-4)y+15=0 \\ \qquad (\text{put in } g=3, f=-4 \text{ and } c=15) \\ \qquad x^2+y^2+6x-8y+15=0 \end{array}$$

Note: Using Method 2, the geometric approach gives the same result.

Note: A line perpendicular to a tangent at the point of tangency passes through (contains) the centre of the circle.

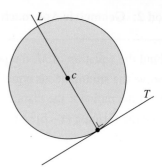

Given two points, *p* and *q*, on the circle and the equation of the tangent at one of these points

Method:

1. Find the equation of *L*, the line perpendicular to the tangent *T* passing through the given point of contact. This line will contain the centre *c*.

2. Now we have two points on the circumference of the circle and the equation of a line that contains the centre of the circle.

3. Use an algebraic approach (as in the previous example) or use a geometric approach.

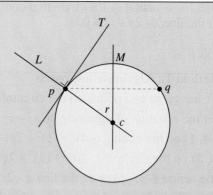

Example ▼

Find the equation of the circle which passes through the points $a(-3, -2)$, and $b(0, -1)$ and where the line $2x - y + 4 = 0$ is a tangent at the point $a(-3, -2)$.

Solution:

Method 2: Geometric approach

The diagram on the right represents the situation. Find the equation of *L*, the line that is perpendicular to the tangent at the point of contact $a(-3, -2)$. This line contains the centre. Find the equation of *M*, the perpendicular bisector of [*ab*]. The centre *c* is the point of intersection of *L* and *M*. The radius is $|ac|$ or $|bc|$.

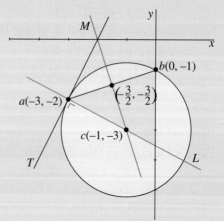

The slope of the tangent

$2x - y + 4 = 0$ is 2

∴ the slope of *L* is $-\frac{1}{2}$.

Slope of $ab = \dfrac{-1+2}{0+3} = \dfrac{1}{3}$

∴ slope of $M = -3$.

Midpoint of $[ab] = \left(\dfrac{-3+0}{2}, \dfrac{-2-1}{2}\right) = (-\tfrac{3}{2}, -\tfrac{3}{2})$

Equation of L [slope $=-\frac{1}{2}$, point $=(-3,-2)$]:

$$(y-y_1)=m(x-x_1)$$

$$(y+2)=-\tfrac{1}{2}(x+3)$$

$$2y+4=-x-3$$

L: $x+2y+7=0$

Equation of M [slope $=-3$, point $=(-\frac{3}{2},-\frac{3}{2})$]:

$$(y-y_1)=m(x-x_1)$$

$$(y+\tfrac{3}{2})=-3(x+\tfrac{3}{2})$$

$$y+\tfrac{3}{2}=-3x-\tfrac{9}{2}$$

M: $3x+y+6=0$

Solving the simultaneous equations L and M gives the centre of the circle $c(-1,-3)$.

Radius:

The radius is $|ac|$ or $|bc|$.

$a(-3,-2)$, $c(-1,-3)$

$$|ac|=\sqrt{(x_2-x_1)^2+(y_2-y_1)^2}=\sqrt{(-1+3)^2+(-3+2)^2}=\sqrt{(2)^2+(-1)^2}=\sqrt{4+1}=\sqrt{5}$$

Thus, the centre of the circle is $(-1,-3)$ and the radius is $\sqrt{5}$.

Equation of the circle:

$$(x-h)^2+(y-k)^2=r^2$$

$$(x+1)^2+(y+3)^2=(\sqrt{5})^2$$

$$(x+1)^2+(y+3)^2=5$$

or

$$x^2+y^2+2x+6y+5=0$$

Note: After finding the equation of the line L, we could have let the equation of the circle be $x^2+y^2+2gx+2fy+c=0$ and used an algebraic approach to find the values of g, f and c.

Exercise 1.8 ▼

1. Find the equation of the circle that contains the points (3, 6) and (5, 4) and whose centre lies on the line $x+y-5=0$.

2. Find the equation of the circle that contains the points (2, –6) and (4, –2) and whose centre lies on the line $2x+y+4=0$.

3. The circle $x^2+y^2+2gx+2fy+c=0$ passes through the points (4, 3) and (6, –3). The line $3x-y-7=0$ passes through the centre of the circle. Find the real numbers g, f and c.

4. Find the equation of the circle which passes through the points (–1, 6) and (–3, 0) and where the line $2x+y+6=0$ is a tangent at the point (–3, 0).

5. Find the equation of the circle which passes through the points (–1, 3) and (3, 5) and where the line $3x-y+6=0$ is a tangent at the point (–1, 3).

6. The circle $x^2+y^2+2gx+2fy+c=0$ passes through the points (4, 1) and (6, –5). The line $2x-y-17=0$ is a tangent to the circle at (6, –5). Find the real numbers g, f and c.

Given the length of the radius

In some questions we are given the radius. When this happens we let $\sqrt{g^2+f^2-c}$ be equal to the given radius. Then we square both sides. We then have to use the other information in the question to form two other equations in g, f and c, and substitute these into the first equation to get a quadratic equation in one variable. In general, we end up with two circles that satisfy the given conditions.

Example ▼

A circle of radius length $\sqrt{20}$ contains the point $(-1, 3)$. Its centre lies on the line $x+y=0$. Find the equations of the two circles that satisfy these conditions.

Solution:

Let the circle be $x^2+y^2+2gx+2fy+c=0$.

Given:

Radius $=\sqrt{20}$

$\therefore$ $\sqrt{g^2+f^2-c}=\sqrt{20}$

$g^2+f^2-c=20$ ①

The centre $(-g, -f)$ is on the line $x+y=0$

$\therefore$ $-g-f=0$

$g+f=0$ ③

Contains the point $(-1, 3)$

$\therefore$ $(-1)^2+(3)^2+2g(-1)+2f(3)+c=0$

$2g-6f-c=10$ ②

We now have to solve between the simultaneous equations ①, ② and ③.

$g+f=0$ ③

$f=-g$

Put $f=-g$ into ② and express c in terms of g only.

$2g-6f-c=10$ ②

$2g-6(-g)-c=10$ $(f=-g)$

$2g+6g-c=10$

$8g-c=10$

$c=8g-10$

We now have f and c in terms of g and we put these into ①:

$g^2+f^2-c=20$ ①

$g^2+(-g)^2-(8g-10)=20$ (put in $f=-g$ and $c=8g-10$)

$g^2+g^2-8g+10=20$

$2g^2-8g-10=0$

$g^2-4g-5=0$

$(g+1)(g-5)=0$

$g=-1$ or $g=5$

Case 1

$g=-1$

$f=-g=-(-1)=1$

$c=8g-10=8(-1)-10=-8-10=-18$

$x^2+y^2+2(-1)x+2(1)y-18=0$

$x^2+y^2-2x+2y-18=0$

Case 2

$g=5$

$f=-g=-5$

$c=8g-10=8(5)-10=40-10=30$

$x^2+y^2+2(5)x+2(-5)y+30=0$

$x^2+y^2+10x-10y+30=0$

These are the equations of the two circles that satisfy the given conditions.

. A circle of radius length 2 contains the point $(1, -1)$. Its centre lies on the line $x = 1$.
Find the equations of the two circles that satisfy these conditions.

. A circle of radius length $\sqrt{20}$ contains the point $(0, 2)$. Its centre lies on the line $x + y = 0$.
Find the equations of the two circles that satisfy these conditions.

. A circle of radius length $\sqrt{10}$ contains the point $(-5, 0)$. Its centre lies on the line $x + 2y = 0$.
Find the equations of the two circles that satisfy these conditions.

. A line L: $2x - 3y = 0$ is a tangent to a circle C at the point $(0, 0)$.
If the radius of C is $\sqrt{13}$, find two possible equations for C.

. Two circles intersect at the points $p(1, 3)$ and $q(3, -1)$.
The line M joining the centres of the circles is the perpendicular bisector of $[pq]$.
(i)   Find the coordinates of r, the midpoint of $[pq]$ and the equation of the line M.
(ii) If the distance from the centre of each circle to r is $\sqrt{20}$, find the radius length of each circle.
(iii) Find the equation of each circle.

. A circle of radius length $\sqrt{10}$ contains the points $(1, 2)$ and $(-1, 4)$.
Find the equations of the two circles that satisfy these conditions.

Equation of a Tangent I

Equation of a tangent to a circle at a given point

A tangent is perpendicular to the radius that joins the centre
of a circle to the point of tangency.

This fact is used to find the slope of the tangent.

In the diagram on the right, the radius, R, is perpendicular
to the tangent, T, at the point of tangency, p.

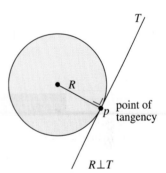

The equation of a tangent to a circle at a given point is found with the following steps:

Step 1: Find the slope of the radius to the point of tangency.

Step 2: Turn this slope upside down and change its sign.
This gives the slope of the tangent.

Step 3: Use the coordinates of the point of contact and the slope of the tangent at this point in
the formula:

$$(y - y_1) = m(x - x_1).$$

This gives the equation of the tangent.

A diagram is often very useful.

Find the equation of the tangent to the circle $x^2 + y^2 - 4x + 6y - 12 = 0$ at the point $(5, -7)$ on the circle.

Solution:

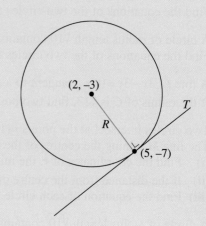

$x^2 + y^2 - 4x + 6y - 12 = 0$

The centre of the circle is $(2, -3)$.

Slope of $R = \dfrac{-7 + 3}{5 - 2} = -\dfrac{4}{3}$

$\therefore$ Slope of $T = \dfrac{3}{4}$

Equation of T: $(y - y_1) = m(x - x_1)$

$(y + 7) = \tfrac{3}{4}(x - 5)$

$4y + 28 = 3x - 15$

$3x - 4y - 43 = 0$

Proving that a line is a tangent to a circle

A line is a tangent to a circle if the perpendicular distance from the centre of the circle to the line is equal to the radius.

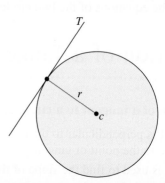

Prove that the line $2x - 3y - 27 = 0$ is a tangent to the circle $x^2 + y^2 - 8x + 4y + 7 = 0$.

Solution:

(As we do not need the point of contact, we use the perpendicular distance method.)

$x^2 + y^2 - 8x + 4y + 7 = 0$

Centre $= (4, -2)$

Radius $= \sqrt{(4)^2 + (-2)^2 - 7} = \sqrt{16 + 4 - 7} = \sqrt{13}$

Perpendicular distance from the centre $(4, -2)$ to the line $2x - 3y - 27 = 0$ is given by:

$d = \dfrac{|ax_1 + by_1 + c|}{\sqrt{a^2 + b^2}} = \dfrac{|2(4) - 3(-2) - 27|}{\sqrt{(2)^2 + (-3)^2}} = \dfrac{|8 + 6 - 27|}{\sqrt{4 + 9}} = \dfrac{|-13|}{\sqrt{13}} = \dfrac{13}{\sqrt{13}} = \sqrt{13}$

As the perpendicular distance from the centre of the circle to the line is equal to the radius, the line is a tangent to the circle.

Length of a tangent to a circle from a point outside the circle

The **length of a tangent** from a point outside a circle
is the distance, d, from the point outside the circle to the
point of tangency.

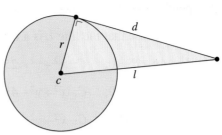

Method:

> 1. Find the centre, c, and radius length, r, of the circle.
> 2. Find the distance, l, between the centre and the point outside the circle.
> 3. Use Pythagoras's theorem to find d, i.e. $l^2 = r^2 + d^2$.

Example ▼

A tangent from the point $p(3, 0)$ touches the circle $x^2 + y^2 + 2x - 4y + 1 = 0$ at q.
Find $|pq|$.

(rough diagram)

Solution:

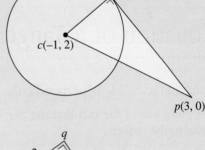

$x^2 + y^2 + 2x - 4y + 1 = 0$

centre $= c(-1, 2)$

radius $= \sqrt{(-1)^2 + (2)^2 - 1} = \sqrt{1 + 4 - 1} = \sqrt{4} = 2$

Distance from the centre $c(-1, 2)$ to the point $p(3, 0)$

$= |pc| = \sqrt{(3+1)^2 + (0-2)^2} = \sqrt{4^2 + (-2)^2} = \sqrt{16 + 4} = \sqrt{20}$

Using Pythagoras's theorem:

$|pq|^2 + |qc|^2 = |pc|^2$

$|pq|^2 + 2^2 = (\sqrt{20})^2$

$|pq|^2 + 4 = 20$

$|pq|^2 = 16$

$|pq| = 4$

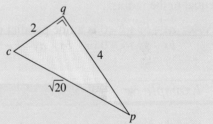

Exercise 1.10 ▼

Find the equation of the tangent to the given circle at the given point:

1. $x^2 + y^2 = 10$;　(3, 1)
2. $x^2 + y^2 = 29$;　$(-2, 5)$
3. $x^2 + y^2 = 50$;　$(-7, -1)$
4. $4x^2 + 4y^2 = 25$;　$\left(2, -\frac{3}{2}\right)$
5. $(x-4)^2 + (y+3)^2 = 10$;　$(7, -4)$
6. $x^2 + (y-5)^2 = 29$;　(5, 3)
7. $x^2 + y^2 + 6x + 2y - 3 = 0$;　$(-5, -4)$
8. $x^2 + y^2 - 2x + 4y - 15 = 0$;　(3, 2)
9. $x^2 + y^2 - 4x - 6y - 12 = 0$;　(5, 7)
10. $x^2 + y^2 - 8x + 14 = 0$;　$(3, -1)$

11. Show that the tangents to the circle $x^2+y^2-2x-2y-3=0$ at the points $(3, 2)$ and $(2, -1)$ are perpendicular to each other.

Verify in each case that the line L is a tangent to the circle C:

12. L: $3x+4y-25=0$; C: $x^2+y^2=25$

13. L: $4x+3y-14=0$; C: $x^2+y^2-4x+6y+4=0$

14. L: $x-4y+31=0$; C: $x^2+y^2+4x-6y-4=0$

15. L: $x-6y-9=0$; C: $x^2+y^2-4x-10y-8=0$

16. L: $x-2y+10=0$; C: $x^2+y^2+8x-16y+60=0$

In each of the following, find the distance from the given point outside the circle to the point of tangency:

17. $(11, -2)$; $x^2+y^2=25$

18. $(0, -4)$; $x^2+y^2-6x-8y+16=0$

19. $(3, 1)$; $x^2+y^2+4x-2y-4=0$

20. $(2, 5)$; $x^2+y^2-2x+4y-20=0$

21. $(0, 0)$; $x^2+y^2-8x-6y+20=0$

22. $(5, 0)$; $x^2+y^2+6x-5=0$

23. The length of the tangent from the point $(3, 2)$ to the circle $x^2+y^2-8x-8y+k=0$ is 2. Find the value of k.

Equation of a Tangent 2

Tangents parallel, or perpendicular, to a given line

We make use of the fact that the perpendicular distance from the centre of a circle to the tangent is equal to the radius.

Note: $ax+by+k=0$ is a line parallel to the line $ax+by+c=0$.
       $bx-ay+k=0$ or $-bx+ay+k=0$ is a line perpendicular to the line $ax+by+c=0$.

Example ▼

Find the equations of the tangents to the circle $x^2+y^2-6x-2y-15=0$ which are parallel to the line $3x+4y+20=0$.

Solution:

$x^2+y^2-6x-2y-15=0$

Centre $=(3, 1)$

Radius $=\sqrt{(3)^2+(1)^2+15}=\sqrt{9+1+15}=\sqrt{25}=5$

Let the equation of the tangent parallel to $3x+4y+20=0$ be $3x+4y+k=0$.

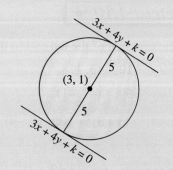

As $3x + 4y + k = 0$ is a tangent to the circle, the perpendicular distance from the centre of the circle, $(3, 1)$, to this line is equal to the radius, 5.

$$\therefore \quad \frac{|3(3) + 4(1) + k|}{\sqrt{(3)^2 + (4)^2}} = 5$$

$$\frac{|9 + 4 + k|}{\sqrt{9 + 16}} = 5$$

$$\frac{|13 + k|}{5} = 5$$

$$|13 + k| = 25$$

$$\therefore \quad 13 + k = 25 \qquad \text{or} \qquad 13 + k = -25$$

$$k = 12 \qquad \text{or} \qquad k = -38$$

Thus, the tangents are $3x + 4y + 12 = 0$ and $3x + 4y - 38 = 0$.

Equations of tangents from a point outside a circle

From a point outside a circle, two tangents can be drawn to touch the circle.

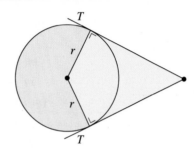

Method for finding the two equations of tangents from a point (x_1, y_1) outside a circle:

1. Find the centre and radius length of the circle (a rough diagram can help).
2. Let the equation be $(y - y_1) = m(x - x_1)$ and write the equation in the form $ax + by + c = 0$.
3. Let the perpendicular distance from the centre of the circle to the tangent equal the radius.
4. Solve this equation to find two values of m.
5. Using these two values of m and the point (x_1, y_1), write down the equations of the two tangents.

Example ▼

Find the equations of the two tangents from the point $(5, -3)$ to the circle $x^2 + y^2 - 4x + 8y + 12 = 0$.

Solution:

$x^2 + y^2 - 4x + 8y + 120$

Centre $= (2, -4)$

Radius $= \sqrt{(2)^2 + (-4)^2 - 12} = \sqrt{4 + 16 - 12} = \sqrt{8}$

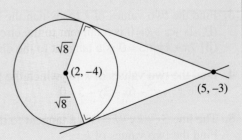

We have a point $(5, -3)$ and we need to find the slopes of the two tangents.

Equation: $(y - y_1) = m(x - x_1)$

$$(y + 3) = m(x - 5)$$

$$y + 3 = mx - 5m$$

$$mx - y + (-5m - 3) = 0 \qquad \text{[in the form } ax + by + c = 0]$$

The perpendicular distance from the centre of the circle $(2, -4)$ to each tangent is equal to the radius, $\sqrt{8}$.

Thus,

$$\frac{|m(2) - 1(-4) + (-5m - 3)|}{\sqrt{m^2 + (-1)^2}} = \sqrt{8}$$

$$\frac{|2m + 4 - 5m - 3|}{\sqrt{m^2 + 1}} = \sqrt{8}$$

$$\frac{|-3m + 1|}{\sqrt{m^2 + 1}} = \sqrt{8}$$

$$\frac{9m^2 - 6m + 1}{m^2 + 1} = 8 \qquad \text{[square both sides]}$$

$$9m^2 - 6m + 1 = 8m^2 + 8 \qquad \text{[multiply both sides by } (m^2 + 1)]$$

$$m^2 - 6m - 7 = 0$$

$$(m + 1)(m - 7) = 0$$

$$m = -1 \quad \text{or} \quad m = 7$$

Equations of the two tangents:

Slope $= -1$; point $= (5, -3)$	Slope $= 7$; point $= (5, -3)$
$(y + 3) = -1(x - 5)$	$(y + 3) = 7(x + 5)$
$y + 3 = -x + 5$	$y + 3 = 7x + 35$
$x + y - 2 = 0$	$7x - y + 32 = 0$

Thus, the equations of the two tangents are $x + y - 2 = 0$ and $7x - y + 32 = 0$.

Exercise 1.11 ▼

1. The line $2x + y + k = 0$ is a tangent to the circle $x^2 + y^2 = 5$. Find the two values of k.

2. The line $3x + y + k = 0$ is a tangent to the circle $x^2 + y^2 - 4x + 8y + 10 = 0$. Find the two values of k.

3. Find the two values of k for which the line:
   (i) $2x + y + k = 0$ is a tangent to the circle $x^2 + y^2 - 4x - 6y + 8 = 0$
   (ii) $2x + ky + 3 = 0$ is a tangent to the circle $x^2 + y^2 - 4x - 4y - 5 = 0$.

4. Find the two values of k for which the line $x + ky - 6 = 0$ is a tangent to the circle $x^2 + y^2 - 6x - 2y + 5 = 0$.

5. The line $3x + ky - k = 0$ is a tangent to the circle $x^2 + y^2 - 10x - 2y + 17 = 0$. Find the two values of k.

6. Find the equations of the tangents to the circle $x^2 + y^2 = 25$ which are parallel to the line $4x - 3y + 10 = 0$.

7. Find the equations of the tangents to the circle $x^2 + y^2 = 10$ which are parallel to the line $3x - y = 0$.

8. Find the equations of the tangents to the circle $x^2 + y^2 + 6x + 10y + 29 = 0$ which are parallel to the line $2x - y - 8 = 0$.

9. Find the equations of the tangents to the circle $x^2 + y^2 - 6x + 4y - 4 = 0$ which are parallel to the line $x + 4y - 3 = 0$.

10. Find the equations of the tangents to the circle $x^2 + y^2 + 6x - 2y - 15 = 0$ which are perpendicular to the line $4x + 3y + 5 = 0$.

11. The line $mx - y = 0$ is a tangent to the circle $x^2 + y^2 - 6x + 2y + 2 = 0$. Find the two values of m.

Find the equations of the tangent from the given point to the given circle:

12. $(5, 0)$; $x^2 + y^2 = 5$

13. $(-10, -10)$; $x^2 + y^2 = 20$

14. $(0, 0)$; $x^2 + y^2 + 4x + 2y + 4 = 0$

15. $(3, -2)$; $x^2 + y^2 + 4x - 6y + 8 = 0$

16. $(0, 1)$; $x^2 + y^2 - 8x - 2y + 9 = 0$

17. $(1, 2)$; $x^2 + y^2 + 8x + 6y + 15 = 0$

18. The line $ax + by = 0$ is a tangent to the circle $x^2 + y^2 - 4x - 2y + 4 = 0$, where $a, b \in \mathbf{R}$ and $b \neq 0$.
   (i) Show that $\dfrac{a}{b} = -\dfrac{4}{3}$.
   (ii) Hence, or otherwise, find the coordinates of the point of contact.

Circles with the Axes as Tangents

If a circle touches an axis (the x- or y-axis is a tangent to the circle), then one of the coordinates of the centre of the circle is equal to the radius.

1. Circle touching the x-axis $\text{radius} = \lvert -f \rvert$ $\sqrt{g^2 + f^2 - c} = \lvert -f \rvert$ $g^2 + f^2 - c = f^2$ $g^2 - c = 0$ $g^2 = c$	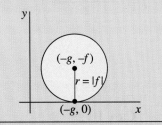
2. Circle touching the y-axis $\text{radius} = \lvert -g \rvert$ $\sqrt{g^2 + f^2 - c} = \lvert -g \rvert$ $g^2 + f^2 - c = g^2$ $f^2 - c = 0$ $f^2 = c$	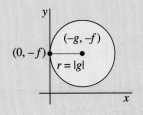

The x-axis is a tangent to the circle $C: x^2 + y^2 + 2gx + 2fy + c = 0$.

Show that $g^2 = c$.

The points (2, 1) and (3, 2) are also on the circle C.

Find two possible equations for C.

Solution:

$$x^2 + y^2 + 2gx + 2fy + c = 0$$

$$\text{centre} = (-g, -f) \qquad \text{radius} = \sqrt{g^2 + f^2 - c}$$

From the diagram,

$$\text{radius} = |-f|$$

$$\sqrt{g^2 + f^2 - c} = |-f|$$

$$g^2 + f^2 - c = f^2$$

$$g^2 - c = 0$$

$$g^2 = c$$

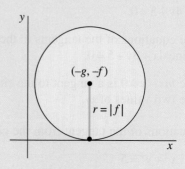

(2, 1) on the circle: $(2)^2 + (1)^2 + 2g(2) + 2f(1) + c = 0 \implies 4g + 2f + c + 5 = 0$

(3, 2) on the circle: $(3)^2 + (2)^2 + 2g(3) + 2f(2) + c = 0 \implies 6g + 4f + c + 13 = 0$

We now have 3 equations:

$$g^2 = c \quad ① \qquad\qquad 4g + 2f + c + 5 = 0 \quad ② \qquad\qquad 6g + 4f + c + 13 = 0 \quad ③$$

Replace c with g^2 in ② and ③:

$4g + 2f + c + 5 = 0 \quad ②$	$6g + 4f + c + 13 = 0 \quad ③$
$4g + 2f + g^2 + 5 = 0 \quad ④$	$6g + 4f + g^2 + 13 = 0 \quad ⑤$

From ④, express f in terms of g and put this into ⑤:

$$4g + 2f + g^2 + 5 = 0 \quad ④ \qquad\qquad\qquad 6g + 4f + g^2 + 13 = 0 \quad ⑤$$

$$2f = -g^2 - 4g - 5 \qquad\qquad 6g + 4\left(\frac{-g^2 - 4g - 5}{2}\right) + g^2 + 13 = 0$$

$$f = \left(\frac{-g^2 - 4g - 5}{2}\right) \qquad\qquad 6g - 2g^2 - 8g - 10 + g^2 + 13 = 0$$

put this into ⑤.

$$-g^2 - 2g + 3 = 0$$

$$g^2 + 2g - 3 = 0$$

$$(g + 3)(g - 1) = 0$$

$$g = -3 \quad \text{or} \quad g = 1$$

Case 1	**Case 2**
$g = -3$	$g = 1$
$c = g^2 = (-3)^2 = 9$	$c = g^2 = (1)^2 = 1$
$f = \dfrac{-g^2 - 4g - 5}{2} = \dfrac{-9 + 12 - 5}{2} = \dfrac{-2}{2} = -1$	$f = \dfrac{-g^2 - 4g - 5}{2} = \dfrac{-1 - 4 - 5}{2} = \dfrac{-10}{2} = -5$
$x^2 + y^2 + 2(-3)x + 2(-1)y + 9 = 0$	$x^2 + y^2 + 2(1)x + 2(-5)y + 1 = 0$
$x^2 + y^2 - 6x - 2y + 9 = 0$	$x^2 + y^2 + 2x - 10y + 1 = 0$

1. Find the equation of the circle with centre $(2, 5)$ and which has the x-axis as a tangent.

2. Find the equation of the circle with centre $(-3, 4)$ and which has the y-axis as a tangent.

3. Show that the circle $x^2 + y^2 - 4x - 4y + 4 = 0$ touches the x- and y-axes.

4. The x-axis is a tangent to the circle $x^2 + y^2 + 2gx + 2fy + c = 0$.
   Show that $g^2 = c$.
   The x-axis is a tangent to a circle C at the point $(5, 0)$.
   The point $(1, 4)$ is on C. Find the equation of C.

5. The y-axis is a tangent to the circle $x^2 + y^2 + 2gx + 2fy + c = 0$.
   Show that $f^2 = c$.
   The y-axis is a tangent to a circle K at the point $(0, 2)$.
   The point $(2, -2)$ is on K. Find the equation of K.

6. A circle has its centre in the first quadrant and touches the x- and y-axes.
   If the distance from the centre of the circle to the origin is $2\sqrt{2}$, find the equation of the circle.

7. The x-axis and the y-axis are tangents to the circle $x^2 + y^2 + 2gx + 2fy + c = 0$.
   Show that: **(i)** $g^2 = c$ **(ii)** $g^2 = f^2$.
   The circle $C: x^2 + y^2 + 2gx + 2fy + c = 0$ has its centre in the first quadrant.
   The x- and y-axes are tangents to C. The point $(3, 6)$ is on C.
   Find two equations for C.

8. Show that the circle $x^2 + y^2 - 2rx - 2ry + r^2 = 0$ has radius r and has the x- and y-axes as tangents.
   Find the equations of the two circles which contain the point $(1, 2)$ and have the x- and y-axes as tangents.

Touching Circles

Two circles are said to be **touching** if they have only one point of intersection. To investigate whether two circles touch, we compare the distance between their centres with the sum or difference of their radii.

Consider two circles of radius r_1 and r_2 (where $r_1 > r_2$) and let d be the distance between their centres.

1. Circles touch externally	**2. Circles touch internally**
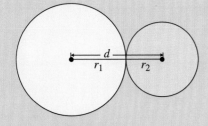	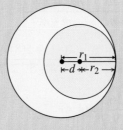
$d = r_1 + r_2$	$d = r_1 - r_2$
Distance between their centres	Distance between their centres
= sum of their radii	= difference of their radii

$S: x^2 + y^2 - 16y + 32 = 0$ and $K: x^2 + y^2 - 18x + 2y + 32 = 0$ are two circles.

Show that the circles touch externally and find their point of contact.

Solution:

$S: x^2 + y^2 + 0x - 16y + 32 = 0$

centre $= (0, 8) = c_1$

radius $= \sqrt{0^2 + 8^2 - 32}$

$\quad = \sqrt{64 - 32} = \sqrt{32} = 4\sqrt{2}$

$K: x^2 + y^2 - 18x + 2y + 32 = 0$

centre $= (9, -1) = c_2$

radius $= \sqrt{9^2 + (-1^2) - 32}$

$\quad = \sqrt{81 + 1 - 32} = \sqrt{50} = 5\sqrt{2}$

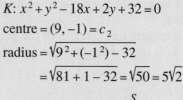

$r_1 + r_2 = 4\sqrt{2} + 5\sqrt{2} = 9\sqrt{2}$

distance between centres

$= \sqrt{(9 - 0)^2 + (-1 - 8)^2} = \sqrt{81 + 81} = \sqrt{162} = 9\sqrt{2}$

Thus, the circles touch externally, as $r_1 + r_2 = |c_1 c_2|$.

To determine the point of contact, divide the line segment joining the centres in the ratio 4:5.

Let the point of contact be (x, y).

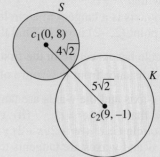

$$
\begin{array}{ccccc}
 & 4 & & 5 & \\
\bullet & & \bullet & & \bullet \\
c_1(0, 8) & m & (x, y) & n & c_2(9, -1)
\end{array}
$$

Method 1:

$\dfrac{x - 0}{9 - x} = \dfrac{4}{5}$

$\quad 5x = 36 - 4x$

$\quad 9x = 36$

$\quad x = 4$

$\dfrac{y - 8}{-1 - y} = \dfrac{4}{5}$

$\quad 5y - 40 = -4 - 4x$

$\quad 9y = 36$

$\quad y = 4$

Thus, the point of contact is $(4, 4)$.

Method 2: Using the formula,

$$(x, y) = \left(\frac{mx_2 + nx_1}{m + n}, \frac{my_2 + ny_1}{m + n} \right)$$

$$= \left(\frac{4(9) + 5(0)}{4 + 5}, \frac{4(-1) + 5(8)}{4 + 5} \right)$$

$$= \left(\frac{36}{9}, \frac{36}{9} \right) = (4, 4)$$

Thus, the point of contact is $(4, 4)$.

1. Prove that the circles $x^2+y^2+2x+2y-7=0$ and $x^2+y^2-6x-4y+9=0$ touch externally.

2. Prove that the circles $x^2+y^2+6x+16y+9=0$ and $x^2+y^2-4x-8y-5=0$ touch externally.

3. Prove that the circles $x^2+y^2+12x-6y-76=0$ and $x^2+y^2-4x+6y+12=0$ touch internally.

4. Prove that the circles $x^2+y^2=80$ and $x^2+y^2-12x-6y+40=0$ touch internally.

5. Prove that the circles $x^2+y^2-2x-4y-20=0$ and $x^2+y^2-18x-16y+120=0$ touch externally and find their point of contact.

6. Prove that the circles $x^2+y^2+14x-10y-26=0$ and $x^2+y^2-4x+14y+28=0$ touch externally and find their point of contact.

7. Prove that the circles $x^2+y^2-6x+4y+11=0$ and $x^2+y^2+4x-6y-19=0$ touch externally and find their point of contact.

8. Prove that the circles $x^2+y^2+4x+6y-19=0$ and $x^2+y^2-2x-1=0$ touch internally and find their point of contact.

9. Prove that the circles $x^2+y^2+8x-8y+24=0$ and $x^2+y^2+2x-2y=0$ touch externally and find their point of contact.

10. The diagram shows the circle $C_1: x+y^2=16$ and the circle C_2 with centre $(12, 5)$.

    If C_1 and C_2 touch externally, find the equation of C_2.

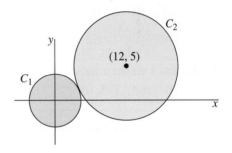

11. If the circles $x^2+y^2+4x+6y+k=0$ and $x^2+y^2-6x-4y+11=0$ touch externally, find the value of k.

12. $C_1: x^2+y^2-6x-4y-3=0$ and

    $C_2: x^2+y^2-18x-4y+81=0$ are two circles.

    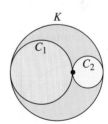

    (i) Prove that C_1 and C_2 touch externally.
    (ii) Find the point of contact of C_1 and C_2.
    (iii) K is a third circle.
    Both C_1 and C_2 touch K internally.
    Find the equation of K.

    Note: All three centres lie on a straight line.

Chords of a Circle

Circles Intersecting the Axes

To find where a circle intersects the axes, we use the following:

> The circle intersects the x-axis at $y = 0$.
> The circle intersects the y-axis at $x = 0$.

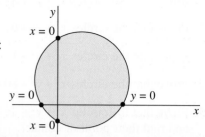

Example ▼

Find the coordinates of the points where the circle $x^2 + y^2 + 4x - 4y - 5 = 0$ intersects:

(i) the x-axis **(ii)** the y-axis.

Solution:

$$x^2 + y^2 + 4x - 4y - 5 = 0$$

(i) On the x-axis $y = 0$
    (put in $y = 0$)
$$x^2 + 4x - 5 = 0$$
$$(x - 1)(x + 5) = 0$$
$$x = 1 \quad \text{or} \quad x = -5$$
Coordinates on the x-axis:
    $(1, 0)$ and $(-5, 0)$

(ii) On the y-axis $x = 0$
    (put in $x = 0$)
$$y^2 - 4y - 5 = 0$$
$$(y + 1)(y - 5) = 0$$
$$y = -1 \quad \text{or} \quad y = 5$$
Coordinates on the y-axis:
    $(0, -1)$ and $(0, 5)$

Common Chord or Common Tangent

> If $S_1 = 0$ and $S_2 = 0$ are the equations of two circles in standard form, then
> $S_1 - S_2 = 0$ is the equation of the common chord or common tangent of the two circles.

Common Chord	**Common Tangent**
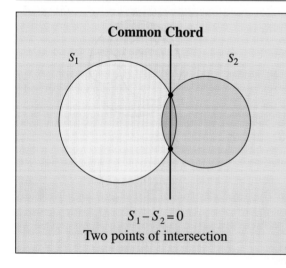	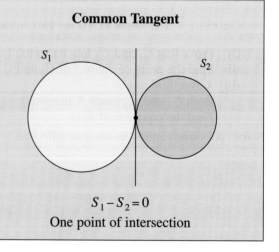
$S_1 - S_2 = 0$ Two points of intersection	$S_1 - S_2 = 0$ One point of intersection

Note: To find the equation of the common chord, or common tangent, of two circles, $S_1 = 0$ and $S_2 = 0$, the coefficients of x^2 and y^2 must be the same for both circles.

To find the coordinates of the points of intersection of two circles, do the following:

1. Find the equation of the common chord ($S_1 - S_2 = 0$).
2. Solve between the equation of the common chord and the equation of one of the circles.

Example ▼

The circles $x^2 + y^2 - 6x + 4y - 7 = 0$ and $x^2 + y^2 - 16x - 6y + 63 = 0$ intersect at the points p and q. Find the equation of the line pq.

Solution:

The equation of the line pq is given by: $\quad S_1 - S_2 = 0$
$$(x^2 + y^2 - 6x + 4y - 7) - (x^2 + y^2 - 16x - 6y + 63) = 0$$
$$x^2 + y^2 - 6x + 4y - 7 - x^2 - y^2 + 16x + 6y - 63 = 0$$
$$10x + 10y - 70 = 0$$
$$x + y - 7 = 0$$

Thus, the equation of the line pq (common chord) is $x + y - 7 = 0$.

Note: To find the coordinates of p and q, solve between the equations

$$x + y - 7 = 0 \quad \text{and} \quad x^2 + y^2 - 6x + 4y - 7 = 0 \quad \text{or} \quad x^2 + y^2 - 16x - 6y + 63 = 0.$$

Radius Perpendicular to a Chord

A radius (or part of a radius) that is perpendicular to a chord bisects that chord. This also enables us to use Pythagoras's Theorem:

$$d^2 + x^2 = r^2$$

Thus, knowing two of d, x and r, we can find the third.

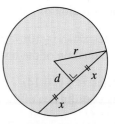

Example ▼

A circle K has centre $(2, 3)$ and makes a chord of $8\sqrt{2}$ units on the y-axis. Find the equation of K.

Solution:

A rough diagram is very useful.

We have the centre and require the radius.

The length of the perpendicular from the centre $(2, 3)$ to the y-axis is 2.

The length of the chord on the y-axis is $8\sqrt{2}$.

The perpendicular from the centre bisects the chord.

Thus, this length is $4\sqrt{2}$.

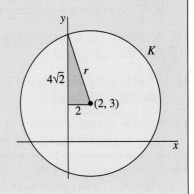

Using Pythagoras's theorem:
$$r^2 = (4\sqrt{2})^2 + (2)^2 = 32 + 4 = 36$$
$$\therefore \ r = 6$$
Equation: $(x-h)^2 + (y-k)^2 = r^2$
$$(x-2)^2 + (y-3)^2 = 6^2$$
$$(x-2)^2 + (y-3)^2 = 36$$

or

$$x^2 + y^2 - 4x - 6y - 23 = 0$$

Exercise 1.14 ▼

1. Find the coordinates of the points where the circle $x^2 + y^2 - 6x + 6y - 16 = 0$ intersects:
   (i) the x-axis   **(ii)** the y-axis.

2. Find the length of the chord the y-axis makes with the circle $x^2 + y^2 - 8x - 10y + 16 = 0$.

3. Find the length of the chord the x-axis makes with the circle $x^2 + y^2 - 6x + 4y - 7 = 0$.

4. Find the equations of the tangents to the circle $x^2 + y^2 + 2x + 4y - 3 = 0$ at the points where the circle cuts the x-axis, and show that these tangents are perpendicular to each other.

5. The circles $x^2 + y^2 + 4x - 10y + 20 = 0$ and $x^2 + y^2 - 4x - 2y + 12 = 0$ intersect at the points a and b. Find the equation of the line ab.

6. The circles $x^2 + y^2 - 6x + 4 = 0$ and $x^2 + y^2 - 2x + 12y + 12 = 0$ intersect at the points p and q. Find the equation of the line pq.

7. The circles $x^2 + y^2 - 10x - 10y + 40 = 0$ and $x^2 + y^2 - 16x + 2y + 40 = 0$ intersect at the points a and b. Find the equation of the line ab, the coordinates of the point a and the coordinates of the point b.

8. The circles $x^2 + y^2 + 14x - 12y + 65 = 0$ and $x^2 + y^2 + 4x - 2y - 5 = 0$ intersect at the points a and b. Find the coordinates of the point a and the coordinates of the point b.

9. The circles $x^2 + y^2 + 8x + 2y + 7 = 0$ and $x^2 + y^2 + 2x - 16y + 25 = 0$ intersect at the point p. Find the coordinates of the point p.

10. The line $2x + y - 10 = 0$ is a common tangent to the circles $x^2 + y^2 - 2x + 4y + h = 0$ and $x^2 + y^2 - 14x - 2y + k = 0$.
    Find the value of h and the value of k.

11. A circle C has centre $(5, 3)$ and makes a chord of 4 units on the y-axis. Find the equation of C.

12. A circle S has centre $(2, 0)$ and makes a chord of 6 units on the y-axis. Find the equation of S.

13. A circle of radius length 5 units has its centre in the first quadrant, touches the x-axis and intercepts a chord of length 6 units on the y-axis. Find the equation of this circle.

14. Find the equation of the circle with its centre in the first quadrant if it touches the y-axis at the point $(0, 2)$ and makes a chord of length $4\sqrt{3}$ units on the x-axis.

15. $L: 3x - 4y - 5 = 0$ is a line and $C: x^2 + y^2 - 4x + 12y + k = 0$ is a circle.

The line L contains a chord of length 10 units of the circle C.

Find: **(i)** the radius length of C **(ii)** the value of k.

16. The equation of a circle C is $x^2 + y^2 + 4x - 2y + k$. Write down its centre.

The midpoint of a chord of length $4\sqrt{2}$ is $(1, 4)$.

Find: **(i)**   the distance from the centre of the circle to the chord.

    (ii) the radius length of C and the value of k.

17. Find the equation of the circle with centre $(4, 1)$ and which makes an intercept of length 4 units on the line $3x - 4y + 2 = 0$.

2

COMPLEX NUMBERS

Imaginary Numbers: the Symbol i

The square root of a negative number is called an **imaginary** number, e.g. $\sqrt{-4}, \sqrt{-9}, \sqrt{-64}, \sqrt{-100}$ are imaginary numbers.

Imaginary numbers cannot be represented by a real number, as there is no real number whose square is a negative number.

To overcome this problem, the letter i is introduced to represent $\sqrt{-1}$.

$$i = \sqrt{-1}$$

All imaginary numbers can now be expressed in terms of i, for example:

$$\sqrt{-36} = \sqrt{36 \times -1} = \sqrt{36}\sqrt{-1} = 6i$$

$$\sqrt{-50} = \sqrt{50 \times -1} = \sqrt{25 \times 2 \times -1} = \sqrt{25}\sqrt{2}\sqrt{-1} = 5\sqrt{2}i$$

Integer Powers of i

Every integer power of i is a member of the set $\{1, -1, i, -i\}$.

$$i = \sqrt{-1}$$
$$i^2 = -1$$
$$i^3 = i^2 \cdot i = (-1)i = -i$$
$$i^4 = i^2 \cdot i^2 = (-1)(-1) = 1$$

$$i = \sqrt{-1}$$
$$i^2 = -1$$
$$i^3 = -i$$
$$i^4 = 1$$

Simplify: **(i)** i^{21} **(ii)** i^{10} **(iii)** i^{-13}.

Solution:

(i) i^{21}

$= i^4 \cdot i^4 \cdot i^4 \cdot i^4 \cdot i^4 \cdot i$

$= (1)(1)(1)(1)(1)i$

$= i$

Alternatively,

$i^{21} = i^{20} \cdot i$

$\quad = (i^4)^5 \cdot i$

$\quad = (1)^5 \cdot i = i$

(ii) i^{10}

$= i^{10}$

$= i^4 \cdot i^4 \cdot i^2$

$= (1)(1)(-1)$

$= -1$

Alternatively,

$i^{10} = i^8 \cdot i^2$

$\quad = (i^4)^2 \cdot i^2$

$\quad = (1)^2 \cdot (-1)$

$\quad = -1$

(iii) i^{-13}

$= \dfrac{1}{i^{13}}$

$= \dfrac{1}{i^{13}} \times \dfrac{i^3}{i^3}$

$= \dfrac{i^3}{i^{16}}$

$= \dfrac{i^3}{1}$

$= i^3 = -i$

Complex Numbers

A complex number has two parts, a **real** part and an **imaginary** part.
Some examples are $3 + 4i$, $2 - 5i$, $-6 + 0i$, $0 - i$.
Consider the complex number $4 + 3i$:

    4 is called the **real** part,
    3 is called the **imaginary** part.

Note: $3i$ is **not** the imaginary part.

> Complex number = (Real Part) + (Imaginary Part) i

The set of complex numbers is denoted by $\boldsymbol{C}$.
The letter z is usually used to represent a complex number, e.g.

$$z_1 = 2 + 3i, \qquad z_2 = -2 - i, \qquad z_3 = -5i$$

If $z = a + bi$, then:

(i) a is called the real part of z and is written $\boldsymbol{Re(z) = a}$
(ii) b is called the imaginary part of z and is written $\boldsymbol{Im(z) = b}$.

Write down the real and imaginary parts of each of the following complex numbers:

(i) $5-4i$ (ii) $-3+2i$ (iii) 6   (iv) $-5i$.

Solution:

	Real Part	Imaginary Part
(i) $5-4i$	5	-4
(ii) $-3+2i$	-3	2
(iii) $6=6+0i$	6	0
(iv) $-5i=0-5i$	0	-5

Notes: *i* **never** appears in the imaginary part.
If $Im(z)=0$, then z is a **real** number.
If $Re(z)=0$, then z is a **purely imaginary** number.

Addition and Subtraction of Complex Numbers

To add or subtract complex numbers do the following:

> Add or subtract the real and the imaginary parts separately.

For example:

$$(3+5i)-(2-3i)=3+5i-2+3i=1+8i$$
$$2(-1+3i)-3(1+4i)=-2+6i-3-12i=-5-6i$$

Multiplication of Complex Numbers

Multiplication of complex numbers is performed using the usual algebraic method, except that:

$$i^2 \text{ is replaced with } -1.$$

For example:

$$
\begin{aligned}
(3-2i)(-4+5i) &= 3(-4+5i)-2i(-4+5i) \\
&= -12+15i+8i-10i^2 \\
&= -12+15i+8i-10(-1) \qquad (i^2=-1) \\
&= -12+15i+8i+10 \\
&= -2+23i
\end{aligned}
$$

If $z_1 = 3 + 2i$ and $z_2 = -1 + 5i$, express in the form $a + bi$, $a, b \in \mathbf{R}$:

(i) $2z_1 - iz_2$ **(ii)** $z_1 z_2$ **(iii)** z_1^2.

Solution:

(i) $2z_1 - iz_2$
$$= 2(3 + 2i) - i(-1 + 5i)$$
$$= 6 + 4i + i - 5i^2$$
$$= 6 + 4i + i + 5$$
$$\quad (i^2 = -1)$$
$$= 11 + 5i$$

(ii) $z_1 z_2$
$$= (3 + 2i)(-1 + 5i)$$
$$= 3(-1 + 5i) + 2i(-1 + 5i)$$
$$= -3 + 15i - 2i + 10i^2$$
$$= -3 + 15i - 2i - 10 \qquad (i^2 = -1)$$
$$= -13 + 13i$$

(iii) z_1^2
$$= (3 + 2i)^2$$
$$= (3 + 2i)(3 + 2i)$$
$$= 3(3 + 2i) + 2i(3 + 2i)$$
$$= 9 + 6i + 6i + 4i^2$$
$$= 9 + 6i + 6i - 4 \qquad (i^2 = -1)$$
$$= 5 + 12i$$

Given that $z = 1 - \sqrt{3}i$, find the real number k such that $z^2 + kz$ is:

(i) real   **(ii)** purely imaginary.

Solution:

$$z = 1 - \sqrt{3}i$$
$$z^2 = (1 - \sqrt{3}i)^2$$
$$= (1 - \sqrt{3}i)(1 - \sqrt{3}i)$$
$$= 1(1 - \sqrt{3}i) - \sqrt{3}i(1 - \sqrt{3}i)$$
$$= 1 - \sqrt{3}i - \sqrt{3}i + 3i^2$$
$$= 1 - \sqrt{3}i - \sqrt{3}i - 3$$
$$= -2 - 2\sqrt{3}i$$

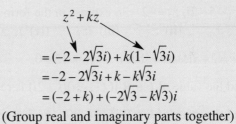

$$z^2 + kz$$
$$= (-2 - 2\sqrt{3}i) + k(1 - \sqrt{3}i)$$
$$= -2 - 2\sqrt{3}i + k - k\sqrt{3}i$$
$$= (-2 + k) + (-2\sqrt{3} - k\sqrt{3})i$$

(Group real and imaginary parts together)

(i) If $z^2 + kz$ is real, then the imaginary part is zero,
$$\therefore \quad -2\sqrt{3} - k\sqrt{3} = 0$$
$$-2 - k = 0$$
$$k = -2$$

(ii) If $z^2 + kz$ is imaginary, then the real part is zero,
$$\therefore \quad -2 + k = 0$$
$$k = 2$$

Note: $\sqrt{3}i$ is often written as $i\sqrt{3}$ to avoid the error $\sqrt{3i}$.

Exercise 2.1 ▼

Express each of the following in the form ai, where $a \in \mathbf{N}$:

1. $\sqrt{-4}$ **2.** $\sqrt{-25}$ **3.** $\sqrt{-49}$ **4.** $\sqrt{-100}$ **5.** $\sqrt{-16}$ **6.** $\sqrt{-144}$

7. $\sqrt{-9}$ **8.** $\sqrt{-121}$ **9.** $\sqrt{-400}$ **10.** $\sqrt{-196}$ **11.** $\sqrt{-169}$ **12.** $\sqrt{-289}$

Express each of the following in the form $a\sqrt{b}i$, $a, b \in \mathbf{N}$ and b is prime:

13. $\sqrt{-8}$ **14.** $\sqrt{-12}$ **15.** $\sqrt{-18}$ **16.** $\sqrt{-50}$ **17.** $\sqrt{-80}$ **18.** $\sqrt{-63}$

Express each of the following as an element of the set $\{1, -1, i, -i\}$:

19. i^6 **20.** i^7 **21.** i^8 **22.** i^{13} **23.** i^{20} **24.** i^{22}

25. i^{27} **26.** i^{102} **27.** i^{-3} **28.** i^{-2} **29.** i^{-1} **30.** i^{-20}

31. Write down the real part and imaginary parts of z if:

    (i) $z = 2 + 5i$ **(ii)** $z = -3 - 4i$ **(iii)** $z = -7 - \sqrt{3}i$ **(iv)** $z = -7i$

Express each of the following in the form $a + bi$, $a, b \in \mathbf{R}$ and $i^2 = -1$:

32. $(3 + 2i) - 2(5 - 4i)$ **33.** $2(2 - 3i) - 3(2 - 7i)$

34. $(2 + 3i)(-3 + 4i)$ **35.** $(3 + i)(-2 - 5i)$

36. $3 + 2i(3 + 4i) - i$ **37.** $i(-2 + 5i) - 5(-1 + 2i)$

38. $i(3 - 5i)(4 + i)$ **39.** $4i(2 - 3i)(-2 - 4i)$

40. $(1 + 2i)^2 - 2(5 - 3i)$ **41.** $(1 + \sqrt{3}i)^2 - \sqrt{3}(-\sqrt{3} + 2i)$

42. If $z = 1 - 3i$, where $i^2 = -1$, evaluate $z^2 - 3z$.

43. If $z_1 = 5 - 2i$, $z_2 = -2 - 3i$, express in the form $a + bi$, $a, b \in \mathbf{R}$ and $i^2 = -1$:
    (i) $z_1 z_2$ **(ii)** z_2^2 **(iii)** iz_1 **(iv)** $iz_1 z_2$.

44. If $w = 2 + 3i$, show that $w^2 - 4w + 13 = 0$.

45. Find the value of $k \in \mathbf{R}$ if $(1 - 3i)(k + 2i)$ is real, where $i^2 = -1$.

46. Find the value of $k \in \mathbf{R}$ if $(2 + i)(k - 5i)$ is purely imaginary, where $i^2 = -1$.

47. Given that $z = 1 + 3i$, find the real number k such that $z^2 + kz$ is real.

48. Given that $z = 1 + \sqrt{2}i$, find the real number t such that $z^2 + tz$ is:
    (i) real   **(ii)** purely imaginary.

49. Given that $z = (-1 + \sqrt{5}i)$, find the real number k such that $z^2 - kz + \sqrt{5}i$ is:
    (i) real   **(ii)** purely imaginary.

Conjugate and Division

Conjugate of a Complex Number

Two complex numbers which differ only in the sign of their imaginary parts are called **conjugate complex numbers**, each being the conjugate of the other.

Thus $3 + 4i$ and $3 - 4i$ are conjugates, and $-2 - 3i$ is the conjugate of $-2 + 3i$ and vice versa.

In general, $a + bi$ and $a - bi$ are conjugates.

If $z = a + bi$, then its conjugate, $a - bi$, is denoted by $\bar{z}$.

$$z = a + bi \quad \Rightarrow \quad \bar{z} = a - bi$$

To find the conjugate, simply **change the sign** of the imaginary part only.

For example, if $z = -6 - 5i$ then $\bar{z} = -6 + 5i$.

Example ▼

If $z = -3 + 5i$, where $i^2 = -1$, simplify: **(i)** $z + \bar{z}$ **(ii)** $z - \bar{z}$ **(iii)** $z\bar{z}$.

Solution:

If $z = -3 + 5i$, then $\bar{z} = -3 - 5i$ (change sign of the imaginary part only).

(i) $z + \bar{z}$
$$= (-3 + 5i) + (-3 - 5i)$$
$$= -3 + 5i - 3 - 5i$$
$$= -6 \quad \text{(a real number)}$$

(ii) $z - \bar{z}$
$$= (-3 + 5i) - (-3 - 5i)$$
$$= -3 + 5i + 3 + 5i$$
$$= 10i \quad \text{(a purely imaginary number)}$$

(iii) $z\bar{z}$
$$= (-3 + 5i)(-3 - 5i)$$
$$= -3(-3 - 5i) + 5i(-3 - 5i)$$
$$= 9 + 15i - 15i - 25i^2$$
$$= 9 + 25 \quad (i^2 = -1)$$
$$= 34 \quad \text{(a real number)}$$

Note: If a complex number is added to, or multiplied by, its conjugate the imaginary parts cancel and the result will **always** be a real number.

If $z = a + bi$, then:

> 1. $z + \bar{z} = (a + bi) + (a - bi) = a + bi + a - bi = 2a$ (a real number)
> 2. $z\bar{z} = (a + bi)(a - bi) = a^2 - abi + abi - b^2 i^2 = a^2 + b^2$ (a real number)

Division by a Complex Number

> Multiply the top and bottom by the conjugate of the bottom.

This will convert the complex number on the bottom into a real number. The division is then performed by dividing the real number on the bottom into each part on the top.

If $z = \dfrac{2+i}{1-i}$, find the real part of z.

Solution:

First write z in the form $a + bi$:

$$z = \frac{2+i}{1-i}$$

$$= \frac{2+i}{1-i} \cdot \frac{1+i}{1-i} \qquad \left(\begin{array}{l}\text{multiply the top and bottom by } 1+i,\\ \text{the conjugate of } 1-i\end{array}\right)$$

$$= \frac{2+2i+i+i^2}{1+i-i-i^2}$$

$$= \frac{2+2i+i-1}{1+i-i+1} \qquad (i^2 = -1)$$

$$= \frac{1+3i}{2}$$

$$= \tfrac{1}{2} + \tfrac{3}{2}i \qquad \text{(divide the bottom into \textbf{each} part on top)}$$

Thus, the real part of z is $\tfrac{1}{2}$.

Simplify $\dfrac{4+3i}{3-4i}$ and, hence, evaluate $\left(\dfrac{4+3i}{3-4i}\right)^{10}$.

Solution:

$$\frac{4+3i}{3-4i}$$

$$= \frac{4+3i}{3-4i} \cdot \frac{3+4i}{3+4i}$$

$$= \frac{12+16i+9i+12i^2}{9+12i-12i-16i^2}$$

$$= \frac{25i}{25} \qquad (i^2 = -1)$$

$$= i$$

$$\frac{4+3i}{3-4i} = i$$

$$\therefore \quad \left(\frac{4+3i}{3-4i}\right)^{10} = i^{10}$$

$$= i^4 \cdot i^4 \cdot i^2$$

$$= (1)(1)(-1)$$

$$= -1$$

Express each of the following in the form $a + bi$, where $a, b \in \mathbf{R}$ and $i^2 = -1$:

1. $\dfrac{3+4i}{2+i}$

2. $\dfrac{7+4i}{2-i}$

3. $\dfrac{1+5i}{3+2i}$

4. $\dfrac{7-17i}{5-i}$

5. $\dfrac{1}{1-i}$

6. $\dfrac{2+i}{1+2i}$

7. $\dfrac{2-i}{3+2i}$

8. $\dfrac{3+4i}{1-i}$

9. If $a + bi = \dfrac{9 - 7i}{2 - 3i}$, find the value of a and the value of b, $\quad a, b \in \mathbf{R}$.

10. If $p + qi = \dfrac{2 - i}{1 - 2i}$, $\quad p, q \in \mathbf{R}$, evaluate $p^2 + q^2$.

11. Given that $(4 + 3i)z = 1 + 7i$, express the complex number z in the form $a + bi$.

12. (i) Express $(1 - 2i)^2$ in the form $a + bi$.

    (ii) Hence, find the real part of $\dfrac{1}{(1 - 2i)^2}$.

13. Show that of $\dfrac{1}{(1 + i)^2}$ is a purely imaginary number and write down the imaginary part.

14. Evaluate: $\left(\dfrac{1}{2 + i} + \dfrac{2}{3 - i} \right)^{100}$.

15. (i) Evaluate $\dfrac{a + bi}{b - ai}$, where $a, b \in \mathbf{R}$ and $i^2 = -1$.

    Hence, or otherwise, evaluate:

    (ii) $\left(\dfrac{5 + 2i}{2 - 5i} \right)^4$ **(iii)** $\left(\dfrac{3 + 4i}{4 - 3i} \right)^4$ **(iv)** $\left(\dfrac{-3 + 2i}{2 + 3i} \right)^{21}$ **(v)** $\left(\dfrac{2 + i}{1 - 2i} \right)^{31}$

Evaluate each of the following:

16. $\left(\dfrac{8 - 4i}{2 - i} \right)^3$ **17.** $\left(\dfrac{-6 + 8i}{4 + 3i} \right)^8$ **18.** $\left(\dfrac{2 - 3i}{9 + 6i} \right)^4$ **19.** $\left(\dfrac{-1 + \sqrt{2}i}{\sqrt{2} + i} \right)^{34}$

20. k is a real number such that $\dfrac{-1 + \sqrt{3}i}{-5\sqrt{3} - 5i} = ki$. Find k.

Equality of Complex Numbers

If two complex numbers are equal then:
their real parts are equal and their imaginary parts are also equal.

For example, if $a + bi = c + di$,

    then $a = c$ and $b = d$.

This definition is very useful when dealing with equations involving complex numbers.

Equations involving complex numbers are usually solved with the following steps:

> 1. Remove the brackets.
> 2. Put an R under the real parts and an I under the imaginary parts to identify them.
> 3. Let the real parts equal the real parts and the imaginary parts equal the imaginary parts.
> 4. Solve these resultant equations (usually simultaneous equations).

Note: If one side of the equation does not contain a real part or an imaginary part, it should be replaced with 0 or $0i$, respectively.

$z_1 = 4 - 2i$, $z_2 = -2 - 6i$. If $z_2 - pz_1 = qi$, $p, q \in \mathbf{R}$, find p and q.

Solution:

$$z_2 - pz_1 = qi$$

The right-hand side has no real part, hence a 0, representing the real part, should be placed on the right-hand side.

Now the equation is:

$z_2 - pz_1 = 0 + qi$	(put 0 in for real part)
$(-2 - 6i) - p(4 - 2i) = 0 + qi$	(substitute for z_1 and z_2)
$-2 - 6i - 4p + 2pi = 0 + qi$	(remove the brackets)
$\quad R \quad I \quad R \quad I \quad R \quad I$	(identify real and imaginary parts)

Real parts = Real parts	**Imaginary parts = Imaginary parts**
$-2 - 4p = 0$ .... ①	$-6 + 2p = q$ .... ②

Solve between the equations ① and ②:

$-2 - 4p = 0 \qquad$ ①	Substitute $p = -\frac{1}{2}$ into equation ②:
$-4p = 2$	$-6 + 2p = q \qquad$ ②
$4p = -2$	$-6 + 2(-\frac{1}{2}) = q$
$p = -\frac{2}{4} = -\frac{1}{2}$	$-6 - 1 = q$
	$-7 = q$

Solution: $p = -\frac{1}{2}, q = -7$

$w = a + bi$ is a complex number such that: $w\bar{w} - 2iw = 17 - 6i$.
Find the two possible values of w.

Solution:

$$w = a + bi \qquad \therefore \quad \bar{w} = a - bi$$

Given:

$$w\bar{w} - 2iw = 17 - 6i$$

$$\therefore \quad (a + bi)(a - bi) - 2i(a + bi) = 17 - 6i$$

$a^2 - abi + abi - b^2i^2 - 2ai - 2bi^2 = 17 - 6i$	(remove brackets)
$a^2 + b^2 - 2ai + 2b = 17 - 6i$	($i^2 = -1$)
$\quad R \quad R \quad I \quad R \quad R \quad I$	(identify real and imaginary parts)

Real parts = Real parts	**Imaginary parts = Imaginary parts**
$a^2 + b^2 + 2b = 17 \qquad$ ①	$-2a = -6 \qquad$ ②

Solve between equations ① and ②:

$$-2a = -6 \quad ②$$
$$2a = 6$$
$$a = 3$$

$$a^2 + b^2 + 2b = 17$$
$$9 + b^2 + 2b = 17 \quad (a = 3)$$
$$b^2 + 2b - 8 = 0$$
$$(b + 4)(b - 2) = 0$$
$$b = -4 \quad \text{or} \quad b = 2$$

$w = a + bi$

Thus, $w = 3 - 4i$ or $w = 3 + 2i$.

Exercise 2.3 ▼

Solve for $x, y \in \mathbf{R}$:

1. $x(3 + 4i) + y(2 - 3i) = 8 + 5i$

2. $x(3 - 2i) + y(i - 2) = 5 - 4i$

3. $3x - i(x + y + 5) = (1 + 3i)i + 2(3 - y)$

4. $(x + y) - (xi - y) = (3 + 2i)^2 - 7i$

5. If $2(h - 2) - k + i = i(2k - h)$, find h and k, $h, k \in \mathbf{R}$.

6. If $2p - q + i(7i + 3) = 2(2i - q) - i(p + 3q)$, find p and q, $p, q \in \mathbf{R}$.

7. $z_1 = 4 - 3i$, $z_2 = 5(1 + i)$. If $z_1 + tz_2 = k$, find t and k, $t, k \in \mathbf{R}$.

8. $z_1 = 5 + 7i$, $z_2 = 3 - i$. If $k(z_1 + z_2) = 16 + (t + 2)i$, find t and k, $t, k \in \mathbf{R}$.

9. $z = 2 - 3i$. If $z + i + 3(a + bi) = iz - 5$, find a and b, $a, b \in \mathbf{R}$.

10. $z_1 = 2 + 3i$, $z_2 = -4 - 3i$. If $lz_1 - z_2 = ki$, find l and k, $l, k \in \mathbf{R}$.

11. $z_1 = 6 - 8i$, $z_2 = 4 - 3i$. If $pi = z_2 + lz_3$, find p and l, where $z_1 - z_3 = z_2$ and $p, l \in \mathbf{R}$.

Express z in the form $a + bi$ if:

12. $iz = 2(3 - \bar{z})$

13. $z(1 + 3i) - 5(1 + 3i) = 2z$

14. $z = a + bi$ is a complex number such that $z + \bar{z} = 8$ and $z\bar{z} = 25$.
Find two values of z.

15. $w = a + bi$ is a complex number such that $w\bar{w} - 3iw = 5(7 - 3i)$.
Find two values of w.

16. $z = p + qi$ is a complex number such that $z\bar{z} - i\bar{z} = 11 - 3i$.
Find two values of z.

17. If $a(a + i) - bi(3 + bi) = 10(1 + i)$, find a, b, $a, b \in \mathbf{R}$.

18. If $a^2 + 2abi - b^2 = -15 + 8i$, find the values of a, b, $a, b \in \mathbf{R}$.

Argand Diagram and Modulus

Argand Diagram

An Argand diagram is used to plot complex numbers. It is very similar to the *x*- and *y*-axes used in coordinate geometry, except that the **horizontal** axis is called the **real axis (Re)** and the **vertical** axis is called the imaginary axis (**Im**). It is also called the **complex plane**.

To represent a complex number on an Argand diagram, it must be written in the form $a + bi$. The complex number $a + bi$ is represented by the point with coordinates (a, b).

Example ▼

If $z_1 = 2 - 3i$ and $z_2 = 6 - 5i$, represent on an Argand diagram:

(i) $\bar{z}_1$ **(ii)** $2z_1 - z_2$.

Solution:

(i) $z_1 = 2 - 3i$

$\bar{z}_1 = 2 + 3i$

(ii) $2z_1 - z_2$

$= 2(2 - 3i) - (6 - 5i)$

$= 4 - 6i - 6 + 5i$

$= -2 - i$

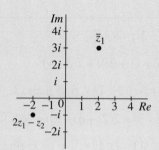

Modulus of a Complex Number

The **modulus** of a complex number is the distance from the origin to the point representing the complex number on the Argand diagram.

If $z = a + bi$, then the modulus of z is written $|z|$ or $|a + bi|$.

The point z represents the complex number $a + bi$.

The modulus of z is the distance from the origin, *o*, to the complex number $a + bi$.

Using the theorem of Pythagoras, $|z| = \sqrt{a^2 + b^2}$.

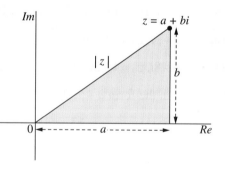

> If $z = a + bi$, then
>
> $|z| = |a + bi| = \sqrt{a^2 + b^2}$.

Notes:

1. *i* **never** appears when the modulus formula is used.
2. The modulus of a complex number is **always positive**.
3. Before using the formula a complex number must be in the form $a + bi$.

For example, if $z = -2 + 5i$, then:

$|z| = |-2 + 5i| = \sqrt{(-2)^2 + (5)^2} = \sqrt{4 + 25} = \sqrt{29}$

Let $z = (k-1) + 7i$ and $w = 8 - i$.

If $|z| = |w|$, find two values of k, $k \in \mathbf{R}$.

Given: $\qquad\qquad |z| = |w|$

$\therefore \qquad\qquad |(k-1) + 7i| = |8 - i|$

$$\sqrt{(k-1)^2 + (7)^2} = \sqrt{8^2 + (-1)^2} \qquad\qquad \left(|a + bi| = \sqrt{a^2 + b^2} \right)$$

$$(k-1)^2 + (7)^2 = 8^2 + (-1)^2 \qquad\qquad \text{(square both sides)}$$

$$k^2 - 2k + 1 + 49 = 64 + 1$$

$$k^2 - 2k - 15 = 0$$

$$(k-5)(k+3) = 0$$

$$k = 5 \quad \text{or} \quad k = -3$$

Exercise 2.4 ▼

For questions $1 - 11$, construct an Argand diagram from -6 to 6 on the real axis and $-5i$ to $5i$ on the imaginary axis.

If $z = 1 + i$ and $w = -6 + 4i$, represent each of the following on an Argand diagram:

1. z **2.** $\bar{z}$ **3.** w **4.** $\bar{w}$ **5.** $2\bar{z} + w$

6. $\frac{1}{2}z\bar{w}$ **7.** $\dfrac{w}{z}$ **8.** $\dfrac{\bar{z} - w + 3}{\bar{z} + 1}$ **9.** $\dfrac{i\bar{w}}{z}$ **10.** $\dfrac{w}{z^2}$

11. Let $w = 9 + 7i$ and $u = \dfrac{5 + i}{1 - i}$. Represent on an Argand diagram:

     (i) u **(ii)** $\dfrac{w}{u}$ **(iii)** $\dfrac{w - 4(u - 1)}{3 - u}$.

     Hence, evaluate $\left| \dfrac{w - 4(u - 1)}{3 - u} \right|$.

12. Evaluate each of the following:

     (i) $|12 - 5i|$ **(ii)** $|-3 - 5i|$ **(iii)** $|\sqrt{2} + i|$ **(iv)** $|1 - \sqrt{3}i|$

     (v) $|2 - 2\sqrt{3}i|$ **(vi)** $|-2 - \frac{3}{2}i|$ **(vii)** $|-\frac{1}{2} + \frac{\sqrt{3}}{2}i|$ **(viii)** $|\frac{1}{\sqrt{2}} - \frac{1}{\sqrt{2}}i|$

13. Let $w = \dfrac{4 - 2i}{2 + i}$.

     (i) Express w in the form $a + bi$, where $a, b \in \mathbf{R}$.   **(ii)** Evaluate $|w|$.

14. Let $z = 4 - 3i$ and $w = \dfrac{1 - \sqrt{3}i}{1 + \sqrt{3}i}$. Evaluate: **(i)** $\left| \dfrac{1}{z} \right|$ **(ii)** $|w|$.

15. Let $z = 1 + 7i$ and $w = -1 + i$. Express $\dfrac{z}{w}$ in the form $a + bi$, $\quad a, b \in \mathbf{R}$ and $i^2 = -1$.

     Verify that: **(i)** $|z| \cdot |w| = |zw|$ **(ii)** $\dfrac{|z|}{|w|} = \left| \dfrac{z}{w} \right|$.

     Solve, for real h and k: $\quad hz = \left| \dfrac{z}{w} \right| kw + 16i$.

16. If $|8 + ki| = 10$, $k \in \mathbf{R}$, find two possible values of k.

17. If $|a + ai| = |1 - 7i|$, $a \in \mathbf{R}$, find two possible values of a.

18. Let $z = (k - 1) - 5i$ and $w = -2 + 11i$.
If $|z| = |w|$, find two possible values of $k \in \mathbf{R}$.

19. Let $z = a + bi$, where a, $b \in \mathbf{R}$.
If $z - \bar{z} + |z| = 17 + 16i$, find two values of z.

20. Let $w = a + bi$. Find the complex number w such that $\sqrt{3}|w| + iw = 2 + \sqrt{2}i$.

Quadratic Equations with Complex Roots

> The equation $az^2 + bz + c = 0$ has roots given by:
> $$z = \frac{-b \pm \sqrt{b^2 - 4ac}}{2a}.$$

If $b^2 - 4ac < 0$, then the number under the square root sign will be negative, and so the solutions will be complex numbers.

Example ▼

Solve the equations: **(i)** $z^2 - 4z + 13 = 0$ **(ii)** $2z^2 + 2z + 1 = 0$.

Solution:

(i) $z^2 - 4z + 13 = 0$

$az^2 + bz + c = 0$

$a = 1, \quad b = -4, \quad c = 13$

$z = \dfrac{-b \pm \sqrt{b^2 - 4ac}}{2a}$

$z = \dfrac{4 \pm \sqrt{(-4)^2 - 4(1)(13)}}{2(1)}$

$z = \dfrac{4 \pm \sqrt{16 - 52}}{2}$

$z = \dfrac{4 \pm \sqrt{-36}}{2}$

$z = \dfrac{4 \pm 6i}{2}$

$z = 2 \pm 3i$

∴   the roots are $2 + 3i$ and $2 - 3i$.

(ii) $2z^2 + 2z + 1 = 0$

$az^2 + bz + c = 0$

$a = 2, \quad b = 2, \quad c = 1$

$z = \dfrac{-b \pm \sqrt{b^2 - 4ac}}{2a}$

$z = \dfrac{-2 \pm \sqrt{(2)^2 - 4(2)(1)}}{2(2)}$

$z = \dfrac{-2 \pm \sqrt{4 - 8}}{4}$

$z = \dfrac{-2 \pm \sqrt{-4}}{4}$

$z = \dfrac{-2 \pm 2i}{4} = \dfrac{-1 \pm i}{2}$

$z = -\tfrac{1}{2} \pm \tfrac{1}{2}i$

∴   the roots are $-\tfrac{1}{2} + \tfrac{1}{2}i$ and $-\tfrac{1}{2} - \tfrac{1}{2}i$.

Note: Notice that in both solutions the roots occur in conjugate pairs. If one root of a quadratic equation, with real coefficients, is a complex number, then the other root must also be complex and the conjugate of the first.

i.e. if $3-4i$ is a root, then $3+4i$ is also a root;
if $-2-5i$ is a root, then $-2+5i$ is also a root;
if $a+bi$ is a root, then $a-bi$ is also a root.

Conjugate Roots Theorem

> If all the coefficients of a polynomial equation are **real**, then all complex roots occur as conjugate pairs.

In other words, if one root is a complex number, then its conjugate is also a root. The Conjugate Roots Theorem can be used only if **all** the coefficients in the equation are **real**. If even one coefficient is non-real (contains an i), then the Conjugate Roots Theorem cannot be used.

The roots of the equation $z^2 - 2z + 10 = 0$ are $1+3i$ and $1-3i$.
The complex roots occur as conjugate pairs, since all the coefficients, $1, -2$ and 10, are real.
The roots of the equation $z^2 + (i-2)z + (3-i) = 0$ are $1+i$ and $1-2i$.
The complex roots do **not** occur as conjugate pairs, because the coefficients, $1, i-2$ and $3-i$ are **not** all real numbers.

Example ▼

Solve $z^2 - (2-i)z + 7 - i = 0$. Explain why the roots do not occur in conjugate pairs.

Solution:

$$z^2 - (2-i)z + 7 - i = 0$$
$$z^2 + (-2+i)z + (7-i) = 0 \qquad \text{(write in the form } az^2 + bz + c = 0)$$

$$z = \frac{-b \pm \sqrt{b^2 - 4ac}}{2a}$$

$$= \frac{-(-2+i) \pm \sqrt{(-2+i)^2 - 4(1)(7-i)}}{2(1)}$$

$$= \frac{2 - i \pm \sqrt{4 - 4i - 1 - 28 + 4i}}{2}$$

$$= \frac{2 - i \pm \sqrt{-25}}{2} = \frac{2 - i \pm 5i}{2}$$

$$z_1 = \frac{2 - i + 5i}{2} = \frac{2 + 4i}{2} = 1 + 2i$$

$$z_2 = \frac{2 - i - 5i}{2} = \frac{2 - 6i}{2} = 1 - 3i$$

Thus, the roots are $1+2i$ and $1-3i$.
They are not complex conjugates because **not** all the coefficients are real.

The results concerning the roots of a quadratic equation also hold for quadratic equations that contain complex roots.

If α and β are the roots of the equation $az^2 + bz + c = 0$, then:

$$\alpha + \beta = -\frac{b}{a} \quad \text{and} \quad \alpha\beta = \frac{c}{a}.$$

The quadratic equation can be written:

$$z^2 - (\alpha + \beta)z + \alpha\beta = 0$$

or

$$z^2 - (\text{sum of the roots})z + (\text{product of the roots}) = 0.$$

Example ▼

If $-2 + 5i$ is a root of the equation $z^2 + pz + q = 0$, $p, q \in \mathbf{R}$, write down the other root and, hence, find the value of p and the value of q.

Solution:

All the coefficients are real (given). Thus we can use the Conjugate Root Theorem.

Therefore, as $-2 + 5i$ is a root, then $-2 - 5i$ is also a root.

$z^2 - (\text{sum of the roots})z + (\text{product of the roots}) = 0$

$\quad z^2 - (-4)z + 29 = 0$

$\quad\quad z^2 + 4z + 29 = 0$

Compare to: $z^2 + pz + q = 0$

$\therefore\ p = 4 \quad \text{and} \quad q = 29$

sum of the roots
$= -2 + 5i - 2 - 5i = -4$
product of the roots
$= (-2 + 5i)(-2 - 5i) = 29$

Example ▼

Find the value of p and the value of q, $p, q \in \mathbf{R}$, if $(-1 + i)$ is a root of the equation $z^2 + (-1 + pi)z + (q - i) = 0$, and find the other root.

Solution:

$\quad\quad\quad z^2 + (-1 + pi)z + (q - i) = 0$

$(-1 + i)^2 + (-1 + pi)(-1 + i) + (q - i) = 0$ \qquad (put in $(-1 + i)$ for z)

$\quad\quad 1 - 2i - 1 + 1 - i - pi - p + q - i = 0$

$\quad\quad\quad (-p + q + 1) + (-p - 4)i = 0$ \qquad (group real and imaginary parts together)

$\therefore\ -p + q + 1 = 0$ ① $\quad$ and $\quad -p - 4 = 0$ ②

Solving the simultaneous equations ① and ② gives $p = -4$ and $q = -5$.

Thus, $\qquad z^2 + (-1 + pi)z + (q - i) = 0$

becomes $\quad z^2 + (-1 - 4i)z + (-5 - i) = 0$ $\qquad$ (put in $p = -4$ and $q = -5$)

Let $a + bi$ be the other root.

Thus, the roots are $a + bi$ and $-1 + i$.

The sum of the roots $= -(-1 - 4i) = 1 + 4i$

$\therefore \qquad a + bi - 1 + i = 1 + 4i$

$\qquad\qquad a + bi = 1 + 4i + 1 - i$

$\qquad\qquad a + bi = 2 + 3i$

Thus, the other root is $2 + 3i$.

Exercise 2.5 ▼

Solve each of the following equations for $z \in \mathbf{C}$:

1. $z^2 - 2z + 2 = 0$ $\qquad\qquad$ **2.** $z^2 - 2z + 5 = 0$ $\qquad\qquad$ **3.** $z^2 + 10z + 34 = 0$

4. $2z^2 - 2z + 1 = 0$ $\qquad\qquad$ **5.** $2z^2 + 6z + 5 = 0$ $\qquad\qquad$ **6.** $5z^2 - 2z + 10 = 0$

7. $z^2 - (1 + 4i)z - 2(3 - i) = 0$ $\qquad$ **8.** $z^2 - (3 - 2i)z - (1 + 3i) = 0$

9. $z^2 - (2 + 5i)z + 5(i - 1) = 0$ $\qquad$ **10.** $z^2 - 2(1 + i)z + (4 + 2i) = 0$

Find a quadratic equation whose roots are:

11. $-2 \pm i$ $\qquad$ **12.** $3 \pm 2i$ $\qquad$ **13.** $-1 \pm 5i$ $\qquad$ **14.** $\pm 3i$

15. $-1 \pm \sqrt{2}i$ $\qquad$ **16.** $2 \pm \sqrt{5}i$ $\qquad$ **17.** $\frac{1}{2} \pm \frac{1}{2}i$ $\qquad$ **18.** $-\frac{1}{3} \pm \frac{2}{3}i$

19. If $3 + 5i$ is a root of $z^2 + pz + q = 0$, $\quad p, q \in \mathbf{R}$, find p and q.

20. Express $\dfrac{1 + 7i}{1 - 3i}$ in the form $p + qi$.

Hence, show that $\dfrac{1 + 7i}{1 - 3i}$ is a root of the equation $z^2 + 4z + 5 = 0$, and write down the other

root in the form $a + bi$, $\quad a, b \in \mathbf{R}$.

21. Show that $\dfrac{11 - 7i}{2 + i}$ is a root of the equation $z^2 - 6z + 34 = 0$ and write down the other root in the

form $p + qi$, $\quad p, q \in \mathbf{R}$.

22. If $\dfrac{7 - 17i}{5 - i}$ is a root of $z^2 + az + b = 0$, $\quad a, b \in \mathbf{R}$, find the values of a and b.

23. If $z = \dfrac{19 - 4i}{3 - 2i} = a + bi$, find the value of a and the value of b, $\quad a, b \in \mathbf{R}$.

Verify that $z^2 - 10z + 29 = 0$.

Hence, find two complex numbers, u, such that $(u + 3i)^2 - 10(u + 3i) + 29 = 0$.

24. Show that $2 + i$ is a root of the equation $z^2 - 3(1 + i)z + 5i = 0$, and find the other root.

25. Find the value of $k \in \mathbf{R}$ if $1 + 2i$ is a root of the equation $z^2 + kz + 7 + 4i = 0$.

26. One root of the equation $z^2 + (-1 + pi)z + q(2 - i) = 0$ is $-7i$.
Find: **(i)** the value of p and the value of q **(ii)** the other root.

27. One root of the equation $z^2 - (p + i)z + qi = 0$ is $2 + 3i$.
Find the value of p, the value of q and the other root.

28. One root of the equation $z^2 - (a + 2i)z + b(1 + i) = 0$ is $2 - i$, where $a, b \in \mathbf{R}$.
Find the value of a, the value of b and the other root.

29. The equation $z^2 - 2(1 - i)z + 2(2 - i) = 0$ has roots α and β.
Evaluate: **(i)** $\alpha + \beta$ **(ii)** $\alpha\beta$ **(iii)** $\alpha^2 + \beta^2$.
Construct a quadratic equation with roots $\alpha + i$ and $\beta + i$.

Square Roots and Quadratic Equations with Complex Roots

In some problems we have to find the square root of a complex number in order to find the roots of a quadratic equation.

Example ▼

(i) Express $\sqrt{5 + 12i}$ in the form $a + bi$, $a, b \in \mathbf{R}$.

(ii) Hence, determine the two roots of the equation $z^2 - (1 + 4i)z - 5 - i = 0$.

Solution:

(i)   Let $a + bi = \sqrt{5 + 12i}$, $a, b \in \mathbf{R}$.

$$(a + bi)^2 = (\sqrt{5 + 12i})^2 \qquad \text{[square both sides]}$$
$$a^2 + 2abi - b^2 = 5 + 12i \qquad \text{[remove brackets]}$$
$$\begin{array}{ccccc} R & I & R & R & I \end{array} \qquad \text{[identify real and imaginary parts]}$$

Real parts = Real parts	**Imaginary parts = Imaginary parts**
$a^2 - b^2 = 5 \quad$ ①	$2ab = 12 \quad$ ②

Solve between equations ① and ②:

$$2ab = 12 \quad ②$$
$$ab = 6$$
$$b = \left(\frac{6}{a}\right)$$

put this into equation ①

$$a^2 - b^2 = 5 \quad ①$$
$$a^2 - \left(\frac{6}{a}\right)^2 = 5 \qquad \left[\text{replace } b \text{ with } \frac{6}{a}\right]$$
$$a^2 - \frac{36}{a^2} = 5$$
$$a^4 - 36 = 5a^2$$
$$a^4 - 5a^2 - 36 = 0$$

$$(a^2 - 9)(a^2 + 4) = 0$$
$$a^2 - 9 = 0 \quad \text{or} \quad a^2 + 4 = 0$$
$$a^2 = 9 \quad \text{or} \quad a^2 = -4$$
$$a = \pm 3 \quad \text{or} \quad a = \pm 2i$$

As $a, b \in \mathbf{R}$, the result $a = \pm 2i$ is rejected.

$$b = \frac{6}{a}$$

$a = 3$	$a = -3$
$b = \dfrac{6}{3}$	$b = \dfrac{6}{-3}$
$= 2$	$= -2$
$a = 3, \quad b = 2$	$a = -3, \quad b = -2$

Thus, $\sqrt{5 + 12i} = 3 + 2i$

or $\quad \sqrt{5 + 12i} = -3 - 2i$

[i.e. $\pm(3 + 2i)$]

(ii) $\quad z^2 - (1 + 4i)z - 5 - i = 0$

$$z^2 + (-1 - 4i)z + (-5 - i) = 0 \qquad \text{[write in the form } az^2 + bz + c = 0]$$

$$z = \frac{-b \pm \sqrt{b^2 - 4ac}}{2a}$$

$$= \frac{-(-1 - 4i) \pm \sqrt{(-1 - 4i)^2 - 4(1)(-5 - i)}}{2(1)}$$

$$= \frac{1 + 4i \pm \sqrt{1 + 8i - 16 + 20 + 4i}}{2}$$

$$= \frac{1 + 4i \pm \sqrt{5 + 12i}}{2}$$

$$= \frac{1 + 4i \pm (3 + 2i)}{2} \qquad \text{[put in } (3 + 2i) \text{ for } \sqrt{5 + 12i}]$$

$$z_1 = \frac{1 + 4i + (3 + 2i)}{2} = \frac{1 + 4i + 3 + 2i}{2} = \frac{4 + 6i}{2} = 2 + 3i$$

$$z_2 = \frac{1 + 4i - (3 + 2i)}{2} = \frac{1 + 4i - 3 - 2i}{2} = \frac{-2 + 2i}{2} = -1 + i$$

Thus the roots of $z^2 - (1 + 4i)z - 5 - i = 0$ are $2 + 3i$ and $-1 + i$.

Note: It makes no difference if we substitute $3 + 2i$ or $-3 - 2i$ for $\sqrt{5 + 12i}$.

Note: Another way of asking for $\sqrt{5 + 12i}$ to be expressed in the form $a + bi$ is:
  1. If $(a + bi)^2 = 5 + 12i$, find the values of a and b, $\quad a, b \in \mathbf{R}$.
  2. If $z^2 = 5 + 12i$ or $z = \sqrt{5 + 12i}$, find all the values of z.

1. Find two complex numbers $a + bi$ such that $(a + bi)^2 = -15 + 8i$, $\quad a, b \in \mathbf{R}$.

Express each of the following in the form $a + bi$, $\quad a, b \in \mathbf{R}$ and $i^2 = -1$:

2. $\sqrt{-3 - 4i}$ **3.** $\sqrt{8 - 6i}$ **4.** $\sqrt{-5 + 12i}$ **5.** $\sqrt{15 - 8i}$

6. $\sqrt{-21 + 20i}$ **7.** $\sqrt{-7 - 24i}$ **8.** $\sqrt{-9 - 40i}$ **9.** $\sqrt{2i}$

10. Express $\sqrt{-3 + 4i}$ in the form $a + bi$, $\quad a, b \in \mathbf{R}$ and $i^2 = -1$.
Hence, solve the equation $z^2 - 3z + (3 - i) = 0$.

11. Express $\sqrt{-24 + 10i}$ in the form $a + bi$, $\quad a, b \in \mathbf{R}$ and $i^2 = -1$.
Hence, solve the equation $z^2 - 3(1 + i)z + 2(3 + i) = 0$.

12. Express $\sqrt{15 + 8i}$ in the form $p + qi$, $\quad p, q \in \mathbf{R}$.
Hence, show that one of the roots of the equation $z^2 + (2 + i)z - (3 + i) = 0$ is real and the other is complex.

13. Express $\sqrt{3 + 4i}$ in the form $a + bi$, $\quad a, b \in \mathbf{R}$ and $i^2 = -1$.
Hence, show that one root of the equation $z^2 + (2 - i)z - 2i = 0$ is real and the other is complex.

14. Determine real numbers x and y such that $(x + yi)^2 = 5 - 12i$.
Hence, determine the two roots of the equations:
   (i) $z^2 + z + (3i - 1) = 0$ **(ii)** $z^2 - 2(1 + i)z + 5(1 - 2i) = 0$.

15. If $z^2 = 2 - 2\sqrt{3}i$, express z in the form $a + bi$, $\quad a, b \in \mathbf{R}$ and $i^2 = -1$.

Cubic Equations with Complex Roots

The Conjugate Root Theorem also applies to cubic equations.

Conjugate Root Theorem

> If all the coefficients of a polynomial equation are **real**, then all complex roots occur as conjugate pairs.

In other words, if one root is a complex number then its conjugate is also a root, provided all the coefficients are real.

Show that $-1 + 2i$ is a root of $z^3 - 2z^2 - 3z - 20 = 0$ and find the other two roots.

Solution:

Put in $(-1 + 2i)$ for z:

$z^3 - 2z^2 - 3z - 20$

$(-1 + 2i)^3 - 2(-1 + 2i)^2 - 3(-1 + 2i) - 20$

$= (11 - 2i) - 2(-3 - 4i) - 3(-1 + 2i) - 20$

$= 11 - 2i + 6 + 8i + 3 - 6i - 20$

$= 20 - 20 + 8i - 8i$

$= 0$

$\therefore$ $-1 + 2i$ is a root.

$\therefore$ $-1 - 2i$ is also a root (roots occur in conjugate pairs, as all the coefficients are real).

$(-1 + 2i)^2$
$= (-1 + 2i)(-1 + 2i)$
$= -3 - 4i$
$(-1 + 2i)^3$
$= (-1 + 2i)^2(-1 + 2i)$
$= (-3 - 4i)(-1 + 2i)$
$= 11 - 2i$

We now construct the quadratic factor using:

$z^2 - (\text{sum of the roots})z + (\text{product of the roots})$

$z^2 - (-1 + 2i - 1 - 2i)z + (-1 + 2i)(-1 - 2i)$

$z^2 + 2z + 5$

Division:

$$
\begin{array}{r}
z - 4 \\
z^2 + 2z + 5 \overline{\big)\, z^3 - 2z^2 - 3z - 20} \\
\underline{z^3 + 2z^2 + 5z} \\
-4z^2 - 8z - 20 \\
\underline{-4z^2 - 8z - 20} \\
0
\end{array}
$$

Dividing $z^3 - 2z^2 - 3z - 20$ by $z^2 + 2z + 5$ gives $z - 4$.

$\therefore$ the third factor is $z - 4$.

Let $z - 4 = 0$

$\therefore$ $z = 4$

Thus, the other two roots are $-1 - 2i$ and 4.

Note: We did not have to use long division to get the third factor.

Let the third factor be $z + k$.

$\therefore$ $(z + k)(z^2 + 2z + 5) = z^3 - 2z^2 - 3z - 20$

Comparing constants on both sides, we get:

$5k = -20$

$\therefore$ $k = -4$

Thus, the third factor is $z - 4$.

One root of the equation $z^3 + az^2 + bz - 52 = 0$, $a, b \in \mathbf{R}$ is $2 - 3i$.
Find the value of a and the value of b.

Solution:

Method 1:

$(2 - 3i)^2 = (2 - 3i)(2 - 3i) = -5 - 12i$

$(2 - 3i)^3 = (2 - 3i)^2(2 - 3i) = (-5 - 12i)(2 - 3i) = -46 - 9i$

$$z^3 + az^2 + bz - 52 = 0$$

$(2 - 3i)^3 + a(2 - 3i)^2 + b(2 - 3i) - 52 = 0$ (put in $(2 - 3i)$ for z)

$(-46 - 9i) + a(-5 - 12i) + b(2 - 3i) - 52 = 0$

$-46 - 9i - 5a - 12ai + 2b - 3bi - 52 = 0$

$(-5a + 2b - 98) + (-12a - 3b - 9)i = 0$ (group real and imaginary parts together)

∴ $-5a + 2b - 98 = 0$ ①   and $-12a - 3b - 9 = 0$ ②

Solving the simultaneous equations ① and ② gives $a = -8$ and $b = 29$.

Method 2:

If $2 - 3i$ is a root, then $2 + 3i$ is also a root.
(Roots occur in conjugate pairs as all the coefficients are real.)

The quadratic factor is given by:

$z^2 - (\text{sum of the roots})z + (\text{product of the roots})$

$z^2 - (2 - 3i + 2 + 3i)z + (2 - 3i)(2 + 3i)$

$z^2 - 4z + 13$

Let the third factor be $z + k$.

$(z + k)(z^2 - 4z + 13) = z(z^2 - 4z + 13) + k(z^2 - 4z + 13)$

$\qquad\qquad = z^3 - 4z^2 + 13z + kz^2 - 4kz + 13k$

$\qquad\qquad = z^3 + (-4 + k)z^2 + (13 - 4k)z + 13k$

∴ $z^3 + (-4 + k)z^2 + (13 - 4k)z + 13k = z^3 + az^2 + bz - 52$

Equating coefficients of like terms:

$-4 + k = a$ ① $13 - 4k = b$ ② $13k = -52$ ③

    $13k = -52$ ③

∴ $k = -4$ (replace k with -4 in ① and ②).

$-4 + k = a$ ①	$13 - 4k = b$ ②
$-4 - 4 = a$	$13 - 4(-4) = b$
$-8 = a$	$13 + 16 = b$
	$29 = b$

Thus, $a = -8$ and $b = 29$.

1. If $1 + 2i$ is a root of $z^3 + 2z^2 - 3z + 20 = 0$, find the other two roots.

2. If $-2 + 3i$ is a root of $z^3 - z^2 - 7z - 65 = 0$, find the other two roots.

3. Show that $z = 2$ is a root of the equation $z^3 - 8z^2 + 46z - 68 = 0$ and find the other two roots.

4. (i) Express in the form $a + bi$: **(a)** $(1 + i)^2$ **(b)** $(1 + i)^3$.
   (ii) Show that $1 + i$ is a root of $z^3 - 5z^2 + 8z - 6 = 0$ and find the other two roots.

5. Verify that $1 + 3i$ is a root of the equation $z^3 - 7z^2 + 20z - 50 = 0$ and find the other roots.

6. Verify that $-2 + 2i$ is a root of the equation $z^3 + 3z^2 + 4z - 8 = 0$ and find the other roots.

7. Verify that $2 - i$ is a root of the equation $z^3 - 11z + 20 = 0$ and find the other roots.

8. Verify that $2 + 3i$ is a root of the equation $2z^3 - 9z^2 + 30z - 13 = 0$ and find the other roots.

9. Verify that i is a root of the equation $z^3 - iz^2 - 9z + 9i = 0$ and find the other roots.

10. (i) Express in the form $a + bi$: **(a)** $(1 - i)^2$ **(b)** $(1 - i)^3$.
    (ii) If $1 - i$ is a root of the equation $z^3 - 4z^2 + 6z + k = 0$, $k \in \mathbf{R}$, find the value of k and the other roots.

11. If $1 - 2i$ is a root of the equation $z^3 + kz^2 + 7z + k - 2 = 0$, $k \in \mathbf{R}$, find the value of k and the other roots.

12. One root of the equation $z^3 + az^2 + bz - 4 = 0$, $a, b \in \mathbf{R}$, is $1 + i$.
    Find the value of a and the value of b.

13. One root of the equation $z^3 + pz^2 + z + q = 0$, $p, q \in \mathbf{R}$, is $4 - i$.
    Find the value of p and the value of q.

14. If $(z - 2)(z^2 + az + b) = z^3 - 4z^2 + 6z - 4$, $a, b \in \mathbf{Z}$,
    find the value of a and the value of b.

15. Let $p(z) = z^3 + (4 - 2i)z^2 + (5 - 8i)z - 10i$, where $i^2 = -1$.
    Determine the real numbers a and b if $p(z) = (z - 2i)(z^2 + az + b)$.

16. (i) Factorise $z^2 - 5z + 6$ and, hence, solve the equation $z^2 - 5z + 6 = 0$.
    (ii) Show that $z^2 - 5z + 6$ is a factor of $z^3 + (-4 + i)z^2 + (1 - 5i)z + 6(1 + i)$.
    (iii) Find the three roots of the equation $z^3 + (-4 + i)z^2 + (1 - 5i)z + 6(1 + i) = 0$.

17. (i) Factorise $z^2 - 4$ and, hence or otherwise, solve the equation $z^2 - 4 = 0$.
    (ii) Show that $z^2 - 4$ is a factor of $z^3 + (3 + i)z^2 - 4z - 4(3 + i)$.
    (iii) Find the three roots of the equation $z^3 + (3 + i)z^2 - 4z - 4(3 + i) = 0$.

18. ki is a root of the equation $2z^3 - z^2 + 18z - 9 = 0$, $k \in \mathbf{R}$.
    Find the values of k and the three roots of the equation $2z^3 - z^2 + 18z - 9 = 0$.

Polar Coordinates and the Polar Form of a Complex Number

Polar Coordinates

Consider the complex number $z = x + yi$. The position of z on the Argand diagram can be given by Cartesian, or rectangular coordinates, (x, y). An alternative way of describing the position of z is to give its **modulus, r** and its **argument, θ**.

(r, θ) are called the polar coordinates of the complex number.

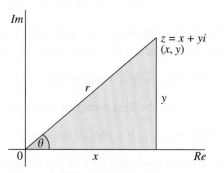

1. Modulus	2. Argument
The modulus $= r = \lvert z \rvert = \sqrt{x^2 + y^2}$.	The argument $= \theta$ (usually in radians).
The modulus is the distance from the origin to the point representing the complex number on the Argand diagram.	The argument, θ, is the angle between the positive real-axis and the line from the origin to the point $z = x + yi$.

Note: Drawing a diagram can be a very good aid in calculating θ.

Polar Form

Having calculated r and θ, there is a simple connection between the Cartesian coordinates (x, y) and the polar coordinates (r, θ).

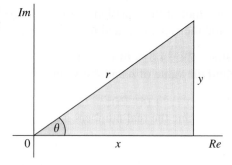

$$\frac{x}{r} = \cos\theta \qquad \Big| \qquad \frac{y}{r} = \sin\theta$$
$$x = r\cos\theta \qquad \Big| \qquad y = r\sin\theta$$

Now we can write $z = x + yi$ in terms of r and θ.

$$z = x + yi$$
$$z = (r\cos\theta) + (r\sin\theta)i$$
$$z = r(\cos\theta + i\sin\theta)$$

This is called the **polar form** of the complex number.

> The polar form of the complex number $z = x + yi$ is:
> $$z = r(\cos\theta + i\sin\theta).$$

Note: It is conventional to write i before $\sin\theta$.
In other words, $i\sin\theta$ is preferable to $\sin\theta i$.

Express each of these complex numbers in the form $r(\cos\theta + i\sin\theta)$, where $i^2 = -1$:

(i) $-1 + i$ **(ii)** $-\sqrt{3} - i$ **(iii)** $\dfrac{1}{2} + \dfrac{\sqrt{3}}{2}i$ **(iv)** $-6i$.

Solution:

(i) $-1 + i = (-1,\ 1)$

$r = |-1 + i| = \sqrt{(-1)^2 + (1)^2} = \sqrt{1 + 1} = \sqrt{2}$

$\tan\alpha = \dfrac{1}{1} = 1 \quad\Rightarrow\quad \alpha = \dfrac{\pi}{4}$

$\therefore\quad \theta = \pi - \dfrac{\pi}{4} = \dfrac{3\pi}{4}$

$\therefore\quad -1 + i = \sqrt{2}\left(\cos\dfrac{3\pi}{4} + i\sin\dfrac{3\pi}{4}\right)$

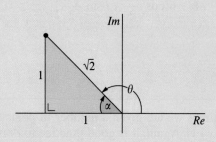

(ii) $-\sqrt{3} - i = (-\sqrt{3},\ -1)$

$r = |-\sqrt{3} - i| = \sqrt{(-\sqrt{3})^2 + (-1)^2} = \sqrt{3 + 1} = \sqrt{4} = 2$

$\tan\alpha = \dfrac{1}{\sqrt{3}} \quad\Rightarrow\quad \alpha = \dfrac{\pi}{6}$

$\therefore\quad \theta = \pi + \dfrac{\pi}{6} = \dfrac{7\pi}{6}$

$\therefore\quad -\sqrt{3} - i = 2\left(\cos\dfrac{7\pi}{6} + i\sin\dfrac{7\pi}{6}\right)$

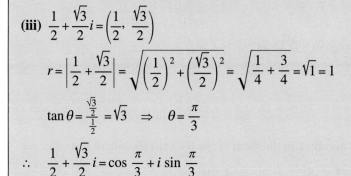

(iii) $\dfrac{1}{2} + \dfrac{\sqrt{3}}{2}i = \left(\dfrac{1}{2},\ \dfrac{\sqrt{3}}{2}\right)$

$r = \left|\dfrac{1}{2} + \dfrac{\sqrt{3}}{2}\right| = \sqrt{\left(\dfrac{1}{2}\right)^2 + \left(\dfrac{\sqrt{3}}{2}\right)^2} = \sqrt{\dfrac{1}{4} + \dfrac{3}{4}} = \sqrt{1} = 1$

$\tan\theta = \dfrac{\frac{\sqrt{3}}{2}}{\frac{1}{2}} = \sqrt{3} \quad\Rightarrow\quad \theta = \dfrac{\pi}{3}$

$\therefore\quad \dfrac{1}{2} + \dfrac{\sqrt{3}}{2}i = \cos\dfrac{\pi}{3} + i\sin\dfrac{\pi}{3}$

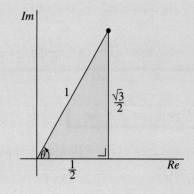

(iv) $-6i = 0 - 6i = (0, -6)$

$r = |0 - 6i| = \sqrt{0^2 + (-6)^2} = \sqrt{0 + 36} = \sqrt{36} = 6$

$\theta = \dfrac{3\pi}{2}$

$\therefore \quad -6i = 6\left(\cos\dfrac{3\pi}{2} + i\sin\dfrac{3\pi}{2}\right)$

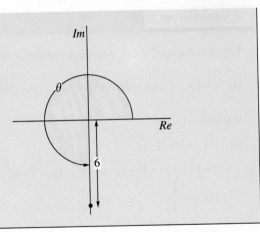

Sometimes we are given a number in polar form $r(\cos\theta + i\sin\theta)$, and asked to write it in Cartesian form, $x + yi$. Again, it is good practice to draw a diagram.

Example ▼

Express $4\left(\cos\dfrac{5\pi}{6} + i\sin\dfrac{5\pi}{6}\right)$ in the form $x + yi$.

Solution:

$\dfrac{5\pi}{6}$ is in the 2nd quadrant, so:

$\cos\dfrac{5\pi}{6} = -\cos\dfrac{\pi}{6} = -\dfrac{\sqrt{3}}{2}$

$\sin\dfrac{5\pi}{6} = \sin\dfrac{\pi}{6} = \dfrac{1}{2}$

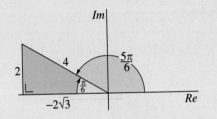

$\therefore \quad 4\left(\cos\dfrac{5\pi}{6} + i\sin\dfrac{5\pi}{6}\right) = 4\left(-\dfrac{\sqrt{3}}{2} + \dfrac{1}{2}i\right) = -2\sqrt{3} + 2i$

Exercise 2.8 ▼

Express each of the following complex numbers in the form $r(\cos\theta + i\sin\theta)$, where $i^2 = -1$:

1. $1 + i$ 　　　**2.** $\sqrt{3} + i$ 　　　**3.** -5 　　　**4.** $3i$

5. $-2i$ 　　　**6.** $-1 - \sqrt{3}i$ 　　　**7.** $1 - i$ 　　　**8.** $2 - 2i$

9. $-\sqrt{2} - \sqrt{2}i$ 　　**10.** $-3 + \sqrt{3}i$ 　　**11.** $\dfrac{1}{2} - \dfrac{\sqrt{3}}{2}i$ 　　**12.** $-\dfrac{1}{\sqrt{2}} + \dfrac{1}{\sqrt{2}}i$

Express each of the following in the form $a + bi$:

13. $\cos\dfrac{\pi}{2} + i\sin\dfrac{\pi}{2}$ 　　　**14.** $\sqrt{2}\left(\cos\dfrac{\pi}{4} + i\sin\dfrac{\pi}{4}\right)$ 　　　**15.** $6\left(\cos\dfrac{2\pi}{3} + i\sin\dfrac{2\pi}{3}\right)$

16. $2\sqrt{2}\left(\cos\dfrac{3\pi}{4} + i\sin\dfrac{3\pi}{4}\right)$ 　　**17.** $10\left(\cos\dfrac{5\pi}{6} + i\sin\dfrac{5\pi}{6}\right)$ 　　**18.** $2\left(\cos\dfrac{4\pi}{3} + i\sin\dfrac{4\pi}{3}\right)$

Express each of the following complex numbers in the form $r(\cos \theta + i \sin \theta)$, where $i^2 = -1$:

19. $(1+i)^2$

20. $\dfrac{2}{1-i}$

21. $\dfrac{2}{\sqrt{3}+i}$

22. $\dfrac{1}{(1-i)^2}$

23. $z_1 = 2(\cos \pi + i \sin \pi)$ and $z_2 = 5\left(\cos \dfrac{\pi}{2} + i \sin \dfrac{\pi}{2}\right)$, where $i^2 = -1$.

Calculate $z_1 z_2$ in the form $x + yi$, where $x, y \in \mathbf{R}$.

24. $z_1 = \sqrt{2}\left(\cos \dfrac{\pi}{4} + i \sin \dfrac{\pi}{4}\right)$ and $z_2 = 4\left(\cos \dfrac{3\pi}{2} + i \sin \dfrac{3\pi}{2}\right)$, where $i^2 = -1$.

Calculate $z_1 z_2$ in the form $x + yi$, where $x, y \in \mathbf{R}$.

25. $z_1 = 4\left(\cos \dfrac{\pi}{3} + i \sin \dfrac{\pi}{3}\right)$ and $z_2 = 2\left(\cos \dfrac{2\pi}{3} + i \sin \dfrac{2\pi}{3}\right)$, where $i^2 = -1$.

Calculate $\sqrt{z_1 z_2}$.

26. $z_1 = 2\left(\cos \dfrac{\pi}{2} + i \sin \dfrac{\pi}{2}\right)$ and $z_2 = \left(\cos \dfrac{\pi}{6} + i \sin \dfrac{\pi}{6}\right)$.

Calculate $\dfrac{z_1}{z_2}$ in the form $x + yi$, where $x, y \in \mathbf{R}$

27. $(a + bi)(2 + 5i) = 7 + 3i$. Express $a + bi$ in the form $r \cos \theta + i \sin \theta$.

De Moivre's Theorem

$$[r(\cos \theta + i \sin \theta)]^n = r^n(\cos n\theta + i \sin n\theta)], \text{ where } n \in \mathbf{Q}.$$

There are three applications of De Moivre's Theorem

1. Finding powers of complex numbers
2. Proving trigonometric identities
3. Finding roots of complex numbers.

I. Finding Powers of Complex Numbers

Method:

1. Write the number in polar form.
2. Apply De Moivre's Theorem.
3. Simplify the result.

Note: After applying De Moivre's Theorem the angle can be very large. However, we can keep subtracting 2π until the angle is in the range $0 \leqslant \theta \leqslant 2\pi$.

Express $(-1+i)^{10}$ in the form $x + yi$, $\quad x, y \in \mathbf{R}$ and $i^2 = -1$.

Solution:

1. $r = |-1 + i| = \sqrt{(-1)^2 + 1^2} = \sqrt{1 + 1} = \sqrt{2}$

$\tan \alpha = \dfrac{1}{1} = 1 \quad \Rightarrow \quad \alpha = \dfrac{\pi}{4}$

$\theta = \pi - \dfrac{\pi}{4} = \dfrac{3\pi}{4}$

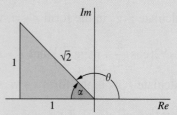

$\therefore \quad (-1 + i) = \sqrt{2}\left(\cos \dfrac{3\pi}{4} + i \sin \dfrac{3\pi}{4}\right)$ (rectangular form to polar form)

2. $\therefore \quad (-1 + i)^{10} = \left[\sqrt{2}\left(\cos \dfrac{3\pi}{4} + i \sin \dfrac{3\pi}{4}\right)\right]^{10}$ (raise both sides to the power of 10)

$= (\sqrt{2})^{10}\left[\cos 10\left(\dfrac{3\pi}{4}\right) + i \sin 10\left(\dfrac{3\pi}{4}\right)\right]$ (apply De Moivre's Theorem)

3. $\quad = 32\left(\cos \dfrac{30\pi}{4} + i \sin \dfrac{30\pi}{4}\right)$ $\left((\sqrt{2})^{10} = (2^{1/2})^{10} = 2^5 = 32\right)$

$= 32\left(\cos \dfrac{3\pi}{2} + i \sin \dfrac{3\pi}{2}\right)$ $\left(\tfrac{30}{4}\pi = 7\tfrac{1}{2}\pi = \tfrac{3}{2}\pi + 6\pi = \tfrac{3}{2}\pi + 3(2\pi)\right)$

$= 32(0 - i) = 0 - 32i$

$\therefore \quad (-1 + i)^{10} = 0 - 32i$

Use De Moivre's Theorem to write each of the following in the form $a + bi$:

1. $\left(\cos \dfrac{\pi}{3} + i \sin \dfrac{\pi}{3}\right)^6$ **2.** $\left(\cos \dfrac{\pi}{5} + i \sin \dfrac{\pi}{5}\right)^5$

3. $\left(\cos \dfrac{\pi}{4} + i \sin \dfrac{\pi}{4}\right)^{10}$ **4.** $\left(\cos \dfrac{\pi}{8} + i \sin \dfrac{\pi}{8}\right)^{12}$

5. $\left[2\left(\cos \dfrac{\pi}{3} + i \sin \dfrac{\pi}{3}\right)\right]^6$ **6.** $\left[\sqrt{2}\left(\cos \dfrac{\pi}{4} + i \sin \dfrac{\pi}{4}\right)\right]^6$

7. $\left(\cos \dfrac{\pi}{12} + i \sin \dfrac{\pi}{12}\right)^8$ **8.** $\left(\cos \dfrac{\pi}{6} + i \sin \dfrac{\pi}{6}\right)^7$

9. Express $\sqrt{3} + i$ in the form $r(\cos \theta + i \sin \theta)$, where $i^2 = -1$.
Hence, use De Moivre's Theorem to express $(\sqrt{3} + i)^3$ in the form $a + bi$.

Use De Moivre's Theorem to write each of the following in the form $x + yi$:

10. $(1 + i)^8$ **11.** $(-1 + i)^4$ **12.** $(-\sqrt{3} - i)^3$ **13.** $(-2 - 2i)^5$

14. $(\sqrt{2} - \sqrt{2}i)^6$ **15.** $(2 - 2\sqrt{3}i)^4$ **16.** $\left(\dfrac{\sqrt{3}}{2} + \dfrac{1}{2}i\right)^9$ **17.** $\left(\dfrac{1}{2} - \dfrac{\sqrt{3}}{2}i\right)^{20}$

18. Show that: $2(1 - i)^4 = (1 + \sqrt{3}i)^3$.

19. Evaluate: $\left(\cos \dfrac{2\pi}{3} + i \sin \dfrac{2\pi}{3}\right)^4 \left(\cos \dfrac{\pi}{3} + i \sin \dfrac{\pi}{3}\right)^2$.

20. Express $\dfrac{1 + 3i}{2 + i}$ in the form $r(\cos \theta + i \sin \theta)$, where $i^2 = -1$.

     Hence, evaluate $\left(\dfrac{1 + 3i}{2 + i}\right)^{10}$.

21. $z = \dfrac{1 + \sqrt{3}i}{2}$. Show that $z^{13} = z$.

22. (i) Express $\dfrac{\sqrt{3} + i}{1 + \sqrt{3}i}$ in the form $r(\cos \theta + i \sin \theta)$, where $i^2 = -1$.

     (ii) Hence, evaluate $\left(\dfrac{\sqrt{3} + i}{1 + \sqrt{3}i}\right)^6$.

2. Proving Trigonometric Identities

De Moivre's Theorem can be used to prove trigonometric identities by expressing $\cos n\theta$ and $\sin n\theta$ as polynomials in $\cos \theta$ and $\sin \theta$, respectively.

Example ▼

Using De Moivre's Theorem, prove that: $\cos 3\theta = 4 \cos^3 \theta - 3 \cos \theta$.

Solution:

De Moivre's Theorem: $(\cos \theta + i \sin \theta)^n = \cos n\theta + i \sin n\theta$.

Therefore, by De Moivre's Theorem:

$\cos 3\theta + i \sin 3\theta = (\cos \theta + i \sin \theta)^3$ (put in 3 for n on both sides)

$$= \binom{3}{0} \cos^3 \theta + \binom{3}{1} \cos^2 \theta (i \sin \theta) + \binom{3}{2} \cos \theta (i \sin \theta)^2 + \binom{3}{3} (i \sin \theta)^3$$

$$= \cos^3 \theta + 3 \cos^2 \theta (i \sin \theta) + 3 \cos \theta (i^2 \sin^2 \theta) + i^3 \sin^3 \theta$$

$\cos 3\theta + i \sin 3\theta = \cos^3 \theta + i\, 3 \cos^2 \theta \sin \theta - 3 \cos \theta \sin^2 \theta - i \sin^3 \theta$ $(i^2 = -1,\ i^3 = -i)$

   R I R I R I

Equating the real parts:

$\cos 3\theta = \cos^3 \theta - 3 \cos \theta \sin^2 \theta$

$\cos 3\theta = \cos^3 \theta - 3 \cos \theta (1 - \cos^2 \theta)$ $(\sin^2 \theta = 1 - \cos^2 \theta)$

$\cos 3\theta = \cos^3 \theta - 3 \cos \theta + 3 \cos^3 \theta$

$\cos 3\theta = 4 \cos^3 \theta - 3 \cos \theta$

1. Using De Moivre's Theorem, prove that:
   (i) $\sin 2\theta = 2 \sin \theta \cos \theta$ **(ii)** $\cos 2\theta = \cos^2 \theta - \sin^2 \theta$.
   Hence, express $\tan 2\theta$ in terms of $\tan \theta$.

2. Using De Moivre's Theorem, prove that:
   (i) $\sin 3\theta = 3 \cos^2 \theta \sin \theta - \sin^3 \theta = 3 \sin \theta - 4 \sin^3 \theta$
   (ii) $\cos 3\theta = \cos^3 \theta - 3 \cos \theta \sin^2 \theta = 4 \cos^3 \theta - 3 \cos \theta$.
   Hence, express $\tan 3\theta$ in terms of $\tan \theta$.

3. Using De Moivre's Theorem, prove that:
   (i) $\cos 4\theta = 8 \cos^4 \theta - 8 \cos^2 \theta + 1$
   (ii) $\sin 4\theta = 4 \cos^3 \theta \sin \theta - 4 \cos \theta \sin^3 \theta$.
   Hence, express $\tan 4\theta$ in terms of $\tan \theta$.

4. Using De Moivre's Theorem, prove that:
   (i) $\sin 5\theta = 16 \sin^5 \theta - 20 \sin^3 \theta + 5 \sin \theta$
   (ii) $\cos 5\theta = 16 \cos^5 \theta - 20 \cos^3 \theta + 5 \cos \theta$.

3. Finding Roots of Complex Numbers

From trigonometry we know that:

$\cos \theta = \cos(\theta \pm 2\pi) = \cos(\theta \pm 4\pi) = \cos(\theta \pm 6\pi) = \cos(\theta \pm 2n\pi), \quad n \in \mathbf{Z}.$
$\sin \theta = \sin(\theta \pm 2\pi) = \cos(\theta \pm 4\pi) = \cos(\theta \pm 6\pi) = \cos(\theta \pm 2n\pi), \quad n \in \mathbf{Z}.$

In other words, when 2π, 4π, 6π, ... is added to, or subtracted from, an angle, the value of sine or cosine is unchanged.

Thus, we can write:

$r(\cos \theta + i \sin \theta) = r[\cos(\theta + 2n\pi) + i \sin(\theta + 2n\pi)]$, for $n \in \mathbf{Z}.$

When a complex number is written in the form $r[\cos(\theta + 2n\pi) + i \sin(\theta + 2n\pi)]$, the complex number is said to be written in **general polar form**.

Method for Finding Roots:

> **1.** Write the number in polar form.
> **2.** Write the number in general polar form.
> **3.** Apply De Moivre's Theorem.
> **4.** Let $n = 0, 1, 2, ...$ (as required).

Use De Moivre's Theorem to find the three roots of the equation $z^3 - 8i = 0$.

Solution:

$$z^3 - 8i = 0$$
$$z^3 = 8i$$
$$z^3 = 0 + 8i \qquad \text{(rectangular form)}$$

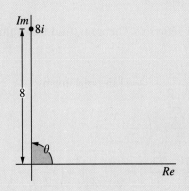

1. Write $0 + 8i$ in polar form.

$$0 + 8i = (0, 8)$$
$$r = 8 \quad \text{and} \quad \theta = \frac{\pi}{2}$$

Polar form: $0 + 8i = 8\left(\cos \dfrac{\pi}{2} + i \sin \dfrac{\pi}{2}\right)$

2. Write in general polar form.

$$8\left[\cos\left(\frac{\pi}{2} + 2n\pi\right) + i \sin\left(\frac{\pi}{2} + 2n\pi\right)\right] \qquad \text{(add } 2n\pi \text{ to the angle)}$$
$$= 8\left[\cos\left(\frac{\pi + 4n\pi}{2}\right) + i \sin\left(\frac{\pi + 4n\pi}{2}\right)\right] \qquad \left(\frac{\pi}{2} + 2n\pi = \frac{\pi + 4n\pi}{2}\right)$$

3. Apply De Moivre's Theorem.

$$z^3 = 8\left[\cos\left(\frac{\pi + 4n\pi}{2}\right) + i \sin\left(\frac{\pi + 4n\pi}{2}\right)\right]$$
$$z = \left[8\left[\cos\left(\frac{\pi + 4n\pi}{2}\right) + i \sin\left(\frac{\pi + 4n\pi}{2}\right)\right]\right]^{1/3} \qquad \text{(take the cube root of both sides)}$$
$$z = 8^{1/3}\left[\cos\frac{1}{3}\left(\frac{\pi + 4n\pi}{2}\right) + i \sin\frac{1}{3}\left(\frac{\pi + 4n\pi}{2}\right)\right] \qquad \text{(apply De Moivre's Theorem)}$$
$$z = 2\left[\cos\left(\frac{\pi + 4n\pi}{6}\right) + i \sin\left(\frac{\pi + 4n\pi}{6}\right)\right]$$

4. Let $n = 0$, 1 and 2 to get the three different roots.

(**Note:** Letting $n = 3, 4, 5, \ldots$ merely regenerates the same roots.)

$n = 0$: $\quad z = 2\left(\cos \dfrac{\pi}{6} + i \sin \dfrac{\pi}{6}\right) = 2\left(\dfrac{\sqrt{3}}{2} + \dfrac{1}{2}i\right) = \sqrt{3} + i$

$n = 1$: $\quad z = 2\left(\cos \dfrac{5\pi}{6} + i \sin \dfrac{5\pi}{6}\right) = 2\left(-\dfrac{\sqrt{3}}{2} + \dfrac{1}{2}i\right) = -\sqrt{3} + i$

$n = 2$: $\quad z = 2\left(\cos \dfrac{9\pi}{6} + i \sin \dfrac{9\pi}{6}\right) = 2\left(\cos \dfrac{3\pi}{2} + i \sin \dfrac{3\pi}{2}\right) = 2(0 - i) = -2i$

Notes: **1.** The same method is used if the index is a rational number (fraction).
For example, $(1 - \sqrt{3}i)^{3/2}$.

2. The number of different roots is the same as the bottom number in the fraction.
Thus, $(1 - \sqrt{3}i)^{3/2}$ will have two different roots.

Express $-\dfrac{1}{2}+\dfrac{\sqrt{3}}{2}i$ in the form $r(\cos\theta + i\sin\theta)$ where $i^2 = -1$.

Using De Moivre's Theorem, find two values of $\left(-\dfrac{1}{2}+\dfrac{\sqrt{3}}{2}i\right)^{3/2}$.

Solution:

1. Write $\left(-\dfrac{1}{2}+\dfrac{\sqrt{3}}{2}i\right)$ in polar form.

$$-\frac{1}{2}+\frac{\sqrt{3}}{2}i = \left(-\frac{1}{2},\frac{\sqrt{3}}{2}\right)$$

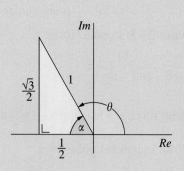

$$r = \left|-\frac{1}{2}+\frac{\sqrt{3}}{2}i\right| = \sqrt{\left(-\frac{1}{2}\right)^2 + \left(\frac{\sqrt{3}}{2}\right)^2} = \sqrt{\frac{1}{4}+\frac{3}{4}} = \sqrt{1} = 1$$

$$\tan\alpha = \frac{\frac{\sqrt{3}}{2}}{\frac{1}{2}} = \sqrt{3} \quad\Rightarrow\quad \alpha = \frac{\pi}{3}$$

$$\therefore\ \theta = \pi - \frac{\pi}{3} = \frac{2\pi}{3}$$

$$\therefore\ -\frac{1}{2}+\frac{\sqrt{3}}{2}i = 1\left(\cos\frac{2\pi}{3}+i\sin\frac{2\pi}{3}\right) = \cos\frac{2\pi}{3}+i\sin\frac{2\pi}{3}$$

2. Write in general polar form.

$$\cos\left(\frac{2\pi}{3}+2n\pi\right)+i\sin\left(\frac{2\pi}{3}+2n\pi\right) \qquad \text{(add } 2n\pi \text{ to the angle)}$$

$$= \cos\left(\frac{2\pi+6n\pi}{3}\right)+i\sin\left(\frac{2\pi+6n\pi}{3}\right) \qquad \left(\frac{2\pi}{3}+2n\pi = \frac{2\pi+6n\pi}{3}\right)$$

3. Apply De Moivre's Theorem.

$$\left(-\frac{1}{2}+\frac{\sqrt{3}}{2}i\right) = \cos\left(\frac{2\pi+6n\pi}{3}\right)+i\sin\left(\frac{2\pi+6n\pi}{3}\right)$$

$$\left(-\frac{1}{2}+\frac{\sqrt{3}}{2}i\right)^{3/2} = \left[\cos\left(\frac{2\pi+6n\pi}{3}\right)+i\sin\left(\frac{2\pi+6n\pi}{3}\right)\right]^{3/2} \qquad \left(\begin{array}{c}\text{raise both sides to the}\\ \text{power of } \frac{3}{2}\end{array}\right)$$

$$\left(-\frac{1}{2}+\frac{\sqrt{3}}{2}i\right)^{3/2} = \cos\frac{3}{2}\left(\frac{2\pi+6n\pi}{3}\right)+i\sin\frac{3}{2}\left(\frac{2\pi+6n\pi}{3}\right) \qquad \text{(apply De Moivre's Theorem)}$$

$$\left(-\frac{1}{2}+\frac{\sqrt{3}}{2}i\right)^{3/2} = \cos(\pi+3n\pi)+i\sin(\pi+3n\pi)$$

4. Let $n=0$ and 1 to find the two roots.

(**Note:** Letting $n = 2, 3, 4, ...$ merely regenerates the same roots.)

$n=0$: $\quad \cos\pi + i\sin\pi = -1+i(0) = -1$

$n=1$: $\quad \cos 4\pi + i\sin 4\pi = \cos 2\pi + i\sin 2\pi = 1+i(0) = 1$

1. Express -1 in the form $r(\cos \theta + i \sin \theta)$, where $i^2 = -1$.
   Use De Moivre's Theorem to find the three roots of the equation $z^3 = -1$.
   If the roots are z_1, z_2 and z_3, show that $z_1 + z_2 + z_3 = 0$.

2. Express $-8i$ in the form $r(\cos \theta + i \sin \theta)$, where $i^2 = -1$.
   Use De Moivre's Theorem to find the three roots of the equation $z^3 + 8i = 0$.
   If the roots are α, β and γ, show that $\alpha + \beta + \gamma = 0$.

Use De Moivre's Theorem to find all the solutions of each of the following equations:

3. $z^2 = -4i$

4. $z^2 = 2 - 2\sqrt{3}i$

5. $z^3 = -8$

6. $z^4 = 1$

7. $z^3 = -64i$

8. $z^3 = 27i$

9. Use De Moivre's Theorem to find the six roots of the equation $z^6 + 64 = 0$.

10. Write $-8 - 8\sqrt{3}i$ in the form $r(\cos \theta + i \sin \theta)$, where $i^2 = -1$.
    Use De Moivre's Theorem to find the four roots of the equation $z^4 = -8 - 8\sqrt{3}i$.

11. Write $\dfrac{1}{2} - \dfrac{\sqrt{3}}{2}i$ in the form $r(\cos \theta + i \sin \theta)$, where $i^2 = -1$.

    Using De Moivre's Theorem, find the two values of $\left(\dfrac{1}{2} - \dfrac{\sqrt{3}}{2}i\right)^{3/2}$.

12. Write $2(-1 + \sqrt{3}i)$ in the form $r(\cos \theta + i \sin \theta)$, where $i^2 = -1$.
    Using De Moivre's Theorem, find the two values of $[2(-1 + \sqrt{3}i)]^{3/2}$.

13. Write $4i$ in the form $r(\cos \theta + i \sin \theta)$, where $i^2 = -1$.
    Using De Moivre's Theorem, find the two values of $(4i)^{5/2}$.

MATRICES

Matrices

Information can be neatly presented as an array of rows (horizontal lines of numbers) and columns (vertical lines of numbers).
Train timetables and football league results very often use this form of presentation.
Such an arrangement is called a '**matrix**'.

The first matrix on the right shows the number of matches won (W), drawn (D) and lost (L) by four teams, A, B, C and D in a league. The matrix has 4 rows and 3 columns and is said to be a 4×3 matrix. The second matrix, points (Pt), shows that there are 3 points for a win, 1 for a draw and 0 if a team loses. The matrix has 3 rows and 1 column and is said to be a 3×1 matrix.

$$
\begin{array}{c}
\begin{array}{cccc} W & D & L & Pt \end{array} \\
\begin{array}{c} A \\ B \\ C \\ D \end{array}
\begin{pmatrix} 4 & 1 & 1 \\ 2 & 2 & 2 \\ 2 & 1 & 3 \\ 1 & 2 & 3 \end{pmatrix}
\begin{pmatrix} 3 \\ 1 \\ 0 \end{pmatrix}
\end{array}
$$

If you multiply a row in the first matrix by the column in the second, you get the number of points a team achieved (where the row represents the team's performance).
For example: number of points for $A = 4(3) + 1(1) + 1(0) = 12 + 1 + 0 = 13$ (similarly for B, C and D).

Dimensions of a Matrix

The dimensions of a matrix are: (number of rows) × (number of columns).
A matrix with m rows and n columns is said to be an $m \times n$ matrix.
On our course we will meet only matrices of order 1×2, 2×2 and 2×1.
Here are some examples of matrices:

$$A = (5 \quad 8)$$

order
1×2

$$B = \begin{pmatrix} 1 & -2 \\ -3 & 5 \end{pmatrix}$$

order
2×2

$$C = \begin{pmatrix} -4 \\ 7 \end{pmatrix}$$

order
2×1

Note: Matrices are indicated by capital letters.
The numbers in a matrix are called **elements** of the matrix.

Square Matrix

A square matrix has the same number of rows and columns; its order is of the form $m \times m$.

For example, $\begin{pmatrix} -1 & 2 \\ 3 & -8 \end{pmatrix}$ is a square matrix.

Equal Matrices

If two matrices are equal, then their corresponding elements must be equal.

Consider the matrices $M = \begin{pmatrix} a & c \\ b & d \end{pmatrix}$ and $N = \begin{pmatrix} 1 & -2 \\ 3 & 5 \end{pmatrix}$.

If $M = N$, then $a = 1$, $b = 3$, $c = -2$ and $d = 5$.

Multiplication by a Scalar

To multiply a matrix by a scalar (a number), multiply each element of the matrix by the number.

For example: $-3\begin{pmatrix} -2 & 1 \\ 3 & -4 \end{pmatrix} = \begin{pmatrix} 6 & -3 \\ -9 & 12 \end{pmatrix}$.

Addition and Subtraction of Matrices

Matrices can only be added, or subtracted, if they have the same dimensions.
We simply add, or subtract, corresponding elements.

Example ▼

If $A = \begin{pmatrix} 2 & 1 \\ -3 & 4 \end{pmatrix}$ and $B = \begin{pmatrix} 3 & 0 \\ -1 & 5 \end{pmatrix}$,

(i) simplify $3A + 2B$
(ii) find the matrix C such that $C + 2A = B$.

Solution:

(i)

$$3A + 2B$$

$$= 3\begin{pmatrix} 2 & 1 \\ -3 & 4 \end{pmatrix} + 2\begin{pmatrix} 3 & 0 \\ -1 & 5 \end{pmatrix}$$

$$= \begin{pmatrix} 6 & 3 \\ -9 & 12 \end{pmatrix} + \begin{pmatrix} 6 & 0 \\ -2 & 10 \end{pmatrix}$$

$$= \begin{pmatrix} 6+6 & 3+0 \\ -9-2 & 12+10 \end{pmatrix}$$

$$= \begin{pmatrix} 12 & 3 \\ -11 & 22 \end{pmatrix}$$

(ii) $C + 2A = B$

$$C = B - 2A$$

$$C = \begin{pmatrix} 3 & 0 \\ -1 & 5 \end{pmatrix} - 2\begin{pmatrix} 2 & 1 \\ -3 & 4 \end{pmatrix}$$

$$C = \begin{pmatrix} 3 & 0 \\ -1 & 5 \end{pmatrix} - \begin{pmatrix} 4 & 2 \\ -6 & 8 \end{pmatrix}$$

$$C = \begin{pmatrix} 3-4 & 0-2 \\ -1+6 & 5-8 \end{pmatrix}$$

$$C = \begin{pmatrix} -1 & -2 \\ 5 & -3 \end{pmatrix}$$

$$M = \begin{pmatrix} 3 & -1 \\ 2 & 4 \end{pmatrix}, \quad N = \begin{pmatrix} 5 & -2 \\ -3 & 1 \end{pmatrix} \text{ and } X = \begin{pmatrix} -1 & 1 \\ 12 & 10 \end{pmatrix}.$$

If $aM + bN = X$, $\quad a, b \in \mathbf{R}$, find the value of a and the value of b.

Solution:

$$aM + bN = X$$

$$a\begin{pmatrix} 3 & -1 \\ 2 & 4 \end{pmatrix} + b\begin{pmatrix} 5 & -2 \\ -3 & 1 \end{pmatrix} = \begin{pmatrix} -1 & 1 \\ 12 & 10 \end{pmatrix}$$

$$\begin{pmatrix} 3a & -a \\ 2a & 4a \end{pmatrix} + \begin{pmatrix} 5b & -2b \\ -3b & b \end{pmatrix} = \begin{pmatrix} -1 & 1 \\ 12 & 10 \end{pmatrix} \qquad \left(\begin{array}{c}\text{multiply the matrices } M \text{ and } N \\ \text{by the scalars } a \text{ and } b\end{array}\right)$$

$$\begin{pmatrix} 3a + 5b & -a - 2b \\ 2a - 3b & 4a + b \end{pmatrix} = \begin{pmatrix} -1 & 1 \\ 12 & 10 \end{pmatrix} \qquad \text{(add corresponding elements)}$$

$\therefore \quad 3a + 5b = -1 \quad ① \quad \text{and} \quad -a - 2b = 1 \quad ② \qquad \text{(equate corresponding elements)}$

Solving the simultaneous equations ① and ② gives $a = 3$ and $b = -2$.

Note: The other two equations, $2a - 3b = 12$ and $4a + b = 10$, are satisfied by these values.

---

1. If $A = \begin{pmatrix} 3 & 1 \\ 4 & 5 \end{pmatrix}$ and $B = \begin{pmatrix} 2 & 4 \\ 3 & 7 \end{pmatrix}$, find:

   (i) $A + B$ **(ii)** $A - B$ **(iii)** $2A$ **(iv)** $3B$ **(v)** $3B - 2A$.

2. If $A = \begin{pmatrix} 2 & 0 \\ -1 & 3 \end{pmatrix}$, $B = \begin{pmatrix} -3 & 1 \\ 2 & -4 \end{pmatrix}$ and $C = \begin{pmatrix} -1 & -2 \\ 0 & 3 \end{pmatrix}$, find:

   (i) $A + B + C$ **(ii)** $2A - 3B$ **(iii)** $A - 2B + 3C$.

   Show that $A + B = B + A$.

3. If $P = \begin{pmatrix} 1 & 3 \\ -2 & 5 \end{pmatrix}$ and $Q = \begin{pmatrix} 0 & -3 \\ -4 & -2 \end{pmatrix}$, find:

   (i) $2P - Q$ **(ii)** $Q + 2P$ **(iii)** $-2P + 3Q$ **(iv)** $4P - 3Q$.

   Find the matrix M, if $M + Q = P$.

4. $A = \begin{pmatrix} -2 & -1 \\ -4 & 3 \end{pmatrix}$ and $B = \begin{pmatrix} 4 & -1 \\ -2 & 5 \end{pmatrix}$.

   If $M + 2A = B$, find the matrix M.

5. $A = \begin{pmatrix} 5 & 3 \\ -2 & 7 \end{pmatrix}$ and $B = \begin{pmatrix} 3 & -1 \\ 4 & 5 \end{pmatrix}$.

   If $2X + B = 3A$, find the matrix X.

6. If $\begin{pmatrix} p & r \\ q & s \end{pmatrix} = 3\begin{pmatrix} 1 & 0 \\ -2 & -5 \end{pmatrix} - 2\begin{pmatrix} 4 & 3 \\ -2 & -1 \end{pmatrix}$, find the values of p, q, r and s.

7. If $3\begin{pmatrix} a & c \\ b & d \end{pmatrix} + 2\begin{pmatrix} 5 & -1 \\ -4 & 4 \end{pmatrix} = \begin{pmatrix} 1 & 4 \\ 7 & -10 \end{pmatrix}$, find the values of a, b, c and d.

Solve each of the following for x, $y \in \mathbf{R}$:

8. $\begin{pmatrix} 3x & x+2y \\ 4 & -2 \end{pmatrix} = \begin{pmatrix} 12 & 10 \\ 4 & -2 \end{pmatrix}$

9. $\begin{pmatrix} x-y & x+y \\ 7 & -5 \end{pmatrix} = \begin{pmatrix} 6 & 4 \\ 7 & -5 \end{pmatrix}$

10. $\begin{pmatrix} 2x+3y \\ 3x-y \end{pmatrix} = \begin{pmatrix} -6 \\ 13 \end{pmatrix}$

11. $\begin{pmatrix} x+5 & 3 \\ y & -2 \end{pmatrix} = \begin{pmatrix} 2-y & 3 \\ 1-2x & -2 \end{pmatrix}$

Solve each of the following for a, $b \in \mathbf{R}$:

12. $\begin{pmatrix} a^2 \\ a+b \end{pmatrix} = 2\begin{pmatrix} 8 \\ 3\frac{1}{2} \end{pmatrix}$

13. $\begin{pmatrix} 3 \\ 11 \end{pmatrix} + a\begin{pmatrix} -2 \\ b \end{pmatrix} = \begin{pmatrix} -7 \\ 1 \end{pmatrix}$

14. If $\begin{pmatrix} x+y & p-q \\ p+q & x-y \end{pmatrix} = 2\begin{pmatrix} 1 & -7 \\ 1 & 3 \end{pmatrix}$, find the values of x, y, p and q.

15. $A = \begin{pmatrix} 3 & 4 \\ 1 & 2 \end{pmatrix}$, $B = \begin{pmatrix} -1 & 1 \\ 2 & -5 \end{pmatrix}$ and $C = \begin{pmatrix} 4 & 3 \\ -1 & 7 \end{pmatrix}$.

If $lA + mB = C$, $l, m \in \mathbf{R}$, find the value of l and the value of m.

16. $P = \begin{pmatrix} -1 & 2 \\ 4 & -5 \end{pmatrix}$, $Q = \begin{pmatrix} 3 & 1 \\ -2 & 4 \end{pmatrix}$ and $R = \begin{pmatrix} -9 & 4 \\ 16 & -23 \end{pmatrix}$.

If $aP + bQ = R$, $a, b \in \mathbf{R}$, find the value of a and the value of b.

Multiplication of Matrices

Multiply each row of the first matrix by each column of the second matrix.

Memory Aid: Row by Column.

Two matrices can be multiplied only if:

The number of columns in the first matrix = The number of rows in the second matrix.

If A is a $p \times q$ matrix and B is a $q \times r$ matrix,
then the product AB will be a $p \times r$ matrix.

$$A \,.\, B \quad = \quad AB$$
$$(p \times q) \,.\, (q \times r) \quad (p \times r)$$

Multiplying a 2 × 2 Matrix by a 2 × 2 Matrix

If $A = \begin{pmatrix} a & c \\ b & d \end{pmatrix}$ and $B = \begin{pmatrix} p & r \\ q & s \end{pmatrix}$, then the product AB will be a 2 × 2 matrix.

The product is found as follows (remember: row by column):

$$\begin{pmatrix} (\text{row 1 of } A) \cdot (\text{column 1 of } B) & (\text{row 1 of } A) \cdot (\text{column 2 of } B) \\ (\text{row 2 of } A) \cdot (\text{column 1 of } B) & (\text{row 2 of } A) \cdot (\text{column 2 of } B) \end{pmatrix}$$

Thus, $AB = \begin{pmatrix} a & c \\ b & d \end{pmatrix}\begin{pmatrix} p & r \\ q & s \end{pmatrix} = \begin{pmatrix} ap + cq & ar + cs \\ bp + dq & br + ds \end{pmatrix}$.

Multiplying a 2 × 2 Matrix by a 2 × 1 Matrix

If $M = \begin{pmatrix} a & c \\ b & d \end{pmatrix}$ and $N = \begin{pmatrix} p \\ q \end{pmatrix}$, then the product MN will be a 2 × 1 matrix.

The product is found as follows:

$$\begin{pmatrix} (\text{row 1 of } M) \cdot (\text{column 1 of } N) \\ (\text{row 2 of } M) \cdot (\text{column 1 of } N) \end{pmatrix}$$

Thus, $AB = \begin{pmatrix} a & c \\ b & d \end{pmatrix}\begin{pmatrix} p \\ q \end{pmatrix} = \begin{pmatrix} ap + cq \\ bp + dq \end{pmatrix}$.

Multiplying a 1 × 2 Matrix by a 2 × 1 Matrix

If $P = (a \quad b)$ and $Q = \begin{pmatrix} c \\ d \end{pmatrix}$, then the product PQ will be a 1 × 1 matrix, i.e. a real number.

$$((\text{row 1 of } P) \cdot (\text{column 1 of } Q))$$

Thus, $PQ = (a \quad b)\begin{pmatrix} c \\ d \end{pmatrix} = ac + bd$.

Note: To multiply three, or more, matrices, multiply them two at a time.
Keep the order given in the question,
i.e. $ABC = (AB)C = A(BC)$.

Example ▼

$A = \begin{pmatrix} 2 & -1 \\ 3 & 5 \end{pmatrix}$ and $B = \begin{pmatrix} 3 & 1 \\ 2 & -4 \end{pmatrix}$. Show that $AB \neq BA$.

Solution:

(i) AB

$= \begin{pmatrix} 2 & -1 \\ 3 & 5 \end{pmatrix}\begin{pmatrix} 3 & 1 \\ 2 & -4 \end{pmatrix}$

$= \begin{pmatrix} (2)(3) + (-1)(2) & (2)(1) + (-1)(-4) \\ (3)(3) + (5)(2) & (3)(1) + (5)(-4) \end{pmatrix}$

$= \begin{pmatrix} 6 - 2 & 2 + 4 \\ 9 + 10 & 3 - 20 \end{pmatrix} = \begin{pmatrix} 4 & 6 \\ 19 & -17 \end{pmatrix}$

(ii) BA

$= \begin{pmatrix} 3 & 1 \\ 2 & -4 \end{pmatrix}\begin{pmatrix} 2 & -1 \\ 3 & 5 \end{pmatrix}$

$= \begin{pmatrix} (3)(2) + (1)(3) & (3)(-1) + (1)(5) \\ (2)(2) + (-4)(3) & (2)(-1) + (-4)(5) \end{pmatrix}$

$= \begin{pmatrix} 6 + 3 & -3 + 5 \\ 4 - 12 & -2 - 20 \end{pmatrix} = \begin{pmatrix} 9 & 2 \\ -8 & -22 \end{pmatrix}$

Thus, $AB \neq BA$.

Notes:

1. In general, multiplication of matrices is **not** commutative,
   i.e., in general $AB \neq BA$.
2. $A^2 = AA$ and $A^3 = AAA$.

Example ▼

If $A = (2 \quad 1)$, $B = \begin{pmatrix} -2 & 1 \\ 5 & 4 \end{pmatrix}$ and $C = \begin{pmatrix} 3 \\ -1 \end{pmatrix}$, evaluate:

(i) AC **(ii)** BC **(iii)** ABC.

Solution:

(i) $A_{1 \times 2} C_{2 \times 1} = (AC)_{1 \times 1}$ (a real number)

$= (2 \quad 1)\begin{pmatrix} 3 \\ -1 \end{pmatrix}$

$= (2)(3) + (1)(-1)$

$= 6 - 1$

$= 5$

(ii) $B_{2 \times 2} C_{2 \times 1} = (BC)_{2 \times 1}$

$= \begin{pmatrix} -2 & 1 \\ 5 & 4 \end{pmatrix}\begin{pmatrix} 3 \\ -1 \end{pmatrix}$

$= \begin{pmatrix} (-2)(3) + (1)(-1) \\ (5)(3) + (4)(-1) \end{pmatrix}$

$= \begin{pmatrix} -6 - 1 \\ 15 - 4 \end{pmatrix} = \begin{pmatrix} -7 \\ 11 \end{pmatrix}$

(iii) $A_{1 \times 2} B_{2 \times 2} C_{2 \times 1} = (ABC)_{1 \times 1}$ (a real number)

$= A(BC)$

$= (2 \quad 1)\begin{pmatrix} -7 \\ 11 \end{pmatrix}$ $\left[BC = \begin{pmatrix} -7 \\ 11 \end{pmatrix} \right]$

$= (2)(-7) + (1)(11)$

$= -14 + 11$

$= -3$

Note: For 2×2 matrices:

The **zero matrix** is given by:

$$O = \begin{pmatrix} 0 & 0 \\ 0 & 0 \end{pmatrix}$$

$$M + O = O + M = M$$

The **identity matrix** is given by:

$$I = \begin{pmatrix} 1 & 0 \\ 0 & 1 \end{pmatrix}$$

$$MI = IM = M$$

1. Calculate each of the following:

(i) $\begin{pmatrix} 2 & 1 \\ 3 & 5 \end{pmatrix}\begin{pmatrix} 1 & 2 \\ 4 & 6 \end{pmatrix}$ (ii) $\begin{pmatrix} -3 & -1 \\ 1 & 4 \end{pmatrix}\begin{pmatrix} 6 & 1 \\ 7 & -2 \end{pmatrix}$ (iii) $\begin{pmatrix} 3 & 4 \\ -2 & 5 \end{pmatrix}\begin{pmatrix} 3 \\ -1 \end{pmatrix}$ (iv) $(3 \quad -1)\begin{pmatrix} 2 \\ 5 \end{pmatrix}$.

2. If $A = \begin{pmatrix} -1 & 1 \\ 2 & 3 \end{pmatrix}$ and $B = \begin{pmatrix} 0 & 3 \\ 2 & -2 \end{pmatrix}$, calculate:

(i) AB (ii) BA (iii) A^2 (iv) B^2.

Show that $A(A + B) = A^2 + AB$.

3. If $A = \begin{pmatrix} 2 & -1 \\ 4 & 3 \end{pmatrix}$, $B = \begin{pmatrix} 1 & 4 \\ 3 & -2 \end{pmatrix}$, $C = \begin{pmatrix} 3 \\ 2 \end{pmatrix}$ and $D = (-1 \quad 3)$, calculate:

(i) AC (ii) DC (iii) DBC.

4. If $P = \begin{pmatrix} 2 & 1 \\ 3 & 4 \end{pmatrix}$, $Q = \begin{pmatrix} 1 & 3 \\ -1 & 4 \end{pmatrix}$ and $R = \begin{pmatrix} 5 & -2 \\ -1 & 3 \end{pmatrix}$, calculate:

(i) PQ (ii) PR (iii) $R(2P - Q)$ (iv) $R(P - 3Q)$.

Show that: $P(Q + R) = PQ + PR$.

5. If $A = \begin{pmatrix} 4 & 2 \\ 1 & 3 \end{pmatrix}$, $B = \begin{pmatrix} 3 & 0 \\ 5 & 6 \end{pmatrix}$ and $C = \begin{pmatrix} 1 & 1 \\ 1 & 1 \end{pmatrix}$, show that $(AB)C = A(BC)$.

6. $A = \begin{pmatrix} 2 & 1 \\ 2 & 3 \end{pmatrix}$. Show that $A^2 - 5A + 4I = 0$.

7. If $M = \begin{pmatrix} 2 & 3 \\ -4 & -1 \end{pmatrix}$, show that $M - M^2 = 10I$.

8. $M = \begin{pmatrix} 2 & -1 \\ -3 & 4 \end{pmatrix}$. If $M^2 + kI = 6M$, find the value of k, $k \in \mathbf{R}$.

9. If $M = \begin{pmatrix} 2 & -1 \\ 3 & 2 \end{pmatrix}$ and $N = \begin{pmatrix} p & 1 \\ q & 1 \end{pmatrix}$, find the values of p and q such that $MN = NM$.

10. $M = \begin{pmatrix} x & y \\ 0 & x \end{pmatrix}$ and $N = \begin{pmatrix} -2 \\ 1 \end{pmatrix}$. If $MN = \begin{pmatrix} 1 \\ 2 \end{pmatrix}$, find the values of x and y.

11. $A = \begin{pmatrix} 1 & 2 \\ -3 & 0 \end{pmatrix}$ and $B = \begin{pmatrix} x & -2 \\ y & 5 \end{pmatrix}$.

Find the values of x and y such that $AB = BA$.

12. If $M = \begin{pmatrix} 2 & -3 \\ 1 & -2 \end{pmatrix}$, evaluate: (i) M^2 (ii) M^{20}.

13. Let $M = \begin{pmatrix} 6 & -2 \\ 5 & -1 \end{pmatrix}$. If $M\begin{pmatrix} 2 \\ 5 \end{pmatrix} = \lambda\begin{pmatrix} 2 \\ 5 \end{pmatrix}$, find the value of λ, $\lambda \in \mathbf{R}$.

14. Find x and y, given that $\begin{pmatrix} 2x & x \\ 3y & -y \end{pmatrix}\begin{pmatrix} 2 \\ -1 \end{pmatrix} = \begin{pmatrix} 12 \\ -14 \end{pmatrix}$.

15. Solve for x and y: $(x \quad y)\begin{pmatrix} 4 & 2 \\ 0 & -3 \end{pmatrix} = (-8 \quad -25)$.

16. $M = \begin{pmatrix} x & 3 \\ 2 & x \end{pmatrix}$. If $M^2 = \begin{pmatrix} 22 & 6x \\ 4x & 22 \end{pmatrix}$, find the two values of x.

17. Write $(x \quad y)\begin{pmatrix} 5 & 8 \\ 8 & 13 \end{pmatrix}\begin{pmatrix} x \\ y \end{pmatrix}$ in the form $ax^2 + bxy + cy^2$.

18. Evaluate: **(i)** $(1 \quad 2)\begin{pmatrix} 3 & 4 \\ -2 & 1 \end{pmatrix}\begin{pmatrix} 1 \\ 2 \end{pmatrix}$ **(ii)** $(1 \quad i)\begin{pmatrix} 3 & 2-i \\ 2+i & 3 \end{pmatrix}\begin{pmatrix} 1 \\ -i \end{pmatrix}$.

19. Find the coefficient of xy in:

(i) $(x \quad y)\begin{pmatrix} 3 & 1 \\ 1 & 1 \end{pmatrix}\begin{pmatrix} x \\ y \end{pmatrix}$ **(ii)** $(x + yi)\begin{pmatrix} 1 & 1-i \\ 1+i & -1 \end{pmatrix}\begin{pmatrix} x \\ -yi \end{pmatrix}$.

20. Simplify: $\cos\theta\begin{pmatrix} \cos\theta & \sin\theta \\ -\sin\theta & \cos\theta \end{pmatrix} + \sin\theta\begin{pmatrix} \sin\theta & -\cos\theta \\ \cos\theta & \sin\theta \end{pmatrix}$.

Inverse Matrices

The **determinant** of a matrix A is written as $\det(A)$. It is a real number which acts as a measure of the matrix (similarly to how the modulus of a vector measures the size of a vector).

> **Determinant of a 2×2 matrix**
>
> If $A = \begin{pmatrix} a & c \\ b & d \end{pmatrix}$, then $\det(A) = ad - bc$.

For example, if $A = \begin{pmatrix} 4 & -2 \\ -3 & 5 \end{pmatrix}$, then $\det(A) = (4)(5) - (-2)(-3) = 20 - 6 = 14$.

A determinant can be positive, negative or zero.

Inverse of a Matrix

The inverse of a matrix A is written as A^{-1}. It has the property that:

> $$A^{-1}A = I = AA^{-1}$$

where $I = \begin{pmatrix} 1 & 0 \\ 0 & 1 \end{pmatrix}$.

In other words, when we multiply a matrix by its inverse, in either order, the result is always the identity matrix $I = \begin{pmatrix} 1 & 0 \\ 0 & 1 \end{pmatrix}$.

Finding the Inverse of a 2×2 Matrix

> If $A = \begin{pmatrix} a & c \\ b & d \end{pmatrix}$, then $A^{-1} = \dfrac{1}{ad - bc}\begin{pmatrix} d & -c \\ -b & a \end{pmatrix}$.

1. Exchange the elements in the leading diagonal: $\begin{pmatrix} d & c \\ b & a \end{pmatrix}$

2. Change the signs of the elements on the other diagonal: $\begin{pmatrix} d & -c \\ -b & a \end{pmatrix}$

3. Multiply by $\dfrac{1}{ad-bc}$: $\dfrac{1}{ad-bc}\begin{pmatrix} d & -c \\ -b & a \end{pmatrix}$

Note: If the determinant of a matrix A is zero, then the inverse matrix, A^{-1}, does not exist, since
$\dfrac{1}{ad-bc} = \dfrac{1}{0}$ which is undefined.

If the determinant is zero, a matrix is said to be singular.

Inverse matrices can be used to solve matrix equations involving products. A matrix can be removed by **premultiplying** or **postmultiplying** both sides by an inverse matrix. For example:

If **(i)** $AX = B$ and **(ii)** $XA = B$, express X in terms of A and B.

(i) $\qquad AX = B$

$A^{-1}AX = A^{-1}B$

(premultiply both sides by A^{-1})

$IX = A^{-1}B$

$X = A^{-1}B$

(ii) $\qquad XA = B$

$XAA^{-1} = BA^{-1}$

(postmultiply both sides by A^{-1})

$XI = BA^{-1}$

$X = BA^{-1}$

Note: Using matrices in this way is called 'matrix algebra'.

Example ▼

Let $A = \begin{pmatrix} 5 & 2 \\ 1 & 1 \end{pmatrix}$ and $B = \begin{pmatrix} 3 & 2 \\ 6 & -5 \end{pmatrix}$.

Find: **(i)** A^{-1} **(ii)** $A^{-1}B$.

If $AC = A + B$, express C in matrix form.

Solution:

(i) $A = \begin{pmatrix} 5 & 2 \\ 1 & 1 \end{pmatrix}$

$A^{-1} = \dfrac{1}{(5)(1)-(2)(1)}\begin{pmatrix} 1 & -2 \\ -1 & 5 \end{pmatrix}$

$= \dfrac{1}{3}\begin{pmatrix} 1 & -2 \\ -1 & 5 \end{pmatrix}$

$AC = A + B$

$A^{-1}AC = A^{-1}A + A^{-1}B$

$IC = I + A^{-1}B$

$C = \begin{pmatrix} 1 & 0 \\ 0 & 1 \end{pmatrix} + \begin{pmatrix} -3 & 4 \\ 9 & -9 \end{pmatrix}$

$= \begin{pmatrix} -2 & 4 \\ 9 & -8 \end{pmatrix}$

(ii) $A^{-1}B$

$= \dfrac{1}{3}\begin{pmatrix} 1 & -2 \\ -1 & 5 \end{pmatrix}\begin{pmatrix} 3 & 2 \\ 6 & -5 \end{pmatrix}$

$= \dfrac{1}{3}\begin{pmatrix} -9 & 12 \\ 27 & -27 \end{pmatrix} = \begin{pmatrix} -3 & 4 \\ 9 & -9 \end{pmatrix}$

[premultiply each matrix by A^{-1}]

$\left[A^{-1}B = \begin{pmatrix} -3 & 4 \\ 9 & -9 \end{pmatrix} \text{ from } \textbf{(ii)} \right]$

Alternatively, add A and B and then premultiply both sides by A^{-1}:

$$AC = A + B$$
$$AC = (A + B) \qquad \text{[add } A \text{ and } B\text{]}$$
$$A^{-1}AC = A^{-1}(A + B) \qquad \text{[premultiply both sides by } A^{-1}\text{]}$$
$$C = A^{-1}(A + B) \qquad [A^{-1}AC = IC = C]$$

$$= \frac{1}{3}\begin{pmatrix} 1 & -2 \\ -1 & 5 \end{pmatrix}\left[\begin{pmatrix} 5 & 2 \\ 1 & 1 \end{pmatrix} + \begin{pmatrix} 3 & 2 \\ 6 & -5 \end{pmatrix}\right]$$

$$= \frac{1}{3}\begin{pmatrix} 1 & -2 \\ -1 & 5 \end{pmatrix}\begin{pmatrix} 8 & 4 \\ 7 & -4 \end{pmatrix}$$

$$= \frac{1}{3}\begin{pmatrix} -6 & 12 \\ 27 & -24 \end{pmatrix} = \begin{pmatrix} -2 & 4 \\ 9 & -8 \end{pmatrix}$$

Example ▼

$M = \begin{pmatrix} x+2 & 7 \\ 2 & x-3 \end{pmatrix}$, $x \in \mathbf{R}$.

If the determinant of M is zero (i.e. M is singular), find the values of x.

Solution:

Given: $\det(M) = 0$

$\therefore \quad (x+2)(x-3) - (7)(2) = 0 \qquad [\det(M) = ad - bc]$

$\qquad\qquad x^2 - x - 6 - 14 = 0$

$\qquad\qquad\qquad x^2 - x - 20 = 0$

$\qquad\qquad (x - 5)(x + 4) = 0$

$\qquad\qquad\qquad x = 5 \quad \text{or} \quad x = -4$

Using Matrices to Solve Simultaneous Equations

Matrices can be used to solve simultaneous equations.
Consider the simultaneous equations:

$$3x - 2y = 16$$
$$5x + 4y = -10$$

These equations can be written as a matrix equation:

$$\begin{pmatrix} 3 & -2 \\ 5 & 4 \end{pmatrix}\begin{pmatrix} x \\ y \end{pmatrix} = \begin{pmatrix} 16 \\ -10 \end{pmatrix}$$

To find the values of x and y, we premultiply both sides by the inverse of $\begin{pmatrix} 3 & -2 \\ 5 & 4 \end{pmatrix}$.

(i) Write the simultaneous equations: $3x - y = 7$

$$2x + 5y = -18$$

in the form $M\begin{pmatrix} x \\ y \end{pmatrix} = \begin{pmatrix} a \\ b \end{pmatrix}$, where M is a 2×2 matrix.

(ii) Find M^{-1}, the inverse of the matrix M.

(iii) Hence, use M^{-1} to solve the equations for x and y.

Solution:

(i)

$$3x - y = 7$$
$$2x + 5y = -18$$

in matrix form gives:

$$\begin{pmatrix} 3 & -1 \\ 2 & 5 \end{pmatrix}\begin{pmatrix} x \\ y \end{pmatrix} = \begin{pmatrix} 7 \\ -18 \end{pmatrix}$$

(ii) $\qquad M = \begin{pmatrix} 3 & -1 \\ 2 & 5 \end{pmatrix}$ (from **(i)**)

$$M^{-1} = \frac{1}{(3)(5) - (-1)(2)}\begin{pmatrix} 5 & 1 \\ -2 & 3 \end{pmatrix}$$

$$M^{-1} = \frac{1}{17}\begin{pmatrix} 5 & 1 \\ -2 & 3 \end{pmatrix}$$

(iii)

$$3x - y = 7$$
$$2x + 5y = -18$$

$$\begin{pmatrix} 3 & -1 \\ 2 & 5 \end{pmatrix}\begin{pmatrix} x \\ y \end{pmatrix} = \begin{pmatrix} 7 \\ -18 \end{pmatrix} \qquad \text{(in matrix form)}$$

$$\frac{1}{17}\begin{pmatrix} 5 & 1 \\ -2 & 3 \end{pmatrix}\begin{pmatrix} 3 & -1 \\ 2 & 5 \end{pmatrix}\begin{pmatrix} x \\ y \end{pmatrix} = \frac{1}{17}\begin{pmatrix} 5 & 1 \\ -2 & 3 \end{pmatrix}\begin{pmatrix} 7 \\ -18 \end{pmatrix} \left(\text{premultiply both sides by the inverse of } \begin{pmatrix} 3 & -1 \\ 2 & 5 \end{pmatrix}\right)$$

$$\begin{pmatrix} 1 & 0 \\ 0 & 1 \end{pmatrix}\begin{pmatrix} x \\ y \end{pmatrix} = \frac{1}{17}\begin{pmatrix} 17 \\ -68 \end{pmatrix} \qquad \left(M^{-1}M = \begin{pmatrix} 1 & 0 \\ 0 & 1 \end{pmatrix}\right)$$

$$\begin{pmatrix} x \\ y \end{pmatrix} = \begin{pmatrix} 1 \\ -4 \end{pmatrix}$$

Thus, $x = 1$, $y = -4$.

Exercise 3.3 ▼

In each of the following, find **(i)** det(M)   **(ii)** M^{-1}:

1. $M = \begin{pmatrix} 3 & 5 \\ 2 & 4 \end{pmatrix}$
2. $M = \begin{pmatrix} 4 & 3 \\ 1 & 2 \end{pmatrix}$
3. $M = \begin{pmatrix} 3 & 2 \\ 2 & 5 \end{pmatrix}$
4. $M = \begin{pmatrix} 1 & 6 \\ 1 & 2 \end{pmatrix}$

5. $M = \begin{pmatrix} 3 & -1 \\ 2 & 1 \end{pmatrix}$
6. $M = \begin{pmatrix} 3 & -5 \\ -1 & 2 \end{pmatrix}$
7. $M = \begin{pmatrix} 5 & -2 \\ 0 & 4 \end{pmatrix}$
8. $M = \begin{pmatrix} 1 & -2 \\ 3 & -1 \end{pmatrix}$

9. If $A = \begin{pmatrix} 10 & 2 \\ 4 & -6 \end{pmatrix}$ and $B = \begin{pmatrix} -7 & -3 \\ 1 & 4 \end{pmatrix}$, express $(A + B)^{-1}$ in the form $\begin{pmatrix} a & c \\ b & d \end{pmatrix}$.

10. $M = \begin{pmatrix} 3 & 2 \\ -1 & 1 \end{pmatrix}$. Find M^{-1} and verify that $M^{-1}M = I$, where $I = \begin{pmatrix} 1 & 0 \\ 0 & 1 \end{pmatrix}$.

11. $A = \begin{pmatrix} 3 & 1 \\ 4 & 2 \end{pmatrix}$ and $B = \begin{pmatrix} 4 & -1 \\ -5 & 2 \end{pmatrix}$. Find: **(i)** A^{-1} **(ii)** B^{-1}.

Show that $(AB)^{-1} = B^{-1}A^{-1}$.

12. If $A = \begin{pmatrix} 3 & -1 \\ 1 & 3 \end{pmatrix}$ and $B = \begin{pmatrix} 4 & 3 \\ 3 & -4 \end{pmatrix}$, find $B - 2A^{-1}B$.

13. If $A = \begin{pmatrix} 3 & 4 \\ 1 & 2 \end{pmatrix}$ and $B = \begin{pmatrix} 2 & -4 \\ -1 & 3 \end{pmatrix}$, express A^{-1} in terms of B.

14. The matrix $A = \begin{pmatrix} 2 & 1 \\ 4 & 3 \end{pmatrix}$. Find A^{-1}.

Hence, find the matrix B such that $AB = \begin{pmatrix} -7 & 7 \\ -15 & 17 \end{pmatrix}$.

15. $A = \begin{pmatrix} 3 & 1 \\ 5 & 2 \end{pmatrix}$ and $B = \begin{pmatrix} 5 & -8 \\ -1 & 2 \end{pmatrix}$.

(i) If $AX = B$, express X in terms of A and B, where X is a 2×2 matrix.
(ii) Hence, find the matrix X.

16. Let $N = \begin{pmatrix} 4 & -1 \\ 1 & 5 \end{pmatrix}$. Find the values of a, b, c and d, if $N^{-1} \begin{pmatrix} a & c \\ b & d \end{pmatrix} = N$.

17. $M = \begin{pmatrix} 1 & 2 \\ -1 & -3 \end{pmatrix}$ and $N = \begin{pmatrix} p & q \\ -3 & -1 \end{pmatrix}$.

Find: **(i)** M^{-1} **(ii)** the value of p and the value of q if $M^{-1}NM = \begin{pmatrix} 2 & 0 \\ 0 & 1 \end{pmatrix}$.

18. Let $M = \begin{pmatrix} 3 & -7 \\ 1 & -2 \end{pmatrix}$ and $N = \begin{pmatrix} 5 & 3 \\ 2 & 1 \end{pmatrix}$.

(i) Simplify $M^{-1}N$.   **(ii)** If $MA = 3M + N$, express A in matrix form.

19. Let $A = \begin{pmatrix} 3 & 5 \\ 2 & 4 \end{pmatrix}$ and $B = \begin{pmatrix} 3 & -1 \\ 4 & 2 \end{pmatrix}$.

(i) Simplify $A^{-1}B$.   **(ii)** If $AM = 2A + B$, express M in matrix form.

20. $M = \begin{pmatrix} 3 & 6 \\ -2 & k \end{pmatrix}$, $k \in \mathbf{R}$. If the determinant of M is zero, find the value of k.

21. $A = \begin{pmatrix} x-1 & x+4 \\ x-1 & x+2 \end{pmatrix}$, $x \in \mathbf{R}$. If the determinant of A is zero, find the value of x.

22. **(i)** Write the simultaneous equations: $3x + 5y = 27$
$x + 2y = 10$
in the form $M\begin{pmatrix} x \\ y \end{pmatrix} = \begin{pmatrix} a \\ b \end{pmatrix}$, where M is a 2×2 matrix.

(ii) Find M^{-1}, the inverse of the matrix M.
(iii) Hence, use M^{-1} to solve the equations for x and y.

23. (i) Write the simultaneous equations: $3x - 2y + 16 = 0$

$$5x - 4y + 30 = 0$$

in the form $M\begin{pmatrix} x \\ y \end{pmatrix} = \begin{pmatrix} a \\ b \end{pmatrix}$, where M is a 2×2 matrix.

(ii) Find M^{-1}, the inverse of the matrix M.

(iii) Hence, use M^{-1} to solve the equations for x and y.

Express each of the following pairs of simultaneous equations in matrix form and use matrix methods to solve them:

24. $3x + 5y = 13$

$\quad\ x + 2y = 5$

25. $4x + 5y = 7$

$\quad\ 2x + 3y = 5$

26. $3x - 2y = 8$

$\quad\ x + y = 6$

27. $4x + 3y = -23$

$\quad\ x + 2y = -12$

28. $2x + y - 4 = 0$

$\quad\ 3x - 2y - 27 = 0$

29. $x - \sqrt{2}y = 1$

$\quad\ \sqrt{2}x + y = 4\sqrt{2}$

Diagonal Matrices

A **2 × 2 diagonal matrix** is a matrix of the form $\begin{pmatrix} a & 0 \\ 0 & b \end{pmatrix}$.

It is a square matrix in which all the elements **off** the leading diagonal (from top left-hand corner to the bottom right-hand corner) are zero.

Powers of Diagonal Matrices

Diagonal matrices have the following property:

$$\begin{pmatrix} a & 0 \\ 0 & b \end{pmatrix}^n = \begin{pmatrix} a^n & 0 \\ 0 & b^n \end{pmatrix}$$

For example,

$$\begin{pmatrix} 3 & 0 \\ 0 & -2 \end{pmatrix}^6 = \begin{pmatrix} 3^6 & 0 \\ 0 & (-2)^6 \end{pmatrix} = \begin{pmatrix} 729 & 0 \\ 0 & 64 \end{pmatrix}$$

Power Property

$$(M^{-1}AM)^n = M^{-1}A^nM$$

This power property occurs quite often in the applications of matrices.

If $M^{-1}AM$ is a diagonal matrix, then we can use $(M^{-1}AM)^n$ to calculate A^n by using matrix algebra.

If $M = \begin{pmatrix} 2 & 2 \\ 1 & 3 \end{pmatrix}$ and $A = \begin{pmatrix} 3 & -4 \\ 3 & -5 \end{pmatrix}$,

(i) find M^{-1} **(ii)** show that $M^{-1}AM$ is of the form $\begin{pmatrix} a & 0 \\ 0 & b \end{pmatrix}$, $a, b \in \mathbf{Z}$.

(iii) show that $(M^{-1}AM)^4 = M^{-1}A^4M$ **(iv)** hence, calculate A^4.

Solution:

(i) $M = \begin{pmatrix} 2 & 2 \\ 1 & 3 \end{pmatrix}$

$M^{-1} = \dfrac{1}{(2)(3) - (2)(1)} \begin{pmatrix} 3 & -2 \\ -1 & 2 \end{pmatrix}$

$M^{-1} = \dfrac{1}{4} \begin{pmatrix} 3 & -2 \\ -1 & 2 \end{pmatrix}$

(ii) $M^{-1}AM$

$= \dfrac{1}{4} \begin{pmatrix} 3 & -2 \\ -1 & 2 \end{pmatrix} \begin{pmatrix} 3 & -4 \\ 3 & -5 \end{pmatrix} \begin{pmatrix} 2 & 2 \\ 1 & 3 \end{pmatrix}$

$= \dfrac{1}{4} \begin{pmatrix} 3 & -2 \\ -1 & 2 \end{pmatrix} \begin{pmatrix} 2 & -6 \\ 1 & -9 \end{pmatrix}$ (calculate AM first)

$= \dfrac{1}{4} \begin{pmatrix} 4 & 0 \\ 0 & -12 \end{pmatrix}$

$= \begin{pmatrix} 1 & 0 \\ 0 & -3 \end{pmatrix}$ $\left(\text{a matrix of the form } \begin{pmatrix} a & 0 \\ 0 & b \end{pmatrix}\right)$

(iii) $(M^{-1}AM)^4 = M^{-1}AM \cdot M^{-1}AM \cdot M^{-1}AM \cdot M^{-1}AM$

              $= M^{-1}AIAIAIAM$ $(MM^{-1} = I)$

              $= M^{-1}A^4M$ $(AI = A)$

$\therefore$ $(M^{-1}AM)^4 = M^{-1}A^4M$

(iv) $M^{-1}AM = \begin{pmatrix} 1 & 0 \\ 0 & -3 \end{pmatrix}$

$\therefore$ $(M^{-1}AM)^4 = \begin{pmatrix} 1 & 0 \\ 0 & -3 \end{pmatrix}^4$ (raise both sides to the power of 4)

$\therefore$ $M^{-1}A^4M = \begin{pmatrix} 1^4 & 0 \\ 0 & (-3)^4 \end{pmatrix}$ $\left((M^{-1}AM)^4 = M^{-1}A^4M \right.$

$M^{-1}A^4M = \begin{pmatrix} 1 & 0 \\ 0 & 81 \end{pmatrix}$ $\left. \text{and } \begin{pmatrix} 1 & 0 \\ 0 & -3 \end{pmatrix}^4 = \begin{pmatrix} 1^4 & 0 \\ 0 & (-3)^4 \end{pmatrix}\right)$

We now premultiply both sides by M and postmultiply both sides by M^{-1}. This gives A^4 on its own.

$$M^{-1}A^4M = \begin{pmatrix} 1 & 0 \\ 0 & 81 \end{pmatrix}$$

$$MM^{-1}A^4MM^{-1} = M\begin{pmatrix} 1 & 0 \\ 0 & 81 \end{pmatrix}M^{-1}$$

$$IA^4I = \begin{pmatrix} 2 & 2 \\ 1 & 3 \end{pmatrix}\begin{pmatrix} 1 & 0 \\ 0 & 81 \end{pmatrix}\frac{1}{4}\begin{pmatrix} 3 & -2 \\ -1 & 2 \end{pmatrix} \qquad (MM^{-1}=I=MM^{-1})$$

$$A^4 = \frac{1}{4}\begin{pmatrix} 2 & 2 \\ 1 & 3 \end{pmatrix}\begin{pmatrix} 1 & 0 \\ 0 & 81 \end{pmatrix}\begin{pmatrix} 3 & -2 \\ -1 & 2 \end{pmatrix} \qquad \text{(put } \tfrac{1}{4} \text{ to the front)}$$

$$= \frac{1}{4}\begin{pmatrix} 2 & 2 \\ 1 & 3 \end{pmatrix}\begin{pmatrix} 3 & -2 \\ -81 & 162 \end{pmatrix}$$

$$= \frac{1}{4}\begin{pmatrix} -156 & 320 \\ -240 & 484 \end{pmatrix} = \begin{pmatrix} -39 & 80 \\ -60 & 121 \end{pmatrix}$$

Note: To calculate A^4 we could have used $A.A.A.A$, but this was not allowed in the question. However, the technique above is better if we need to calculate large powers, for example, A^{40}.

Exercise 3.4 ▼

Write each of the following in the form $\begin{pmatrix} a & 0 \\ 0 & b \end{pmatrix}$:

1. $\begin{pmatrix} 2 & 0 \\ 0 & 3 \end{pmatrix}^5$ **2.** $\begin{pmatrix} 1 & 0 \\ 0 & -2 \end{pmatrix}^6$ **3.** $\begin{pmatrix} -3 & 0 \\ 0 & 2 \end{pmatrix}^7$ **4.** $\begin{pmatrix} -1 & 0 \\ 0 & 4 \end{pmatrix}^8$

5. Let $A = \begin{pmatrix} 1 & 0 \\ 0 & 2 \end{pmatrix}$. Calculate: **(i)** A^2 **(ii)** A^3 **(iii)** A^5.

Show that $A^2.A^3 = A^5$.

6. $A = \begin{pmatrix} 2 & 1 \\ -1 & -2 \end{pmatrix}$ and $B = \begin{pmatrix} 2 & 2 \\ -2 & -3 \end{pmatrix}$.

Show that $A^{-1}BA$ is of the form $\begin{pmatrix} p & 0 \\ 0 & q \end{pmatrix}$, where $p, q \in \mathbf{Z}$.

7. Let $M = \begin{pmatrix} 19 & 4 \\ 1 & 16 \end{pmatrix}$ and $N = \begin{pmatrix} 1 & 4 \\ -1 & 1 \end{pmatrix}$.

Express $N^{-1}MN$ in the form $a\begin{pmatrix} b & 0 \\ 0 & c \end{pmatrix}$, $a, b, c \in \mathbf{N}$ and $a > 1$.

8. $A = \begin{pmatrix} 2 & 2 \\ 3 & 1 \end{pmatrix}$ and $B = \begin{pmatrix} 2 & 1 \\ -3 & 1 \end{pmatrix}$. If $M = B^{-1}AB$, calculate M^5.

9. $M = \begin{pmatrix} 5 & 4 \\ 1 & 2 \end{pmatrix}$ and $N = \begin{pmatrix} 4 & 1 \\ 1 & -1 \end{pmatrix}$. If $A = N^{-1}MN$, calculate A^4.

10. If $M = \begin{pmatrix} -2 & 1 \\ 1 & 2 \end{pmatrix}$ and $M^{-1}AM = \begin{pmatrix} -3 & 0 \\ 0 & 2 \end{pmatrix}$, find the matrix A.

11. If $P = \begin{pmatrix} 3 & -1 \\ 1 & 3 \end{pmatrix}$ and $P^{-1}AP = \begin{pmatrix} 5 & 0 \\ 0 & -5 \end{pmatrix}$, find the matrix A.

12. $A = \begin{pmatrix} 2 & 1 \\ -3 & -2 \end{pmatrix}$ and $P = \begin{pmatrix} 1 & 1 \\ -1 & -3 \end{pmatrix}$.

Calculate: **(i)** P^{-1} **(ii)** AP **(iii)** $P^{-1}AP$ **(iv)** $(P^{-1}AP)^5$.
Hence, show that $A^5 = A$.

13. $A = \begin{pmatrix} 3 & 4 \\ -2 & -3 \end{pmatrix}$ and $P = \begin{pmatrix} -1 & 2 \\ 1 & -1 \end{pmatrix}$.

Calculate: **(i)** P^{-1} **(ii)** AP **(iii)** $P^{-1}AP$.
Show that $(P^{-1}AP)^3 = P^{-1}A^3P$ and, hence, calculate A^3.
Explain why $A^3 = A^5 = A^7 = A^{2n+1}$, where $n \in \mathbf{N}$.
Calculate A^{100}.

14. $A = \begin{pmatrix} 2 & 2 \\ -2 & -3 \end{pmatrix}$ and $M = \begin{pmatrix} 2 & 1 \\ -1 & -2 \end{pmatrix}$.

Calculate: **(i)** M^{-1} **(ii)** $M^{-1}AM$ **(iii)** $(M^{-1}AM)^7$.
Hence, calculate A^7.

15. $A = \begin{pmatrix} -1 & 2 \\ 2 & -1 \end{pmatrix}$ and $P = \begin{pmatrix} 1 & 1 \\ 1 & -1 \end{pmatrix}$.

Calculate: **(i)** P^{-1} **(ii)** $P^{-1}AP$ **(iii)** $(P^{-1}AP)^4$.
Hence, calculate A^4.

16. If $M = \begin{pmatrix} 1 & 1 \\ 5 & 1 \end{pmatrix}$ and $A = \begin{pmatrix} -4 & 1 \\ -5 & 2 \end{pmatrix}$,

(i) find M^{-1} **(ii)** show that $M^{-1}AM$ is of the form $\begin{pmatrix} a & 0 \\ 0 & b \end{pmatrix}$, $a, b \in \mathbf{Z}$.
(iii) show that $(M^{-1}AM)^5 = M^{-1}A^5M$ **(iv)** hence, calculate A^5.

17. $M = \begin{pmatrix} 3 & 3 \\ -2 & -4 \end{pmatrix}$. Find the value of a and the value of b, $a, b \in \mathbf{R}$, if:

$$M\begin{pmatrix} 1 \\ a \end{pmatrix} = -3\begin{pmatrix} 1 \\ a \end{pmatrix} \text{ and } M\begin{pmatrix} 1 \\ b \end{pmatrix} = -2\begin{pmatrix} 0 \\ b \end{pmatrix}.$$

If $N = \begin{pmatrix} -b & -3b \\ a & b \end{pmatrix}$, find $N^{-1}MN$ and, hence, calculate M^6.

VECTORS

Definition of a Vector

A vector is a movement over a certain distance and in a certain direction.
We can represent a vector with a line segment. The length of the line represents the size (magnitude) of the vector and the direction of the line shows which way the vector points, indicated by an arrow.

The diagram on the right shows the movement from p to q, in other words, the vector from p to q.

This is written as $\overrightarrow{pq}$.

Notice the arrow points from p to q, i.e., from the start to the finish, as indicated in the diagram.

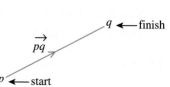

Notes: The length of a vector is called the **modulus** or **norm** of the vector.

The modulus of the vector $\overrightarrow{pq}$ is written $|\overrightarrow{pq}|$.

In the diagram opposite, the length of the vector $\overrightarrow{pq}$ is 3 cm.

This is written: $|\overrightarrow{pq}| = 3$ cm.

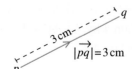

Equality of Vectors

Equal vectors have **three common characteristics:**

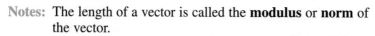

| 1. Parallel | 2. Same length | 3. Same direction |

The characteristic 'parallel' can be dropped because 'same direction' implies parallel.
In other words: equal vectors have the same length and direction.

On the right are shown two vectors, $\overrightarrow{ab}$ and $\overrightarrow{cd}$.

They are **parallel**, have the **same length** and point in the **same direction**.

Therefore they are equal vectors.

Thus we write: $\overrightarrow{ab} = \overrightarrow{cd}$.

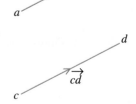

It follows from this that a vector may be represented by any accurate line segment, provided we keep its correct length and direction. Its location does not matter. In other words we can move a vector anywhere, provided we maintain its **original** length and direction.

Negative Vectors

The vectors $\overrightarrow{ab}$ and $\overrightarrow{ba}$ are parallel and equal in length, but point in opposite directions.

We say $\overrightarrow{ab}$ and $\overrightarrow{ba}$ are the negative of each other. To get the negative of a vector, simply change its direction.

The negative of $\overrightarrow{ab}$ is written $-\overrightarrow{ab}$.

From the diagram it can be seen that $-\overrightarrow{ab} = \overrightarrow{ba}$.

Thus, a negative sign in front of a vector can be changed to a positive sign simply by changing the order of the letters.

$$\text{e.g.,} \qquad -\overrightarrow{pq} = \overrightarrow{qp}, \qquad -\overrightarrow{xy} = \overrightarrow{yx}, \qquad -\overrightarrow{dc} = \overrightarrow{cd}, \qquad \text{etc.}$$

> **Negative Vector**
>
> $$\overrightarrow{ab} = -\overrightarrow{ba}$$

Remember: Equal vectors have the **same** length and direction.

Consider the parallelogram *abcd* opposite.

$$\overrightarrow{ab} = \overrightarrow{dc}$$

$$\overrightarrow{bc} = \overrightarrow{ad}$$

$$-\overrightarrow{ab} = \overrightarrow{ba} = \overrightarrow{cd}$$

$$-\overrightarrow{ad} = \overrightarrow{da} = \overrightarrow{cb} \qquad \text{etc.}$$

Multiplication by a Scalar (Number)

A scalar is a number. If we multiply a vector by a number, we change its size or its length. If the scalar is a **negative** number, we also change the direction of the vector. However, the new vector will always remain parallel to the original vector.

Consider the vector $\overrightarrow{ab}$.

A **multiple** of this vector is a vector of the form $k\overrightarrow{ab}$, where $k \in \mathbf{R}$.

1. **$k > 0$**
   If $k > 0$, then $k\overrightarrow{ab}$ has the same direction as $\overrightarrow{ab}$.
2. **$k < 0$**
   If $k < 0$, then $k\overrightarrow{ab}$ has the opposite direction to $\overrightarrow{ab}$.

In each case, the length of $k\overrightarrow{ab}$ is $|k|$ times the length of $\overrightarrow{ab}$.

For example:

$5\overrightarrow{ab}$ is 5 times as long as $\overrightarrow{ab}$ and in the same direction as $\overrightarrow{ab}$.

$-3\overrightarrow{ab}$ is 3 times as long as $\overrightarrow{ab}$ but in the opposite direction to $\overrightarrow{ab}$.

Parallel Vectors

If $\vec{u} \parallel \vec{v}$, then $\vec{v} = k\vec{u}$,
where $k \in \mathbf{R}$.

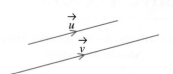

In particular, if $\vec{a} = h\vec{u}$, and $\vec{b} = k\vec{u}$, where, $h, k \in \mathbf{R}$, then $\vec{a} \parallel \vec{b}$.

Similarly for collinear vectors.

If a, c and b are collinear, then:

$$\vec{ac} = h\,\vec{ab}$$

or $\vec{ab} = k\,\vec{ac}$

or $\vec{cb} = m\,\vec{ab}$

where h, k, $m \in \mathbf{R}$.

Example ▼

Given the vector $\vec{pq}$, construct the vectors:

(i) $2\vec{pq}$ **(ii)** $\frac{2}{3}\vec{pq}$ **(iii)** $-3\vec{pq}$.

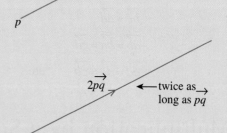

Solution:

(i) $2\vec{pq}$

The vector $2\vec{pq}$ is parallel to and pointing in the
same direction as $\vec{pq}$; however, it is **twice** the length
of $\vec{pq}$.

←—twice as long as pq

(ii) $\frac{2}{3}\vec{pq}$

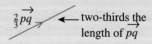

←—two-thirds the length of pq

The vector $\frac{2}{3}\vec{pq}$ is parallel to and pointing in the
same direction as $\vec{pq}$; however, it
is only **two-thirds** the length of
$\vec{pq}$.

(iii) $-3\vec{pq} = 3\vec{qp}$ (change sign and
change order of letters).

The vector $-3\vec{pq}$ is parallel to $\vec{pq}$,
three times as long; however, it
points in the **opposite** direction.

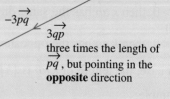

three times the length of
$\vec{pq}$, but pointing in the
opposite direction

Adding Vectors

There are two methods of adding vectors:

Triangle Law

To add the two vectors $\vec{ab}$ and $\vec{cd}$, using the Triangle Law, do the following:

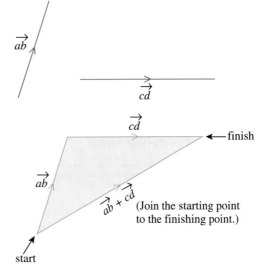

> **1.** Place the beginning of the second vector to the end of the first vector.
> (The order chosen is not important.)
>
> **2.** Join the beginning of the first vector to the end of the second vector.
> This is the required vector (as shown).

Parallelogram Law

To add the two vectors $\vec{ab}$ and $\vec{cd}$, using the Parallelogram Law, do the following:

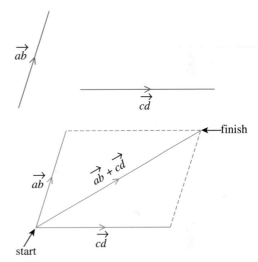

> **1.** Place the starting point of each at the same point.
> **2.** Complete the parallelogram (as shown).
> **3.** Join the common starting point to the opposite vertex.
> This diagonal is the vector required (as shown).

Notes:
1. The Parallelogram Law and the Triangle Law give the same result. However, use one or the other: never use the two methods together.
2. The Triangle Law is easier to use, especially if more than two vectors are to be added or subtracted.
3. The **order** in which vectors are added or subtracted is **not** important.
4. A very useful result is to look for **linkage**:

e.g.
$$\vec{ab} + \vec{bc} = \vec{ac}$$

If the letter at the end of the first vector is equal to the letter at the start of the second vector, the result of adding the two vectors is straightforward to write down. Simply write the letter at the start of the first vector followed by the letter at the end of the second vector together and put an arrow over them.

e.g. $\vec{pq} + \vec{qr} = \vec{pr}$ $\vec{xy} - \vec{zy} = \vec{xy} + \vec{yz} = \vec{xz}$

$-\vec{pm} + \vec{qm} = \vec{mp} + \vec{qm} = \vec{qm} + \vec{mp} = \vec{qp}$

(change order of addition)

Any number of vectors can be added in this way. The resultant vector joins the **start** of the **first** vector to the **end** of the **last** vector.

i.e., $\vec{ab} + \vec{bc} + \vec{cd} + \vec{de} + \vec{ef} = \vec{af}$

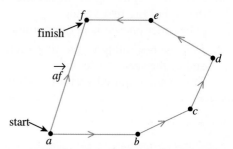

Using a diagram:

Notice that the arrows all **follow** each other.
The result is simply obtained by joining the start to the finish.
(Notice the linkage of the vectors.)

Example ▼

pqrs is a parallelogram. The diagonals intersect at the point t.
Express each of the following as a single vector:

(i) $\vec{pq} + \vec{qt}$ (ii) $\vec{pq} + \vec{ps}$
(iii) $\vec{pr} - \vec{pq}$ (iv) $\frac{1}{2}\vec{pr} + \frac{1}{2}\vec{sq}$

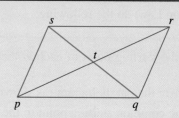

Solution:

Using the Triangle Law:

(i) $\vec{pq} + \vec{qt} = \vec{pt}$

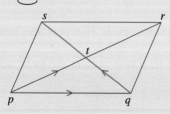

(ii) $\vec{pq} + \vec{ps} = \vec{pq} + \vec{qr} = \vec{pr}$

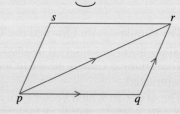

(iii) $\vec{pr} - \vec{pq} = \vec{pr} + \vec{qp} = \vec{pr} + \vec{rs} = \vec{ps}$

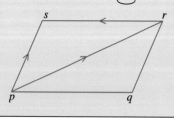

(iv) $\frac{1}{2}\vec{pr} + \frac{1}{2}\vec{sq} = \vec{pt} + \vec{st} = \vec{pt} + \vec{tq} = \vec{pq}$

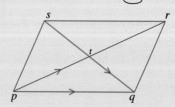

Example ▼

abcd is a rectangle.
Copy the diagram and construct the point k, such
that $\vec{ak} = \vec{bd}$.

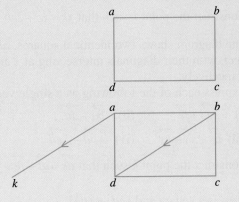

Solution:

Construct the vector $\vec{bd}$.
From a, construct the vector $\vec{ak}$, such that it is:

(i) parallel to $\vec{bd}$

(ii) the same length as $\vec{bd}$

(iii) in the same direction as $\vec{bd}$.

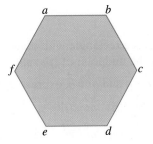

Exercise 4.1 ▼

1. The diagram shows a regular hexagon abcdef.
   Name a vector equal to:

   (i) $\vec{ab}$ **(ii)** $\vec{cd}$ **(iii)** $\vec{fe}$

   (iv) $\vec{db}$ **(v)** $\vec{fb}$ **(vi)** $-\vec{bc}$

   (vii) $\vec{fc}$

2. xyzw is a parallelogram. The diagonals intersect at the point g.
   Express each of the following as a single vector:

   (i) $\vec{xy} + \vec{yz}$ **(ii)** $\vec{xw} + \vec{wg}$

   (iii) $\vec{xy} + \vec{xw}$ **(iv)** $\vec{xz} - \vec{xy}$

   Show that:
   $\frac{1}{2}\vec{xz} + \frac{1}{2}\vec{wy} = \vec{xw} + \vec{xy} - \vec{yz}$.

3. rstu is a square, and ustv is a parallelogram.
   Express each of the following as a single vector:

   (i) $\vec{sr} + \vec{ru}$ **(ii)** $\vec{su} + \vec{ts}$ **(iii)** $\vec{su} + \frac{1}{2}\vec{rv}$

   Show that:
   $\frac{1}{2}\vec{rv} + \vec{rs} = \vec{ru} + \vec{us} - \vec{vu}$.

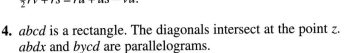
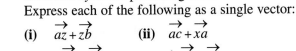

4. abcd is a rectangle. The diagonals intersect at the point z.
   abdx and bycd are parallelograms.
   Express each of the following as a single vector:

   (i) $\vec{az} + \vec{zb}$ **(ii)** $\vec{ac} + \vec{xa}$

   (iii) $2\vec{xd} + \vec{cb}$ **(iv)** $\frac{1}{2}(\vec{xa} + \vec{ay})$

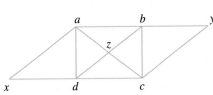

(v) $\overrightarrow{xz} + \overrightarrow{az}$ **(vi)** $\overrightarrow{xa} + \overrightarrow{by} - \overrightarrow{cb}$

(vii) $\frac{1}{2}\overrightarrow{db} + \frac{1}{2}\overrightarrow{az}$

Construct the point k such that $\overrightarrow{xk} = \overrightarrow{xc} + 2\overrightarrow{cb}$.

5. The diagram shows two identical squares, $abcd$ and $dcef$, with their diagonals intersecting at x and y, respectively.

Express each of the following as a single vector:

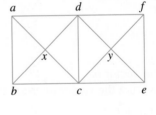

(i) $2\overrightarrow{ad} + \overrightarrow{fe}$ **(ii)** $\overrightarrow{ba} - \overrightarrow{da}$

(iii) $\overrightarrow{bx} + \overrightarrow{xy} - \overrightarrow{ey}$ **(iv)** $\frac{1}{2}\overrightarrow{bd} - \frac{1}{2}\overrightarrow{ed}$

Construct the point k such that $\overrightarrow{ak} = \overrightarrow{af} + \overrightarrow{fe} + \overrightarrow{fc}$.

6. $abcd$ is a square and $|cd| = |de|$.

If $\overrightarrow{ba} = \overrightarrow{u}$ and $\overrightarrow{bc} = \overrightarrow{v}$, express $\overrightarrow{be}$ in

terms of $\overrightarrow{u}$ and $\overrightarrow{v}$.

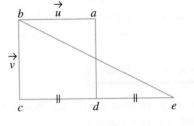

7. $pqrs$ is a rectangle with diagonals intersecting at t. h is the midpoint of $[ps]$ and k is the midpoint of $[sr]$.

If $\overrightarrow{pq} = \overrightarrow{a}$ and $\overrightarrow{qr} = \overrightarrow{b}$, express in terms of $\overrightarrow{a}$ and $\overrightarrow{b}$:

(i) $\overrightarrow{pr}$ **(ii)** $\overrightarrow{pt}$ **(iii)** $\overrightarrow{st}$ **(iv)** $\overrightarrow{ht}$

(v) $\overrightarrow{hk}$ **(vi)** $\overrightarrow{qt} - \overrightarrow{rt}$ **(vii)** $2\overrightarrow{pr} + \overrightarrow{qr}$

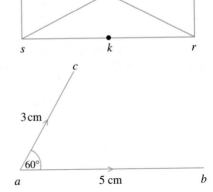

8. $\overrightarrow{ab}$ and $\overrightarrow{ac}$ are two vectors, as shown.

$|\overrightarrow{ab}| = 5$ cm, $|\overrightarrow{ac}| = 3$ cm and $|\angle bac| = 60°$.

Copy the diagram and show on it $\overrightarrow{ar}$ and $\overrightarrow{as}$ such that:

$\overrightarrow{ar} = -\overrightarrow{ab}$ and $\overrightarrow{as} = 2\overrightarrow{ac}$.

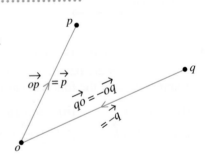

Representing Vectors With Single Letters

We can choose any point in the plane as the origin o.

If a vector starts or ends at the origin, we can represent it with a single letter.

Consider the three points o, p, q opposite.

The vector from o to p is written $\overrightarrow{op}$.

The vector from q to o is written $\overrightarrow{qo}$ or $-\overrightarrow{oq}$.

The letter o **at the beginning** can be dropped.

Thus $\boxed{\vec{op} = \vec{p}}$ and $\boxed{\vec{qo} = -\vec{oq} = -\vec{q}}$

Notes: A vector which **starts** from the origin is known as a **position vector**.

A vector which starts and finishes at the same point is called the **null**, or **zero** vector.

It is denoted by $\vec{o}$. It has no size or direction.

Representing any Two-letter Vectors as a Combination of two Single-letter Vectors

The following results are very useful and should be memorised:

$$\vec{ab} = \vec{b} - \vec{a}$$

(second letter minus the first letter)

The result can be used to express any two-letter vector as a combination of two single-letter vectors:

e.g., $\quad \vec{pq} = \vec{q} - \vec{p}, \qquad \vec{xy} = \vec{y} - \vec{x}, \qquad \vec{dc} = \vec{c} - \vec{d}, \qquad$ etc.

Midpoint

If m is the midpoint of $[ab]$, then: $\quad \boxed{\vec{m} = \tfrac{1}{2}\vec{a} + \tfrac{1}{2}\vec{b}}$

These results, which are proved in the next example, can be used directly.

Example ▼

oab is a triangle, where o is the origin and m is the midpoint of $[ab]$.

Prove that: **(i)** $\vec{ab} = \vec{b} - \vec{a}$

(ii) $\vec{m} = \tfrac{1}{2}\vec{a} + \tfrac{1}{2}\vec{b}$.

Solution:

(i) Using the Triangle Law:

$\vec{ab} = \vec{ao} + \vec{ob}$

$\vec{ab} = -\vec{oa} + \vec{ob}$

$\vec{ab} = -\vec{a} + \vec{b}$

$\vec{ab} = \vec{b} - \vec{a}$

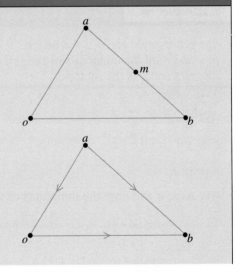

(ii) Using the Triangle Law:

$$\overrightarrow{om} = \overrightarrow{oa} + \overrightarrow{am}$$

$$\overrightarrow{m} = \overrightarrow{a} + \tfrac{1}{2}\overrightarrow{ab}$$

$$\overrightarrow{m} = \overrightarrow{a} + \tfrac{1}{2}(\overrightarrow{b} - \overrightarrow{a})$$

$$\overrightarrow{m} = \overrightarrow{a} + \tfrac{1}{2}\overrightarrow{b} - \tfrac{1}{2}\overrightarrow{a}$$

$$\overrightarrow{m} = \tfrac{1}{2}\overrightarrow{a} + \tfrac{1}{2}\overrightarrow{b}$$

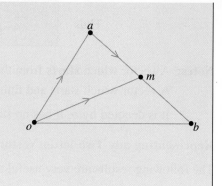

Centroid of a Triangle

A median of a triangle is a line segment from a vertex to the midpoint of the opposite side.

The three medians of a triangle meet at a point called the **centroid**, g in the diagram.
g divides each median in the ratio $2:1$,

i.e.

$$|ag| : |gq| = |bg| : |gr| = |cg| : |gp| = 2:1$$

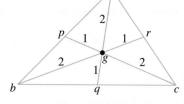

Medians of a triangle and the point where they meet, the centroid, occur frequently when writing vectors in terms of other vectors.

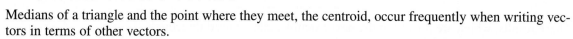

Example ▼

abc is a triangle and o is the origin.
p, q and r are the midpoints of the sides as shown in the diagram and g is the centroid.
Verify that:

(i) $\overrightarrow{p} + \overrightarrow{q} + \overrightarrow{r} = \overrightarrow{a} + \overrightarrow{b} + \overrightarrow{c}$

(ii) $g = \tfrac{1}{3}\overrightarrow{a} + \tfrac{1}{3}\overrightarrow{b} + \tfrac{1}{3}\overrightarrow{c}.$

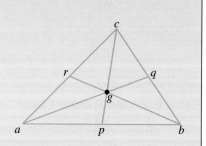

Solution:

(i) As p, q and r are the midpoints of the sides of the triangle,

$$\overrightarrow{p} = \tfrac{1}{2}\overrightarrow{a} + \tfrac{1}{2}\overrightarrow{b}, \qquad \overrightarrow{q} = \tfrac{1}{2}\overrightarrow{b} + \tfrac{1}{2}\overrightarrow{c}, \qquad \overrightarrow{r} = \tfrac{1}{2}\overrightarrow{a} + \tfrac{1}{2}\overrightarrow{c}$$

Thus,

$$\overrightarrow{p} + \overrightarrow{q} + \overrightarrow{r} = \tfrac{1}{2}\overrightarrow{a} + \tfrac{1}{2}\overrightarrow{b} + \tfrac{1}{2}\overrightarrow{b} + \tfrac{1}{2}\overrightarrow{c} + \tfrac{1}{2}\overrightarrow{a} + \tfrac{1}{2}\overrightarrow{c}$$

$$= \overrightarrow{a} + \overrightarrow{b} + \overrightarrow{c}$$

(ii) Using the Triangle Law:

$$\vec{og} = \vec{op} + \vec{pg}$$

$$\vec{g} = \vec{p} + \tfrac{1}{3}\vec{pc} \qquad \text{(as } g \text{ is the centroid)}$$

$$\vec{g} = \tfrac{1}{2}\vec{a} + \tfrac{1}{2}\vec{b} + \tfrac{1}{3}(\vec{c} - \vec{p})$$

$$\vec{g} = \tfrac{1}{2}\vec{a} + \tfrac{1}{2}\vec{b} + \tfrac{1}{3}\vec{c} - \tfrac{1}{3}\vec{p}$$

$$\vec{g} = \tfrac{1}{2}\vec{a} + \tfrac{1}{2}\vec{b} + \tfrac{1}{3}\vec{c} - \tfrac{1}{3}(\tfrac{1}{2}\vec{a} + \tfrac{1}{2}\vec{b})$$

$$\vec{g} = \tfrac{1}{2}\vec{a} + \tfrac{1}{2}\vec{b} + \tfrac{1}{3}\vec{c} - \tfrac{1}{6}\vec{a} - \tfrac{1}{6}\vec{b}$$

$$\vec{g} = \tfrac{1}{3}\vec{a} + \tfrac{1}{3}\vec{b} + \tfrac{1}{3}\vec{c}$$

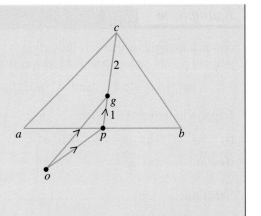

Example ▼

In the diagram, a, x and b are three collinear points and o is the origin.

x divides $[ab]$ in the ratio $m:n$.

Show that: $\vec{x} = \dfrac{n}{m+n}\vec{a} + \dfrac{m}{m+n}\vec{b}$.

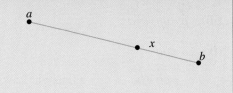

Solution:

$$\vec{ox} = \vec{oa} + \dfrac{m}{m+n}\vec{ab}$$

$$\vec{x} = \vec{a} + \dfrac{m}{m+n}(\vec{b} - \vec{a})$$

$$= \dfrac{(m+n)\vec{a} + m(\vec{b} - \vec{a})}{m+n}$$

$$= \dfrac{m\vec{a} + n\vec{a} + m\vec{b} - m\vec{a}}{m+n}$$

$$= \dfrac{n\vec{a} + m\vec{b}}{m+n} = \dfrac{n}{m+n}\vec{a} + \dfrac{m}{m+n}\vec{b}$$

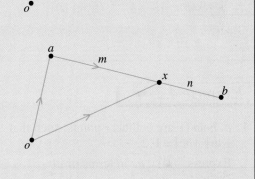

Note: This is often called the '**ratio theorem**' and the result can be written down directly. (It is very similar to the internal divisor formula of a line segment in coordinate geometry.)

For example, if r divides $[ab]$ internally in the ratio $5:3$, then:

$$\vec{r} = \dfrac{3}{5+3}\vec{a} + \dfrac{5}{5+3}\vec{b}$$

$$\vec{r} = \dfrac{3}{8}\vec{a} + \dfrac{5}{8}\vec{b}$$

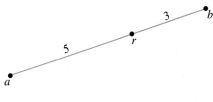

Notice that the sum of the coefficients $\dfrac{3}{8} + \dfrac{5}{8} = 1$.

Similarly $\dfrac{n}{m+n} + \dfrac{m}{m+n} = \dfrac{m+n}{m+n} = 1$.

oab is a triangle, where o is the origin.

p, q are points on $[oa]$ and $[ab]$, respectively, such that:

$$|op| : |pa| = 2:1 \quad \text{and} \quad |bq| : |qa| = 2:3$$

Express in terms of $\vec{a}$ and $\vec{b}$:

(i) $\vec{bq}$ (ii) $\vec{ap}$ (iii) $\vec{p}$

(iv) $\vec{q}$ (v) $\vec{qp}$

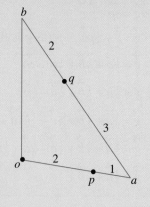

Solution:

(i) $\vec{bq} = \frac{2}{5}\vec{ba} = \frac{2}{5}(\vec{a} - \vec{b}) = \frac{2}{5}\vec{a} - \frac{2}{5}\vec{b}$

(ii) $\vec{ap} = \frac{1}{3}\vec{ao} = -\frac{1}{3}\vec{oa} = -\frac{1}{3}\vec{a}$

(iii) $\vec{p} = \vec{op} = \frac{2}{3}\vec{a}$

(iv) $\vec{q} = \vec{oq}$

     $= \vec{ob} + \vec{bq}$ (Triangle Law)

     $= \vec{b} + \frac{2}{5}\vec{a} - \frac{2}{5}\vec{b}$ (from (i))

     $= \frac{2}{5}\vec{a} + \frac{3}{5}\vec{b}$

(v) $\vec{qp} = \vec{p} - \vec{q}$

     $= \frac{2}{3}\vec{a} - \left(\frac{2}{5}\vec{a} + \frac{3}{5}\vec{b}\right)$ (from (iv))

     $= \frac{2}{3}\vec{a} - \frac{2}{5}\vec{a} - \frac{3}{5}\vec{b}$

     $= \frac{4}{15}\vec{a} - \frac{3}{5}\vec{b}$

Exercise 4.2 ▼

1. a, b and c are collinear points, such that
$|ab| : |bc| = 1:2$.

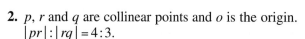

Express: (i) $\vec{ac}$ in terms of $\vec{ab}$

           (ii) $\vec{bc}$ in terms of $\vec{ac}$.

If $\vec{cb} = k\,\vec{ab}$, $k \in \mathbf{R}$, write down the value of k.

2. p, r and q are collinear points and o is the origin.
$|pr| : |rq| = 4:3$.

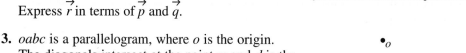

Express $\vec{r}$ in terms of $\vec{p}$ and $\vec{q}$.

3. $oabc$ is a parallelogram, where o is the origin.
The diagonals intersect at the point m and d is the
midpoint of $[ab]$.

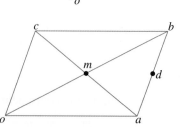

(i)   Express $\vec{cb}$ in terms of $\vec{a}$.

(ii)   Express in terms of $\vec{a}$ and $\vec{c}$:

     (a) $\vec{b}$ (b) $\vec{m}$ (c) $\vec{d}$.

(iii)   Express $\vec{dm} - \vec{bm}$ in terms of $\vec{c}$.

4. opq is a triangle, where o is the origin, r is the midpoint of $[oq]$ and s is the midpoint of $[pr]$.

Express: **(i)** $\vec{r}$ in terms of $\vec{q}$

        (ii) $\vec{s}$ in terms of $\vec{p}$ and $\vec{r}$

        (iii) $\vec{sq}$ in terms of $\vec{p}$, $\vec{q}$ and $\vec{r}$.

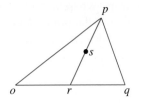

5. $opqr$ is a parallelogram, where o is the origin. The point x divides $[pq]$ in the ratio $2:1$. y is the midpoint of $[qr]$.

Express in terms of $\vec{p}$ and $\vec{r}$:

(i) $\vec{q}$ **(ii)** $\vec{y}$ **(iii)** $\vec{x}$ **(iv)** $\vec{xy}$.

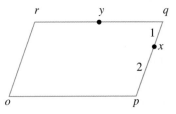

6. In the diagram, x is the midpoint of $[op]$ and $|py|:|yq|=2:1$.

Express in terms of $\vec{p}$ and $\vec{q}$:

(i) $\vec{y}$ **(ii)** $\vec{xy}$

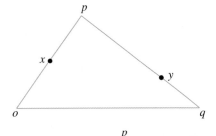

7. opq is a triangle, where o is the origin. x is the midpoint of $[oq]$, y is the midpoint of $[qz]$, and $|oz|:|zp|=3:1$.

(i) Express in terms of $\vec{p}$ and $\vec{q}$:

    (a) $\vec{x}$ **(b)** $\vec{zy}$.

(ii) If $\vec{xy}=k\vec{p}$, $k \in \mathbf{R}$, find the value of k.

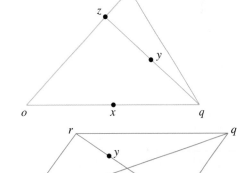

8. $opqr$ is a parallelogram, where o is the origin. $|ox|:|xr|=1:2$ and $|ry|:|yp|=1:2$.

(i) Express $\vec{xy}$ in terms of $\vec{p}$ and $\vec{r}$.

(ii) If $\vec{q}=k\vec{xy}$, $k \in \mathbf{R}$, find the value of k.

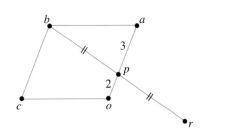

9. In the diagram, $oabc$ is a parallelogram. p is a point on oa such that $|op|:|pa|=2:3$. $[bp]$ is produced to r such that $|bp|=|pr|$.

Taking o as origin:

(i) Express $\vec{bp}$ in terms of $\vec{a}$ and $\vec{c}$.

(ii) Find the values of h and k given that

    $\vec{r}=h\vec{a}+k\vec{c}$, where $h, k \in \mathbf{R}$.

10. *opqr* is a parallelogram, where *o* is the origin. *y* is the midpoint of [*qr*]. *x* is the point of intersection of [*oq*] and [*py*]. *x* divides [*py*] in the ratio 2:1.

    (i) Express $\overrightarrow{ry}$ in terms of $\overrightarrow{p}$.

    (ii) Express in terms of $\overrightarrow{p}$ and $\overrightarrow{r}$:

        (a) $\overrightarrow{y}$ **(b)** $\overrightarrow{px}$.

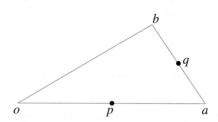

11. *oab* is a triangle, where *o* is the origin.
p is the midpoint of [*oa*].
q is the midpoint of [*ab*].
Prove that: $|\overrightarrow{ob}| = 2|\overrightarrow{pq}|$.

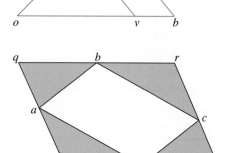

12. *oab* is a triangle, where *o* is the origin.
u is a point on [*oa*] such that $|ou|:|ua| = m:n$.
v is a point on [*ob*] such that $|ov|:|vb| = m:n$.

    (i) Express $\overrightarrow{u}$ in terms of $\overrightarrow{a}$.

    (ii) Express $\overrightarrow{v}$ in terms of $\overrightarrow{b}$.

    (iii) Hence, show that $\overrightarrow{uv} \parallel \overrightarrow{ab}$.

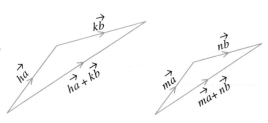

13. *a*, *b*, *c* and *d* are the midpoints of the sides of a quadrilateral *pqrs*.
Using vector methods, prove that *abcd* is a parallelogram.

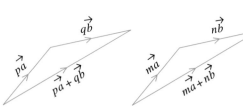

Parallel and Non-parallel Vectors

Parallel Vectors

Consider two parallel vectors $\overrightarrow{p}$ and $\overrightarrow{q}$.
If $\overrightarrow{p} = h\overrightarrow{a} + k\overrightarrow{b}$ and $\overrightarrow{q} = m\overrightarrow{a} + n\overrightarrow{b}$, h, k, m and $n \in \mathbf{R}$,

then: $\dfrac{|\overrightarrow{p}|}{|\overrightarrow{q}|} = \dfrac{h}{m} = \dfrac{k}{n}$.

Non-parallel Vectors

Consider two non-parallel vectors $\overrightarrow{a}$ and $\overrightarrow{b}$.
If $p\overrightarrow{a} + q\overrightarrow{b} = m\overrightarrow{a} + n\overrightarrow{b}$, $p, q, m, n \in \mathbf{R}$,

then: $p = m$ and $q = n$.
Equate the coefficients of $\overrightarrow{a}$ and the coefficients of $\overrightarrow{b}$ on both sides.

Example ▼

oab is a triangle, where *o* is the origin.

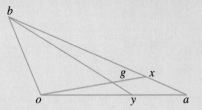

(i) *x* is a point on [*ab*] such that $|ax| : |xb| = 1:3$.
Express $\vec{x}$ in terms of $\vec{a}$ and $\vec{b}$.

(ii) *y* is a point on [*oa*] such that $|oy| : |ya| = 2:1$.
Express $\vec{by}$ in terms of $\vec{a}$ and $\vec{b}$.

(iii) [*ox*] and [*by*] intersect at *g*.
Given that $\vec{g} = m\vec{x}$ and $\vec{bg} = n\,\vec{by}$, where $m, n \in \mathbf{R}$,
find the value of *m* and the value of *n*.

Solution:

(i) $\vec{x} = \vec{ox}$

$= \vec{oa} + \tfrac{1}{4}\vec{ab}$

$= \vec{a} + \tfrac{1}{4}(\vec{b} - \vec{a})$

$= \vec{a} + \tfrac{1}{4}\vec{b} - \tfrac{1}{4}\vec{a}$

$= \tfrac{3}{4}\vec{a} + \tfrac{1}{4}\vec{b}$

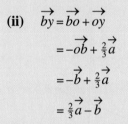

(ii) $\vec{by} = \vec{bo} + \vec{oy}$

$= -\vec{ob} + \tfrac{2}{3}\vec{a}$

$= -\vec{b} + \tfrac{2}{3}\vec{a}$

$= \tfrac{2}{3}\vec{a} - \vec{b}$

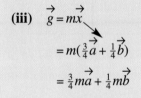

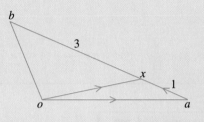

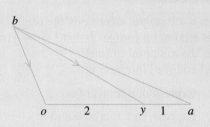

(iii) $\vec{g} = m\vec{x}$

$= m(\tfrac{3}{4}\vec{a} + \tfrac{1}{4}\vec{b})$

$= \tfrac{3}{4}m\vec{a} + \tfrac{1}{4}m\vec{b}$

$\vec{bg} = n\vec{by}$ (given)

$\vec{g} - \vec{b} = n(\tfrac{2}{3}\vec{a} - \vec{b})$

$\vec{g} - \vec{b} = \tfrac{2}{3}n\vec{a} - n\vec{b}$

$\vec{g} = \tfrac{2}{3}n\vec{a} - n\vec{b} + \vec{b}$

$\vec{g} = \tfrac{2}{3}n\vec{a} + (1-n)\vec{b}$

$\vec{g} = \vec{g}$

$\therefore \quad \tfrac{3}{4}m\vec{a} + \tfrac{1}{4}m\vec{b} = \tfrac{2}{3}n\vec{a} + (1-n)\vec{b}$

Equating coefficients:

$$\tfrac{3}{4}m = \tfrac{2}{3}n \qquad \text{and} \qquad \tfrac{1}{4}m = (1-n)$$

$$9m = 8n \qquad \text{and} \qquad m = 4 - 4n$$

$$9m - 8n = 0 \quad ① \qquad \text{and} \qquad m + 4n = 4 \quad ②$$

We now solve the simultaneous equations ① and ②:

$$9m - 8n = 0 \qquad ①$$
$$\underline{2m + 8n = 8 \qquad ② \times 2}$$
$$11m = 8 \quad \text{(add)}$$
$$m = \frac{8}{11}$$

$$9m - 8n = 0 \qquad ①$$
$$\underline{-9m - 36n = -36 \qquad ② \times -9}$$
$$-44n = -36$$
$$44n = 36$$
$$11n = 9$$
$$n = \frac{9}{11}$$

Thus, $m = \dfrac{8}{11}$ and $n = \dfrac{9}{11}$.

Exercise 4.3 ▼

1. oab is a triangle, where o is the origin.
p is a point on $[oa]$ such that $|op| = \tfrac{2}{3}|oa|$.
q is the midpoint of $[ab]$.
$[oq]$ and $[bp]$ intersect at r.

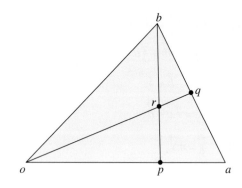

  (i) Express $\overrightarrow{p}$ in terms of $\overrightarrow{a}$.

  (ii) Express, in terms of $\overrightarrow{a}$ and $\overrightarrow{b}$:

    (a) $\overrightarrow{q}$ **(b)** $\overrightarrow{bp}$.

  (iii) Given that $\overrightarrow{r} = x\overrightarrow{q}$ and $\overrightarrow{br} = y\,\overrightarrow{bp}$, where $x, y \in \mathbf{R}$,
    find the value of x and the value of y.

  (iv) Write down the ratios:

    (a) $|or| : |oq|$ **(b)** $|br| : |rp|$.

2. $oabc$ is a rectangle, where o is the origin.
p is the midpoint of $[ab]$.
q is the midpoint of $[bc]$.
$[pc]$ and $[oq]$ intersect at r.

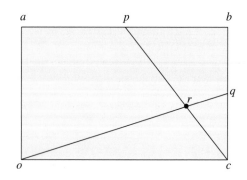

  (i) Express $\overrightarrow{q}$ in terms of $\overrightarrow{a}$ and $\overrightarrow{c}$.

  (ii) Express $\overrightarrow{pc}$ in terms of $\overrightarrow{a}$ and $\overrightarrow{c}$.

  (iii) If $\overrightarrow{r} = h\overrightarrow{q}$ and $\overrightarrow{pr} = k\,\overrightarrow{pc}$, where $h, k \in \mathbf{R}$, find the
    value of h and the value of k.

  (iv) Hence, write down the ratio:

    (a) $|or| : |rq|$ **(b)** $|pr| : |pc|$.

3. *oab* is a triangle, where *o* is the origin.

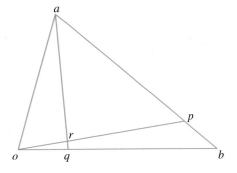

   (i) *p* is a point on [*ab*] such that $|ap|:|pb| = 4:1$.
      Express $\vec{p}$ in terms of $\vec{a}$ and $\vec{b}$.

  (ii) *q* is a point on [*ob*] such that $|oq|:|qb| = 1:3$.
      Express $\vec{aq}$ in terms of $\vec{a}$ and $\vec{b}$.

 (iii) [*op*] and [*aq*] intersect at *r*.
      Given that $\vec{r} = h\vec{p}$ and $\vec{ar} = k\vec{aq}$, where $h, k \in \mathbf{R}$,
      find the value of *h* and the value of *k*.

4. *oabc* is a parallelogram, where *o* is the origin.
y is a point on [*cb*] such that $|cy|:|yb| = 1:4$.
a, *x* and *c* are collinear.

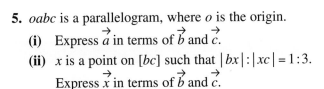

   (i) Express $\vec{y}$ in terms of $\vec{a}$ and $\vec{c}$.

  (ii) $\vec{x} = k\vec{y}$, where $k \in \mathbf{R}$.
      Express $\vec{x}$ in terms of *k*, $\vec{a}$ and $\vec{c}$.

 (iii) $\vec{cx} = t\,\vec{ca}$, where $t \in \mathbf{R}$.
      Show that: $\vec{x} = t\vec{a} + (1-t)\vec{c}$.

 (iv) Find the value of *k* and the value of *t*.

5. *oabc* is a parallelogram, where *o* is the origin.

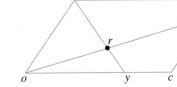

   (i) Express $\vec{a}$ in terms of $\vec{b}$ and $\vec{c}$.

  (ii) *x* is a point on [*bc*] such that $|bx|:|xc| = 1:3$.
      Express $\vec{x}$ in terms of $\vec{b}$ and $\vec{c}$.

 (iii) *y* is a point on [*oc*] such that $|oy|:|yc| = 2:1$.
      Express $\vec{ay}$ in terms of $\vec{b}$ and $\vec{c}$.

 (iv) [*ox*] and [*ay*] intersect at *r*.
      Given that $\vec{r} = m\vec{x}$ and $\vec{ar} = n\vec{ay}$, where $m, n \in \mathbf{R}$,
      find the value of *m* and the value of *n*.

Perpendicular Unit Vectors $\vec{i}$ and $\vec{j}$

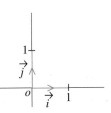

The vector from the origin, (0, 0) to the point (1, 0) on the
horizontal axis is called the $\vec{i}$ **vector**.

The vector from the origin, (0, 0) to the point (0, 1) on the
vertical axis is called the $\vec{j}$ **vector**.

> The vectors $\vec{i}$ and $\vec{j}$ are called perpendicular unit vectors.

Note: $\vec{i}$ and $\vec{j}$ are often called the **unit base vectors**.

Any vector can be written and represented in terms of $\vec{i}$ and $\vec{j}$.

For example, consider the vectors:

$$\vec{a} = 3\vec{i} + \vec{j}$$

$$\vec{b} = -2\vec{i} + \vec{j}$$

$$\vec{c} = -\vec{i} - 2\vec{j}$$

$$\vec{d} = 2\vec{i} - \vec{j}$$

$$\vec{e} = 3\vec{i}$$

$$\vec{f} = 2\vec{j}$$

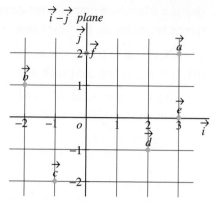

The plane on which these vectors are represented is called the $\vec{i} - \vec{j}$ plane.

It is common practice to represent a vector starting at the origin by its **endpoint only**; however, it must be understood the vector goes from the origin to its endpoint. When we represent vectors by points in this way they are called **position vectors**; for example, $3\vec{i} + 2\vec{j}$ is represented by the point $(3, 2)$.

Note: The vectors $\vec{i}$ and $\vec{j}$ obey all the properties of vectors we met earlier.
If preferred, the origin can be joined to the endpoint with a line.

Example ▼

Let $\vec{p} = 3\vec{i} - 2\vec{j}$ and $\vec{q} = \vec{i} + 3\vec{j}$. Express in terms of $\vec{i}$ and $\vec{j}$:

(i) $\vec{p} + \vec{q}$ (ii) $\vec{pq}$ (iii) $2\vec{p} + 3\vec{q}$.

Illustrate the vectors $\vec{p}, \vec{q}, \vec{p} + \vec{q}, \vec{pq}$ and $2\vec{p} + 3\vec{q}$ on a diagram.

Solution:

(i)
$$\vec{p} + \vec{q}$$
$$= (3\vec{i} - 2\vec{j}) + (\vec{i} + 3\vec{j})$$
$$= 3\vec{i} - 2\vec{j} + \vec{i} + 3\vec{j}$$
$$= 4\vec{i} + \vec{j}$$

(ii)
$$\vec{pq} = \vec{q} - \vec{p}$$
$$= (\vec{i} + 3\vec{j}) - (3\vec{i} - 2\vec{j})$$
$$= \vec{i} + 3\vec{j} - 3\vec{i} + 2\vec{j}$$
$$= -2\vec{i} + 5\vec{j}$$

(iii)
$$2\vec{p} + 3\vec{q}$$
$$= 2(3\vec{i} - 2\vec{j}) + 3(\vec{i} + 3\vec{j})$$
$$= 6\vec{i} - 4\vec{j} + 3\vec{i} + 9\vec{j}$$
$$= 9\vec{i} + 5\vec{j}$$

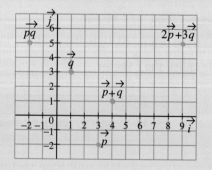

$\vec{a} = 4\vec{i} + 3\vec{j}$, $\vec{b} = 6\vec{i} - 5\vec{j}$ and $\vec{a} = c\vec{b}$. Express $\vec{c}$ in terms of $\vec{i}$ and $\vec{j}$.

Solution:

$$\vec{a} = c\vec{b}$$
$$\vec{a} = \vec{b} - \vec{c}$$
$$\vec{c} = \vec{b} - \vec{a}$$
$$\vec{c} = (6\vec{i} - 5\vec{j}) - (4\vec{i} + 3\vec{j})$$
$$\vec{c} = 6\vec{i} - 5\vec{j} - 4\vec{i} - 3\vec{j}$$
$$\vec{c} = 2\vec{i} - 8\vec{j}$$

$oabc$ is a parallelogram, where o is the origin.

$a = 2\vec{i} - 3\vec{j}$ and $b = 3\vec{i} + \vec{j}$. Express $\vec{c}$ in terms of $\vec{i}$ and $\vec{j}$.

Solution:

Make a rough diagram (keep cyclic order).

Since $oabc$ is a parallelogram:

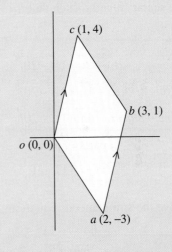

$$\vec{c} = \vec{oc} = \vec{ab}$$
$$= \vec{b} + \vec{a}$$
$$= (3\vec{i} + \vec{j}) - (2\vec{i} - 3\vec{j})$$
$$= 3\vec{i} + \vec{j} - 2\vec{i} + 3\vec{j}$$
$$= \vec{i} + 4\vec{j}$$

Alternatively (using coordinates):

$\vec{ab}$: $(2, -3) \rightarrow (3, 1)$ (add 1 to x, add 4 to y)

$\vec{oc}$: $(0,0) \rightarrow (1,4)$ (add 1 to x, add 4 to y)

∴   the coordinates of c are $(1, 4)$.

Thus, $\vec{c} = \vec{i} + 4\vec{j}$.

Vector Equations Involving $\vec{i}$ and $\vec{j}$

| If two vectors are equal, then |
| their $\vec{i}$ parts are equal and their $\vec{j}$ parts are equal. |

For example, if $a\vec{i} + b\vec{j} = c\vec{i} + d\vec{j}$,

then $a = c$ and $b = d$.

Vector equations involving $\vec{i}$ and $\vec{j}$ are solved with the following steps:

1. Remove the brackets.
2. Let the $\vec{i}$ parts equal the $\vec{i}$ parts and the $\vec{j}$ parts equal the $\vec{j}$ parts.
3. Solve these resultant equations.

Note: If one side of the equation does not contain an $\vec{i}$ part or a $\vec{j}$ part, add in $0\vec{i}$ or $0\vec{j}$, respectively.

Example ▼

$\vec{u} = 6\vec{i} - 8\vec{j}$ and $\vec{v} = \vec{i} + 4\vec{j}$.
Find the scalars h and t, such that $h\vec{u} + t\vec{v} = 11\vec{i} - 20\vec{j}$.

Solution:

$$h\vec{u} + t\vec{v} = 11\vec{i} - 20\vec{j}$$
$$h(6\vec{i} - 8\vec{j}) + t(\vec{i} + 4\vec{j}) = 11\vec{i} - 20\vec{j}$$
$$6h\vec{i} - 8h\vec{j} + t\vec{i} + 4t\vec{j} = 11\vec{i} - 20\vec{j}$$

$\vec{i}$ parts $= \vec{i}$ parts $\vec{j}$ parts $= \vec{j}$ parts

$6h + t = 11$ ① $-8h + 4t = -20$

                                    $-2h + t = -5$ ②

Now solve the simultaneous equations ① and ②:

$6h + t = 11$ ①	$6h + t = 11$ ①
$\underline{2h - t = 5}$ ② $\times -1$	$6(2) + t = 11$
$8h = 16$	$12 + t = 11$
$h = 2$	$t = -1$

Put $h = 2$ into ① or ②.

Thus, $h = 2$ and $t = -1$.

Exercise 4.4 ▼

1. Let $\vec{a} = 5\vec{i} - 3\vec{j}$, $\vec{b} = -\vec{i} + 2\vec{j}$, $\vec{c} = -4\vec{i}$ and $\vec{d} = 3\vec{j}$.

   Express in terms of $\vec{i}$ and $\vec{j}$:

   (i) $3\vec{a}$ **(ii)** $-2\vec{b}$ **(iii)** $\vec{a} + 2\vec{b}$ **(iv)** $\vec{dc}$ **(v)** $\vec{ab}$

   (vi) $2\vec{c} - \vec{d}$ **(vii)** $3\vec{a} - \vec{b}$ **(viii)** $2\vec{ba} - \vec{c}$ **(ix)** $\vec{cd} - \vec{ab}$ **(x)** $2\vec{a} + \vec{ab}$

2. $\vec{a} = 2\vec{i} + 2\vec{j}$ and $\vec{b} = -\vec{i} - 2\vec{j}$.

   Express $\vec{a} + \vec{b}$ and $\vec{ab}$ in terms of $\vec{i}$ and $\vec{j}$.

   Illustrate $\vec{a}$, $\vec{b}$, $\vec{a} + \vec{b}$ and $\vec{ab}$ on a diagram.

3. If $\vec{a} = 3\vec{i} + 4\vec{j}$ and $\vec{ab} = 2\vec{i} - 5\vec{j}$, express $\vec{b}$ in terms of $\vec{i}$ and $\vec{j}$.

4. If $\vec{pq} = -3\vec{i} + 5\vec{j}$ and $\vec{q} = -\vec{i} + \vec{j}$, express $\vec{p}$ in terms of $\vec{i}$ and $\vec{j}$.

5. $\vec{a} = 5\vec{i} - 2\vec{j}$, $\vec{b} = 2\vec{i} + 3\vec{j}$ and $\vec{a} = \vec{cb}$. Express $\vec{c}$ in terms of $\vec{i}$ and $\vec{j}$.

6. $\vec{p} + \vec{q} = 4\vec{i} - 4\vec{j}$ and $\vec{qp} = 2\vec{i} - 2\vec{j}$. Express $\vec{p}$ and $\vec{q}$ in terms of $\vec{i}$ and $\vec{j}$.

7. $\vec{x} + \vec{y} = 5\vec{i} - 3\vec{j}$ and $\vec{xy} = 5\vec{i} + \vec{j}$. Express $\vec{x}$ and $\vec{y}$ in terms of $\vec{i}$ and $\vec{j}$.

8. $oabc$ is a parallelogram where o is the origin, $\vec{a} = -3\vec{i} + \vec{j}$ and $\vec{b} = -4\vec{i} - 3\vec{j}$.

   Express $\vec{c}$ in terms of $\vec{i}$ and $\vec{j}$.

9. $pqrs$ is a parallelogram, where $\vec{p} = \vec{i} - 2\vec{j}$, $\vec{q} = -3\vec{i} + \vec{j}$ and $\vec{r} = 2\vec{i} + 3\vec{j}$.

   Express $\vec{s}$ in terms of $\vec{i}$ and $\vec{j}$.

10. c is an internal point on $[ab]$ such that $|ac| = \frac{3}{4}|ab|$.

    Express $\vec{c}$ in terms of $\vec{a}$ and $\vec{b}$.

    If $\vec{a} = 2\vec{i} + 3\vec{j}$ and $\vec{ab} = 4\vec{i} + 4\vec{j}$, express $\vec{c}$ in terms of $\vec{i}$ and $\vec{j}$.

11. Find the scalars a and b, such that $(1 - 4a)\vec{i} - (2b + 1)\vec{j} = 9\vec{i} - 7\vec{j}$.

12. Find the scalars p and q, such that $p\vec{i} + p\vec{j} + q\vec{i} - q\vec{j} = 7\vec{i} + 3\vec{j}$.

13. Find the scalars h and k, such that $h(2\vec{i} + 3\vec{j}) + k(\vec{i} - 5j) = \vec{i} + 21\vec{j}$.

14. Let $\vec{p} = 3\vec{i} + k\vec{j}$ and $\vec{q} = t\vec{i} + 3\vec{j}$. If $\vec{pq} = -5\vec{i} - 2\vec{j}$, find the values of k and t.

15. Let $\vec{a} = 2\vec{i} - 3\vec{j}$ and $\vec{ab} = -3\vec{i} + 7\vec{j}$.

    Find the scalars p and q, such that $p\vec{a} + q\vec{b} = 7\vec{i} - 18\vec{j}$.

16. If $\vec{x} = h\vec{i} + 4\vec{j}$ and $\vec{y} = 2\vec{i} + k\vec{j}$, find the scalars h and k, such that $\vec{xy} = -\vec{i} + \vec{j}$.

17. *oab* is a triangle, where *o* is the origin.

   p and *q* are points such that:

$$|oq| : |qb| = 2 : 1 = |bp| : |pa|.$$

   If $\vec{a} = 6\vec{i} + 3\vec{j}$ and $\vec{b} = 9\vec{i} + 12\vec{j}$, express $\vec{p}$ and $\vec{q}$ in terms of $\vec{i}$ and $\vec{j}$ and find $h, k \in \mathbf{R}$, such that

$$h\vec{p} + k\vec{q} = 4\vec{i} + 12\vec{j}.$$

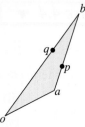

18. Let $\vec{u} = 3\vec{i} + 2\vec{j}$, $\vec{w} = -\vec{i} + 4\vec{j}$. The vector $t\vec{w} + \vec{u}$ is on the $\vec{j}$-axis; find the value of the scalar *t*.

19. Let $\vec{h} = 6\vec{i} - 8\vec{j}$ and $\vec{k} = 4\vec{i} - 3\vec{j}$.

   (i) If *ohkm* is a parallelogram, *o* being the origin, express $\vec{m}$ in terms of $\vec{i}$ and $\vec{j}$.

   (ii) If $\vec{p} = \vec{k} + a\vec{m}$, $a \in \mathbf{R}$, and $\vec{p}$ is a point on the $\vec{j}$-axis, calculate the value of *a*.

Modulus of a Vector

The **modulus** of the vector $a\vec{i} + b\vec{j}$ is the distance from the origin to the point (a, b).

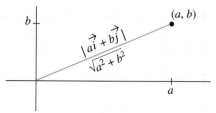

The modulus of the vector $a\vec{i} + b\vec{j}$ is denoted by $|a\vec{i} + b\vec{j}|$ and is given by $\sqrt{a^2 + b^2}$ (by Pythagoras's Theorem).

$$\boxed{|a\vec{i} + b\vec{j}| = \sqrt{a^2 + b^2}}$$

Note: The **modulus** of a vector is often called the **length** of the vector.

Before getting the length of a vector, make sure it is written in the form $a\vec{i} + b\vec{j}$.

Example ▼

If $\vec{p} = 4\vec{i} - 2\vec{j}$ and $\vec{q} = -\vec{i} + 5\vec{j}$, calculate:

(i) $|\vec{p}|$ **(ii)** $|\vec{p} + \vec{q}|$ **(iii)** $|\vec{pq}|$.

Solution:

(i) $|\vec{p}| = |4\vec{i} - 2\vec{j}|$

$= \sqrt{(4)^2 + (-2)^2}$

$= \sqrt{16 + 4}$

$= \sqrt{20}$ or $2\sqrt{5}$

(ii) $\vec{p} + \vec{q} = 4\vec{i} - 2\vec{j} - \vec{i} + 5\vec{j} = 3\vec{i} + 3\vec{j}$

$|\vec{p} + \vec{q}| = |3\vec{i} + 3\vec{j}|$

$= \sqrt{(3)^2 + (3)^2}$

$= \sqrt{9 + 9}$

$= \sqrt{18}$ or $3\sqrt{2}$

(iii) $\vec{pq} = \vec{q} - \vec{p}$

$= (-\vec{i} + 5\vec{j}) - (4\vec{i} - 2\vec{j})$

$= -\vec{i} + 5\vec{j} - 4\vec{i} + 2\vec{j}$

$= -5\vec{i} + 7\vec{j}$

$|\vec{pq}| = |-5\vec{i} + 7\vec{j}|$

$= \sqrt{(-5)^2 + (7)^2}$

$= \sqrt{25 + 49}$

$= \sqrt{74}$

Example ▼

$\vec{a} = 6\vec{i} - 2\vec{j}, \quad \vec{b} = x\vec{i} - 3\vec{j}$. If $|\vec{ab}| = \sqrt{17}$, find two values for x.

Solution:

$\vec{ab} = \vec{b} - \vec{a} = (x\vec{i} - 3\vec{j}) - (6\vec{i} - 2\vec{j})$

$\quad = x\vec{i} - 3\vec{j} - 6\vec{i} + 2\vec{j}$

$\quad = (x - 6)\vec{i} - \vec{j}$

Given: $\qquad\qquad\qquad\qquad\qquad |\vec{ab}| = \sqrt{17}$

$\therefore \qquad\qquad\qquad\qquad |(x-6)\vec{i} - \vec{j}| = \sqrt{17}$

$\therefore \qquad\qquad\qquad \sqrt{(x-6)^2 + (-1)^2} = \sqrt{17}$

$\qquad\qquad\qquad\qquad (x-6)^2 + (-1)^2 = 17 \qquad$ (square both sides)

$\qquad\qquad\qquad\qquad x^2 - 12x + 36 + 1 = 17$

$\qquad\qquad\qquad\qquad\quad x^2 - 12x + 20 = 0$

$\qquad\qquad\qquad\qquad\quad (x-2)(x-10) = 0$

$\qquad\qquad\qquad\quad x - 2 = 0 \quad \text{or} \quad x - 10 = 0$

$\qquad\qquad\qquad\qquad x = 2 \quad \text{or} \qquad x = 10$

Unit Vector

If $\vec{v}$ is any vector, then the **unit vector** in the direction of $\vec{v}$ is given by $\dfrac{\vec{v}}{|\vec{v}|}$.
It has the same direction as $\vec{v}$ and its length is one unit.

> The unit vector in the direction of $\vec{v}$ is:
>
> $$\frac{\vec{v}}{|\vec{v}|}$$

Find the unit vector in the direction of the vector $3\vec{i} - 2\vec{j}$.
Verify that its length is 1.

Solution:

$$|3\vec{i} - 2\vec{j}| = \sqrt{(3)^2 + (-2)^2}$$

$$= \sqrt{9 + 4}$$

$$= \sqrt{13}$$

Unit vector in the direction of $3\vec{i} - 2\vec{j}$

$$= \frac{3\vec{i} - 2\vec{j}}{|3\vec{i} - 2\vec{j}|}$$

$$= \frac{3\vec{i} - 2\vec{j}}{\sqrt{13}}$$

$$= \frac{3}{\sqrt{13}}\vec{i} - \frac{2}{\sqrt{13}}\vec{j}$$

$$\left|\frac{3}{\sqrt{13}}\vec{i} - \frac{2}{\sqrt{13}}\vec{j}\right| = \sqrt{\left(\frac{3}{\sqrt{13}}\right)^2 + \left(-\frac{2}{\sqrt{13}}\right)^2} = \sqrt{\frac{9}{13} + \frac{4}{13}} = \sqrt{\frac{13}{13}} = \sqrt{1} = 1$$

Exercise 4.5 ▼

Evaluate each of the following:

1. $|3\vec{i} + 4\vec{j}|$ **2.** $|12\vec{i} - 5\vec{j}|$ **3.** $|-8\vec{i} + 15\vec{j}|$ **4.** $|-21\vec{i} - 20\vec{j}|$

5. $|3\vec{i} - 2\vec{j}|$ **6.** $|4\vec{i} - \vec{j}|$ **7.** $|-5\vec{i} - 2\vec{j}|$ **8.** $|-4\vec{i} - 5\vec{j}|$

If $\vec{a} = 2\vec{i} + 4\vec{j}$, $\vec{b} = -2\vec{i} - \vec{j}$ and $\vec{c} = \vec{i} - 3\vec{j}$, calculate each of the following:

9. $|\vec{a}|$ **10.** $|2\vec{b} - \vec{c}|$ **11.** $|\vec{ab}|$ **12.** $|\vec{cb}|$

13. Let $\vec{p} = 3\vec{i} + 4\vec{j}$ and $\vec{q} = -\vec{i} + 2\vec{j}$.
   (i) Express $\vec{pq}$ in terms of $\vec{i}$ and $\vec{j}$. **(ii)** Verify that: $|\vec{p}| + |\vec{q}| > |\vec{pq}|$.

14. Let $\vec{a} = \vec{i} + 2\vec{j}$, $\vec{b} = \vec{i} + 6\vec{j}$, and $\vec{c} = -2\vec{i} + 6\vec{j}$.
   Verify that: $|\vec{b} - \vec{a}|^2 + |\vec{b} - \vec{c}|^2 = |\vec{a} - \vec{c}|^2$.

15. $\vec{v} = -8\vec{i} + k\vec{j}$. If $|\vec{v}| = \sqrt{73}$, find two possible values of k, $k \in \mathbf{R}$.

16. If $|k\vec{i} + 10\vec{j}| = |2\vec{i} + 11\vec{j}|$, find two possible values of k, $k \in \mathbf{R}$.

17. If $|t\vec{i} + \vec{j}| = |5\vec{i} + 5\vec{j}|$, find two possible values of t, $t \in \mathbf{R}$.

18. $\vec{x} = 2\vec{i} + 3\vec{j}$ and $\vec{y} = k\vec{i} + 2\vec{j}$. If $|\vec{xy}| = \sqrt{37}$, find two possible values of k, $k \in \mathbf{R}$.

19. $\vec{p} = t\vec{i} + 5\vec{j}$ and $\vec{q} = 2\vec{i} + \vec{j}$. If $|\vec{pq}| = \sqrt{41}$, find two possible values of t, $t \in \mathbf{R}$.

20. Find the unit vector in the direction $8\vec{i} + 15\vec{j}$.

21. Find the unit vector in the direction $-5\vec{i} + 2\vec{j}$.

22. If $\vec{p} = \vec{i} + 2\vec{j}$ and $\vec{q} = 5\vec{i} - \vec{j}$, find the unit vector in the direction $\vec{pq}$.

23. If $\vec{a} = 4\vec{i} + \vec{j}$, verify that: $\left| \dfrac{\vec{a}}{|\vec{a}|} \right| = 1$.

24. $\vec{p} = 4\vec{i} + 3\vec{j}$ and $\vec{q} = h\vec{i} + k\vec{j}$.

If $\vec{q} - \dfrac{\vec{q}}{|\vec{p}|} = \vec{p}$, find the value of h and the value of k, $h, k \in \mathbf{R}$.

25. $\vec{a} = 2\vec{i} + \vec{j}$, $\vec{b} = \vec{i} + \vec{j}$ and $\vec{c} = 4\vec{i} + 3\vec{j}$.

$\vec{p} = h\vec{a}$, $\vec{q} = k\vec{b}$ and $\vec{p} + \vec{q} = m\vec{c}$, $h, k, m \in \mathbf{R}$.

If $|\vec{p} + \vec{q}| = 10$, calculate: **(i)** $|\vec{p}|$ **(ii)** $|\vec{q}|$.

Dot Product (or Scalar Product)

If $\vec{x}$ and $\vec{y}$ are two vectors, their dot product is defined as:

$\vec{x} \cdot \vec{y} = |\vec{x}||\vec{y}| \cos \theta$,

where θ is the smaller angle between them.

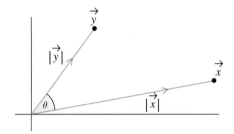

In words:
The length of $\vec{x}$ multiplied by the length of $\vec{y}$ multiplied by the cos of the angle between them.
The result of the dot product is a real number, **not** a vector.

Note: The **dot product** is also called the **scalar product**, because $|\vec{x}|$, $|\vec{y}|$ and $\cos \theta$ are scalars and their product is also a scalar.

The smaller angle θ, is such that $0 \leqslant \theta \leqslant 180$.

If $0° < \theta < 90°$, then $\vec{x} \cdot \vec{y} > 0$ (because $\cos \theta > 0$ in the first quadrant).

If $90° < \theta < 180°$, then $\vec{x} \cdot \vec{y} < 0$ (because $\cos \theta < 0$ in the second quadrant).

Properties of the Dot Product

1.

$$\vec{x} \perp \vec{y} \iff \vec{x} \cdot \vec{y} = 0$$

(where $\vec{x}$ and $\vec{y}$ are non-zero vectors)

If $\vec{x} \perp \vec{y}$, then:

$$\vec{x} \cdot \vec{y} = |\vec{x}| |\vec{y}| \cos 90°$$

$$= |\vec{x}| |\vec{y}| (0) \qquad (\cos 90° = 0)$$

$$= 0$$

$\vec{i}$ and $\vec{j}$ are perpendicular vectors.

Thus, $\vec{i} \cdot \vec{j} = 0$ and $\vec{j} \cdot \vec{i} = 0$.

(i) To prove that two vectors are perpendicular, show that their dot product is zero.

(ii) If we are told that two vectors are perpendicular, then we let their dot product equal zero and use this equation to find any unknown values.

2.

$$\vec{x} \cdot \vec{x} = |\vec{x}|^2$$

$$\vec{x} \cdot \vec{x} = |\vec{x}| |\vec{x}| \cos 0 \qquad \text{(angle between } \vec{x} \text{ and itself is 0)}$$

$$= |\vec{x}| |\vec{x}| (1) \qquad (\cos 0 = 1)$$

$$= |\vec{x}|^2$$

In particular, $\vec{i} \cdot \vec{i} = |\vec{i}|^2 = 1$ and $\vec{j} \cdot \vec{j} = |\vec{j}|^2 = 1$.

3.

$$\text{If } \vec{x} \parallel \vec{y}, \text{ then } \vec{x} \cdot \vec{y} = |\vec{x}| |\vec{y}|$$

If $\vec{x} \parallel \vec{y}$, then:

$$\vec{x} \cdot \vec{y} = |\vec{x}| |\vec{y}| \cos 0 \qquad \text{(angle between } \vec{x} \text{ and } \vec{y} \text{ is zero)}$$

$$= |\vec{x}| |\vec{y}| (1) \qquad (\cos 0 = 1)$$

$$= |\vec{x}| |\vec{y}|$$

4.

$$\vec{x} \cdot \vec{y} = \vec{y} \cdot \vec{x}$$

$$\vec{x} \cdot \vec{y} = |\vec{x}| |\vec{y}| \cos \theta$$

$$= |\vec{y}| |\vec{x}| \cos \theta \qquad (|\vec{x}| |\vec{y}| = |\vec{y}| |\vec{x}|, \text{ as both are real numbers})$$

$$= \vec{y} \cdot \vec{x}$$

5.

$$\vec{a} \cdot (\vec{b} + \vec{c}) = \vec{a} \cdot \vec{b} + \vec{a} \cdot \vec{c}$$

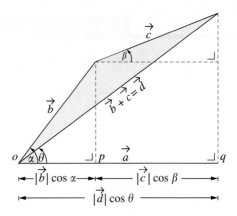

In the diagram $\vec{d} = \vec{b} + \vec{c}$.

$$|oq| = |op| + |pq|$$

$$|\vec{d}| \cos\theta = |\vec{b}| \cos\alpha + |\vec{c}| \cos\beta$$

$$|\vec{a}||\vec{d}| \cos\theta = |\vec{a}||\vec{b}| \cos\alpha + |\vec{a}||\vec{c}| \cos\beta$$

(multiply both sides by $|\vec{a}|$)

$$\vec{a} \cdot \vec{d} = \vec{a} \cdot \vec{b} + \vec{a} \cdot \vec{c}$$

$$\vec{a} \cdot (\vec{b} + \vec{c}) = \vec{a} \cdot \vec{b} + \vec{a} \cdot \vec{c}$$

6.

If $\vec{x} = a\vec{i} + b\vec{j}$ and $\vec{y} = c\vec{i} + d\vec{j}$, then $\vec{x} \cdot \vec{y} = ac + bd$.

Multiply the $\vec{i}$ coefficients, multiply the $\vec{j}$ coefficients and add these results.

$$\vec{x} \cdot \vec{y} = (a\vec{i} + b\vec{j}) \cdot (c\vec{i} + d\vec{j})$$

$$= a\vec{i} \cdot (c\vec{i} + d\vec{j}) + b\vec{j} \cdot (c\vec{i} + d\vec{j})$$

$$= a\vec{i} \cdot c\vec{i} + a\vec{i} \cdot d\vec{j} + b\vec{j} \cdot c\vec{i} + b\vec{j} \cdot d\vec{j}$$

$$= ac\vec{i} \cdot \vec{i} + ad\vec{i} \cdot \vec{j} + bc\vec{j} \cdot \vec{i} + bd\vec{j} \cdot \vec{j}$$

$$= ac(1) + ad(0) + bc(0) + bd(1)$$

$$= ac + bd$$

7.

If θ is the angle between $\vec{x}$ and $\vec{y}$, then:

$$\cos\theta = \frac{\vec{x} \cdot \vec{y}}{|\vec{x}||\vec{y}|}.$$

$$\vec{x} \cdot \vec{y} = |\vec{x}||\vec{y}| \cos\theta$$

$$|\vec{x}||\vec{y}| \cos\theta = \vec{x} \cdot \vec{y}$$

$$\cos\theta = \frac{\vec{x} \cdot \vec{y}}{|\vec{x}||\vec{y}|}$$

(divide both sides by $|\vec{x}|$ and $|\vec{y}|$)

(i) $\vec{a} = -2\vec{i} + \vec{j}$ and $\vec{b} = 3\vec{i} + 6\vec{j}$. Verify that: $\vec{a} \perp \vec{b}$.

(ii) $\vec{p} = -4\vec{i} + 3\vec{j}$ and $\vec{q} = k\vec{i} - 8\vec{j}$. If $\vec{p} \perp \vec{q}$, find the value of k, $k \in \mathbf{R}$.

Solution:

(i) $\vec{a} \cdot \vec{b} = (-2\vec{i} + \vec{j}) \cdot (3\vec{i} + 6\vec{j})$

$= (-2)(3) + (1)(6)$

$= -6 + 6$

$= 0$

$\therefore \quad \vec{a} \perp \vec{b}$

(ii) Given: $\vec{p} \perp \vec{q}$

$\therefore \quad\quad\quad\quad \vec{p} \cdot \vec{q} = 0$

$(-4\vec{i} + 3\vec{j}) \cdot (k\vec{i} - 8\vec{j}) = 0$

$(-4)(k) + (3)(-8) = 0$

$-4k - 24 = 0$

$-4k = 24$

$k = -6$

$\vec{a} = 4\vec{i} + 4\vec{j}$, $\vec{b} = -2\vec{i} + 6\vec{j}$ and $\vec{c} = -4\vec{j}$. Find $|\angle bac|$, correct to one decimal place.

Solution:

Let $|\angle bac| = \theta$.

$\vec{ab} \cdot \vec{ac} = |\vec{ab}| \cdot |\vec{ac}| \cos\theta$

$\cos\theta = \dfrac{\vec{ab} \cdot \vec{ac}}{|\vec{ab}||\vec{ac}|}$

$\vec{ab} = \vec{b} - \vec{a} = -2\vec{i} + 6\vec{j} - 4\vec{i} - 4\vec{j} = -6\vec{i} + 2\vec{j}$

$\therefore \quad |\vec{ab}| = |-6\vec{i} + 2\vec{j}| = \sqrt{(-6)^2 + (-2)^2} = \sqrt{36 + 4} = \sqrt{40} = 2\sqrt{10}$

$\vec{ac} = \vec{c} - \vec{a} = -4\vec{j} - 4\vec{i} - 4\vec{j} = -4\vec{i} - 8\vec{j}$

$\therefore \quad |\vec{ac}| = |-4\vec{i} - 8\vec{j}| = \sqrt{(-4)^2 + (-8)^2} = \sqrt{16 + 64} = \sqrt{80} = 4\sqrt{5}$

$\vec{ab} \cdot \vec{ac} = (-6\vec{i} + 2\vec{j}) \cdot (-4\vec{i} - 8\vec{j})$

$= (-6)(-4) + (2)(-8) = 24 - 16 = 8$

$\cos\theta = \dfrac{\vec{ab} \cdot \vec{ac}}{|\vec{ab}||\vec{ac}|} = \dfrac{8}{2\sqrt{10} \ 4\sqrt{5}} = \dfrac{1}{\sqrt{10} \ \sqrt{5}} = \dfrac{1}{\sqrt{50}}$

$\therefore \quad \theta = \cos^{-1}\dfrac{1}{\sqrt{50}}$

$\theta = 81.86989765°$

$\theta = 81.9$ (correct to one decimal place)

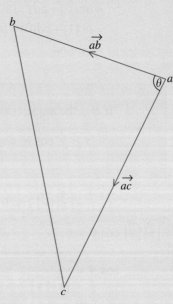

We take the origin of both vectors, in this case a, acting away from the required angle, i.e.,

$\vec{ab} \cdot \vec{ac} = |\vec{ab}||\vec{ac}| \cos\theta.$

Vertices p and r of the parallelogram $opqr$ are $\vec{p} = 4\vec{i} - \vec{j}$ and $\vec{r} = 2\vec{i} + 3\vec{j}$, where o is the origin.

Find:

(i) $\vec{p} + \vec{r}$ and $\vec{p} - \vec{r}$

(ii) $|\vec{p} + \vec{r}|$ and $|\vec{p} - \vec{r}|$.

Show that θ, the acute angle between $\vec{oq}$ and $\vec{rp}$, is given by:

$$\cos^{-1} \frac{1}{5\sqrt{2}}$$

A point d in the plane is such that $\vec{d} = \vec{r} - k\vec{p}$, $k \in \mathbf{R}$ and $\vec{d} \perp \vec{p}$. Find the value of k.

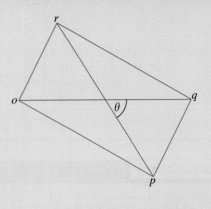

Solution:

(i) $\vec{p} + \vec{r} = 4\vec{i} - \vec{j} + 2\vec{i} + 3\vec{j}$

$\qquad = 6\vec{i} + 2\vec{j}$

$\vec{p} - \vec{r} = (4\vec{i} - \vec{j}) - (2\vec{i} + 3\vec{j})$

$\qquad = 2\vec{i} - 4\vec{j}$

(ii) $|\vec{p} + \vec{r}| = |6\vec{i} + 2\vec{j}|$

$\qquad = \sqrt{36 + 4} = \sqrt{40} = 2\sqrt{10}$

$|\vec{p} - \vec{r}| = |2\vec{i} - 4\vec{j}|$

$\qquad = \sqrt{4 + 16} = \sqrt{20} = 2\sqrt{5}$

$\vec{oq} = \vec{q} = \vec{p} + \vec{r} = 6\vec{i} + 2\vec{j}$

$\vec{rp} = \vec{p} - \vec{r} = 2\vec{i} - 4\vec{j}$

$\vec{oq} \cdot \vec{rp} = |\vec{oq}||\vec{rp}| \cos \theta$

Thus, $\cos \theta = \dfrac{\vec{oq} \cdot \vec{rp}}{|\vec{oq}||\vec{rp}|}$.

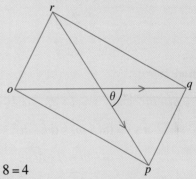

$\vec{oq} \cdot \vec{rp} = (6\vec{i} + 2\vec{j}) \cdot (2\vec{i} - 4\vec{j}) = (6)(2) + (2)(-4) = 12 - 8 = 4$

$|\vec{oq}||\vec{rp}| = |6\vec{i} + 2\vec{j}||2\vec{i} - 4\vec{j}| = \sqrt{40}\sqrt{20} = \sqrt{800} = 20\sqrt{2}$

$\cos \theta = \dfrac{\vec{oq} \cdot \vec{rp}}{|\vec{oq}||\vec{rp}|} = \dfrac{4}{20\sqrt{2}} = \dfrac{1}{5\sqrt{2}}$

$\therefore \quad \theta = \cos^{-1} \dfrac{1}{5\sqrt{2}}$

$\vec{d} = \vec{r} - k\vec{p} = 2\vec{i} + 3\vec{j} - k(4\vec{i} - \vec{j})$

$\qquad = 2\vec{i} + 3\vec{j} - 4k\vec{i} + k\vec{j} = (2 - 4k)\vec{i} + (3 + k)\vec{j}$

Given:
$$\vec{d} \perp \vec{p}$$
$$\therefore \quad \vec{d} \cdot \vec{p} = 0$$
$$[(2-4k)\vec{i} + (k+3)\vec{j}] \cdot [4\vec{i} - \vec{j}] = 0$$
$$(2-4k)(4) + (k+3)(-1) = 0$$
$$8 - 16k - k - 3 = 0$$
$$-17k = -5$$
$$k = \tfrac{5}{17}$$

Example ▼

If $|\vec{x} + \vec{y}| = |\vec{x} - \vec{y}|$, prove that $\vec{x} \perp \vec{y}$.

Solution:

Method 1:

Given:
$$|\vec{x} + \vec{y}| = |\vec{x} - \vec{y}|$$
$$|\vec{x} + \vec{y}|^2 = |\vec{x} - \vec{y}|^2 \qquad \text{(square both sides)}$$
$$(x+y) \cdot (x+y) = (x-y) \cdot (x-y) \qquad (|\vec{x}|^2 = \vec{x} \cdot \vec{x})$$
$$\vec{x} \cdot \vec{x} + \vec{x} \cdot \vec{y} + \vec{y} \cdot \vec{x} + \vec{y} \cdot \vec{y} = \vec{x} \cdot \vec{x} - \vec{x} \cdot \vec{y} - \vec{y} \cdot \vec{x} + \vec{y} \cdot \vec{y}$$
$$2\vec{x} \cdot \vec{y} = -2\vec{x} \cdot \vec{y} \qquad (\vec{x} \cdot \vec{y} = \vec{y} \cdot \vec{x})$$
$$4\vec{x} \cdot \vec{y} = 0$$
$$\vec{x} \cdot \vec{y} = 0$$
$$\therefore \quad \vec{x} \perp \vec{y}$$

Method 2:

Let $\vec{x} = a\vec{i} + b\vec{j}$ and $\vec{y} = c\vec{i} + d\vec{j}$, $\quad a, b, c, d \in \mathbf{R}$.

$\vec{x} + \vec{y} = (a\vec{i} + b\vec{j}) + (c\vec{i} + d\vec{j})$	$\vec{x} - \vec{y} = (a\vec{i} + b\vec{j}) - (c\vec{i} + d\vec{j})$
$= a\vec{i} + b\vec{j} + c\vec{i} + d\vec{j}$	$= a\vec{i} + b\vec{j} - c\vec{i} - d\vec{j}$
$= (a+c)\vec{i} + (b+d)\vec{j}$	$= (a-c)\vec{i} + (b-d)\vec{j}$
$\therefore \ |\vec{x} + \vec{y}| = \sqrt{(a+c)^2 + (b+d)^2}$	$\therefore \ |\vec{x} - \vec{y}| = \sqrt{(a-c)^2 + (b-d)^2}$

Given:
$$|\vec{x} + \vec{y}| = |\vec{x} - \vec{y}|$$
$$\therefore \quad \sqrt{(a+c)^2 + (b+d)^2} = \sqrt{(a-c)^2 + (b-d)^2}$$
$$a^2 + 2ac + c^2 + b^2 + 2bd + d^2 = a^2 - 2ac + c^2 + b^2 - 2bd + d^2$$
$$2ac + 2bd = -2ac - 2bd$$
$$4ac + 4bd = 0$$
$$ac + bd = 0$$
$$\vec{x} \cdot \vec{y} = 0 \qquad (\vec{x} \cdot \vec{y} = ac + bd)$$
$$\therefore \quad \vec{x} \perp \vec{y}$$

Evaluate each of the following:

1. $(3\vec{i}+2\vec{j}) \cdot (5\vec{i}+4\vec{j})$

2. $(-3\vec{i}-2\vec{j}) \cdot (4\vec{i}-3\vec{j})$

3. $(-\vec{i}+4\vec{j}) \cdot (-5\vec{i}+2\vec{j})$

4. $(-2\vec{i}-5\vec{j}) \cdot (-4\vec{i}-8\vec{j})$

5. $(7\vec{i}+6\vec{j}) \cdot (6\vec{i}-2\vec{j})$

6. $(5\vec{i}+4\vec{j}) \cdot (4\vec{i}-5\vec{j})$

7. $(5\vec{i}+3\vec{j}) \cdot 4\vec{i}$

8. $-8\vec{j} \cdot (2\vec{i}+4\vec{j})$

9. $\vec{i} \cdot (4\vec{i}-2\vec{j})$

10. Let $\vec{a}=3\vec{i}+4\vec{j}$ and $\vec{b}=2\vec{i}-\vec{j}$. Calculate $\vec{a} \cdot \vec{b}$.

11. Let $\vec{p}=-2\vec{i}+5\vec{j}$ and $\vec{q}=3\vec{i}+2\vec{j}$. Calculate $\vec{p} \cdot \vec{q}$.

12. Let $\vec{a}=2\vec{i}+\vec{j}$, $\vec{b}=4\vec{i}-2\vec{j}$ and $\vec{c}=\vec{i}+3\vec{j}$.

Show that: **(i)** $\vec{a} \cdot (\vec{b}+\vec{c}) = \vec{a} \cdot \vec{b} + \vec{a} \cdot \vec{c}$ **(ii)** $\vec{a} \cdot \vec{a} = |\vec{a}|^2$.

13. Let $\vec{x}=4\vec{i}+\vec{j}$ and $\vec{y}=2\vec{i}-5\vec{j}$.

(i) Express in terms of $\vec{i}$ and $\vec{j}$: **(a)** $\vec{x}+\vec{y}$ **(b)** $\vec{xy}$.

(ii) Calculate: **(a)** $\vec{x} \cdot \vec{y}$ **(b)** $(\vec{x}+\vec{y}) \cdot \vec{xy}$ **(c)** $3\vec{x} \cdot 2\vec{y}$.

14. Let $\vec{x}=-\vec{i}+6\vec{j}$ and $\vec{y}=3\vec{i}+2\vec{j}$. Express $\vec{xy}$ in terms of $\vec{i}$ and $\vec{j}$.

(i) Evaluate $\vec{x} \cdot \vec{xy}$ **(ii)** Show that: $\vec{x} \cdot \vec{xy} = \vec{x} \cdot \vec{y} - |\vec{x}|^2$.

15. If $|\vec{x}| = 4$, $|\vec{y}| = 5$ and $|\angle xoy| = 60°$, calculate $\vec{x} \cdot \vec{y}$.

16. If $\vec{p}=3\vec{i}+\vec{j}$ and $\vec{q}=2\vec{i}+4\vec{j}$, calculate $|\angle poq|$.

17. If $\vec{a}=-\vec{i}+2\vec{j}$ and $\vec{b}=-\vec{i}-3\vec{j}$, calculate $|\angle aob|$.

18. If $\vec{a}=5\vec{i}$ and $\vec{b}=\vec{i}+\sqrt{3}\vec{j}$, calculate $|\angle aob|$.

19. If $\vec{a}=4\vec{i}+\vec{j}$ and $\vec{b}=2\vec{i}+3\vec{j}$, calculate $|\angle boa|$, correct to one decimal place.

20. $\vec{a}=\vec{i}-2\vec{j}$, $\vec{b}=-\vec{i}-5\vec{j}$ and $\vec{c}=5\vec{i}-9\vec{j}$. Show that $\cos \angle cab = \dfrac{1}{\sqrt{5}}$.

21. $\vec{p}=2\vec{i}+2\vec{j}$, $\vec{q}=-\vec{i}+4\vec{j}$ and $\vec{r}=-\vec{j}$. Calculate $|\angle qpr|$.

22. $\vec{a}=-2\vec{i}+4\vec{j}$, $\vec{b}=\vec{i}+6\vec{j}$ and $\vec{c}=2\vec{i}-2\vec{j}$. Calculate $|\angle abc|$, correct to the nearest degree.

23. Let $\vec{p}=2\vec{i}-5\vec{j}$ and $\vec{q}=5\vec{i}+2\vec{j}$. Verify that $\vec{p} \perp \vec{q}$.

24. Let $\vec{x}=-3\vec{i}+\vec{j}$ and $\vec{y}=-2\vec{i}-6\vec{j}$. Verify that $\vec{x} \perp \vec{y}$.

25. Let $\vec{a}=3\vec{i}+2\vec{j}$ and $\vec{b}=-8\vec{i}+k\vec{j}$. If $\vec{a} \perp \vec{b}$, find the value of k.

26. Let $\vec{x}=2\vec{i}+5\vec{j}$ and $\vec{y}=-20\vec{i}+h\vec{j}$. If $\vec{x} \perp \vec{y}$, find the value of h.

27. Let $\vec{a}=h\vec{i}+30\vec{j}$ and $\vec{b}=-6\vec{i}+2\vec{j}$. Find the value of h if:

(i) $\vec{a} \perp \vec{b}$ **(ii)** $\vec{a} \cdot \vec{b} = 12$ **(iii)** $\vec{a} \cdot \vec{b} = 72$.

28. Let $\vec{x}=4\vec{i}-2\vec{j}$ and $\vec{y}=k\vec{i}-8\vec{j}$. If $\vec{x} \perp \vec{xy}$, find the value of k.

29. $\vec{a} = 4\vec{i} + 2\vec{j}$, $\vec{b} = -\vec{i} + 4\vec{j}$ and $\vec{c} = k\vec{i} - \vec{j}$. If $\vec{ab} \perp \vec{bc}$, find the value of k, $k \in \mathbf{R}$.

30. $\vec{p} = \vec{i} - 8\vec{j}$ and $\vec{q} = 5\vec{i} + 12\vec{j}$. r is an internal point on $[pq]$ such that $|pr| : |rq| = 1 : 3$ and s is the midpoint of $[pq]$.

    (i) Express $\vec{r}$ and $\vec{s}$ in terms of $\vec{i}$ and $\vec{j}$.

    (ii) Using vector methods, calculate: **(a)** $|\angle ros|$ **(b)** $|\angle pro|$, where o is the origin.

31. $\vec{a} = 4\vec{i} + \vec{j}$, $\vec{b} = 8\vec{i} + 5\vec{j}$ and $\vec{c} = -3\vec{i} + 2\vec{j}$.

    (i) Verify that: $\cos \angle bac = -\dfrac{3}{5}$.

    (ii) Calculate: **(a)** $\sin \angle bac$ **(b)** area of triangle abc.

32. $\vec{p} = 2\vec{i} + \vec{j}$. $\vec{q}$ is a vector, such that $|\vec{q}| = \sqrt{10}$ and $\vec{p} \cdot \vec{q} = 5$.

    (i) Calculate $|\angle poq|$.   **(ii)** Find two possible values of $\vec{q}$, in terms of $\vec{i}$ and $\vec{j}$.

    (Hint: Let $\vec{q} = a\vec{i} + b\vec{j}$.)

33. $\vec{p} = 2\vec{i} + \vec{j}$ and $\vec{q} = \vec{i} + k\vec{j}$. If $|\angle poq| = \dfrac{\pi}{4}$, find two values of k.

34. If $\vec{a} \perp \vec{b}$, simplify $\vec{a} \cdot (\vec{a} + \vec{b})$.

35. If $|\vec{p}| = |\vec{q}|$, show that $(\vec{p} + \vec{q}) \cdot (\vec{p} - \vec{q}) = 0$.

36. **(i)** If $\vec{pq} \perp \vec{rs}$, find the value of $(\vec{q} - \vec{p}) \cdot (\vec{s} - \vec{r})$.

    (ii) Simplify: $\vec{a} \cdot (\vec{a} - \vec{b}) - \vec{b} \cdot (\vec{a} - \vec{b})$.

37. **(i)** $\vec{o}, \vec{x}$ and $\vec{y}$ are three non-collinear vectors, where o is the origin.

    Show that $\vec{x} \cdot \vec{x} = |\vec{x}|^2$ and $\vec{x} \cdot \vec{y} = \vec{y} \cdot \vec{x}$.

    (ii) Calculate the value of: **(a)** $(\vec{p} + \vec{q}) \cdot (\vec{p} + \vec{q})$ **(b)** $(\vec{p} - \vec{q}) \cdot (\vec{p} - \vec{q})$,

    given that $|\vec{p}| = 4$, $|\vec{q}| = 7$ and $\vec{p} \cdot \vec{q} = 8$.

    Hence, calculate the value of: **(c)** $|\vec{p} + \vec{q}|$ **(d)** $|\vec{p} - \vec{q}|$.

38. $\vec{c} = \dfrac{\vec{a} \cdot \vec{b}}{|\vec{a}|^2} \vec{a} - \vec{b}$. Show that $\vec{c} \perp \vec{a}$.

39. Express $\vec{ab}$ in terms of $\vec{a}$ and $\vec{b}$.

In the diagram, $\vec{ac} \perp \vec{cb}$.

Show that:

$|\vec{c}|^2 = \vec{a} \cdot \vec{c} + \vec{b} \cdot \vec{c} - \vec{a} \cdot \vec{b}$.

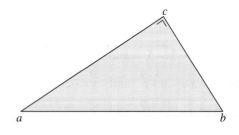

40. *oabc* is a parallelogram, where *o* is the origin.

    (i) Express in terms of $\vec{a}$ and $\vec{b}$: **(a)** $\vec{ba}$ **(b)** $\vec{c}$.

    (ii) Prove that: $|\vec{a}+\vec{b}|^2+|\vec{a}-\vec{b}|^2=2|\vec{a}|^2+2|\vec{b}|^2$.

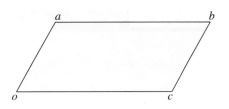

41. *oab* is a triangle, where *o* is the origin and $\theta=\angle aob$.
   p is a point on [*ob*] such that $ap\perp ob$.

    (i) Show that:

      (a) $|\vec{p}|=|\vec{a}|\cos\theta$ **(b)** $|\vec{p}|=\dfrac{\vec{a}.\vec{b}}{|\vec{b}|}$.

    (ii) If $\vec{p}=k\vec{b}$, where $k\in\mathbf{R}$ and $o<k<1$, show that:

      (a) $k=\dfrac{\vec{a}.\vec{b}}{|\vec{b}|^2}$ **(b)** $\vec{p}=\dfrac{\vec{a}.\vec{b}}{|\vec{b}|^2}\vec{b}$.

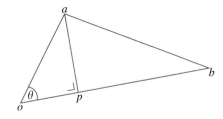

Related Perpendicular Vector $r^{\perp}$

The **related vector** $r^{\perp}$ is obtained by rotating $\vec{r}$ anticlockwise, about the origin, through 90°.

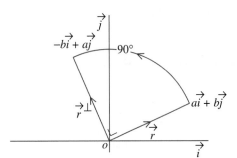

> If $\vec{r}=a\vec{i}+b\vec{j}$,
>
> then: $\vec{r}^{\perp}=-b\vec{i}+a\vec{j}$.
>
> In short: Swop the coefficients and **then** change
> the sign of the coefficient of $\vec{i}$.

If $\vec{a}=2\vec{i}+3\vec{j}$,   then $\vec{a}^{\perp}=-3\vec{i}+2\vec{j}$.

If $\vec{p}=-4\vec{i}-5\vec{j}$,   then $\vec{p}^{\perp}=5\vec{i}-4\vec{j}$.

Notes: **(i)** $\vec{r}.\vec{r}^{\perp}=0$ **(ii)** $|\vec{r}|=|\vec{r}^{\perp}|$

       (iii) $-r^{\perp}$ is another vector perpendicular to $\vec{r}$.

$\vec{a} = 2\vec{i} + \vec{j}$ and $\vec{b} = 5\vec{i} - 3\vec{j}$. Find a unit vector in the direction of $(\vec{ab})^{\perp}$.

Solution:

$$\vec{ab} = \vec{b} - \vec{a}$$
$$= (5\vec{i} - 3\vec{j}) - (2\vec{i} + \vec{j})$$
$$= 5\vec{i} - 3\vec{j} - 2\vec{i} - \vec{j}$$
$$= 3\vec{i} - 4\vec{j}$$
$$\therefore \quad (\vec{ab})^{\perp} = 4\vec{i} + 3\vec{j}$$
$$\text{and } |(\vec{ab})^{\perp}| = |4\vec{i} + 3\vec{j}|$$
$$= \sqrt{(4)^2 + (3)^2} = \sqrt{16 + 9} = \sqrt{25} = 5$$

A unit vector in the direction of $(\vec{ab})^{\perp}$

$$= \frac{(\vec{ab})^{\perp}}{|(\vec{ab})^{\perp}|}$$
$$= \frac{4\vec{i} + 3\vec{j}}{5}$$
$$= \frac{4}{5}\vec{i} + \frac{3}{5}\vec{j}$$

By writing $\vec{v} = h\vec{r} + k\vec{r}^{\perp}$, $h, k \in \mathbf{R}$, we can write a given vector, $\vec{v}$, as a linear combination of $\vec{r}$ and $\vec{r}^{\perp}$. In other words, we can write a given vector, $\vec{v}$, in terms of a vector parallel to $\vec{r}$ and a vector perpendicular to $\vec{r}$. We then use simultaneous equations to find the constants h and k.

Write $22\vec{i} + 7\vec{j}$ as the sum of a vector parallel to $2\vec{i} + 3\vec{j}$ and a vector perpendicular to $2\vec{i} + 3\vec{j}$.

Solution:

Let $\vec{r} = 2\vec{i} + 3\vec{j}$; then $\vec{r}^{\perp} = -3\vec{i} + 2\vec{j}$.

Let
$$h\vec{r} + k\vec{r}^{\perp} = 22\vec{i} + 7\vec{j}$$
$$\therefore \quad h(2\vec{i} + 3\vec{j}) + k(-3\vec{i} + 2\vec{j}) = 22\vec{i} + 7\vec{j}$$
$$2h\vec{i} + 3h\vec{j} - 3k\vec{i} + 2k\vec{j} = 22\vec{i} + 7\vec{j}$$

$\vec{i}$ parts $= \vec{i}$ parts	$\vec{j}$ parts $= \vec{j}$ parts
$2h - 3k = 22$ ①	$3h + 2k = 7$ ②

Now solve the simultaneous equations ① and ②:

$$4h - 6k = 44 \quad ① \times 2$$
$$\underline{9h + 6k = 21 \quad ② \times 3}$$
$$13h = 65$$
$$h = 5$$
Put $h = 5$ into ① or ②.

$$3h + 2k = 7$$
$$3(5) + 2k = 7$$
$$15 + 2k = 7$$
$$2k = -8$$
$$k = -4$$

Thus, $\quad 22\vec{i} + 7\vec{j} = 5(2\vec{i} + 3\vec{j}) - 4(-3\vec{i} + 2\vec{j})$
$$22\vec{i} + 7\vec{j} = (10\vec{i} + 15\vec{j}) + (12\vec{i} - 8\vec{j}).$$

(i) Show that, for all vectors $\vec{r}$: **(a)** $\vec{r} \perp \vec{r}^{\perp}$ **(b)** $(k\vec{r})^{\perp} = k\vec{r}^{\perp}$, $k \in \mathbf{R}$.

(ii) Show that, for all vectors $\vec{r}$ and $\vec{s}$: $(\vec{r} + \vec{s})^{\perp} = \vec{r}^{\perp} + \vec{s}^{\perp}$.

Solution:

(i) Let $\vec{r} = a\vec{i} + b\vec{j}$; then $\vec{r}^{\perp} = -b\vec{i} + a\vec{j}$.

(a)
$$\vec{r} \cdot \vec{r}^{\perp} = (a\vec{i} + b\vec{j}) \cdot (-b\vec{i} + a\vec{j})$$
$$= -ab + ab$$
$$= 0$$
$$\therefore \quad \vec{r} \perp \vec{r}^{\perp}$$

(b)
$$k\vec{r} = k(a\vec{i} + b\vec{j}) \qquad\qquad k\vec{r}^{\perp} = k(-b\vec{i} + a\vec{j})$$
$$k\vec{r} = ka\vec{i} + kb\vec{j} \qquad\qquad\quad = -kb\vec{i} + ka\vec{j}$$
$$\therefore \quad (k\vec{r})^{\perp} = -kb\vec{i} + ka\vec{j}$$
$$\therefore \quad (k\vec{r})^{\perp} = k\vec{r}^{\perp}$$

(ii) Let $\vec{r} = a\vec{i} + b\vec{j}$ and $\vec{s} = c\vec{i} + d\vec{j}$

$$\therefore \quad \vec{r}^{\perp} = -b\vec{i} + a\vec{j} \text{ and } \vec{s}^{\perp} = -d\vec{i} + c\vec{j}$$

$$\vec{r} + \vec{s} = a\vec{i} + b\vec{j} + c\vec{i} + d\vec{j} \qquad\qquad \vec{r}^{\perp} + \vec{s}^{\perp} = -b\vec{i} + a\vec{j} - d\vec{i} + c\vec{j}$$
$$= (a+c)\vec{i} + (b+d)\vec{j} \qquad\qquad\qquad = (-b-d)\vec{i} + (a+c)\vec{j}$$
$$\therefore \quad (\vec{r} + \vec{s})^{\perp} = -(b+d)\vec{i} + (a+c)\vec{j} \qquad\qquad = -(b+d)\vec{i} + (a+c)\vec{j}$$

$$\text{Thus, } (\vec{r} + \vec{s})^{\perp} = \vec{r}^{\perp} + \vec{s}^{\perp}$$

Exercise 4.7 ▼

In each case write down the related perpendicular vector $\vec{r}^{\perp}$:

1. $\vec{r} = 4\vec{i} + 3\vec{j}$ **2.** $\vec{r} = 2\vec{i} + 5\vec{j}$ **3.** $\vec{r} = 4\vec{i} - 2\vec{j}$ **4.** $\vec{r} = 6\vec{i} - 5\vec{j}$

5. $\vec{r} = -2\vec{i} - 3\vec{j}$ **6.** $\vec{r} = -7\vec{i} - \vec{j}$ **7.** $\vec{r} = -3\vec{i} + 4\vec{j}$ **9.** $\vec{r} = -2\vec{i} + 7\vec{j}$

9. Let $\vec{x} = 8\vec{i} + 15\vec{j}$. Express $\vec{x}^{\perp}$ in terms of $\vec{i}$ and $\vec{j}$. Show that $|\vec{x}| = |\vec{x}^{\perp}|$.

10. Let $\vec{a} = 5\vec{i} + 2\vec{j}$. Express $\vec{a}^{\perp}$ in terms of $\vec{i}$ and $\vec{j}$. Show that $|\vec{a}|^2 = |\vec{a}^{\perp}|^2$.

11. Let $\vec{a} = -5\vec{i} + 3\vec{j}$ and $\vec{b} = -4\vec{i} + 7\vec{j}$.

Let $\vec{p} = \vec{a}^{\perp}$ and $\vec{q} = \vec{b}^{\perp}$. Investigate whether $\vec{ab} \perp \vec{pq}$.

12. Let $\vec{p} = -12\vec{i} + 5\vec{j}$ and $\vec{q} = 4\vec{i} + 3\vec{j}$.

(i) Write down $\vec{p}^{\perp}$ and $\vec{q}^{\perp}$ in terms of $\vec{i}$ and $\vec{j}$.

(ii) Evaluate $|\vec{p}^{\perp}|$ and $|\vec{q}^{\perp}|$.

(iii) Find the scalar k, such that $|\vec{p}^{\perp} + \vec{q}^{\perp}| = k[|\vec{p}^{\perp}| - |\vec{q}^{\perp}|]$.

13. Let $\vec{x} = t\vec{i} + 3\vec{j}$ and $\vec{y} = -2\vec{i} - \vec{j}$.

Find the value of the scalars t and k, such that $2\vec{x}^{\perp} + k\vec{y}^{\perp} = -2(\vec{i} - 4\vec{j})$.

14. Let $\vec{x} = 8\vec{i} - 2\vec{j}$ and $\vec{y} = 2\vec{i} + 4\vec{j}$.

Find the value of the scalar m and the value of the scalar n for which $\vec{x}^{\perp} + m\vec{y}^{\perp} = 3\vec{i} - n\vec{j}$.

15. Let $\vec{u} = 2\vec{i} - 3\vec{j}$, $\vec{v} = 2\vec{i} - \vec{j}$ and $\vec{s} = 2\vec{i} - 7\vec{j}$.

Find the scalars h and k, such that $h\vec{u}^{\perp} + k\vec{v}^{\perp} = \vec{s}^{\perp}$.

16. $\vec{a} = -6\vec{i} - x\vec{j}$, $\vec{b} = x\vec{i} - 4\vec{j}$ and $\vec{c} = -2x\vec{i} - \vec{j}$.

Find the two values of the scalar x, such that $x\vec{a}^{\perp} + x\vec{b}^{\perp} - 5\vec{j} = 5\vec{c}^{\perp}$.

17. Write $16\vec{i} + 11\vec{j}$ as the sum of a vector parallel to $2\vec{i} + 5\vec{j}$ and a vector perpendicular to $2\vec{i} + 5\vec{j}$.

18. Write $-16\vec{i} - 2\vec{j}$ as the sum of a vector parallel to $-3\vec{i} - 2\vec{j}$ and a vector perpendicular to $-3\vec{i} - 2\vec{j}$.

19. $\vec{r} = 3\vec{i} + 2\vec{j}$. Find the unit vector in the direction of $\vec{r}^{\perp}$.

20. $\vec{a} = 8\vec{i} + 9\vec{j}$ and $\vec{b} = -4\vec{i} + 4\vec{j}$. Find a unit vector perpendicular to $\vec{ab}$.

21. $\vec{p} = -5\vec{i} - 10\vec{j}$ and $\vec{q} = 3\vec{i} + 5\vec{j}$. Find the unit vector in the direction of $(\vec{pq})^{\perp}$.

22. $\vec{a} = 4\vec{i} - \vec{j}$ and $\vec{b} = 2\vec{i} + k\vec{j}$, where $k \in \mathbf{R}$.

If $(\vec{a} + \vec{b}) \perp (\vec{ab})^{\perp}$, find the value of k.

23. For all vectors $\vec{r}$, show that $(\vec{r}^{\perp})^{\perp} = -\vec{r}$.

24. For all vectors $\vec{r}$ and $\vec{s}$, investigate whether each of the following is true or false:

(i) $(\vec{r} - \vec{s})^{\perp} = \vec{r}^{\perp} - \vec{s}^{\perp}$ (ii) $\vec{r}^{\perp} . \vec{s} = \vec{r} . \vec{s}^{\perp}$ (iii) $\vec{r} . \vec{s} = -\vec{r}^{\perp} . \vec{s}$.

25. $\vec{p} = 3\vec{i} - 2\vec{j}$. Let $\vec{q} = \vec{p}^{\perp} - \vec{p}$ and $\vec{r} = \vec{q}^{\perp} + \vec{q}$.

(i) Express $\vec{q}$ and $\vec{r}$ in terms of $\vec{i}$ and $\vec{j}$.   (ii) Calculate $|\angle qor|$, where o is the origin.

26. $\vec{a} = \vec{i} + \vec{j}$ and $\vec{b} = 3\vec{i} + 3\vec{j}$. $\vec{r} = \frac{1}{2}(\vec{a} + \vec{b}) + t(\vec{b} - \vec{a})^{\perp}$, where $t \in \mathbf{R}$.

(i) Express $\vec{r}$ in terms of t, $\vec{i}$ and $\vec{j}$.

(ii) Show that: $|\vec{ra}| = |\vec{rb}|$.   (iii) Verify that: $\left| \dfrac{\vec{ra}}{|\vec{ra}|} \right| = 1$.

CHAPTER 5

PERMUTATIONS, COMBINATIONS AND PROBABILITY

Operations

. . . .

The result of an operation is called an '**outcome**'.
For example, if we throw a die one possible outcome is 5.
If we throw a die there are 6 possible outcomes: 1, 2, 3, 4, 5 or 6.

Fundamental Principle of Counting 1

Suppose one operation has *m* possible outcomes and that a second operation has *n* outcomes. The number of possible outcomes when performing the first operation **followed by** the second operation is $m \times n$.

Performing one operation **and** another operation means we **multiply** the number of possible outcomes.

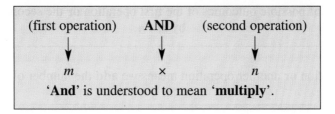

Note: We assume that the outcome of one operation does not affect the number of possible outcomes of the other operation.

The fundamental principle 1 of counting can be extended to three or more operations.

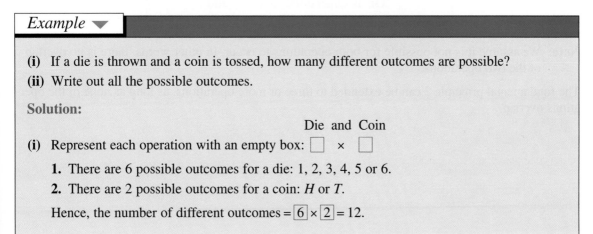

Example ▼

(i) If a die is thrown and a coin is tossed, how many different outcomes are possible?
(ii) Write out all the possible outcomes.

Solution:

Die and Coin

(i) Represent each operation with an empty box: ☐ × ☐

    1. There are 6 possible outcomes for a die: 1, 2, 3, 4, 5 or 6.
    2. There are 2 possible outcomes for a coin: *H* or *T*.

Hence, the number of different outcomes = 6 × 2 = 12.

(ii)

T	•	•	•	•	•	•
H	•	•	•	•	•	•
	1	**2**	**3**	**4**	**5**	**6**

$(1, H), (2, H), (3, H), (4, H), (5, H), (6, H)$
$(1, T), (2, T), (3, T), (4, T), (5, T), (6, T)$

Note: It can help to write down one possible outcome above the box.

	Die	and	Coin
One possible outcome:	5	↓	T
Number of outcomes:	$\boxed{6}$ ×		$\boxed{2}$ = 12

This is very useful when trying to decide the number of possible outcomes at a particular stage, especially when certain choices are restricted. For example, the letter v cannot be in the second place, or the number must be even.

Fundamental Principle of Counting 2

Suppose one operation has m possible outcomes and that a second operation has n outcomes. Then the number of possible outcomes of the first operation **or** the second operation is given by $m + n$.

Performing one operation **or** another operation means we **add** the number of possible outcomes.

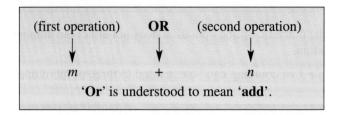

Note: We assume it is not possible for both operations to occur. In other words, there is no overlap of the two operations.

The fundamental principle 2 can be extended to three or more operations, as long as none of the operations overlap.

Example ▼

A bag contains nine discs, numbered from 1 to 9. A disc is drawn from the bag.
If the number is even, then a coin is tossed. If the number is odd, then a die is thrown.
How many outcomes are possible?

Solution:

Break the experiment into two different experiments and work out the number of outcomes
separately. Then add these results.

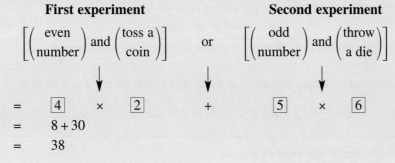

$$= \quad \boxed{4} \quad \times \quad \boxed{2} \quad + \quad \boxed{5} \quad \times \quad \boxed{6}$$
$$= \quad 8 + 30$$
$$= \quad 38$$

Permutations (Arrangements)

> A permutation is an arrangement of a number of objects in a definite order.

Consider the three letters P, Q and R. If these letters are written down in a row, there are six different
possible arrangements:

$$PQR \text{ or } PRQ \text{ or } QPR \text{ or } QRP \text{ or } RPQ \text{ or } RQP$$

There is a choice of 3 letters for the first place, then there is a choice of 2 letters for the second place
and there is only 1 choice for the third place.
Thus the three operations can be performed in $\boxed{3} \times \boxed{2} \times \boxed{1} = 6$ ways.
The boxes are an aid in helping to fill in the number of ways each choice can be made at each position.
In an arrangement, or permutation, the order of the objects chosen is important.

> If we have n **different** objects to arrange, then:
> The total number of arrangements $= n!$
> $n! = n(n-1)(n-2)(n-3) \cdots \times 3 \times 2 \times 1$

For example, $6! = 6 \times 5 \times 4 \times 3 \times 2 \times 1 = 720$
Using a calculator: $6 \boxed{n!} \boxed{=} 720$

Suppose we have 5 different objects, and we want to find the number of possible arrangements taking
3 objects at a time. We could use the fundamental principle of counting 1, i.e.

$$\begin{array}{ccccc} \text{1st} & \text{and} & \text{2nd} & \text{and} & \text{3rd} \\ \boxed{5} & \times & \boxed{4} & \times & \boxed{3} & = & 60 \end{array}$$

However, we can also do this type of calculation using factorials.

$$5 \times 4 \times 3 = \frac{5 \times 4 \times 3 \times 2 \times 1}{2 \times 1} = \frac{5!}{2!} = \frac{5!}{(5-3)!}$$

Similarly:

$$6 \times 5 = \frac{6 \times 5 \times 4 \times 3 \times 2 \times 1}{4 \times 3 \times 2 \times 1} = \frac{6!}{4!} = \frac{6!}{(6-2)!}$$

$$7 \times 6 \times 5 \times 4 = \frac{7 \times 6 \times 5 \times 4 \times 3 \times 2 \times 1}{3 \times 2 \times 1} = \frac{7!}{3!} = \frac{7!}{(7-4)!}$$

Notice that in each case the number of arrangements is given by:

$$\frac{\text{(Total number of objects)!}}{\text{(Total number of objects} - \text{number of objects to be arranged)!}}$$

> The number of arrangements of n different objects taking r at a time is:
> $$^nP_r = \frac{n!}{(n-r)!} = n(n-1)(n-2) \cdots (n-r+1)$$

Note: There is an 'nPr' button on most calculators.

Example ▼

How many arrangements can be made of the letters P, Q, R, S, T, taking two letters at a time, if no letter can be repeated?

Solution:

Method 1: (using the fundamental principle 1 of counting)

1st   and   2nd

$\boxed{5}$ × $\boxed{4}$ = 20

Method 2: (using factorials)

We have 5 letters and want to arrange two.

$$^5P_2 = \frac{5!}{(5-2)!} = \frac{5!}{3!} = \frac{120}{6} = 20$$

Example ▼

How many different arrangements can be made from the letters V, W, X, Y, Z, taking all the letters at a time, if V must be second and Z can never be last?

Solution:

Represent each choice with a box:

	1st		2nd		3rd		4th		5th	
Possible outcome:	W		V		Z		Y		X	
Number of ways:	$\boxed{3}$	×	$\boxed{1}$	×	$\boxed{2}$	×	$\boxed{1}$	×	$\boxed{3}$	= 18

(most restrictive, must be V)   (second most restrictive, cannot use V or Z)

Start with the choice that has most restrictions and choose a possible letter each time.

In some questions we make use of the following fact:

$$\left(\begin{array}{c}\text{The number of arrangements in which}\\\text{an outcome does \textbf{not} occur}\end{array}\right)=\left(\begin{array}{c}\text{Total number}\\\text{of arrangements}\end{array}\right)-\left(\begin{array}{c}\text{The number of arrangements}\\\text{in which the outcome \textbf{does} occur}\end{array}\right)$$

Example ▼

A, B, C, D, E and F are six students. In how many ways can they be seated in a row if:
(i) there are no restrictions on the seating;
(ii) A and B must sit beside each other;
(iii) A and B must not sit beside each other;
(iv) D, E and F must sit beside each other;
(v) A and F must sit at the end of each row?

Solution:

(i) no restrictions

number of arrangements $= \boxed{6}\times\boxed{5}\times\boxed{4}\times\boxed{3}\times\boxed{2}\times\boxed{1}=6!=720.$

(ii) A and B must sit beside each other

Consider A and B as one person.

$\boxed{A,B},\boxed{C},\boxed{D},\boxed{E},\boxed{F}$

The 5 persons can be arranged in 5! ways.
But A and B can be arranged in 2! ways while seated together (i.e. AB or BA).
Thus, the number of arrangements $= 2! \times 5! = 2 \times 120 = 240.$

(iii) A and B must not sit beside each other

$$\left(\begin{array}{c}\text{Number of arrangements with}\\A\text{ and }B\text{ not together}\end{array}\right)=\left(\begin{array}{c}\text{Total number}\\\text{of arrangements}\end{array}\right)-\left(\begin{array}{c}\text{Number of arrangements}\\\text{with }A\text{ and }B\text{ together}\end{array}\right)$$

$$= 720 - 240 = 480$$

(iv) D, E and F must sit beside each other

Consider D, E and F as one person.

$\boxed{A},\boxed{B},\boxed{C},\boxed{D,E,F}$

The 4 persons can be arranged in 4! ways.
But D, E and F can be arranged in 3! ways while seated together.
Thus, the number of arrangements $= 3! \times 4! = 6 \times 24 = 144.$

(v) A and F must sit at the end of each row

Put A and F at the ends and B, C, D and E in between them.

$\boxed{A},\boxed{B,C,D,E},\boxed{F}$

B, C, D and E can be arranged in 4! ways while seated together.
A and F can exchange places.
Thus, the first and last can be arranged in 2! ways.
Thus, the number of arrangements $= 2! \times 4! = 2 \times 24 = 48.$

How many different four-digit numbers greater than 6,000 can be formed using the digits 1, 2, 4, 5, 6, 7 if (**i**) no digit can be repeated;   (**ii**) repetitions are allowed?

Solution:

Represent each choice with a box. The number must be greater than 6,000; thus, the first place can be filled in only 2 ways (with 6 or 7). Fill this in first, then fill the other places. Only use 4 boxes, as our choice is restricted to 4 digits at a time.

(**i**) No digit can be repeated

$\boxed{2} \times \boxed{5} \times \boxed{4} \times \boxed{3} = 120$

(**ii**) Repetitions are allowed

$\boxed{2} \times \boxed{6} \times \boxed{6} \times \boxed{6} = 432$

How many different five-digit numbers can be formed from the digits, 1, 2, 3, 4 and 5 if:
(**i**)   there are no restrictions on digits and repetitions are allowed;

(**ii**) the number is odd and no repetitions are allowed;

(**iii**) the number is even and repetitions are allowed;

(**iv**) the number is greater than 50,000 and no repetitions are allowed?

Solution:

Represent each choice with a box.

(**i**)   no restrictions and repetitions allowed

$\boxed{5} \times \boxed{5} \times \boxed{5} \times \boxed{5} \times \boxed{5} = 3,125$

(**ii**) must be odd and no repetitions

Thus, the last place can be filled in only 3 ways (1, 3 or 5). Fill this in first, then fill in the other places.

$\boxed{4} \times \boxed{3} \times \boxed{2} \times \boxed{1} \times \boxed{3} = 72$

(**iii**) must be even and repetitions allowed

Thus, the last place can be filled in only 2 ways (2 or 4). Fill this in first, then fill in the other places.

$\boxed{5} \times \boxed{5} \times \boxed{5} \times \boxed{5} \times \boxed{2} = 1,250$

(**iv**) must be greater than 50,000 and no repetitions

Thus, the first place can be filled in only 1 way (with 5). Fill this in first, then fill in the other places.

$\boxed{1} \times \boxed{4} \times \boxed{3} \times \boxed{2} \times \boxed{1} = 24$

1. A game consists of spinning an unbiased, five-sided spinner which can land on A, B, C, D or E, and throwing an unbiased die. How many different outcomes of the game are possible?

2. A fifth-year student must choose one subject from each of the following three groups:
Group 1: Music, Technical Graphics, Applied Mathematics or Classical Studies
Group 2: Physics, Chemistry or Biology
Group 3: Economics or Accounting
In how many ways can the student choose the three subjects?

3. A bag contains five discs, numbered from 1 to 5 inclusive. A disc is drawn from the bag. If the number is even, then a die is thrown. If the number is odd, then a coin is tossed. How many outcomes are possible?

4. A bag contains seven discs, numbered from 1 to 7 inclusive. A disc is drawn at random from the bag and **not** replaced. If the number is even, a second disc is drawn from the bag. If the first number is odd, then a die is thrown. How many outcomes are possible?

5. How many different arrangements can be made from the letters *P, Q, R, S, T*, if no letter can be repeated and taking:
   (i) five letters **(ii)** four letters **(iii)** three letters **(iv)** two letters, at a time?

6. Ten horses run in a race. In how many ways can the first, second and third places be filled if there are no dead heats?

7. How many different arrangements can be made using all the letters of the word *DUBLIN*?
   (i) How many arrangements begin with the letter *D*?
   (ii) How many arrangements begin with B and end in *L*?
   (iii) How many arrangements begin with a vowel?
   (iv) How many arrangements begin and end with a vowel?
   (v) How many arrangements end with *LIN*?
   (vi) How many arrangements begin with *D* and end in *LIN*?

8. Taking all the letters of the word *ALGEBRA*, in how many arrangements are the two *A*s together?

9. **(i)** In how many ways can three girls and two boys be seated in a row of 5 seats?
   (ii) In how many ways can this be done if the boys must sit together?
   (iii) In how many ways can this be done if the boys must not sit together?

10. How many arrangements of the letters of the word *FORMULAS* are possible if:
   (i) all letters are used in the arrangement?
   (ii) the three vowels must come together in the arrangement?
   (iii) the three vowels must not **all** come together in the arrangement?

11. Six children are to be seated in a row on a bench.
   (i) How many arrangements are possible?
   (ii) How many arrangements are possible if the youngest child must sit at the left-hand end and the oldest child must sit at the right-hand end?
   If two of the children are twins, in how many ways can the children be arranged if:
   (iii) the twins are together   **(iv)** the twins are not together?

12. In how many ways can four letters of the word *NUMBER* be arranged in a row, if no letter is repeated?

13. A permutation lock has four rings which can be rotated about an axle. There are 10 digits (0, 1, 2, . . . , 8, 9) on each ring. If no digit can be repeated and 0 can never be first, find the maximum number of such locks that could be manufactured if no two locks have the same code, and the lock will open only when a certain code of 4 digits is in line (see diagram).

14. Raffle tickets are printed in three colours, Purple, Green or Yellow. Each ticket contains a letter followed by two digits (e.g. Purple Q47, Yellow K00). How many different tickets can be printed?

15. A number-plate is to consist of three letters of the English alphabet and two digits. If no letter or digit can be repeated and 0 can never be used as the first digit, how many different plates can be manufactured?

BAT 45

(an example)

16. How many different three-digit numbers can be formed using the digits 0, 1, 2, 3, 4 if 0 cannot be the first digit and:
    (i) no digit may be repeated   **(ii)** repetitions are allowed?

17. How many four-digit numbers can be formed from the digits 1, 2, 3, 5, 6 and 8 if:
    (i)   there are no restrictions and repetitions are allowed;
    (ii) the number is odd and no repetitions are allowed;
    (iii) the number is divisible by 5 and repetitions are allowed;
    (iv) the number is greater than 5,000, divisible by 5 and no repetitions are allowed?

18. How many numbers between 2,000 and 4,000 can be made with the digits 1, 2, 3 and 4, if no digit may be repeated?

19. How many numbers between 100 and 1,000 use only odd digits, if no digits are repeated?

20. How many odd numbers between 2,000 and 3,000 can be formed from the digits 1, 2, 3, 4, 5 and 6, if:
    (i) repetitions are allowed   **(ii)** repetitions are not allowed?

21. **(i)**   How many different numbers, each with 3 digits or fewer, can be formed from the digits 2, 3, 4, 5, 6? Each digit can be used only once in each number.
    (ii) How many of the above numbers are odd?

22. How many odd numbers between 4,000 and 6,000 can be formed from the digits 3, 4, 5, 6, 7 and 8, if no digit can be repeated?

23. How many different three-digit numbers can be formed using the digits 0 to 9 inclusive, if no digit can be used more than once and 0 cannot be the first digit?
    (i) If one of the digits must be 7, how many different numbers can be formed?
    (ii) If the digits 2 and 5 cannot be used together, how many different numbers can be formed?

Combinations (Selections)

> A combination is a selection of a number of objects in any order.

In making a selection of a number of objects from a given set, only the contents of the group selected are important, not the order in which the items are selected.

For example, *AB* and *BA* represent the same selection.
However, *AB* and *BA* represent different arrangements.

Note: What is called a 'combination lock' should really be called a 'permutation lock', as the order of the digits is essential.

The $\binom{n}{r}$ Notation

> $\binom{n}{r}$ gives the number of ways of choosing r objects from n different objects.
>
> Its value can be calculated in two ways:
>
> **1.** $\binom{n}{r} = \dfrac{n!}{r!(n-r)!}$ (definition)
>
> **2.** $\binom{n}{r} = \dfrac{n(n-1)(n-2)\ldots(n-r+1)}{r!}$ (in practice)

Both give the same result; however, the second is easier to use in practical questions.
For example:

1. $\binom{6}{2} = \dfrac{6!}{2!(6-2)!} = \dfrac{6!}{2!4!} = \dfrac{720}{2 \times 24} = 15$

2. $\binom{6}{2} = \dfrac{6.5}{2.1}$ $\rightarrow$ start at 6, go down two terms
                   $\rightarrow$ start at 2, go down two terms

     $= 15$

Notes: **1.** $\binom{n}{r}$ is pronounced '*n-c-r*' or '*n*-choose-*r*'.

         2. $\binom{n}{0} = 1$, i.e., there is only one way of choosing no objects out of n objects.

         3. $\binom{n}{n} = 1$, i.e., there is only one way of choosing n objects out of n objects.

         4. $\binom{n}{r} = \binom{n}{n-r}$; use this when r is greater than $\dfrac{n}{2}$.

Explanation for Note 4:

Let's assume you have 13 soccer players and you can pick only 11 to play.

The number of ways of choosing 11 from 13 is given by $\binom{13}{11}$.

$$\binom{13}{11} = \frac{13 \times 12 \times 11 \times 10 \times 9 \times 8 \times 7 \times 6 \times 5 \times 4 \times 3}{11 \times 10 \times 9 \times 8 \times 7 \times 6 \times 5 \times 4 \times 3 \times 2 \times 1} = 78$$

However, every time you choose 11 to play, you choose 2 who cannot play.

Thus $\binom{13}{11} = \binom{13}{2} = \frac{13 \times 12}{2 \times 1} = 78$ (same as before).

Notice that $11 + 2 = 13$

Similarly,　　$\binom{20}{17} = \binom{20}{3}$ as $17 + 3 = 20$

and　　　　$\binom{100}{98} = \binom{100}{2}$ as $98 + 2 = 100$

If r is large, your calculator may not be able to do the calculation: thus use $\binom{n}{r} = \binom{n}{n-r}$.

Note: $\binom{n}{r}$ is sometimes written as ^nC_r or $_nC_r$.

Example ▼

Ten people take part in a chess competition. How many games will be played if every person must play each of the others?

Solution:

We **have** 10 people to choose from, of whom we want to **choose** 2 (as 2 people play in each game). Thus, $n = 10$, $r = 2$.

$$\text{Number of games} = \binom{10}{2} = \frac{10 \times 9}{2 \times 1} = 45.$$

Example ▼

(i) In how many ways can a committee of 4 people be chosen from a panel of 10 people?
(ii) If a certain person must be on the committee, in how many ways can the committee be chosen?
(iii) If a certain person must not be on the committee, in how many ways can the committee be chosen?

Solution:

(i) We **have** a panel of 10 people to choose from, and we need to **choose** a committee of 4.

$$\therefore \quad n = 10, \ r = 4$$

$$\binom{10}{4} = \frac{10 \times 9 \times 8 \times 7}{4 \times 3 \times 2 \times 1} = 210$$

Thus, from a panel of 10 people, we can choose 210 different committees of 4 people.

(ii) One particular person **must** be on the committee.

Thus, we **have** a panel of 9 people to choose from, and we need to **choose** 3 (as one person is already chosen).

$$\therefore \quad n = 9, r = 3$$

$$\binom{9}{3} = \frac{9 \times 8 \times 7}{3 \times 2 \times 1} = 84$$

Thus, from a panel of 10 people, we can choose 84 different committees of 4 people, if one particular person of the 10 must be on every committee.

(iii) One particular person **must not** be on the committee.

Thus, we **have** a panel of 9 to choose from (as one person cannot be chosen), and we need to **choose** 4.

$$\therefore \quad n = 9, r = 4$$

$$\binom{9}{4} = \frac{9 \times 8 \times 7 \times 6}{4 \times 3 \times 2 \times 1} = 126$$

Thus from a panel of 10 people, we can choose 126 different committees of 4 people, if one particular person of the 10 must not be on the committee.

Example ▼

(i) In how many ways can a group of five be selected from nine people?

(ii) How many groups can be selected if two particular people from the nine cannot be in the same group?

Solution:

(i) We have nine from whom we want to choose five. Thus, $n = 9, r = 5$.

$$\binom{9}{5} = \frac{9 \times 8 \times 7 \times 6 \times 5}{5 \times 4 \times 3 \times 2 \times 1} = 126$$

(ii) In order to calculate how many groups of 5 can be selected if two particular people cannot be included, we first need to calculate the number of ways of selecting 5 people with these particular two people always included, i.e. we have 7 from whom we choose 3 (because two are already selected). Thus $n = 7, r = 3$.

$$\binom{7}{5} = \frac{7 \times 6 \times 5}{3 \times 2 \times 1} = 35$$

$$\begin{pmatrix} \text{The number of ways of selecting} \\ \text{a group of 5 people from 9} \\ \text{when two particular people are} \\ \text{not to be in the same group} \end{pmatrix} = \begin{pmatrix} \text{Total number} \\ \text{of ways of} \\ \text{selecting a group} \\ \text{of 5 from 9} \end{pmatrix} - \begin{pmatrix} \text{The number of ways of} \\ \text{selecting a group of 5} \\ \text{people from 9 with} \\ \text{these two particular people} \end{pmatrix}$$

$$= 126 - 35$$

$$= 91$$

In how many ways may 10 people be divided into three groups of 5, 3 and 2 people?

Solution:

The first group of five can be selected in $\binom{10}{5} = 252$ ways.

Once this is done, the second group of 3 can be selected in $\binom{5}{3} = 10$ ways.

The remaining 2 people can now be selected in $\binom{2}{2} = 1$ way.

Thus, the total number of ways 10 people can be divided into groups of 5, 3 and 2:

$$= \binom{10}{5} \times \binom{5}{3} \times \binom{2}{2} = 252 \times 10 \times 1 = 2,520$$

Four letters are selected from the word *SECTIONAL*.
(i) How many different selections are possible?
(ii) How many of these selections contain at least one vowel?

Solution:

(i) We have 9 different letters to choose from and we need to select 4,

$$\therefore \quad n = 9, \, r = 4$$

$$\binom{9}{4} = \frac{9 \times 8 \times 7 \times 6}{4 \times 3 \times 2 \times 1} = 126$$

(ii) Split the word *SECTIONAL* up into vowels and consonants.
The four vowels are *E, I, O, A* and the five consonants are *S, C, T, N, L*.
'At least one vowel' means one vowel, two vowels, three vowels or four vowels.
It is easier to calculate the number of selections containing no vowels (i.e., four consonants), and subtract this from the number of ways of selecting four letters without any restrictions.

Number of selections containing no vowels

$$= \text{Number of selections containing four consonants} = \binom{5}{4} = \frac{5 \times 4 \times 3 \times 2}{4 \times 3 \times 2 \times 1} = 5.$$

(There are five consonants, and we want to select four, thus $n = 5$ and $r = 4$.)
In every other selection there must be at least one vowel.
Thus, the number of selections containing at least one vowel

$$= \text{(total number of selections)} - \text{(number of selections containing no vowels)}$$

$$= 126 - 5$$

$$= 121$$

Sometimes we have to deal with problems where objects are chosen from two different groups. This involves choosing a number of objects from one group **AND** then choosing a number of objects from the other group.

Notes: There are two key words when applying the fundamental principle of counting:
    1. 'And' is understood to mean '**multiply**'. Thus, and $= \times$.
    2. 'Or' is understood to mean '**add**'. Thus, or $= +$.

How many different basketball teams, each consisting of 3 boys and 2 girls, can be formed from 7 boys and 5 girls?

Solution:

And = ×		Or = +

We have 7 boys and 5 girls. These are the upper numbers in the combination bracket.
A team must consist of 5 players.
We need to choose '3 boys and 2 girls'. These are the lower numbers in the combination bracket.

Number of ways of choosing 3 boys from 7 boys $= \binom{7}{3} = 35$

Number of ways of choosing 2 girls from 5 girls $= \binom{5}{2} = 10$

∴   the number of basketball teams consisting of 3 boys and 2 girls $= 35 \times 10 = 350$.

There are 5 women and 4 men in a club. A team of four has to be chosen. How many different teams can be chosen if there must be either exactly one woman or exactly two women on the team?

Solution:

And = ×		Or = +

We have 5 women and 4 men and these are **always** the upper numbers in the combination bracket.
A team must consist of 4 people.
Thus, exactly one woman on the team means '1 woman **and** 3 men';
and exactly two women on the team means '2 women **and** 2 men'.
Thus, we need to choose '1 woman **and** 3 men' **or** '2 women **and** 2 men'.
Let W stand for women and let M stand for men.

$$
\begin{array}{cccccc}
\text{1W and 3M} & \text{or} & \text{2W and 2M} & \text{(lower numbers in each case)} \\
\downarrow \; \downarrow \; \downarrow & \downarrow & \downarrow \; \downarrow \; \downarrow \\
\binom{5}{1} \times \binom{4}{3} & + & \binom{5}{2} \times \binom{4}{2} \\
= \quad 5 \times 4 & + & 10 \times 6 \\
= \quad 20 + 60 \\
= \quad 80
\end{array}
$$

Thus, 80 teams can have either one woman or two women on the team.

How many bundles of 5 different books can be made from 8 Maths books and 6 Physics books, if the number of Maths books must always be greater than the number of Physics books?

Solution:

We have 8 Maths books and 6 Physics books and these are **always** the upper numbers in the combination bracket.

A bundle must consist of 5 books. We need to have more Maths books than Physics books. Therefore, we need to choose:

(5 Maths and 0 Physics books) **or** (4 Maths and 1 Physics books) **or** (3 Maths and 2 Physics books).

Let M stand for a Maths book and P stand for a Physics book.

Possibilities:

$$5M \text{ and } 0P \quad \text{or} \quad 4M \text{ and } 1P \quad \text{or} \quad 3M \text{ and } 2P \qquad \text{(lower numbers in each case)}$$

$$\binom{5}{8} \times \binom{6}{0} \quad + \quad \binom{8}{4} \times \binom{6}{1} \quad + \quad \binom{8}{3} \times \binom{6}{2}$$

$$= 56 \times 1 \quad + \quad 70 \times 6 \quad + \quad 56 \times 15$$

$$= 56 + 420 + 840$$

$$= 1,316$$

Exercise 5.2 ▼

Calculate:

1. $\binom{5}{2}$
2. $\binom{8}{3}$
3. $\binom{9}{5}$
4. $\binom{10}{0}$
5. $\binom{20}{18}$
6. $\binom{30}{27}$

7. In how many ways can a committee of 4 people be chosen from 7 people?

8. There are 15 pupils in a class. How many teams of 11 can be selected from the class? If one person in the class is made captain and must always be included in each team, how many teams can now be selected? If 2 pupils in the class refuse to play, how many teams can now be selected, if the captain must still be on every team?

9. In how many ways can a party of 6 children be chosen from a group of 10 children if:
   (i)   any child may be selected?
   (ii) the oldest child must not be selected?
   (iii) the youngest child must be selected?
   (iv) the youngest and the oldest must both be selected?

10. A fifth-year student has to choose 4 subjects from the following list: Accounting, Biology, Chemistry, Physics, French, Applied Maths and Classical Studies.
   (i)   How many different choices are possible?
   (ii) How many choices include French?
   (iii) How many choices do not include French?
   (iv) How many choices include Accounting and Biology?
   (v)   How many choices include Applied Maths but not Chemistry?

11. Three delegates to form a committee are to be selected from eight members of a club. How many different committees can be formed if:
   (i) there are no restrictions?
   (ii) a certain member must be on each committee?
   (iii) two particular members cannot both be on the committee?

12. Twelve distinct points are taken on the circumference of a circle (as shown).
   (i) (a) Calculate the number of different chords that can be formed using these points as end points.
   (b) How many different triangles can be formed using these points as vertices?
   (ii) (a) Calculate the number of different quadrilaterals that can be formed using these points as vertices.
   (b) Two of the ten points are labelled x and y respectively. How many of the above quadrilaterals have x and y as vertices?
   (c) How many of the quadrilaterals do not have x and y as vertices?

13. From a set of six different coins, in how many ways can four or more coins be selected?

14. In how many ways can 12 different objects be divided into groups of 6, 4 and 2?

15. 5 Irishmen, 3 Frenchmen and 4 Germans are available for selection to a European committee of 4. If each nation has to be represented on each committee, in how many ways can the committee be selected?

16. (i) Find the number of different selections of 4 letters that can be made from the letters of the word *SPHERICAL*.
   (ii) How many of these selections do not contain a vowel?
   (iii) How many of these selections contain at least one vowel?

17. Find the number of different selections of 5 letters that can be made from the letters of the word *CHEMISTRY*.
   How many of these selections contain at least one vowel?

18. A team of 6 players is to be chosen from a group of 10 players. One of the 6 is then to be elected as captain and another as vice-captain. In how many ways can this be done? (Hint: Select and then arrange.)

19. In how many ways can a committee of 7 people be selected from 4 men and 6 women, if the committee must have at least 4 women on it?

20. A committee of six is to be formed from eight students and five teachers. How many different committees can be formed if there are to be more teachers than students?

21. An examination consists of ten questions, four in section A and the remainder in section B. A candidate must attempt 5 questions, at least two of which must be from each section.
   In how many different ways may the candidate select the five questions?

22. In how many ways can a committee of six be selected from five men and four women, if each committee consists of:
   (i) an equal number of men and women?
   (ii) at least three men?

23. A team of 5 players is to be chosen from 6 boys and 5 girls. If there must be more boys than girls, how many different teams can be formed?

24. A group consists of 5 men and 7 women. A committee of 4 must be chosen from the group. How many committees can be chosen in which there are an odd number of men?

25. A club has only 5 women and 4 men as members. A team of 3 is to be chosen to represent the club. In how many ways can this be done if:
   (i) there are no restrictions?
   (ii) the club captain must be on the team?
   (iii) there must be at least one woman on the team?
   (iv) there must be more women than men on the team?

Probability

Probability involves the study of the laws of chance. It is a measure of the chance, or likelihood, of something happening.

toss coins

throw dice

spin a spinner

draw a card

If you carry out an operation, or experiment, using coins, dice, spinners or cards, then each toss, throw, spin or draw is called a **trial**.

The possible things that can happen from a trial are called **outcomes**. The outcomes of interest are called an **event**. In other words, an event is the set of successful outcomes.

For example, if you throw a die and you are interested in the probability of an even number, then the event is 2, 4, 6, the successful outcomes.

If E is an event, then $P(E)$ stands for the probability that the event occurs.

$P(E)$ is read 'the probability of E'.

Definition

> The measure of the probability of an event, E, is given by:
> $$P(E) = \frac{\text{number of successful outcomes}}{\text{number of possible outcomes}}.$$

The probability of an event is a number between 0 and 1, including 0 and 1.

$$0 \leqslant P(E) \leqslant 1$$

The value of $P(E)$ can be given as a fraction, decimal or percentage.

Note: $P(E) = \mathbf{0}$ means that an event is **impossible**.
       $P(E) = \mathbf{1}$ means that an event is **certain**.

The set of all possible outcomes is called the 'sample space'.
For example, the sample space for a normal die is 1, 2, 3, 4, 5 and 6.

Probability of an Event not Happening

If E is any event, then 'not E' is the event that E does not occur. Clearly E and 'not E' cannot occur at the same time. Either E or not E must occur. Thus, we have the following relationship between the probabilities of E and not E:

$$P(E) + P(\text{not } E) = 1$$
$$\text{or}$$
$$P(\text{not } E) = 1 - P(E)$$

Notes: **1.** It is very important **not** to count an outcome twice in an event when calculating probabilities.
2. In questions on probability, objects which are identical are treated as different.
3. The phrase '**drawn at random**' means each object is **equally likely** to be picked.
'**Unbiased**' means '**fair**'. '**Biased**' means '**unfair**' in some way.

Example ▼

A bag contains 8 red, 3 blue and 13 yellow discs. A disc is selected at random from the bag.
What is the probability that the disc selected is:
(i) red   **(ii)** blue   **(iii)** yellow   **(iv)** not yellow?

Solution:

There are $8 + 3 + 13 = 24$ discs in the bag.

(i) $P(\text{red disc}) = \dfrac{\text{number of red discs}}{\text{total number of discs}} = \dfrac{8}{24} = \dfrac{1}{3}$

(ii) $P(\text{blue disc}) = \dfrac{\text{number of blue discs}}{\text{total number of discs}} = \dfrac{3}{24} = \dfrac{1}{8}$

(iii) $P(\text{yellow disc}) = \dfrac{\text{number of yellow discs}}{\text{total number of discs}} = \dfrac{13}{24}$

(iv) We are certain that the disc selected is yellow or not yellow.

$\therefore \quad P(\text{yellow disc}) + P(\text{not a yellow disc}) = 1$

$\qquad P(\text{not a yellow disc}) = 1 - P(\text{yellow disc})$

$$= 1 - \frac{13}{24} = \frac{11}{24}$$

Alternatively:

$P(\text{not a yellow disc}) = \dfrac{\text{number of non-yellow discs}}{\text{total number of discs}} = \dfrac{11}{24}$

(number of non-yellow discs = number of red discs + number of blue discs = $8 + 3 = 11$)

A pack of cards consists of 52 cards divided into four suits: Clubs (black), Diamonds (red), Hearts (red) and Spades (black). Each suit consists of 13 cards bearing the following values: 2, 3, 4, 5, 6, 7, 8, 9, 10, Jack, Queen, King and Ace. The Jack, Queen and King are called 'picture cards'. So the total number of outcomes if one card is picked is 52.

A card is drawn at random from a normal pack of 52 playing cards.
What is the probability that the card will be:

(i) an ace   **(ii)** a spade   **(iii)** black   **(iv)** odd-numbered?

Solution:

(i) $P(\text{ace}) = \dfrac{\text{number of aces}}{\text{number of cards}} = \dfrac{4}{52} = \dfrac{1}{13}$

(ii) $P(\text{spade}) = \dfrac{\text{number of spades}}{\text{number of cards}} = \dfrac{13}{52} = \dfrac{1}{4}$

(iii) $P(\text{black card}) = \dfrac{\text{number of black cards}}{\text{number of cards}} = \dfrac{26}{52} = \dfrac{1}{2}$

(iv)   Each suit has four odd numbers, 3, 5, 7 and 9. There are four suits.
Therefore, there are 16 cards with an odd number.

$$P(\text{odd-numbered card}) = \frac{\text{number of cards with an odd number}}{\text{number of cards}} = \frac{16}{52} = \frac{4}{13}$$

Conditional Probability

With conditional probability we are given some prior knowledge, or some extra condition, about the outcome. This usually reduces the size of the sample space. Consider parts **(iv)** and **(v)** of the next example.

Example ▼

In a class, there are 21 boys and 15 girls. Three boys wear glasses and five girls wear glasses. A pupil is picked at random from the class.

(i)   What is the probability that the pupil is a boy?
(ii)   What is the probability that the pupil wears glasses?
(iii)   What is the probability that the pupil is a boy who wears glasses?

A girl is picked at random from the class.
(iv)   What is the probability that she wears glasses?

A pupil wearing glasses is picked at random from the class.
(v)   What is the probability that it is a boy?

Solution:

It is good practice to represent the information in a table (including the totals for each column and row).

	Boy	Girl	Total
Does not wear glasses	18	10	28
Wears glasses	3	5	8
Total	21	15	36

There are $21 + 15 = 36$ pupils in the class.

(i) $P(\text{boy}) = \dfrac{\text{number of boys}}{\text{number of pupils in the class}} = \dfrac{21}{36} = \dfrac{7}{12}$

(ii) $P(\text{pupil wears glasses}) = \dfrac{\text{number of pupils who wear glasses}}{\text{number of pupils in the class}} = \dfrac{8}{36} = \dfrac{2}{9}$

(iii) $P(\text{boy who wears glasses}) = \dfrac{\text{number of boys who wear glasses}}{\text{number of pupils in the class}} = \dfrac{3}{36} = \dfrac{1}{12}$

The next two questions require the use of conditional probability, where the size of the sample space has been reduced.

(iv) We are certain that the pupil picked is a girl. There are 15 girls in the class. 5 of these wear glasses.

$P(\text{when a girl is picked she wears glasses})$

$= \dfrac{\text{number of girls in the class who wear glasses}}{\text{number of girls in the class}} = \dfrac{5}{15} = \dfrac{1}{3}$

(v) We are certain that the pupil picked wears glasses. There are 8 pupils who wear glasses. 3 of these pupils are boys.

$P(\text{when a pupil who wears glasses is picked, the pupil is a boy})$

$= \dfrac{\text{number of boys in the class who wear glasses}}{\text{number of pupils in the class who wear glasses}} = \dfrac{3}{8}$

Combining Two Events

There are many situations where we have to consider two outcomes. In these situations all the possible outcomes, the **sample space**, can be listed in a sample space diagram (often called a '**two-way table**').

Example ▼

Two dice, one red and the other blue, are thrown. What is the probability of getting two equal scores or of the scores adding up to 10?

Solution:

sample space diagram

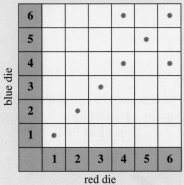

red die

36 possible outcomes (6×6)

The dots indicate where the two scores are equal and/or they add up to 10.

There are 8 dots.

$\therefore \quad P(\text{two equal scores or a total of 10}) = \dfrac{8}{36} = \dfrac{2}{9}$

Note: (5, 5) is **not** counted twice.

Note: Be careful if after the first selection there is no replacement, as in the next example.

Of five balls in a bag, one bears the number 1, another the number 3, two others the number 4 and one the number 6. Two balls are drawn together. If an outcome is the product of the numbers on the two balls, write out the probability for each of the possible outcomes.

Solution:

Note: 'Product' means 'multiply'.

Picking two numbers at a time is the same as picking one after another without replacement.

sample space diagram

second selection					
⑥	6	18	24	24	
④	4	12	16		24
④	4	12		16	24
③	3		12	12	18
①		3	4	4	6
	①	③	④	④	⑥

first selection

The shaded regions indicate that you cannot pick the same ball twice.

From the diagram:

$$P(3) = \frac{2}{20} = \frac{1}{10} \qquad P(4) = \frac{4}{20} = \frac{1}{5} \qquad P(6) = \frac{2}{20} = \frac{1}{10}$$

$$P(12) = \frac{4}{20} = \frac{1}{5} \qquad P(16) = \frac{2}{20} = \frac{1}{10} \qquad P(18) = \frac{2}{20} = \frac{1}{10}$$

$$P(24) = \frac{4}{20} = \frac{1}{5}$$

Exercise 5.3 ▼

1. A box contains 36 coloured balls. 12 are red, 15 are blue, 3 are yellow and the rest are white. One ball is selected at random from the box. Calculate the probability of selecting a:
   (i) red ball **(ii)** blue ball **(iii)** yellow ball **(iv)** white ball.

2. A fair spinner has eight sides as shown.
   The sides are labelled *A, B, B, C, C, C, C* and *F*.
   The spinner is spun once.
   What is the probability that the spinner lands on:
   (i) *A* **(ii)** *B* **(iii)** *C*?

3. The numbers 1 to 30 inclusive are written on 30 identical slips of paper, placed in a box and thoroughly mixed. One slip of paper is chosen at random from the box. Find the probability that the number printed on the slip is:

(i) odd (ii) less than 7 (iii) divisible by 5 (iv) divisible by 9

(v) a two-digit number (vi) a perfect square (vii) a prime number.

4. A card is drawn at random from a normal pack of 52 playing cards.
What is the probability that the card will be:

(i) the nine of spades (ii) a red card (iii) a club

(iv) a king (v) a picture card (vi) a black picture card

(vii) an even number (viii) not a queen (ix) a joker?

5. A die is thrown 120 times. How many times would you expect the die to land on six?

6. 1,000 tickets are sold in a raffle. There is only one prize.
How many tickets does a person need to buy to have exactly 1 chance in 5 (i.e. $\frac{1}{5}$) of winning?

7. A bag contains 3 red, 3 green and 4 blue discs. A disc is selected at random from the bag.
What is the probability of selecting a blue disc?

The selected disc is to be put back into the bag, plus a certain number of red discs. This causes the probability of selecting a red disc to equal $\frac{1}{2}$.

Find the number of extra red discs that were placed in the bag.

8. When a die is thrown, an odd number occurs. What is the probability that the number is prime?

9. A card is chosen at random from a set of twenty-five cards numbered from 1 to 25. What is the probability that the card chosen is a multiple of 4, given that it is greater than 15?

10. Two fair dice are thrown. Find the probability that one of the dice shows a four, given that the total on the two dice is 10.

11. A box contains 20 blue counters and 30 green counters. Each counter is numbered with an even or odd number. 5 of the blue and 20 of the green counters are odd. Complete the table opposite.

	Even	Odd	Total
Blue			20
Green			
Total			50

One of the counters is chosen at random.
What is the probability that the counter is:

(i) blue (ii) green (iii) blue and even (iv) green and odd?

A green counter is chosen at random.
(v) What is the probability that it is odd?

An odd-numbered counter is chosen at random.
(vi) What is the probability that it is blue?

12. There are 80 members in a club, 32 male and 48 female. 4 of the males and 8 of the females wear glasses. A club member is selected at random.

What is the probability that the club member is a:

(i) male (ii) female (iii) person wearing glasses

(iv) female not wearing glasses (v) male wearing glasses?

A male from the club is selected at random.
(vi) What is the probability that he wears glasses?

A member who wears glasses is selected at random.
(vii) What is the probability that it is a female?

13. A game is played with two fair spinners, as shown. Both are spun at the same time and the outcomes are added to get a score. How many scores are possible?

Calculate the probability of a score:
(i) of 4
(ii) of 6
(iii) greater than 6
(iv) less than or equal to 5.

14. A box contains 4 discs, numbered 1, 3, 3 and 4. A disc is drawn from the box and replaced. Then a second disc is drawn. A score is the sum of the two numbers drawn.

Calculate the probability that:
(i) the sum of the numbers is 4
(ii) the sum of the numbers is 6 or 7
(iii) the numbers drawn are the same
(iv) the difference between the numbers is less than 2.

15. Two unbiased dice are thrown, one red and the other black.
(i) How many outcomes are possible?
(ii) If the scores are added together, calculate the probability that the sum of the scores is:
    (a) less than 6
    (b) 7
    (c) greater than 10.

16. Two unbiased dice are thrown. Find the probability that the product of the scores is:
(i) even
(ii) a multiple of 4
(iii) a multiple of 12.

17. A bag A contains 6 blue discs and 2 yellow discs. A bag B contains 4 blue discs and 2 yellow discs. A disc is drawn from bag A and then a disc is drawn from bag B.

Calculate the probability that:
(i) both discs are yellow
(ii) both discs are the same colour
(iii) the disc from bag A is blue and the disc from bag B is yellow.

18. A bag contains five discs, numbered 1, 2, 3, 4 and 5. A disc is drawn from the bag and not replaced. Then a second disc is drawn from the bag.

How many outcomes are possible?

Calculate the probability that:
(i) the sum of the outcomes is less than 5
(ii) one outcome is exactly 3 greater than the other
(iii) the difference between the outcomes is 2.

19. A box contains five cards, numbered 2, 3, 4, 4 and 5. One card is picked from the bag and not replaced. Then a second card is picked. Using a sample space diagram, or otherwise, find the probability that the numbers on the cards:
(i) are both odd
(ii) have a sum of 6
(iii) have a sum of 7 or less.

Addition Rule (OR)

If A and B are two different events of the same experiment, then the probability that the two events, A or B, can happen is given by:

$$P(A \text{ or } B) = P(A) + P(B) - P(A \text{ and } B)$$

$\uparrow$

(removes double counting)

It is often called the **or** rule. It is important to remember that $P(A \text{ or } B)$ means A occurs, or B occurs, or both occur. By subtracting $P(A \text{ and } B)$, the possibility of double counting is removed.

Example ▼

An unbiased twenty-sided die, numbered 1 to 20, is thrown.
What is the probability of obtaining a number divisible by 4 or by 5?

Solution:

There are 20 possible outcomes.

Numbers divisible by 4 are 4, 8, 12, 16 or 20 $\therefore$ $P(\text{divisible by 4}) = \dfrac{5}{20}$

Numbers divisible by 5 are 5, 10, 15 or 20 $\therefore$ $P(\text{divisible by 5}) = \dfrac{4}{20}$

Number divisible by 4 and 5 is 20 $\therefore$ $P(\text{divisible by 4 and 5}) = \dfrac{1}{20}$

$P(\text{number divisible by 4 or 5})$

$= P(\text{number divisible by 4}) + P(\text{number divisible by 5}) - P(\text{number divisible by 4 and 5})$

(removes the double counting of the number 20)

$= \dfrac{5}{20} + \dfrac{4}{20} - \dfrac{1}{20}$

$= \dfrac{8}{20} = \dfrac{2}{5}$

The number 20 is common to both events and if the probabilities were simply added, then the number 20 would have been counted twice.

A single card is drawn at random from a pack of 52. What is the probability that it is a king or a spade? What is the probability that it is not a king or spade?

Solution:

Let K represent that a king is chosen and S represent that a spade is chosen.

The pack contains 52 cards.

There are 4 kings in the pack, $\qquad\qquad\qquad$ $\therefore$ $P(K) = \dfrac{4}{52}$

There are 13 spades in the pack, $\qquad\qquad$ $\therefore$ $P(S) = \dfrac{13}{52}$

One card is both a king and a spade, $\qquad$ $\therefore$ $P(K \text{ and } S) = \dfrac{1}{52}$

(i) $P(K \text{ or } S) = P(K) + P(S) - P(K \text{ and } S)$

$\qquad\qquad = \dfrac{4}{52} + \dfrac{13}{52} - \dfrac{1}{52}$

$\qquad\qquad = \dfrac{16}{52} = \dfrac{4}{13}$

(ii) $P(\text{not } K \text{ or } S) = 1 - P(K \text{ or } S)$

$\qquad\qquad\quad = 1 - \dfrac{4}{13}$

$\qquad\qquad\quad = \dfrac{9}{13}$

A bag contains five red, three blue and two yellow discs. The red discs are numbered 1, 2, 3, 4 and 5; the blue discs are numbered 6, 7 and 8; and the yellow discs are numbered 9 and 10. A single disc is drawn at random from the bag. What is the probability that the disc is blue or even?

Solution:

There are 10 possible outcomes.

Let B represent that a blue disc is chosen and E represent that a disc with an even number is chosen.

$\qquad P(B \text{ or } E) = P(B) + P(E) - P(B \text{ and } E)$

$\qquad\qquad = \dfrac{3}{10} + \dfrac{5}{10} - \dfrac{2}{10} \qquad$ (removes double counting)

$\qquad\qquad = \dfrac{6}{10} = \dfrac{3}{5}$

1. An unbiased die is thrown.
   Find the probability that the number obtained is:
   (i) even   (ii) prime   (iii) even or prime.

2. A number is chosen at random from the whole numbers 1 to 12 inclusive.
   What is the probability that it is:
   (i) even   (ii) divisible by 3   (iii) even or divisible by 3   (iv) not even or divisible by 3?

3. A number is chosen at random from the whole numbers 1 to 30 inclusive.
   What is the probability that it is divisible by:
   (i) 3   (ii) 5   (iii) 3 or 5   (iv) not 3 or 5?

4. A letter is selected at random from the word *EXERCISES*.
   Find the probability that the letter is:
   (i) *I*   (ii) *S*   (iii) a vowel   (iv) a vowel or an *S*   (v) not a vowel or an *S*.

5. A bag contains three blue discs, five white discs and four red discs.
   A disc is chosen at random.
   Find the probability that the disc chosen is:
   (i) red   (ii) blue or white   (iii) red or white   (iv) not red or white.

6. In a class of 20 students, 4 of the 9 girls and 3 of the 11 boys play on the school hockey team.
   A student from the class is chosen at random. What is the probability that the student chosen is:
   (i)   on the hockey team   (ii)   a boy
   (iii) a boy or on the hockey team   (iv) a girl or not on the hockey team?

7. In lotto, there are 42 numbers, numbered from 1 to 42.
   Find the probability that the first number drawn is:
   (i)   an even number   (ii)   a number greater than 24
   (iii) an odd number or a number greater than 24   (iv) a number divisible by 6
   (v)   a number divisible by 4   (vi) a number divisible by 6 or 4
   (vii) not a number divisible by 6 or 4.

8. A card is selected at random from a pack of 52.
   Find the probability that the card is:
   (i)   a spade or a club   (ii)   a queen or a red card
   (iii) a heart or a red picture card   (iv) not a heart or a red picture card.

9. Two unbiased dice, one red and the other blue, are thrown together.
   Calculate the probability that:
   (i)   the numbers are the same or the sum of the numbers is 6
   (ii) the sum of the numbers is 8 or the difference between the two numbers is 2.

10. A bag contains five red discs and three blue discs. The red discs are numbered 1, 2, 2, 3 and 3, while the blue discs are numbered 4, 5 and 5. A single disc is drawn at random from the bag.
    What is the probability that the disc is:
    (i) red   (ii) even   (iii) red or even   (iv) neither red nor even?

11. A bag contains five purple markers, four green markers and three black markers. The purple markers are numbered 1, 2, 3, 4, and 5; the green markers are numbered 6, 7, 8 and 9; while the black markers are numbered 10, 11 and 12. A single marker is drawn from the bag.
    What is the probability that the marker is:
    (i) odd   (ii) black   (iii) black or odd   (iv) purple or even
    (v) green or even   (iv) not green or even?

Multiplication Rule (AND)

Successive Events

> The probability that two events, A and then B, both happen and in that order, is given by:
> $$P(A \text{ and } B) = P(A) \times P(B)$$
> where $P(B)$ has been worked out assuming that A has already occurred.

Order must be taken into account. Also, be very careful where the outcome at one stage does affect the outcome at the next stage. This rule also applies to more than two events.

> When the question says **and**, then multiply.

Example ▼

A bag contains 3 red and 2 yellow discs only. When a disc is drawn from the bag, it is returned before the next draw. What is the probability that two draws will yield both discs the same colour?

Solution:

Method 1: Using a sample space diagram

Let R represent that a red disc is chosen and let Y represent that a yellow disc is chosen.

sample space diagram

first selection

There are 25 possible outcomes
(5 for the first draw and 5 for the second draw).
The dots indicate where the colours are the same, successful outcome, either two reds or two yellows. There are 13 dots.

$$P(\text{both discs the same colour}) = \frac{13}{25}$$

Method 2: Picking one at a time with replacement

Let R_1 represent that a red disc is chosen first, Y_2 represent that a yellow disc is chosen second, and so on.

$P(\text{both discs the same colour})$

$= P(R_1 \text{ and } R_2) \quad \text{or} \quad P(Y_1 \text{ and } Y_2)$

$= P(R_1) \times P(R_2) \quad + \quad P(Y_1) \times P(Y_2)$

$= \dfrac{3}{5} \times \dfrac{3}{5} \quad + \quad \dfrac{2}{5} \times \dfrac{2}{5}$

$= \dfrac{9}{25} + \dfrac{4}{25}$

$= \dfrac{13}{25}$

> red and then a red
> or
> yellow and then a yellow

Method 3: Using arrangements

$$\begin{array}{ccccc} & \text{red and red} & \text{or} & \text{yellow and yellow} & \\ \text{Number of desirable outcomes} = & 3 \times 3 & + & 2 \times 2 & \text{(discs are replaced)} \\ & = 9 + 4 = 13 & & & \end{array}$$

Number of possible outcomes $= 5 \times 5 = 25$

$\therefore P(\text{both discs the same colour}) = \dfrac{13}{25}$

Note: A combinations approach will not work in this example, as the disc was returned before the next disc was picked.

Example ▼

A bag contains four red discs and five blue discs. Three discs are selected at random. Find the probability that two are red and one is blue.

Solution:

(i) Let R_1 represent that a red disc is chosen first, B_2 represent that a blue disc is chosen second, and so on. Three discs selected at random is equivalent to selecting one disc after another **without** replacement.

Method 1: Picking one at a time without replacement

Two reds and one blue can occur in three ways:

$\quad R_1$ and R_2 and $B_3 \qquad$ or $\qquad R_1$ and B_2 and $R_3 \qquad$ or $\qquad B_1$ and R_2 and R_3

$P(\text{two red and blue})$

$= P(R_1 \text{ and } R_2 \text{ and } B_3) \quad$ or $\quad P(R_1 \text{ and } B_2 \text{ and } R_3) \quad$ or $\quad P(B_1 \text{ and } R_2 \text{ and } R_3)$

$= \quad \dfrac{4}{9} \times \dfrac{3}{8} \times \dfrac{5}{7} \qquad + \qquad \dfrac{4}{9} \times \dfrac{5}{8} \times \dfrac{3}{7} \qquad + \qquad \dfrac{5}{9} \times \dfrac{4}{8} \times \dfrac{3}{7}$

$= \quad \dfrac{5}{42} \qquad\qquad + \qquad\quad \dfrac{5}{42} \qquad\qquad + \qquad\quad \dfrac{5}{42}$

$= \quad \dfrac{15}{42} = \dfrac{5}{14}$

Method 2: Using combinations

There are 9 discs and we want to choose 3.

$\qquad$ The total number of selections of 3 from $9 = \dbinom{9}{3} = 84.$

$\qquad$ The number of ways of selecting two red and one blue $= \dbinom{4}{2} \times \dbinom{5}{1} = 6 \times 5 = 30$

$\therefore \quad P(\text{two red and one blue}) = \dfrac{30}{84} = \dfrac{5}{14}$

Method 3: Using arrangements

$$\begin{array}{ccccccc} \text{Number of desirable outcomes} = & R\,R\,B & \text{or} & R\,B\,R & \text{or} & B\,R\,R & \\ & = 4 \times 3 \times 5 & + & 4 \times 5 \times 3 & + & 5 \times 4 \times 3 & \\ & = 60 & + & 60 & + & 60 & = 180 \end{array}$$

Number of possible outcomes $= 9 \times 8 \times 7 = 504$

$\therefore \quad P(\text{two red and one blue}) = \dfrac{180}{504} = \dfrac{5}{14}$

A box contains four blue spheres and two yellow spheres. One sphere is removed at random and not replaced. Then a second sphere is removed at random. Find the probability that one sphere is blue and the other is yellow.

Solution:

Let B_1 represent that a blue sphere is chosen first, Y_2 represent that a yellow is chosen second, and so on.

Diagram of the situation

There are two possible sample spaces for the second choice. It depends on whether a blue sphere is chosen first or a yellow sphere is chosen first.

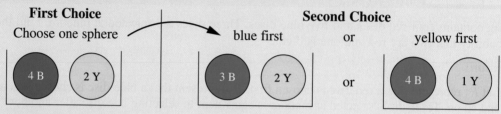

Method 1: Picking one at a time without replacement

P(one sphere is blue and the other is yellow)

$$= P(B_1 \text{ and } Y_2) \qquad \text{or} \qquad P(Y_1 \text{ and } B_2)$$

$$= P(B_1) \times P(Y_2) \qquad + \qquad P(Y_1) \times P(B_2)$$

$$= \quad \frac{4}{6} \times \frac{2}{5} \qquad + \qquad \frac{2}{6} \times \frac{4}{5}$$

$$= \quad \frac{8}{30} + \frac{8}{30} = \frac{16}{30} = \frac{8}{15}$$

> blue first and then a yellow second
> or
> yellow first and then a blue second

Method 2: Using a probability tree diagram

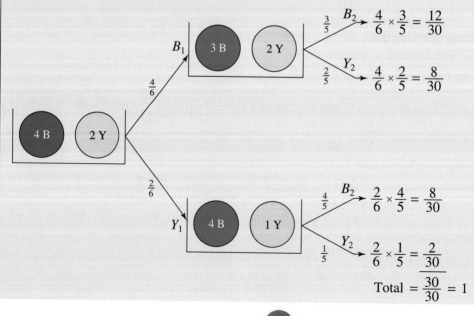

Multiply the probabilities along the branches to get the end results.
If more than one end result is required, add these results together.

P(one sphere is blue and the other is yellow) $= \dfrac{8}{30} + \dfrac{8}{30} = \dfrac{16}{30} = \dfrac{8}{15}$

Method 3: Using combinations
As the first sphere is not replaced, combinations can be used.
There are 6 spheres and we want to choose 2.
The total number of selections of 2 from $6 = \binom{6}{2} = 15$.

The number of ways of selecting one blue and one yellow $= \binom{4}{1} \times \binom{2}{1} = 4 \times 2 = 8$.

$\therefore$ P(one sphere is blue and the other is yellow) $= \dfrac{8}{15}$

Method 4: Using arrangements

$$
\begin{array}{ccc}
B \text{ and } Y & \text{or} & Y \text{ and } B
\end{array}
$$

Number of desirable outcomes $= \quad 4 \times 2 \quad + \quad 2 \times 4$

$\qquad\qquad\qquad\qquad = \quad 8 + 8 = 16$

Number of possible outcomes $= 6 \times 5 = 30$ $\qquad$ (sphere not replaced)

$\therefore$ P(one sphere is blue and the other is yellow) $= \dfrac{16}{30} = \dfrac{8}{15}$

Example ▼

A bag contains 16 marbles, 6 of which are white and the remainder black.
Three marbles are removed at random, one at a time, without replacement.
Find the probability that:
(i) all are black $\qquad$ **(ii)** at least one is white.

Solution:

Let B_1 represent that a black marble is chosen first, B_2 that a black marble is chosen second,
and B_3 that a black marble is chosen third.
There are 20 marbles, 6 white, 10 black.

(i) P(all are black) $= P(B_1) \times P(B_2) \times P(B_3)$

$\qquad\qquad = \dfrac{10}{16} \times \dfrac{9}{15} \times \dfrac{8}{14}$

$\qquad\qquad = \dfrac{3}{14}$

$$P(B_1) = \frac{10}{16}$$

$$P(B_2) = \frac{9}{15} \quad \left(\begin{array}{l}\text{1 black removed,}\\ \text{9 black and 6 white left}\end{array}\right)$$

$$P(B_3) = \frac{8}{14} \quad \left(\begin{array}{l}\text{2 blacks removed,}\\ \text{8 black and 6 white left}\end{array}\right)$$

(ii) In every other case there is **at least** one white.

$\qquad P$(at least one white) $= 1 - P$(none is white)

$\qquad\qquad\qquad\qquad = 1 - P$(all are black)

$\qquad\qquad\qquad\qquad = 1 - \dfrac{3}{14}$

$\qquad\qquad\qquad\qquad = \dfrac{11}{14}$

Note: A combinations or arrangement approach would also work.

149

Ten discs, each marked with a different whole number from 1 to 10, are placed in a box. Three of the discs, are drawn at random (without replacement) from the box.

(i) What is the probability that the disc with the number 7 is drawn?

(ii) What is the probability that the three numbers on the discs drawn are odd?

(iii) What is the probability that the product of the three numbers on the discs drawn is even?

(iv) What is the probability that the smallest number on the discs drawn is 4?

Solution:

10 discs, numbered from 1 to 10 inclusive.

Method 1: Picking one at a time without replacement

(i) $P(\text{disc with the number 7})$

$= P(7, \text{not } 7, \text{not } 7) \quad \text{or} \quad P(\text{not } 7, 7, \text{not } 7) \quad \text{or} \quad P(\text{not } 7, \text{not } 7, 7)$

$$= \frac{1}{10} \times \frac{9}{9} \times \frac{8}{8} \quad + \quad \frac{9}{10} \times \frac{1}{9} \times \frac{8}{8} \quad + \quad \frac{9}{10} \times \frac{8}{9} \times \frac{1}{8}$$

$$= \frac{1}{10} + \frac{1}{10} + \frac{1}{10} = \frac{3}{10}$$

(ii) $P(\text{three numbers on the discs are odd})$

$= P(\text{1st odd}) \times P(\text{2nd odd}) \times P(\text{3rd odd})$

$$= \frac{5}{10} \times \frac{4}{9} \times \frac{3}{8} = \frac{60}{720} = \frac{1}{12}$$

(iii) Product means the result of multiplying.

If at least one number is even, then the product of the three numbers will be even.

$P(\text{product of the three numbers on the discs is even})$

$= P(\text{at least one even number})$

$= 1 - P(\text{three numbers on the discs are odd})$

$$= 1 - \frac{1}{12} = \frac{11}{12}$$

Alternatively, let E_1 represent that an even number is picked first, O_2 represent that an odd number is picked second, and so on.

$P(\text{product of the three numbers on the discs is even})$

$= P(E_1, E_2, E_3) + P(E_1, E_2, O_3) + P(E_1, O_2, E_3) + P(O_1, E_2, E_3) + P(E_1, O_2, O_3) + P(O_1, E_2, O_3)$
$\quad + P(O_1, O_2, E_3)$

$= P(E_1, E_2, E_3) + 3P(E_1, E_2, O_3) + 3P(E_1, O_2, O_3)$

$$= \frac{5}{10} \times \frac{4}{9} \times \frac{3}{8} + 3 \times \frac{5}{10} \times \frac{4}{9} \times \frac{5}{8} + 3 \times \frac{5}{10} \times \frac{5}{9} \times \frac{4}{8}$$

$$= \frac{60}{720} + \frac{300}{720} + \frac{300}{720} = \frac{660}{720} = \frac{11}{12}$$

(iv) For the smallest number to be 4, we need to choose 4 and any two from 5, 6, 7, 8, 9, 10.

P(smallest number is 4)

$= P(4, \text{not } 4, \text{not } 4) + P(\text{not } 4, 4, \text{not } 4) + P(\text{not } 4, \text{not } 4, 4)$

$= \dfrac{1}{10} \times \dfrac{6}{9} \times \dfrac{5}{8} + \dfrac{6}{10} \times \dfrac{1}{9} \times \dfrac{5}{8} + \dfrac{6}{10} \times \dfrac{5}{9} \times \dfrac{1}{8}$

$= \dfrac{30}{720} + \dfrac{30}{720} + \dfrac{30}{720} = \dfrac{90}{720} = \dfrac{1}{8}$

Method 2: Using combinations

As the discs are **not** replaced, we can use combinations.

In each case the number of possible outcomes $= \dbinom{10}{3} = 120$.

(i) One 7 and any two others:

Number of favourable outcomes $= \dbinom{1}{1} \times \dbinom{9}{2} = 1 \times 36 = 36$

$P(\text{disc with the number 7}) = \dfrac{36}{120} = \dfrac{3}{10}$

(ii) Three numbers on the discs are odd:

Number of favourable outcomes $= \dbinom{5}{3} = 10$

$P(\text{three numbers on the discs are odd}) = \dfrac{10}{120} = \dfrac{1}{12}$

(iii) Product of the three numbers on the discs is even:

The product of the three numbers is either even or odd.

$\therefore$ $\begin{pmatrix} \text{number of possible} \\ \text{outcomes} \end{pmatrix} = \begin{pmatrix} \text{number of outcomes} \\ \text{where the product is even} \end{pmatrix} + \begin{pmatrix} \text{number of outcomes} \\ \text{where the product is odd} \end{pmatrix}$

$\begin{pmatrix} \text{number of outcomes where} \\ \text{the product is even} \end{pmatrix} = \begin{pmatrix} \text{number of possible} \\ \text{outcomes} \end{pmatrix} - \begin{pmatrix} \text{number of outcomes where} \\ \text{the product is odd} \end{pmatrix}$

$= \dbinom{10}{3} - \dbinom{5}{3}$

$= 120 - 10 = 110$

$P(\text{product of the three numbers on the disc is even}) = \dfrac{110}{120} = \dfrac{11}{12}$

(iv) The smallest number on the discs is 4:

choose 4 and any two from 5, 6, 7, 8, 9, 10.

Number of favourable outcomes $= \dbinom{1}{1} \times \dbinom{6}{2} = 1 \times 15 = 15$

$P(\text{smallest number is 4}) = \dfrac{15}{120} = \dfrac{1}{8}$

In a particular week (Monday to Sunday inclusive), three students, *A*, *B* and *C*, celebrate their birthdays. Assume that the birthdays are equally likely to fall on any day of the week and that the birthdays are independent of each other. What is the probability that:

(i) *A* has a birthday on Tuesday

(ii) *B* and *C* have their birthday on a Wednesday

(iii) *B* and *C* have their birthday on the same day

(iv) none of them has a birthday on Sunday

(v) at least two of them share the same birthday?

Solution:

P(any person has a birthday on a particular day of the week) $= \dfrac{1}{7}$

P(any person does **not** have a birthday on a particular day of the week) $= \dfrac{6}{7}$

(i) P(*A* has a birthday on Tuesday) $= \dfrac{1}{7}$

(ii) P(*B* and *C* have their birthday on Wednesday)

$= P$(*B* has a birthday on Wednesday) $\times P$(*C* has a birthday on Wednesday)

$= \dfrac{1}{7} \times \dfrac{1}{7} = \dfrac{1}{49}$

(iii) P(*B* and *C* have their birthday on the same day)

Method 1:

P(*B* and *C* have their birthday on the same day)

$= P\left(\begin{array}{c}\text{both born on Monday \quad or \quad Tuesday \quad or \quad Wednesday \quad or \quad Thursday \quad or \quad Friday}\\ \text{or \quad Saturday \quad or \quad Sunday}\end{array}\right)$

$= \dfrac{1}{7} \times \dfrac{1}{7} + \dfrac{1}{7} \times \dfrac{1}{7} + \dfrac{1}{7} \times \dfrac{1}{7} + \dfrac{1}{7} \times \dfrac{1}{7} + \dfrac{1}{7} \times \dfrac{1}{7} + \dfrac{1}{7} \times \dfrac{1}{7} + \dfrac{1}{7} \times \dfrac{1}{7}$

$= \dfrac{1}{49} + \dfrac{1}{49} + \dfrac{1}{49} + \dfrac{1}{49} + \dfrac{1}{49} + \dfrac{1}{49} + \dfrac{1}{49} = \dfrac{7}{49} = \dfrac{1}{7}$

Method 2:

P(*B* and *C* have their birthday on the same day)

$= P$(*B* has a birthday on some day of the week) $\times P$(*C* has a birthday on the same day)

$= \dfrac{7}{7} \times \dfrac{1}{7} = \dfrac{1}{7}$

(iv) P(none of them has a birthday on Sunday)

$= P\left(\begin{array}{c}A \text{ does not have a}\\ \text{birthday on Sunday}\end{array} \text{ and } \begin{array}{c}B \text{ does not have a}\\ \text{birthday on Sunday}\end{array} \text{ and } \begin{array}{c}C \text{ does not have a}\\ \text{birthday on Sunday}\end{array}\right)$

$= \dfrac{6}{7} \times \dfrac{6}{7} \times \dfrac{6}{7} = \dfrac{216}{343}$

(v) *P*(at least two of them share the same birthday)

$P(A \text{ has a birthday on some day of the week}) = \dfrac{7}{7} = 1$

$P(B \text{ has a birthday on a different day from } A) = \dfrac{6}{7}$

$P(C \text{ has a birthday on a different day from } A \text{ and } B) = \dfrac{5}{7}$

∴   *P*(all three have birthdays on different days) $= 1 \times \dfrac{6}{7} \times \dfrac{5}{7} = \dfrac{30}{49}$

∴   *P*(at least two of them share the same birthday)

$= 1 - P(\text{all three have birthdays on different days})$

$= 1 - \dfrac{30}{49} = \dfrac{19}{49}$

Example ▼

A box contains seven silver coins, four gold coins and x copper coins.
Two coins are picked at random, and without replacement, from the box.
Write down an expression in x for the probability that the two coins are both copper.

If it is known that the probability of picking two copper coins is $\dfrac{3}{14}$, how many copper coins are in the box?

Solution:

7 silver coins, 4 gold coins and x copper coins.

Thus, the total number of coins $= x + 11$

$P(\text{copper coin first}) = \dfrac{x}{x+11}$

> **First draw**
>
> x copper coins
> and
> $x + 11$ coins in total

$P(\text{copper coin second}) = \dfrac{x-1}{x+10}$

> **Second draw**
>
> Assuming a copper coin is drawn first:
> $x - 1$ copper coins left
> and
> $x + 10$ coins in total

Given: $P(\text{copper and then a copper coin}) = \dfrac{3}{14}$

$P(\text{copper first}) \times P(\text{copper second}) = \dfrac{3}{14}$

$\dfrac{x}{x+11} \times \dfrac{x-1}{x+10} = \dfrac{3}{14}$

$\dfrac{x^2 - x}{x^2 + 21x + 110} = \dfrac{3}{14}$

$$14x^2 - 14x = 3x^2 + 63x + 330 \qquad \text{(multiply both sides by 14 and } x^2 + 21x + 110)$$
$$11x^2 - 77x - 330 = 0$$
$$x^2 - 7x - 30 = 0$$
$$(x - 10)(x + 3) = 0$$
$$x - 10 = 0 \quad \text{or} \quad x + 3 = 0$$
$$x = 10 \quad \text{or} \quad x = -3$$

Thus, $x = 10$ \qquad (reject $x = -3$)

i.e., the number of copper coins is 10.

Exercise 5.5 ▼

1. Two unbiased dice are thrown. What is the probability of getting two 4s?

2. A fair coin is tossed and an unbiased die is thrown.
   Find the probability of:
   (i)   a head and a 4
   (ii) a tail and an odd number
   (iii) a tail and a number greater than 2
   (iv) a head and a number divisible by 3.

3. A spinner used in a game has 10 sections, of which 5 are coloured red, 3 green and 2 blue.
   The spinner is spun twice. What is the probability of obtaining:
   (i)   two reds
   (ii) two blues
   (iii) a red and a blue?

4. A bag contains ten marbles: five red, three blue and two yellow.
   Three marbles are drawn, one after another, without replacement. Find the probability that the first is red, the second is blue and the third is not red.

5. A game consists of spinning an unbiased arrow on a square board and throwing an unbiased die.

   The board contains the letters A, B, C and D. The board is so designed that when the arrow stops spinning it can point at only one letter, and it is equally likely to point at A, B, C or D.

   List all possible outcomes of the game, that is, of spinning the arrow and throwing the die. Find the probability that in any one game the outcome will be:
   (i)   an A and a 6
   (ii) a B and an even number
   (iii) an A and an even number or a B and an odd number
   (iv) a C and a number $\geqslant 4$ or a D and a number $\leqslant 2$.

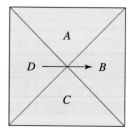

6. An unbiased die has two faces lettered A and four faces lettered B. Two boxes are labelled A and B. Box A contains 6 red and 3 white marbles. Box B contains 4 red and 5 white marbles. The die is rolled and two marbles are drawn at random, without replacement, from the box labelled with the letter uppermost on the die. Find the probability that:
(i) two white marbles are drawn from box A
(ii) both marbles are red.

7. Three coins, a 20c, a 10c and 5c, are tossed. Find the probability of getting:
(i) 3 tails **(ii)** a head and two tails.

8. Twelve blood samples are tested in a laboratory. Of these it is found that five samples are of type A, four of type B and the remaining three are of type O.
Two blood samples are selected at random from the twelve.

What is the probability that:
(i) the two samples are of type A
(ii) one sample is of type B and the other sample is of type O
(iii) the two samples are of the same blood type?

9. A bag contains 8 black discs and 4 white discs. Two discs are picked at random, one after the other, without replacement. Find the probability of drawing discs of different colours if:
(i) the first disc is replaced **(ii)** the first disc is not replaced.

10. A bag contains 5 red, 4 blue and 3 yellow balls. Three balls are removed at random, without replacement. Find the probability that the three balls are of:
(i) the same colour **(ii)** different colours.

11. A bag contains 6 red marbles and 4 white marbles. A marble is chosen at random from the bag, its colour is noted and it is returned to the bag. Then a second marble is drawn and replaced, then a third marble is drawn . Find the probability that:
(i) all three marbles drawn are the same colour
(ii) the first and last marbles are the same colour, but the middle one is different.

12. A bag contains 5 red discs and 4 blue discs. A disc is drawn at random and replaced. Then a second disc is drawn at random. What is the probability that:
(i) both discs are blue **(ii)** the second disc is blue
(iii) the same disc is drawn each time?

13. A bag contains ten blue and ten yellow spheres. Three spheres are removed at random (without replacement). Find the probability that:
(i) all are blue **(ii)** at least one is yellow.

14. Four students work separately on a mathematical problem. The probabilities that the four students have of solving the problem are as follows:

$$\frac{3}{4}, \frac{1}{2}, \frac{4}{7}, \frac{2}{3}.$$

Show that the probability that the problem will be solved by at least one of the four students is $\frac{55}{56}$.

15. Three countries work separately on finding a cure for the common cold. The probabilities that the three countries have of finding a cure are as follows: $\frac{1}{5}, \frac{1}{4}, \frac{1}{3}.$
Find the probability that a cure will be found by at least one country.

16. There are three sets of traffic lights which a woman has to drive through each day on her way to work. The probability that the woman will have to stop at any of these lights is $\frac{1}{3}$. Calculate, for a particular morning, the probability that the woman will have to stop at:

(i) none of the three sets of lights   **(ii)** at least one of the three sets of lights.

17. A box contains one black, one red, one yellow and three purple balls. Three balls are drawn at random from the box (without replacement).

Find the probability that:

(i) three purple balls are drawn

(ii) only two purple balls are drawn

(iii) at least two purple balls are drawn.

18. abc is a triangle. p, q and r are the midpoints of the sides, as shown in the diagram.

(i) A speck of dust falls at random onto, or inside, triangle abc. Find the probability that the speck falls within the smaller triangle pqr.

(ii) If three specks of dust fall at random onto triangle abc, find the probability that at least one falls within the smaller triangle pqr.

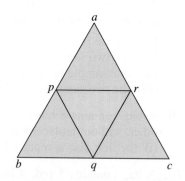

19. In each round of a game, a competitor can score points of 0, 1 or 2 only. Copy and complete the table which shows the points and two of the respective probabilities of these points being scored in a single round.

After two rounds of the game, calculate the probability that a competitor has:

Points	0	1	2
Probability	$\dfrac{1}{2}$	$\dfrac{2}{5}$	

(i) no points   **(ii)** 3 points   **(iii)** an odd number of points.

20. A man has 6 keys, which look very similar, one of which will open his hall door. On a dark night he chooses from the 6 keys, at random, without replacement, until his front door key is found. Find the probability that he will be able to open his hall door after trying:

(i) 2 keys   **(ii)** 4 keys.

21. There were 9 white and 3 black marbles in a bag. In a second bag there were 7 white and 2 black marbles. If a bag and then a marble were selected at random, what was the probability of a black marble?

22. Three cards are drawn, at random and with replacement, from a pack of 52 playing cards. Find the probability that:

(i) the three cards are red

(ii) two are red and one card is a club

(iii) the three cards are all of the same suit.

23. A bag contains nine counters, numbered 1 to 9 inclusive. Four are drawn at random without replacement. Find the probability that the four counters have digits which are:

(i) all odd   **(ii)** two odd and two even.

24. There are six balls in a bag, numbered as follows: 2, 2, 3, 3, 5, 6. Two of the balls are selected simultaneously from the bag, at random. What is the probability that they will total 8 or more?

25. The letters of the word *TABLE* are arranged at random in order. What is the probability that the two vowels are not side by side?

26. A team of 5 people is to be chosen from 5 men and 4 women.
    (i) Calculate the number of ways this can be done.
    (ii) If one of the men is the husband of one of the women, and the team is selected at random, calculate the probability that the married couple will be chosen.

27. A class consists of 4 boys and 6 girls. It is proposed to use a process of random selection to pick 3 representatives for a school council.
    (i) In how many ways can this be done?
    (ii) How many of the selections consist of all boys or all girls?
    (iii) What is the probability that the selection may be all boys or all girls?

28. A committee of two people is chosen at random from 4 men and 5 women.
    (i) In how many ways can this be done?
    (ii) What is the probability that there will be one man and one woman or two women on the committee?

29. A group consists of 5 boys and 4 girls. If three of the group are picked at random, what is the probability that more girls than boys are picked?

30. Eight discs, each marked with a different whole number from 1 to 8, are placed in a box. Three of the discs are drawn at random (without replacement) from the box.
    (i) What is the probability that the disc with the number 6 is drawn?
    (ii) What is the probability that the three numbers on the discs drawn are odd?
    (iii) What is the probability that the product of the three numbers on the discs drawn is even?
    (iv) What is the probability that the smallest number on the discs drawn is 3?

31. Bag *A* contains 4 blue and 5 yellow counters. Bag *B* contains 3 blue and 6 yellow counters. A counter is picked at random from bag *A* and placed in bag *B*. A counter is then picked at random from bag *B*. Find the probability that the counter picked from bag *B* is yellow.

32. A box contains 6 white discs and 4 black discs. A disc is selected at random from the box and replaced by a disc of the other colour. A second disc is then randomly selected from the box.

Determine the probability that:
    (i) the first disc selected is black and the second disc selected is white
    (ii) both discs selected are white.
Assume that spare white and black discs are available.

33. Aideen and Brendan celebrate their birthdays in a particular week (Monday to Sunday inclusive). Assuming that the birthdays are equally likely to fall on any day of the week, what is the probability that:
    (i) Aideen was born on Tuesday
    (ii) Brendan was not born on Sunday
    (iii) both were born on Friday
    (iv) one was born on Thursday and the other was born on Saturday
    (v) both were born on the same day
    (vi) Aideen and Brendan were born on different days?

34. In a particular week (Monday to Sunday inclusive), three students celebrate their birthdays. Assume that the birthdays are equally likely to fall on any day of the week and that the birthdays are independent of each other.

What is the probability that of these three students:
(i) all were born on Thursday
(ii) all were born on the same day of the week
(iii) all were born on different days of the week
(iv) at least two of them share the same birthday
(v) one was born on Monday and the others were not born on Monday?

35. Three students were chosen at random. Assuming that the probability of being born in any given month is equiprobable, find the probability that:
(i) all three have birthdays on July
(ii) all three have birthdays in the same month
(iii) no two have their birthdays in the same month
(iv) at least two have birthdays in the same month.

36. A bag contains 10 yellow, 6 green and x blue discs. One disc is drawn at random from the bag and **not** replaced.
(i) Write down an expression in x for the probability that the disc is green.
(ii) If the probability of a green disc is $\dfrac{3}{10}$, find the value of x.
(iii) Another disc is then drawn from the bag.
Find the probability that both discs are of the same colour.

37. A drawer contains 6 red and x blue pens. One pen is drawn at random and **not** replaced. Another pen is then drawn at random.
(i) Write down an expression in x for the probability that the two pens are blue.
(ii) If the probability that both are blue is $\dfrac{1}{12}$, find the value of x.
(iii) Find the probability that the two pens are of different colours.

38. A bag contains five yellow marbles, four blue marbles and x red marbles. Two marbles are picked at random, and without replacement, from the box.
(i) Write down an expression in x for the probability that the two marbles are red.
(ii) It is known that the probability of picking two red marbles is $\dfrac{1}{7}$.

(a) Find the value of x. **(b)** How many marbles are in the bag?
(c) What is the probability that the marbles are of different colours?

39. The Venn diagram shows the number of elements in each subset of the set S.
An element is picked at random from S. Write an expression in terms of x and y for the probability that the element came from: **(i)** set A **(ii)** set B.
If $P(A) = \dfrac{3}{10}$ and $P(B) = \dfrac{1}{2}$, find the value of x and the value of y.

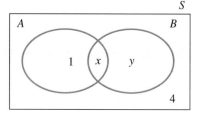

40. A die is weighted so that a score of 5 is three times as likely to appear as a score of 4. A score of 4 is twice as likely as a score of 6, and scores of 1, 2, 3 and 6 are equally likely. On one throw of the die, find the probability of getting an odd number.

STATISTICS AND DIFFERENCE EQUATIONS

Mean

The symbol for the mean is $\bar{x}$ (pronounced 'x bar').

> The mean, $\bar{x}$, of the numbers $x_1, x_2, \ldots, x_n$ is given by:
> $$\bar{x} = \frac{x_1 + x_2 + \cdots + x_n}{n} = \frac{\Sigma x}{n}.$$

In words: 'the sum of all the values divided by the number of values'.

Notes: **1.** A shorthand way of writing $x_1 + x_2 + x_3 + x_4 + x_5 = \displaystyle\sum_{i=1}^{5} x_i$.

2. The symbol Σ (the Greek capital letter 'sigma') is used to denote 'the sum of'. The subscript i is often omitted.

3. Strictly speaking, $\bar{x}$ should be called the '**arithmetic mean**'.

Mean of a Frequency Distribution

Values	x_1	x_2	$\ldots\ldots$	x_n
Frequency	f_1	f_2	$\ldots\ldots$	f_n

$$\text{Mean} = \bar{x} = \frac{\Sigma fx}{\Sigma f}$$

(i) x is the value of each measurement.
(ii) f is the frequency of each measurement.
(iii) Σfx is the sum of all the fx values.
(iv) Σf is the sum of all the frequencies.

Mean of a Grouped Frequency Distribution

Sometimes the range of the values is very wide and it is not suitable to show all the values individually. When this happens we arrange the values into suitable groups called **class intervals**, such as $0 - 10$, $10 - 20$, etc. When the information is arranged in class intervals it is not possible to calculate the exact value of the mean. However, it is possible to estimate it by using the **mid-interval value** of each class interval. The easiest way to find the mid-interval value is to add the two extreme values and divide by 2.

For example, in the class interval $30 - 50$, add 30 and 50 and divide by 2.

i.e., $\dfrac{30 + 50}{2} = \dfrac{80}{2} = 40$ $\qquad \therefore \quad$ 40 is the mid-interval value.

Otherwise, the procedure for estimating the mean is the same as in the previous section.

Use the formula: $\bar{x} = \dfrac{\Sigma fx}{\Sigma f}$, taking x as the mid-interval value.

Example ▼

The mean of the five numbers $2x + 2$, 8, $3x + 1$, 11 and $x - 2$ is 10. Calculate the value of x.

Solution:

Method 1:

Given:

$$\bar{x} = 10$$

$$\therefore \quad \frac{(2x+2) + 8 + (3x+1) + 11 + (x-2)}{5} = 10$$

$$\frac{6x + 20}{5} = 10$$

$$6x + 20 = 50$$

$$6x = 30$$

$$x = 5$$

Method 2:

The mean of the five numbers is 10,

$\therefore$ the numbers must add up to 50

(because $5 \times 10 = 50$ or $\dfrac{50}{5} = 10$).

$$\therefore \quad (2x+2) + 8 + (3x+1) + 11 + (x-2) = 50$$

$$6x + 20 = 50$$

$$6x = 30$$

$$x = 5$$

Example ▼

To obtain a first-class honours degree, a student must obtain a mean of at least 70 marks in four tests. If her mean mark for the first three tests is 66, what is the lowest mark she can obtain in her fourth test to obtain a first-class honours degree?

Solution:

Given, for the three tests:

$$\text{mean} = \bar{x} = 66$$

$$\therefore \quad \frac{x_1 + x_2 + x_3}{3} = 66$$

$$x_1 + x_2 + x_3 = 198 \qquad \text{(multiply both sides by 3)}$$

For the four tests, she wants her mean to be 70 or more.

Required: Mean for the four tests $\geqslant 70$

$$\therefore \quad \frac{x_1 + x_2 + x_3 + x_4}{4} \geqslant 70$$

$$\frac{198 + x_4}{4} \geqslant 70 \qquad (x_1 + x_2 + x_3 = 198)$$

$$198 + x_4 \geqslant 280 \qquad \text{(multiply both sides by 4)}$$

$$x_4 \geqslant 82 \qquad \text{(subtract 198 from each side)}$$

To obtain a first-class honours degree, she must get at least 82 marks in her fourth test.

25 pupils were given a problem to solve. The following grouped frequency distribution table gives the number of pupils who solved the problem in the given time interval.

Time (minutes)	0 – 4	5 – 9	10 – 14	15 – 19
No. of pupils	5	10	7	3

Estimate the mean number of minutes taken per pupil to solve the problem.

Solution:

The table can be rewritten using the mid-interval values.

Time (minutes)	2	7	12	17
No. of pupils	5	10	7	3

$$\text{Mean} = \bar{x} = \frac{\Sigma fx}{\Sigma f} = \frac{5(2) + 10(7) + 7(12) + 3(17)}{5 + 10 + 7 + 3} = \frac{215}{25} = 8.6 \text{ minutes}$$

A die was thrown a number of times and the frequency of each score was as follows:

Value	1	2	3	4	5	6
Frequency	7	7	f	9	5	4

If the mean score was 3.25, find the value of f.

Solution:

Equation given in disguise: mean = 3.25

$$\therefore \quad \frac{7(1) + 7(2) + f(3) + 9(4) + 5(5) + 4(6)}{7 + 7 + f + 9 + 5 + 4} = 3.25$$

$$\frac{7 + 14 + 3f + 36 + 25 + 24}{f + 32} = 3.25$$

$$\frac{3f + 106}{f + 32} = 3.25$$

$$3f + 106 = 3.25(f + 32) \quad \text{[multiply both sides by } (f + 32)\text{]}$$

$$300f + 10,600 = 325(f + 32) \quad \text{[multiply both sides by 100]}$$

$$300f + 10,600 = 325f + 10,400$$

$$-25f = -200$$

$$25f = 200$$

$$f = 8$$

Find the mean of each of the following sets of numbers:

1. 2, 3, 3, 5, 7

2. 4, 0, 2, 6, 8, 2, 6

3. 6.2, 9, 6.4, 7.4, 2.5

4. 2.8, 3.1, 6.7, 1.4, 5.6, 8.6

5. 2, 8, 7, 7, 5, −2, 1, 10

6. −3, 5, 7, −4, −10, 11, 1

Calculate the mean of each of the following frequency distributions:

7.

Value	0	1	2	3	4	5	6
Frequency	1	7	6	5	2	6	3

8.

Value	0 – 5	5 – 10	10 – 20	20 – 35	35 – 40	40 – 50
Frequency	3	5	6	9	5	2

9. The speeds, to the nearest km/h, of 100 vehicles passing a checkpoint were recorded and are grouped in the table below:

Speed (km/h)	31 – 35	36 – 40	41 – 45	46 – 50	51 – 55	56 – 60
No. of vehicles	5	8	27	30	18	12

Estimate the mean speed at the checkpoint.

10. The mean of seven numbers is 8. When one of the numbers is removed the mean is decreased by 1. Find the number that was removed.

11. To obtain an A1 grade in Mathematics for the year a student needs to obtain a mean of at least 90 marks in five tests. If his mean mark for the first four tests is 88, what is the lowest mark he can obtain in his fifth test to obtain a grade A1 for the year?

12. The mean of the six numbers 8, $2x + 1$, 7, $3x$, 4 and 2 is 7. Calculate the value of x.

13. The mean of the following frequency distribution is 13. Find the value of x.

Number	10	12	14	16
Frequency	5	6	x	4

14. People attending a course were asked to choose one of the whole numbers from 1 to 12. The results were recorded as follows:

Number	1 – 3	4 – 6	7 – 9	10 – 12
No. of people	3	x	2	8

Using mid-interval values, 6.5 was calculated as the mean of the numbers chosen. Find the value of x.

15. Show that the mean of the following distribution is independent of the value of x and find the mean:

Number	1	2	3	4	5	6
Frequency	7	9	x	3	7	2

16. (i) Calculate the mean, in terms of k, of the numbers 5, $3k - 6$, 13 and k.

(ii) If the mean is 8, calculate the value of k.

17. The mean of the four numbers $2x$, 2, 3 and 17 is equal to the mean of the five numbers $3x$, 3, 4, 6 and 11. Calculate:

(i) the value of x **(ii)** the mean of the 9 numbers.

18. The mean of the four numbers 2, 7, x and y is 5. Express y in terms of x.

19. If $\bar{x}$ is the mean of the numbers p, q, r and s, express, in terms of $\bar{x}$ and k, the mean of the numbers $3p + 2k$, $3q + 2k$, $3r + 2k$ and $3s + 2k$.

20. Three numbers have a mean of u and four other numbers have a mean of v.

The seven numbers have a mean of w. Express u in terms of v and w.

Weighted Mean

A weighted mean is one in which the **frequencies** are replaced by **weights**. The weights are a **measure of importance** of a particular value, i.e., each value has a **statistical weight** attached to it.

Note: Calculating a weighted mean is exactly the same as finding the mean of a frequency distribution, except that the frequencies are replaced by weights.

We calculate the weighted mean using the formula:

$$\text{Weighted mean} = \bar{x}_w = \frac{\Sigma wx}{\Sigma w}$$

Example ▼

Two students, P and Q, take an examination in Maths, Economics and French.
The table below shows the marks for each student and the corresponding weights.

Subject		Maths	Economics	French
Marks	P	83	70	50
	Q	54	75	81
Weight		5	3	4

Which student has the higher weighted mean?

Solution:

Weighted mean for P

$$= \frac{\Sigma wx}{\Sigma w}$$

$$= \frac{5(83) + 3(70) + 4(50)}{5 + 3 + 4}$$

$$= \frac{415 + 210 + 200}{12}$$

$$= \frac{825}{12} = 68.75$$

Weighted mean for Q

$$= \frac{\Sigma wx}{\Sigma w}$$

$$= \frac{5(54) + 3(75) + 4(81)}{5 + 3 + 4}$$

$$= \frac{270 + 225 + 324}{12}$$

$$= \frac{819}{12} = 68.25$$

Thus P had the higher weighted mean.

Example ▼

The table below shows the prices of various commodities in the year 2004 as a percentage of their prices in 2003. These are called price relatives.

(For example, the price relative for Housing is 108, indicating that the cost of Housing was 8% greater in 2004 than in 2003.)

The table below shows the weight assigned to each commodity. The weight represents the importance of the commodity to the average consumer.

Commodity	Weight	Price in 2004 as a % of price in 2003
Housing	12	108
Fuel and transport	19	107
Food, drink and other goods	40	105
Services	14	118
Clothing and durable goods	10	106

(i) Calculate the weighted mean of the price relatives in the table.

(ii) Calculate the change in the weighted mean if Fuel and transport is removed from consideration.

Solution:

(i)

w	x
12	108
19	107
40	105
14	118
10	106

Weighted mean

$$= \bar{x}_w$$

$$= \frac{\Sigma wx}{\Sigma w}$$

$$= \frac{12(108) + 19(107) + 40(105) + 14(118) + 10(106)}{12 + 19 + 40 + 14 + 10}$$

$$= \frac{1296 + 2033 + 4200 + 1652 + 1060}{95}$$

$$= \frac{10241}{95}$$

$$= 107.8\%$$

(ii) Fuel and transport removed

w	x
12	108
40	105
14	118
10	106

Weighted mean

$$= \bar{x}_w$$

$$= \frac{\Sigma wx}{\Sigma w}$$

$$= \frac{12(108) + 40(105) + 14(118) + 10(106)}{12 + 40 + 14 + 10}$$

$$= \frac{1296 + 4200 + 1652 + 1060}{76}$$

$$= \frac{8208}{76}$$

$$= 108\%$$

Change in weighted mean $= 108 - 107.8 = 0.2\%$, i.e. an increase of 0.2%.

Example ▼

The weighted mean of the data below is €3.60.

Item	P	Q	R	S
Price in €	4.50	2.80	3.40	4.20
Weight	6	7	x	2

Find the value of x.

Solution:

Given: weighted mean = €3.60

$$\therefore \quad \frac{6(4.50) + 7(2.80) + x(3.40) + 2(4.20)}{6 + 7 + x + 2} = 3.60$$

$$\frac{27 + 19.60 + 3.40x + 8.40}{x + 15} = 3.60$$

$$\frac{3.40x + 55}{x + 15} = 3.60$$

$$3.40x + 55 = 3.60(x + 15) \quad \text{[multiply both sides by } (x + 15)]$$
$$34x + 550 = 36(x + 15) \quad \text{[multiply both sides by 10]}$$
$$34x + 550 = 36x + 540$$
$$-2x = -10$$
$$2x = 10$$
$$x = 5$$

Exercise 6.2 ▼

1. The values 6, 2, 5, 4, 8 have, respectively, the weights 5, 4, 1, 2, 3. Calculate the weighted mean.

2. Calculate the weighted mean of the values 10, 6, 7, 3, given the respective weights 14, 6, 10, 9.

3. A composite index number is constructed by taking the weighted mean.
   The following table gives the index and weighting for each of four commodities:

Commodity	Food	Fuel	Mortgage	Clothing
Index	120	110	90	80
Weight	8	5	4	3

   Calculate the composite index number.

4. In their Leaving Certificate, two students, A and B, obtained the following points:

Subject		Maths	Irish	English	Biology	French	Accounting
Points	A	5	2	1	3	4	2
	B	4	1	3	5	2	2

   How many points had each student?
   A university attached weights of 4, 3, 4, 2, 1, 1, respectively, to the six subjects as written above.
   If there was only one place left in the university, which student obtained the place?
   If the weights were 5, 4, 3, 2, 1, 5, respectively, who now obtained the place?

5. Two supermarkets, S_1 and S_2, make reductions in prices, in cents, of four items A, B, C, D, as shown in the table:

Item	A	B	C	D
S_1	11	2	6	5
S_2	8	3	7	10

   Which supermarket had the best average reduction per item?
   If the sales of the four items A, B, C, D in each supermarket were in the ratio $4:2:3:1$, respectively, which now had the best average reduction?

6. The table below shows the prices of various commodities in the year 2004, as a percentage of their prices in 2003. These are called *price relatives*.

The table also shows the weight assigned to each commodity. The weight represents the importance of the commodity to the average consumer.

Commodity	Weight	Price in 2004 as % of price in 2003
Housing	13	110
Fuel and transport	16	106
Tobacco	4	112
Services	19	108
Clothing & durable goods	9	95
Food, drink & other goods	34	105

   (i) Calculate the weighted mean of the price relatives in the table.
   (ii) Calculate the change in the weighted mean if Services is removed from consideration.

7. The percentage change, and corresponding weights, in the price of four consumer items during one year is shown in the table below:

Item	Entertainment	Fuel	Clothing	Transport
Percentage change	10	−3	−1	7
Weight	2	5	7	6

   (i) Calculate the weighted mean of the percentage changes.
   (ii) If the weighting for Fuel is doubled, calculate the change in the weighted mean.
   (iii) If Clothing is removed from consideration, calculate the change in the weighted mean, correct to two decimal places.

8. The percentage change, and corresponding weights, in the price of five items A, B, C, D and E during one year are shown in the table below:

Item	A	B	C	D	E
Percentage change	5	−2	3	4	−3
Weight	6	7	8	w	4

   (i) If the weighted mean of the percentage changes is 1.6, calculate the value of w.
   (ii) If the item A is removed from consideration, find the change in the weighted mean.

9. Two students, A and B, take examinations in Maths, English and Economics. The table shows the marks for each student and the corresponding weights. If the weighted means for A and B are the same, calculate:

Subject		Maths	English	Economics
Marks	A	80	72	46
	B	64	82	40
Weight		2	5	w

(i) the value of w **(ii)** the weighted mean.

10. Two students, P and Q, take examinations in Irish and French. The table shows the marks for each student and the corresponding weights. P's weighted mean mark is less than Q's. Find the **least** possible value of x, $x \in N$.

Student		Irish	French
Marks	P	62	73
	Q	66	60
Weight		x	2

Standard Deviation

Consider the two sets of data:

A: 7, 8, 9

Mean for $A = \dfrac{7+8+9}{3} = \dfrac{24}{3} = 8$

B: 2, 7, 15

Mean for $B = \dfrac{2+7+15}{3} = \dfrac{24}{3} = 8$

Both sets have a mean of 8, but the spread of each is different.
The elements of B are more spread out around the mean.
The statistic used to measure the spread (dispersion) of a set of data about its mean is called the '**standard deviation**' and is denoted by σ (the Greek lower-case letter 'sigma').

Standard Deviation

> If $\bar{x}$ is the mean of the set of numbers $x_1, x_2, ..., x_n$, then the standard deviation, σ, is given by:
>
> $$\sigma = \sqrt{\frac{(x_1-\bar{x})^2 + (x_2-\bar{x})^2 + \cdots + (x_n-\bar{x})^2}{n}} = \sqrt{\frac{\Sigma(x-\bar{x})^2}{n}}$$

To calculate σ, do the following:

> 1. Calculate the mean, $\bar{x}$.
> 2. For each value of x, calculate $(x-\bar{x})$, its deviation from the mean.
> 3. Square **each** of these deviations.
> 4. Find the sum of all these squared deviations.
> 5. Find the mean of these squared deviations.
> 6. Take the square root of the answer.

The higher the standard deviation, the more spread out the data are about the mean, and vice versa.
The square root is used to make sure that the standard deviation and the original data are in the same units.
For example, if the original data are in metres, m, then $(x - \bar{x})^2$ would be measured in m^2.
Taking the square root makes sure that the standard deviation is also in metres.

Standard Deviation of a Frequency Distribution

If $\bar{x}$ is the mean of the frequency,

x	x_1	x_2	. . . .	x_n
f	f_1	f_2	. . . .	f_n

then the standard deviation, σ, is given by:

$$\sigma = \sqrt{\frac{f_1(x_1 - \bar{x})^2 + f_2(x_2 - \bar{x})^2 + \cdots + f_n(x_n - \bar{x})^2}{f_1 + f_2 + \cdots + f_n}} = \sqrt{\frac{\Sigma f(x - \bar{x})^2}{\Sigma f}}$$

For a grouped frequency distribution, we take x as the mid-interval value.

Example ▼

Calculate the standard deviation, correct to two decimal places, of the numbers 2, 5, 6, 8, 10, 11.

Solution:

First calculate the mean, $\bar{x}$:

$$\bar{x} = \frac{\Sigma x}{n}$$

$$= \frac{2 + 5 + 6 + 8 + 10 + 11}{6}$$

$$= \frac{42}{6}$$

$$= 7$$

x	$x - \bar{x}$	$(x - \bar{x})^2$
2	−5	25
5	−2	4
6	−1	1
8	1	1
10	3	9
11	4	16
$\Sigma x = 42$		$\Sigma(x - \bar{x})^2 = 56$

$$\sigma = \sqrt{\frac{\Sigma(x - \bar{x})^2}{n}} = \sqrt{\frac{56}{6}} = \sqrt{9.333333333} = 3.055050463$$

$\sigma = 3.06$ (correct to two decimal places)

Estimate, correct to two decimal places, the standard deviation of the distribution:

x	0 – 4	4 – 12	12 – 24	24 – 40
f	3	8	7	2

Note: 0 – 4 means 0 is included but 4 is not, and so on.

Solution:

The mid-interval values are 2, 8, 16 and 32.

First calculate the mean, $\bar{x}$:

$\bar{x} = \dfrac{\Sigma fx}{\Sigma f}$

$= \dfrac{3(2) + 8(8) + 7(18) + 2(32)}{3 + 8 + 7 + 2}$

$= \dfrac{6 + 64 + 126 + 64}{20}$

$= \dfrac{260}{20} = 13$

f	x	$x - \bar{x}$	$(x - \bar{x})^2$	$f(x - \bar{x})^2$
3	2	–11	121	363
8	8	–5	25	200
7	18	5	25	175
2	32	19	361	722
$\Sigma f = 20$				$\Sigma f(x - \bar{x})^2 = 1460$

$\sigma = \sqrt{\dfrac{\Sigma f(x - \bar{x})^2}{\Sigma f}} = \sqrt{\dfrac{1460}{20}} = \sqrt{73} = 8.544003745$

$\sigma = 8.54$ (correct to two decimal places)

Exercise 6.3 ▼

Find the standard deviation, correct to two decimal places, of each of the following sets of numbers:

1. 4, 5, 6, 9   **2.** 1, 2, 2, 3, 4, 6   **3.** 5, 8, 11, 14, 17

4. 2, 4, 5, 7, 11, 13   **5.** 9, 12, 4, 6, 10, 7   **6.** 12, 4, 9, 8, 7, 11, 5

7. The standard deviation of the array of numbers 2, 8, 3, 7, 6, 4, 5 is k. Calculate the value of k.

8. (i)   Find the mean and standard deviation of the two sets of numbers:
      (a) 7, 9, 10, 11, 13   **(b)** 5, 7, 9, 13, 16
 (ii)   What does comparing the two standard deviations tell you about the two sets of numbers?

9. The array of numbers, 1.8, 2.6, 4.8, 7.2 have a mean of $\bar{x}$ and a standard deviation of σ. Verify that $\bar{x} - \sigma = 2$.

10. (i)   The mean, $\bar{x}$, of the five numbers x, 4, 12, 6 and 8 is 9. Calculate the value of x.
 (ii)   Calculate the value of the standard deviation, σ.

Find the standard deviation, correct to two decimal places, of each of the following distributions:

11.

x	2	6	8	9	10	13
f	3	4	2	6	5	2

12.

x	1	5	6	8	11	13	15
f	7	4	7	3	2	2	1

13.

x	0 – 4	4 – 8	8 – 12	12 – 16	16 – 20
f	2	3	9	7	3

14.

x	0 – 20	20 – 40	40 – 60	60 – 80
f	11	14	9	6

15. The mean, $\bar{x}$, of the following distribution is 10.

x	0 – 4	4 – 8	8 – 12	12 – 16	16 – 20
f	2	w	12	6	2

  (i) Find the value of w.

  (ii) Evaluate $\sqrt{\bar{x} + 4\sigma - 1}$, where σ is the standard deviation.

Algebraic Questions on the Mean and Standard Deviation

We often have to deal with algebraic questions on the mean and standard deviation of a set of data.

Example ▼

(i) Show that the mean of the following distribution is independent of the value of x and find the mean.

Number	1	2	3	4	5	6
Frequency	9	9	x	4	7	3

(ii) If the standard deviation is $\sqrt{2.6}$, find the value of x.

Solution:

(i) $\bar{x} = \dfrac{\Sigma fx}{\Sigma f} = \dfrac{9(1)+9(2)+x(3)+4(4)+7(5)+3(6)}{9+9+x+4+7+3}$

$\qquad = \dfrac{9+18+3x+16+35+18}{x+32}$

$\qquad = \dfrac{3x+96}{x+32}$

$\qquad = \dfrac{3(x+32)}{(x+32)}$ [factorise the top]

$\qquad = 3$ [divide top and bottom by $(x+32)$]

Thus, the mean is 3 for any value of x, i.e. the mean is independent of x.

(ii)

f	x	$x-\bar{x}$	$(x-\bar{x})^2$	$f(x-\bar{x})^2$
9	1	2	4	36
9	2	1	1	9
x	3	0	0	0
4	4	1	1	4
7	5	2	4	28
3	6	3	9	27
$\Sigma f = x+32$				$\Sigma f(x-\bar{x})^2 = 104$

Given: Standard deviation $= \sqrt{2.6}$

$\qquad \therefore \sqrt{\dfrac{f(x-\bar{x})^2}{\Sigma f}} = \sqrt{2.6}$

$\qquad\qquad \sqrt{\dfrac{104}{x+32}} = \sqrt{2.6}$

$\qquad\qquad \dfrac{104}{x+32} = 2.6$ [square both sides]

$\qquad\qquad 104 = 2.6(x+32)$ [multiply both sides by $(x+32)$]

$\qquad\qquad 1040 = 26(x+32)$ [multiply both sides by 10]

$\qquad\qquad 1040 = 26x+832$

$\qquad\qquad 26x = 208$

$\qquad\qquad x = 8$

The real numbers 1, x and y have a mean of 5 and a standard deviation of σ.

(i) Express in terms of x: **(a)** y **(b)** σ.

(ii) If $\sigma = \sqrt{14}$, find the value of x and the value of y, where $x < y$.

Solution:

(i) (a) Given: mean $= 5$

$$\therefore \quad \frac{1+x+y}{3} = 5$$

$$1+x+y = 15$$

$$x+y = 14$$

$$y = 14-x$$

(b) In terms of x, the numbers are 1, x and $14-x$ (as $y = 14-x$).

$$\sigma = \sqrt{\frac{\Sigma(x-\bar{x})^2}{n}}$$

$$= \sqrt{\frac{(1-5)^2 + (x-5)^2 + (14-x-5)^2}{3}} \qquad (\bar{x}=5)$$

$$= \sqrt{\frac{(-4)^2 + (x-5)^2 + (9-x)^2}{3}}$$

$$= \sqrt{\frac{16 + x^2 - 10x + 25 + 81 - 18x + x^2}{3}}$$

$$= \sqrt{\frac{2x^2 - 28x + 122}{3}}$$

(ii)   Given: $\sigma = \sqrt{14}$

$$\therefore \quad \sqrt{\frac{2x^2 - 28x + 122}{3}} = \sqrt{14}$$

$$\frac{2x^2 - 28x + 122}{3} = 14 \qquad \text{(square both sides)}$$

$$2x^2 - 28x + 122 = 42 \qquad \text{(multiply both sides by 3)}$$

$$2x^2 - 28x + 80 = 0$$

$$x^2 - 14x + 40 = 0$$

$$(x-4)(x-10) = 0$$

$$x = 4 \quad \text{or} \quad x = 10$$

$x = 4$: $y = 14 - 4 = 10$ or $x = 10$: $y = 14 - 10 = 4$

Thus, $x = 4$ and $y = 10$ (as $x < y$).

Example ▼

The real numbers a, b, c and d have a mean $= \bar{x}$ and a standard deviation $= \sigma$.
Show that the real numbers $pa+q$, $pb+q$, $pc+q$ and $pd+q$ have:

(i) mean $= p\bar{x} + q$ **(ii)** standard deviation $= p\sigma$.

Solution:

(i) a, b, c and d

$$\bar{x} = \frac{a+b+c+d}{4}$$

$$4\bar{x} = a+b+c+d$$

$pa+q$, $pb+q$, $pc+q$ and $pd+q$

$$\text{Mean} = \frac{(pa+q)+(pb+q)+(pc+q)+(pd+q)}{4}$$

$$= \frac{pa+q+pb+q+pc+q+pd+q}{4}$$

$$= \frac{pa+pb+pc+pd+4q}{4}$$

$$= \frac{p(a+b+c+d)+4q}{4}$$

$$= \frac{p(4\bar{x})+4q}{4} \qquad (a+b+c+d=4\bar{x})$$

$$= \frac{p(4\bar{x})}{4} + \frac{4q}{4}$$

$$= p\bar{x}+q$$

(ii) a, b, c and d

Mean $= \bar{x}$

Standard deviation $= \sigma = \sqrt{\dfrac{(a-\bar{x})^2+(b-\bar{x})^2+(c-\bar{x})^2+(d-\bar{x})^2}{4}}$

$pa+q$, $pb+q$, $pc+q$ and $pd+q$

Mean $= p\bar{x}+q$

Standard deviation

$$= \sqrt{\frac{(pa+q-p\bar{x}-q)^2+(pb+q-p\bar{x}-q)^2+(pc+q-p\bar{x}-q)^2+(pd+q-p\bar{x}-q)^2}{4}}$$

$$= \sqrt{\frac{(pa-p\bar{x})^2+(pb-p\bar{x})^2+(pc-p\bar{x})^2+(pd-p\bar{x})^2}{4}}$$

$$= \sqrt{\frac{p^2(a-\bar{x})^2+p^2(b-\bar{x})^2+p^2(c-\bar{x})^2+p^2(d-\bar{x})^2}{4}}$$

$$= \sqrt{p^2}\sqrt{\frac{(a-\bar{x})^2+(b-\bar{x})^2+(c-\bar{x})^2+(d-\bar{x})^2}{4}}$$

$$= p\sigma$$

The two real numbers a and b have a mean of $\bar{x}$ and a standard deviation of σ.

(i) Express $\bar{x}$ in terms of a and b.

(ii) Express σ in terms of a, b and $\bar{x}$.

(iii) Express σ in terms of a and b only.

(iv) Show that: $\bar{x}^2 - \sigma^2 = ab$.

Solution:

(i) $\quad \bar{x} = \dfrac{a+b}{2}$

(ii) $\quad \sigma = \sqrt{\dfrac{\Sigma(x-\bar{x})^2}{n}} = \sqrt{\dfrac{(a-\bar{x})^2 + (b-\bar{x})^2}{2}}$

(iii) $\quad \sigma = \sqrt{\dfrac{(a-\bar{x})^2 + (b-\bar{x})^2}{2}}$

$$= \sqrt{\dfrac{\left(a - \dfrac{a+b}{2}\right)^2 + \left(b - \dfrac{a+b}{2}\right)^2}{2}} \qquad \left(\bar{x} = \dfrac{a+b}{2}\right)$$

$$= \sqrt{\dfrac{\left(\dfrac{2a-a-b}{2}\right)^2 + \left(\dfrac{2b-a-b}{2}\right)^2}{2}}$$

$$= \sqrt{\dfrac{\left(\dfrac{a-b}{2}\right)^2 + \left(\dfrac{b-a}{2}\right)^2}{2}}$$

$$= \sqrt{\dfrac{\dfrac{a^2 - 2ab + b^2}{4} + \dfrac{b^2 - 2ab + a^2}{4}}{2}}$$

$$= \sqrt{\dfrac{a^2 - 2ab + b^2 + b^2 - 2ab + a^2}{8}} \qquad \text{(multiply each part by 4)}$$

$$= \sqrt{\dfrac{2a^2 - 4ab + 2b^2}{8}}$$

$$= \sqrt{\dfrac{a^2 - 2ab + b^2}{4}} \qquad \text{(divide top and bottom by 2)}$$

$$= \sqrt{\dfrac{(a-b)^2}{4}} = \dfrac{a-b}{2}$$

(iv)

$$\bar{x}^2 - \sigma^2$$

$$= \left(\frac{a+b}{2}\right)^2 - \left(\frac{a-b}{2}\right)^2$$

$$= \frac{a^2 + 2ab + b^2}{4} - \frac{a^2 - 2ab + b^2}{4}$$

$$= \frac{a^2 + 2ab + b^2 - a^2 + 2ab - b^2}{4}$$

$$= \frac{4ab}{4}$$

$$= ab$$

Exercise 6.4 ▼

1. $\bar{x}$ is the mean of the real numbers a, b, c and d.
   Express the mean of $4a - 3$, $4b - 3$, $4c - 3$ and $4d - 3$ in terms of $\bar{x}$.

2. The mean of the real numbers $x_1, x_2, x_3, \ldots, x_n$ is $\bar{x}$. Find the mean of:
   (i) $2 - x_1, 2 - x_2, 2 - x_3, \ldots, 2 - x_n$
   (ii) $px_1 + q, px_2 + q, px_3 + q, \ldots, px_n + q$.

3. The mean of the numbers 3, 4, x, y, 6 and 9 is y.
   The mean of the numbers 4, $x + 1$, $2y$ and 10 is 7.
   Find the value of x and y.

4. $\bar{x}$ is the mean of $3a + 2$, $3b + 2$ and $3c + 2$.
   $\bar{y}$ is the mean of $6a + 3$, $6b + 3$ and $6c + 3$.
   Express $\bar{y}$ in terms of $\bar{x}$.

5. The real numbers x_1, x_2, x_3, x_4 have a mean of $\bar{x}$. Show that: $\Sigma(x - \bar{x}) = 0$.

6. The numbers 6, 8, 12, 3, 5, $10 + x$, $10 - x$ and y have a mean of $\bar{x}$ and a standard deviation of σ.
   (i) If $\bar{x} = 8$, find the value of y.   **(ii)** If $\sigma = \sqrt{14.5}$, find the value of x, $x > 0$.

7. The real numbers a, b and c have a mean of $\bar{x}$ and a standard deviation of σ.
   Show that the mean and standard deviations of $2a - 3$, $2b - 3$ and $2c - 3$ are $2\bar{x} - 3$ and 2σ, respectively.

8. The set of numbers $x_1, x_2, x_3, \ldots, x_n$ have a mean of $\bar{x}$ and a standard deviation of σ.
   (i) Show that the set of numbers $x_1 + k, x_2 + k, x_3 + k, \ldots, x_n + k$ have:
       (a) mean $= \bar{x} + k$ **(b)** standard deviation $= \sigma$.
   (ii) Show that the set of numbers $kx_1, kx_2, kx_3, \ldots, kx_n$ have:
       (a) mean $= k\bar{x}$ **(b)** standard deviation $= k\sigma$.

9. The real numbers p, $2p$, $5p$, $10q$ and $14q$, $p, q > 0$ have a mean of $4p$ and a standard deviation of σ.
   (i) Express: **(a)** p in terms of q **(b)** σ^2 in terms of p.
   (ii) If $\sigma = \sqrt{1920}$, find the value of p and the value of q.

10. The real numbers 1, a, $3a$ and 11 have a mean of $\bar{x}$ and a standard deviation of σ.
    (i) Express in terms of a: **(a)** $\bar{x}$ **(b)** σ^2.
    (ii) If $\sigma^2 = 17$, find the two values of a.

11. The real numbers $a+2$, $2a+1$, $2a+3$ and $2-a$, $a>0$, have a mean of $\bar{x}$ and a standard deviation of σ.
    (i) Express $\bar{x}$ in terms of a.   **(ii)** If $\sigma^2 = 14$, find the value of a.

12. The numbers 6, 3, 2, 0, 1, 4, 5, 3, x, y have a mean of $\bar{x}$ and a standard deviation of σ.
    (i) If $\bar{x} = 3$, express y in terms of x.
    (ii) Express σ^2 in terms of x.
    (iii) If $\sigma^2 = \bar{x}$, find the value of x and the value of y, $x > y$.

13. The real numbers $3a$, $2a$, 5, 3 and 2, $a>0$, have a mean of $\bar{x}$ and a standard deviation of σ.
    (i) Express in terms of a: **(a)** $\bar{x}$ **(b)** σ^2.
    (ii) If $\sigma^2 = \dfrac{118}{5}$, find the value of a.

14. The real numbers p, q, 8, 7, 5 have a mean of $\bar{x}$ and a standard deviation of σ.
    (i) If $\bar{x} = 6$, express q in terms of p.
    (ii) If $\sigma = \sqrt{2}$, calculate the value of p and the value of q, $p > q$.

15. The mean of the two real numbers x_1 and x_2 is 5 and their standard deviation is σ. If $x_1^2 + x_2^2 = 58$, calculate σ.

16. The real numbers a and b have a mean of $\bar{x}$ and a standard deviation of σ.
    (i) Express $\bar{x}$ in terms of a and b.
    (ii) Show that: $\sigma^2 = \frac{1}{2}(a^2 + b^2) - \bar{x}^2$.

17. The real numbers x_1, x_2, x_3 have a mean of $\bar{x}$ and a standard deviation of σ.
$$x_1 = p + q_1, \; x_2 = p + q_2, \; x_3 = p + q_3 \text{ and } \bar{q} = \frac{q_1 + q_2 + q_3}{3}.$$
    Show that: **(i)** $\bar{x} = p + \bar{q}$ **(ii)** $\sigma^2 = \frac{1}{3}(q_1^2 + q_2^2 + q_3^2) - \bar{q}^2$.

18. a, b and c are three real numbers with a mean of $\bar{x}$ and a standard deviation of σ.
    If $a + b + c = 9$ and $a^2 + b^2 + c^2 = 4(a + b + c)$:
    (i) calculate $\bar{x}$ **(ii)** show that $\sigma^2 = \bar{x}$.

Difference Equations

A **difference equation** (often called a recurrence equation) is an equation which will generate any term in a sequence from one or more previous terms.
For example, $u_{n+2} = 5u_{n+1} - 6u_n$ is a difference equation.

To get started, we need to know one or two terms at the beginning of the sequence. For example, $u_1 = 3$, $u_2 = 5$. These terms at the beginning are called the **initial conditions**. To get a particular term, it is normally necessary to calculate all the previous terms, which can be very tedious and time-consuming.

Solving a Difference Equation

Solving a difference equation means finding an expression for u_n in terms of n only. From this expression for u_n we can generate the sequence or find a particular term by substituting values for n. In other words, we do **not** need to know all the previous terms to find a particular term.

On our course, we have to solve second-order difference equations with constant coefficients. A **second-order difference equation** with constant coefficients is one of the form:

$$pu_{n+2} + qu_{n+1} + ru_n = 0, \text{ where } p, q \text{ and } r \text{ are constants.}$$

From this equation we can evaluate u_{n+2} if we are given values for u_n and u_{n+1}.

Theorem:

If a and b are the roots of the quadratic equation:
$$px^2 + qx + r = 0$$
and
$$u_n = la^n + mb^n$$
then $pu_{n+2} + qu_{n+1} + ru_n = 0.$

To solve a difference equation of the form $pu_{n+2} + qu_{n+1} + ru_n = 0$, do the following:

1. Solve the **characteristic equation** $px^2 + qx + r = 0$ to find a and b.
2. Write down the general solution $u_n = la^n + mb^n$ and put in the values of a and b.
3. Substitute, separately, the initial conditions into $u_n = la^n + mb^n$ to find two equations in l and m.
4. Solve these equations to find the value of l and m and write down the unique solution.

Example ▼

(i) Solve the difference equation $u_{n+2} - 5u_{n+1} + 6u_n = 0$ for $n \geqslant 1$, given that $u_1 = 2$ and $u_2 = 16$.
(ii) Verify that the solution obtained in (i) satisfies the difference equation.
(iii) Find u_8.

Solution:

(i) Difference equation: $\qquad u_{n+2} - 5u_{n+1} + 6u_n = 0$

Characteristic equation: $\qquad x^2 - 5x + 6 = 0$

$$(x-3)(x-2) = 0$$
$$x = 3 \quad \text{or} \quad x = 2$$
$$\therefore \quad a = 3 \quad \text{and} \quad b = 2$$

(Makes no difference which you label a or b)

General solution: $\qquad u_n = la^n + mb^n = l(3)^n + m(2)^n$

Substitute separately the initial conditions, $u_1 = 2$ and $u_2 = 16$.

$$u_1 = 2 \qquad\qquad\qquad u_2 = 16$$

$$\therefore \quad l(3)^1 + m(2)^1 = 2 \qquad \therefore \quad l(3)^2 + m(2)^2 = 16$$

$$3l + 2m = 2 \quad \text{①} \qquad\qquad 9l + 4m = 16 \quad \text{②}$$

Now solve the simultaneous equations ① and ② to find l and m.

$$-6l - 4m = -4 \quad ① \times -2$$
$$9l + 4m = 16 \quad ②$$
$$\overline{}$$
$$3l = 12$$
$$l = 4$$

$$3l + 2m = 2 \quad ①$$
$$3(4) + 2m = 2$$
$$12 + 2m = 2$$
$$2m = -10$$
$$m = -5$$

Thus, $l = 4$ and $m = -5$

Therefore, the unique solution is $u_n = 4(3)^n - 5(2)^n$.

(ii) Verifying the unique solution:

The basic idea is to express u_{n+1} and u_{n+2} in terms of 3^n and 2^n, the lowest powers of 3 and 2 in u_n, and then substitute these into the given expression.

To find u_{n+1} replace n with $(n+1)$; to find u_{n+2} replace n with $(n+2)$.

$$u_n = 4(3)^n - 5(2)^n$$

$$u_{n+1} = 4(3)^{n+1} - 5(2)^{n+1} = 4.3^1(3)^n - 5.2^1(2)^n = 4.3(3)^n - 5.2(2)^n = 12(3)^n - 10(2)^n$$

$$u_{n+2} = 4(3)^{n+2} - 5(2)^{n+2} = 4.3^2(3)^n - 5.2^2(2)^n = 4.9(3)^n - 5.4(2)^n = 36(3)^n - 20(2)^n$$

$$u_{n+2} \qquad - \qquad 5(u_{n+1}) \qquad + \qquad 6(u_n)$$
$$\downarrow \qquad\qquad\qquad \downarrow \qquad\qquad\qquad \downarrow$$

$$= [36(3)^n - 20(2)^n] - 5[12(3)^n - 10(2)^n] + 6[4(3)^n - 5(2)^n]$$

$$= 36(3)^n - 20(2)^n - 60(3)^n + 50(2)^n + 24(3)^n - 30(2)^n$$

$$= 60(3)^n - 60(3)^n + 50(2)^n - 50(2)^n$$

$$= 0$$

Thus, $u_n = 4(3)^n - 5(2)^n$ satisfies the difference equation.

(iii) $u_n = 4(3)^n - 5(2)^n$

$$u_8 = 4(3)^8 - 5(2)^8 \qquad\qquad\qquad \text{(put in } n = 8 \text{ on both sides)}$$

$$= 4(6561) - 5(256)$$

$$= 26244 - 1280$$

$$= 24964$$

In the next two examples we use the fact that $(\text{any real number})^0 = 1$.

Note: 0^0 is not defined.

Example ▼

Solve the difference equation $2u_{n+2} + 9u_{n+1} - 5u_n = 0$, for $n \geqslant 0$, given that $u_0 = 7$ and $u_1 = -13$.

Solution:

Difference equation: $\qquad\qquad\qquad 2u_{n+2} + 9u_{n+1} - 5u_n = 0$

Characteristic equation: $\qquad\qquad\qquad 2x^2 + 9x - 5 = 0$

$$(2x - 1)(x + 5) = 0$$

$$2x - 1 = 0 \quad \text{or} \quad x + 5 = 0$$

$$x = \frac{1}{2} \quad \text{or} \qquad x = -5$$

$$\therefore \quad a = \frac{1}{2} \quad \text{and} \quad b = -5$$

General solution: $\quad u_n = l(a)^n + m(b)^n = l(\tfrac{1}{2})^n + m(-5)^n$

Substitute separately the initial conditions, $u_0 = 7$ and $u_1 = -13$.

$$u_0 = 7 \qquad\qquad\qquad\qquad u_1 = -13$$

$$\therefore \quad l(\tfrac{1}{2})^0 + m(-5)^0 = 7 \qquad\qquad \therefore \quad l(\tfrac{1}{2})^1 + m(-5)^1 = -13$$

$$l + m = 7 \quad ① \qquad\qquad\qquad \tfrac{1}{2}l - 5m = -13$$

$$\qquad\qquad\qquad\qquad\qquad\qquad l - 10m = -26 \quad ②$$

Now solve the simultaneous equations ① and ② to find l and m:

$$l + m = 7 \qquad ① \qquad\qquad\qquad\qquad l + m = 7$$

$$\underline{-l + 10m = 26 \qquad ② \times -1} \qquad\qquad\qquad l + 3 = 7$$

$$11m = 33 \qquad\qquad\qquad\qquad\qquad l = 4$$

$$m = 3$$

Thus, $l = 4$ and $m = 3$.

The unique solution is $u_n = 4(\tfrac{1}{2})^n + 3(-5)^n$.

Note: If the characteristic equation does not have rational roots (fractions), then we use the '$-b$' formula. However, do not use your calculator. Leave your answers in surd form. It simplifies the work and avoids approximate answers.

Solve the difference equation $u_{n+2} - 4u_{n+1} + u_n = 0$, for $n \geqslant 0$, given that $u_0 = 4$ and $u_1 = 2u_0$.

Solution:

Difference equation: $\qquad\qquad u_{n+2} - 4u_{n+1} + u_n = 0$

Characteristic equation: $\qquad\qquad x^2 - 4x + 1 = 0$

$x^2 - 4x + 1 = 0$ does not have rational roots, so we use the '$-b$' formula.

$$x^2 - 4x + 1 = 0$$

$$x = \frac{4 \pm \sqrt{4^2 - 4(1)(1)}}{2(1)} = \frac{4 \pm \sqrt{16 - 4}}{2} = \frac{4 \pm \sqrt{12}}{2} = \frac{4 \pm 2\sqrt{3}}{2} = 2 \pm \sqrt{3}$$

$$\therefore \quad a = 2 + \sqrt{3} \quad \text{and} \quad b = 2 - \sqrt{3}$$

General solution: $\quad u_n = la^n + mb^n = l(2 + \sqrt{3})^n + m(2 - \sqrt{3})^n$

Substitute separately the initial conditions, $u_0 = 4$ and $u_1 = 2u_0 = 2(4) = 8$.

$u_0 = 4$	$u_1 = 8$
$\therefore \quad l(2 + \sqrt{3})^0 + m(2 - \sqrt{3})^0 = 4$	$\therefore \quad l(2 + \sqrt{3})^1 + m(2 - \sqrt{3})^1 = 8$
$l(1) + m(1) = 4$	$2l + \sqrt{3}l + 2m - \sqrt{3}m = 8$
$l + m = 4$	$2l + \sqrt{3}l + 2(4 - l) - \sqrt{3}(4 - l) = 8$
$m = 4 - l$	[replace m with $(4 - l)$]
	$2l + \sqrt{3}l + 8 - 2l - 4\sqrt{3} + \sqrt{3}l = 8$
	$2\sqrt{3}l - 4\sqrt{3} = 0$
	$2\sqrt{3}l = 4\sqrt{3}$
	$l = 2$
	$m = 4 - l = 4 - 2 = 2$

Thus, $l = 2$ and $m = 2$.

Therefore, the unique solution is $u_n = 2(2 + \sqrt{3})^n + 2(2 - \sqrt{3})^n$.

1. If $u_n = 3(2)^n + 5$, write down u_0, u_1, u_2 and u_3.

2. If $u_n = 4(5)^n - 3(-2)^n$, write down u_0, u_1 and u_3.

3. $u_{n+2} - 7u_{n+1} + 10u_n = 0$, for $n \geq 0$, is a difference equation.
   (i)   Write down and solve the characteristic equation.
   (ii) If $u_0 = 1$ and $u_1 = 14$, find the solution of the difference equation.
         Write your answer in the form $u_n = la^n + mb^n$, where a and b are the roots of the equation in (i).
   (iii) Find u_5.

4. Solve the difference equation $u_{n+2} = 3u_{n+1} - 2u_n$, for $n \geq 1$, given that $2u_1 = u_2 = 2$.
   Write your solution in the form k^{n-1}, where $k \in \mathbf{N}$. Evaluate $\sqrt{u_{13}}$.

5. Solve the difference equation $u_{n+2} = 2u_{n+1} + 3u_n$, for $n \geq 0$, given that $u_0 = 1$ and $u_1 = 11$.

6. Verify that $u_n = 5^n + 2^n$ satisfies the difference equation $u_{n+2} - 7u_{n+1} + 10u_n = 0$.

7. (i)   Solve the difference equation $u_{n+2} - 6u_{n+1} + 5u_n = 0$, for $n \geq 1$, given that $u_1 = 0$ and $u_2 = 20$.
   (ii) Verify that the solution you have obtained in (i) satisfies the difference equation.
   (iii) Find u_5.

8. (i)   Solve the difference equation $s_{n+2} - 5s_{n+1} + 6s_n = 0$, for $n \geq 0$, given that $s_1 = 1$ and $s_2 = 5$.
   (ii) Verify that the solution you have obtained in (i) satisfies the difference equation.
   (iii) Evaluate s_6.

9. (i)   Solve the difference equation $2u_{n+2} - 11u_{n+1} + 5u_n = 0$, for $n \geq 0$, given that $u_0 = 2$ and $u_1 = -4u_0$.
   (ii) Hence, express u_3 in the form $-\dfrac{p}{q}$, where $p, q \in \mathbf{N}$.

10. Solve the difference equation $2u_{n+2} - 13u_{n+1} + 15u_n = 0$, for $n \geq 0$, given that $u_0 = 2$ and $u_1 = -4$.

11. Solve the difference equation $6u_{n+2} - 7u_{n+1} + 2u_n = 0$, for $n \geq 0$, given that $u_0 = 8$ and $u_1 = 5$.
    Express u_2 in the form $\dfrac{p}{q}$, where $p, q \in \mathbf{N}$.

12. (i)   If $u_n = l(3)^n + m(2)^n$, write down u_{n+1} and u_{n+2}.
    (ii) Hence, show that: $u_{n+2} - 5u_{n+1} + 6u_n = 0$.

13. (i)   Solve the equation $x^2 - 2x - 1 = 0$.
    (ii) Solve the difference equation $u_{n+2} - 2u_{n+1} - u_n = 0$, for $n \geq 0$, given that $u_0 = u_1 = 2$.

14. Solve the difference equation $u_{n+2} - 6u_{n+1} + 4u_n = 0$, for $n \geq 0$, given that $u_0 = \frac{1}{3}u_1 = 2$.

15. Solve the difference equation $u_{n+2} - 6u_{n+1} + 7u_n = 0$, for $n \geq 0$, given that $u_0 = 0$ and $u_1 = 4$.

16. (i) $u_n = k(7)^n - 2^n$. If $u_3 = 1707$, find the value of k.
    (ii) Verify that the solution you obtained in (i) satisfies the difference equation
          $u_{n+2} - 9u_{n+1} + 14u_n = 0$.

17. $u_n = h(3)^n + k(5)^n$ is a solution of the difference equation $u_{n+2} + pu_{n+1} + qu_n = 0$, for $n \geqslant 0$.

    (i)   Find the value of p and the value of q.

    (ii) If $u_0 = u_1 = 1$, find the value of h and the value of k.

18. If the general solution of the difference equation $2u_{n+2} - 7u_{n+1} + ku_n = 0$, for $n \geqslant 0$, is

    $u_n = l(\frac{1}{2})^n + m(3)^n$, find the value of k, $k \in \mathbf{R}$.

    If $u_0 = 3$ and $u_1 = 4$, find the unique solution.

19. **(i)**   Solve the equation $x^2 = x + 1$.

    (ii) The Fibonacci sequence is defined by the difference equation

        $u_{n+2} = u_{n+1} + u_n$,   for $n \geqslant 1$, where $u_1 = u_2 = 1$.

        (a) Write down the first eight terms of the sequence.

        (b) Show that the unique solution of the difference equation $u_{n+2} = u_{n+1} + u_n$, for $n \geqslant 1$ and

        given that $u_1 = u_2 = 1$, is:

$$u_n = \frac{1}{\sqrt{5}} \left(\frac{1 + \sqrt{5}}{2} \right)^n - \frac{1}{\sqrt{5}} \left(\frac{1 - \sqrt{5}}{2} \right)^n.$$

20. $u_0 = 0$, $u_1 = 1$, $u_2 = 7$ and $u_3 = 37$ satisfy the difference equation $u_{n+2} + pu_{n+1} + qu_n = 0$.

    Find the value of p and the value of q. Find the unique solution of the difference equation.

7

SEQUENCES AND SERIES

Sequence

> A sequence is a set of numbers, separated by commas, in which each number after the first is formed by some definite rule.

Note: Each number in the set is called a **term** of the sequence.

1. 5, 9, 13, 17, . . .
   Each number after the first is obtained by adding 4 to the previous number.
   In this example, 5 is called the **first term**, 9 the **second term** and so on.

2. 1, 3, 9, 27, . . .
   Each number after the first is obtained by multiplying the previous number by 3.
   In this example, 1 is called the **first term**, 3 the **second term** and so on.

General Term, u_n

The terms of a sequence can be expressed as $u_1, u_2, u_3, u_4, \ldots$
A sequence which follows a regular pattern can be described by a rule, or formula, called the **general term**. We use the symbol u_n to denote the general term. u_n may be used to generate terms of the sequence (sometimes T_n is used instead of u_n).
Consider the sequence whose general term is: $u_n = n^2 + 3n$.
To generate any term of the sequence, put in the appropriate value for n on both sides:

$$u_n = n^2 + 3n \qquad \text{(general term)}$$
$$u_1 = (1)^2 + 3(1) = 1 + 3 = 4 \qquad \text{(first term, put in } n = 1 \text{ on both sides)}$$
$$u_4 = (4)^2 + 3(4) = 16 + 12 = 28 \qquad \text{(fourth term, put in } n = 4 \text{ on both sides)}$$
$$u_7 = (7)^2 + 3(7) = 49 + 21 = 70 \qquad \text{(seventh term, put in } n = 7 \text{ on both sides)}$$

The notation $u_n = n^2 + 3n$ is very similar to function notation where n is the input and u_n is the output, i.e. (input, output) = (n, u_n).

Note: n used with this meaning must always be a non-negative whole number.
It can never be negative or fractional. In other words, $n \in \mathbf{N}$.

A sequence is given by $u_n = n^2 - 3n$, where $n \in \mathbf{N}_0$.

(i) Find u_{10}.　　**(ii)** For what value of $n \in \mathbf{N}_0$ is $u_n = 40$?

Solution:

(i) $u_n = n^2 - 3n$

$u_{10} = (10)^2 - 3(10)$

$\quad = 100 - 30$

$\quad = 70$

Given:　　$u_n = 40$

$\therefore \quad\quad n^2 - 3n = 40$

$\quad\quad n^2 - 3n - 40 = 0$

$\quad\quad (n+5)(n-8) = 0$

$\quad\quad n = -5 \quad \text{or} \quad n = 8$

Thus, $n = 8$, as $n \in \mathbf{N}_0$.

If $u_n = (n - 10)3^n$, verify that: $u_{n+2} - 6u_{n+1} + 9u_n = 0$.

Solution:

The basic idea is to express u_{n+1} and u_{n+2} in terms of n and 3^n, the lowest power of 3, and substitute these into the given expression.

To find u_{n+1}, replace n with $(n + 1)$; to find u_{n+2}, replace n with $(n + 2)$.

$u_n = (n - 10)3^n$

$u_{n+1} = [(n+1) - 10]3^{n+1} = (n + 1 - 10)3^1 \cdot 3^n = (n - 9)3 \cdot 3^n = 3(n-9)3^n$

$u_{n+2} = [(n+2) - 10]3^{n+2} = (n + 2 - 10)3^2 \cdot 3^n = (n - 8)9 \cdot 3^n = 9(n-8)3^n$

$$
\begin{array}{ccccc}
u_{n+2} & - & 6u_{n+1} & + & 9u_n \\
\downarrow & & \downarrow & & \downarrow
\end{array}
$$

$= [9(n-8)3^n] - 6[3(n-9)3^n] + 9[(n-10)3^n]$

$= 9(n-8)3^n - 18(n-9)3^n + 9(n-10)3^n$

$= 3^n[9(n-8) - 18(n-9) + 9(n-10)]$ 　　　　(factor out 3^n)

$= 3^n[9n - 72 - 18n + 162 + 9n - 90]$

$= 3^n[18n - 18n + 162 - 162]$

$= 3^n[0]$

$= 0$

If $u_n = \dfrac{n}{n+1}$, show that $u_{n+1} > u_n$.

Solution:

$$u_n = \frac{n}{n+1} \qquad \therefore \quad u_{n+1} = \frac{(n+1)}{(n+1)+1} = \frac{n+1}{n+2}$$

$$u_{n+1} > u_n$$

$$\frac{n+1}{n+2} > \frac{n}{n+1}$$

$$(n+1)(n+1) > n(n+2) \qquad \left(\begin{array}{l} \text{multiply both sides by } (n+2) \text{ and } (n+1); \\ (n+2) \text{ and } (n+1) \text{ are both positive as } n \in \mathbf{N}_0. \end{array} \right)$$

$$n^2 + 2n + 1 > n^2 + 2n$$

$$1 > 0 \quad \text{true} \qquad \text{(subtract } n^2 \text{ and } 2n \text{ from both sides)}$$

$$\therefore \quad u_{n+1} > u_n$$

Notes: If $u_{n+1} > u_n$, for all $n \in \mathbf{N}$, then the sequence u_n is (monotonic) increasing.
If $u_{n+1} < u_n$, for all $n \in \mathbf{N}$, then the sequence u_n is (monotonic) decreasing.

Exercise 7.1 ▼

1. If $u_n = 3n + 2$, find u_1 and u_2. Show that $u_{n+1} - u_n = 3$.

2. **(i)** If $u_n = n^2 - 3$, find u_1, u_2 and u_{n+1}.
   (ii) If $u_{n+1} - u_n = an + b$, $a, b \in \mathbf{R}$, find the value of a and the value of b.
   (iii) If $u_n = 222$, find the value of n, $n \in \mathbf{N}$.

3. **(i)** If $u_n = n^2 + 5n$, find u_1, u_2 and u_{n+1}.
   (ii) If $u_{n+1} - u_n = pn + q$, $p, q \in \mathbf{R}$, find the value of p and the value of q.
   (iii) If $u_n = 66$, find the value of n, $n \in \mathbf{N}$.
   (iv) Show that: $u_{n+1} > u_n$.

4. $u_n = an^2 + bn$, where $a, b \in \mathbf{R}$. If $u_1 = 7$ and $u_2 = 20$:
   (i) find the values of a and b **(ii)** find the value of $n \in \mathbf{N}$ if $u_n = 64$.

5. If $u_n = 2^n + 1$, find u_1, u_2 and u_{n+1}. Show that $u_{n+1} > u_n$.

6. If $u_n = (5n - 2)3^n$, show that $u_{n+1} - 3u_n = 5(3)^{n+1}$.

7. If $u_n = (n + 1)5^n$, show that $u_{n+2} - 10u_{n+1} + 25u_n = 0$.

8. If $u_n = \frac{1}{3}(9^n - 3^n)$, show that $u_{n+1} = 3u_n + 2(9)^n$.

9. If $u_n = 2^{2n-1} + 2^{n-1}$, show that $u_{n+1} - 2u_n - 2^{2n} = 0$.

10. If $u_n = 3 + n(n-1)^2$, show that $u_{n+1} - u_n = 3n^2 - n$.

11. If $u_n = n^2 + 4n$, find u_1 and u_2. Simplify: $(u_{n+2} - u_{n+1}) - (u_{n+1} - u_n)$.

12. If $u_n = 4(n+1)!$, show that $u_{n+1} - nu_n = 2u_n$.

13. If $u_n = \dfrac{1}{n}$, show that $u_{n+1} < u_n$, where $n \in \mathbf{N}_0$.

14. If $u_n = \dfrac{1}{n^2}$, show that $u_{n+1} < u_n$, where $n \in \mathbf{N}_0$.

15. If $u_n = \dfrac{1}{2^n}$, show that $u_{n+1} < u_n$, where $n \in \mathbf{N}_0$.

16. If $u_n = \dfrac{n+3}{2n+1}$, show that $u_{n+1} < u_n$, where $n \in \mathbf{N}_0$.

17. The nth term of a sequence is given by $u_n = a(2)^n + bn + c$, where $a, b, c \in \mathbf{R}$.
If $u_1 = 0$, $u_2 = 10$ and $u_3 = 26$, find:
(i) the value of a, b and c **(ii)** u_4.

Series and Sigma (Σ) Notation

When the terms of a sequence are added together the sum of the terms is called a **series**.

For example,   Sequence : $1, 4, 7, 10, \ldots$
                         Series : $1 + 4 + 7 + 10 + \cdots$

A **finite series** is one which ends after a finite number of terms.
An **infinite series** is one that continues indefinitely.
The sum of the first n terms of a series is denoted by S_n, where:

$$S_n = u_1 + u_2 + u_3 + \cdots + u_n$$

This is an example of a finite series, as there is a finite number of terms.
The finite series S_n can be expressed more concisely using sigma (Σ) notation.

$$S_n = u_1 + u_2 + u_3 + \cdots + u_n = \sum_{r=1}^{n} u_r$$

Notes: The letter r (called a **dummy variable**) does not appear when $\displaystyle\sum_{r=1}^{n} u_r$ is written out.

$\displaystyle\sum_{r=1}^{n} u_r = u_1 + u_2 + u_3 + \cdots + u_n$.

Any other letter could also have been used, for example $\displaystyle\sum_{i=1}^{n} u_i$ or $\displaystyle\sum_{k=1}^{n} u_k$.

$\displaystyle\sum_{r=1}^{n} u_r$ is read as:

'the sum of u_r from $r=1$ to $r=n$' or 'sigma u_r from $r=1$ to $r=n$'.

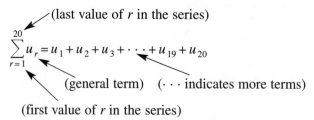

(last value of r in the series)

$$\sum_{r=1}^{20} u_r = u_1 + u_2 + u_3 + \cdots + u_{19} + u_{20}$$

(general term)   ($\cdots$ indicates more terms)

(first value of r in the series)

The values of r increase in steps of 1 from the first term to the last term.

$$\sum_{r=3}^{8} u_r = u_3 + u_4 + u_5 + u_6 + u_7 + u_8$$

i.e., start at the third term, u_3, finish at the eighth term, u_8, and add these terms.

The notation can also be used to describe an infinite series.

$$\sum_{r=1}^{\infty} u_r = u_1 + u_2 + u_3 + \cdots + u_n + \cdots$$

($\cdots$ indicates that the series continues indefinitely)

In this notation, ∞ indicates that there is no upper limit for r.

Note: $S_1 = u_1,$ $S_2 = u_1 + u_2,$ $S_3 = u_1 + u_2 + u_3,$ etc.

Example ▼

Evaluate: **(i)** $\displaystyle\sum_{r=0}^{5}(2r+1)$ **(ii)** $\displaystyle\sum_{r=1}^{4}(-1)^{r+1}\,2^r.$

Solution:

$$\sum_{r=0}^{5}(2r+1) = [2(0)+1] + [2(1)+1] + [2(2)+1] + [2(3)+1] + [2(4)+1] + [2(5)+1]$$
$$= (0+1) + (2+1) + (4+1) + (6+1) + (8+1) + (10+1)$$
$$= 1+3+5+7+9+11$$
$$= 36$$

$$\sum_{r=1}^{4}(-1)^{r+1}\,2^r = (-1)^{1+1}(2)^1 + (-1)^{2+1}(2)^2 + (-1)^{3+1}(2)^3 + (-1)^{4+1}(2)^4$$
$$= (-1)^2(2) + (-1)^3(4) + (-1)^4(8) + (-1)^5(16)$$
$$= (1)(2) + (-1)(4) + (1)(8) + (-1)(16)$$
$$= 2 - 4 + 8 - 16$$
$$= -10$$

Notice that in the second example the series alternates between positive and negative terms.

$(-1)^k = 1$ when k is even.

$(-1)^k = -1$ when k is odd.

Find u_n when Given S_n

$$S_n = u_1 + u_2 + u_3 + \cdots + u_{n-1} + u_n$$

$$\underline{S_{n-1} = u_1 + u_2 + u_3 + \cdots + u_{n-1}}$$

$S_n - S_{n-1} =$ u_n (subtracting)

> If $S_n = u_1 + u_2 + u_3 + \cdots + u_n$, then:
> $$u_n = S_n - S_{n-1}$$

This gives us a nice method to find the general term, u_n, when given S_n in terms of n.

Example ▼

$S_n = u_1 + u_2 + u_3 + \cdots + u_n$.

If $S_n = 2n^2 - 3n$, find an expression for u_n, and hence find u_{10}.

Solution:

$$S_n = 2n^2 - 3n$$
$$S_{n-1} = 2(n-1)^2 - 3(n-1) \qquad \text{[replace } n \text{ with } (n-1)\text{]}$$
$$= 2(n^2 - 2n + 1) - 3(n-1)$$
$$= 2n^2 - 4n + 2 - 3n + 3$$
$$= 2n^2 - 7n + 5$$

$$u_n = S_n - S_{n-1}$$
$$= (2n^2 - 3n) - (2n^2 - 7n + 5)$$
$$= 2n^2 - 3n - 2n^2 + 7n - 5$$
$$u_n = 4n - 5$$

Thus, $u_{10} = 4(10) - 5 = 40 - 5 = 35$.

Exercise 7.2 ▼

Evaluate each of the following:

1. $\displaystyle\sum_{r=1}^{6}(2r+1)$

2. $\displaystyle\sum_{r=0}^{5}(3r-2)$

3. $\displaystyle\sum_{r=1}^{6}r^2$

4. $\displaystyle\sum_{r=1}^{5}n(n+1)$

5. $\displaystyle\sum_{r=1}^{4}(-1)^{r+1}r^3$

6. $\displaystyle\sum_{r=0}^{6}(-1)^r 2^r$

7. Evaluate: **(i)** $\sum_{r=2}^{5}(-1)^r(r+1)(r+3)$ **(ii)** $\sum_{r=3}^{7}\dfrac{(-1)^r}{r-1}$.

8. For a sequence, $u_n = 2n + 5$. Find: **(i)** S_1 **(ii)** S_4.

9. For a sequence, $u_n = 3(2)^n$. Find: **(i)** S_2 **(ii)** S_3.

10. For a sequence, $u_n = \dfrac{n}{n+1}$. Find the value of S_3.

In each of the following find u_n, given $S_n = u_1 + u_2 + u_3 + \cdots + u_n$:

11. $S_n = n^2 + 2n$ **12.** $S_n = n^2 - 5n$ **13.** $S_n = 2n^2 + n$

14. For the series $S_n = u_1 + u_2 + \cdots + u_n$, $S_n = \dfrac{n(n+1)}{2}$.

     Find: **(i)** S_{n-1} **(ii)** u_n **(iii)** u_{20}.

15. For the series $S_n = u_1 + u_2 + \cdots + u_n$, $S_n = 2^n$.
     Find: **(i)** S_{n-1} **(ii)** u_n **(iii)** u_{10} **(iv)** $\sqrt{u_9}$.

16. For the series $S_n = u_1 + u_2 + \cdots + u_n$, $S_n = 2(2)^n + n^2$.
     Find an expression for u_n and, hence, evaluate u_8.

Arithmetic Sequences and Series

Consider the sequence of numbers 2, 5, 8, 11, . . .
Each term, after the first, can be found by adding 3 to the previous term.
This is an example of an arithmetic sequence.

> A sequence in which each term, after the first, is found by
> adding a constant number is called an **arithmetic sequence**.

The first term of an arithmetic sequence is denoted by a.
The constant number, which is added to each term, is called the **common difference** and is denoted by d.
Consider the arithmetic sequence 3, 5, 7, 9, 11, . . .

$$a = 3 \quad \text{and} \quad d = 2$$

Each term after the first is found by adding 2 to the previous term.
Consider the arithmetic sequence 7, 2, –3, –8, . . .

$$a = 7 \quad \text{and} \quad d = -5$$

Each term after the first is found by subtracting 5 from the previous term.
In an arithmetic sequence the common difference, d, between any two consecutive terms is always the same.

> Any term – previous term $= u_n - u_{n-1} = $ constant $= d$.

> If three terms, u_n, u_{n+1}, u_{n+2}, are in arithmetic sequence, then:
>
> $$u_{n+2} - u_{n+1} = u_{n+1} - u_n.$$

General Term of an Arithmetic Sequence

In an arithmetic sequence a is the first term and d is the common difference.
Thus, in an arithmetic sequence:

$$u_1 = a \qquad\qquad = a$$
$$u_2 = a + d \qquad = a + d$$
$$u_3 = (a + d) + d \quad = a + 2d$$
$$u_4 = (a + 2d) + d = a + 3d \quad \text{and so on.}$$

Notice that the coefficient of d is always **one less** than the term number.
Thus, the general term of an arithmetic sequence is given by:

$$\boxed{u_n = a + (n - 1)d}$$

For example: $u_8 = a + 7d$, $\qquad\qquad u_{10} = a + 9d$.

Note: If $u_n = pn + q$, where p and q are constants, then the sequence is arithmetic.

Arithmetic Series

If the sequence u_1, u_2, u_3, . . ., u_n is arithmetic, then the corresponding series,

$S_n = u_1 + u_2 + u_3 + \cdots + u_n$, is an arithmetic series.

The formula for S_n of an arithmetic series can be written in terms of the first term, a, and the common difference, d.

> If $S_n = u_1 + u_2 + u_3 + \cdots + u_n$ is an arithmetic series, then:
>
> $$S_n = \frac{n}{2}[2a + (n - 1)d].$$

To derive this result:

$$S_n = \quad [a] \quad + \quad [a + d] \quad + \cdots + [a + (n - 2)d] + [a + (n - 1)d]$$
$$S_n = [a + (n - 1)d] \; + \; [a + (n - 2)d] \; + \cdots + \quad [a + d] \quad + \quad [a] \qquad \text{(in reverse)}$$
$$\overline{2S_n = [2a + (n - 1)d] + [2a + (n - 1)d] + \cdots + [2a + (n - 1)d] + [2a + (n - 1)d]} \qquad \text{(add)}$$
$$2S_n = n[2a + (n - 1)d]$$
$$S_n = \frac{n}{2}[2a + (n - 1)d]$$

Once we find the first term, a, and the common difference, d, we can answer any question about an arithmetic sequence or series.

Note: If $S_n = pn^2 + qn$, where p and q are constants, then the series is arithmetic.

Example ▼

If $k+2$, $2k+3$, $5k-2$ are three consecutive terms in an arithmetic sequence, find the value of k, $k \in \mathbf{R}$.

Solution:

We use the fact that in an arithmetic sequence the difference between any two consecutive terms is always the same.

Thus:
$$u_{n+2} - u_{n+1} = u_{n+1} - u_n \qquad \text{(common difference)}$$

$$(5k-2) - (2k+3) = (2k+3) - (k+2) \qquad \text{(put in given values)}$$
$$5k - 2 - 2k - 3 = 2k + 3 - k - 2$$
$$3k - 5 = k + 1$$
$$2k = 6$$
$$k = 3$$

Check: When $k = 3$, the terms are 5, 9, 13, which are in arithmetic sequence.

Example ▼

In an arithmetic series, the sum of the first six terms is given by $S_6 = 57$ and the fifth term is given by $u_5 = 14$.
Find the first term, a, and the common difference, d.

Solution:

$$S_n = \frac{n}{2}[2a + (n-1)d] \qquad\qquad u_n = a + (n-1)d$$

Given: $\qquad\qquad S_6 = 57$ **Given:** $\qquad u_5 = 14$

$$\therefore \quad \frac{6}{2}(2a + 5d) = 57 \qquad\qquad \therefore \quad a + 4d = 14 \quad ②$$

$$3(2a + 5d) = 57$$

$$2a + 5d = 19 \quad ①$$

We now solve the simultaneous equations ① and ② to find a and d.

$$
\begin{array}{ll}
2a + 8d = 28 & ② \times 2 \\
-2a - 5d = -19 & ① \times -1 \\
\hline
3d = 9 & \\
d = 3 &
\end{array}
\qquad\qquad
\begin{array}{l}
a + 4d = 14 \quad ② \\
a + 4(3) = 14 \\
a + 12 = 14 \\
a = 2
\end{array}
$$

Thus, the first term is $a = 2$ and the common difference is $d = 3$.

Find the sum of the series $5 + 8 + 11 + \cdots + 65$.

Solution:

We are given $a = 5$ and $d = 3$. We need to find which term of the series is 65.

Given: $\qquad\qquad u_n = 65$

$$\therefore \quad a + (n-1)d = 65 \qquad \text{(we know } a \text{ and } d; \text{ find } n)$$
$$5 + (n-1)(3) = 65 \qquad \text{(put in } a = 5 \text{ and } d = 3)$$
$$5 + 3n - 3 = 65$$
$$3n + 2 = 65$$
$$3n = 63$$
$$n = 21$$

Thus, there are 21 terms in the series. We need to find S_{21}.

$$S_n = \frac{n}{2}[2a + (n-1)d]$$
$$S_{21} = \frac{21}{2}[2(5) + (20)(3)]$$
$$= \frac{21}{2}(10 + 60)$$
$$= \frac{21}{2}(70)$$
$$= 735$$

To verify that a sequence is arithmetic, we must show the following:

$$\boxed{u_n - u_{n-1} = \text{constant.}}$$

To show that a sequence is **not arithmetic**, it is necessary only to show that the difference between any two consecutive terms is not the same. In practice, this usually involves showing that $u_3 - u_2 \neq u_2 - u_1$ or similar.

(i) The nth term of a sequence is $u_n = 3n - 2$. Verify that the sequence is arithmetic.

(ii) The nth term of a sequence is $u_n = n^2 - 2n + 5$. Verify that the sequence is **not** arithmetic.

Solution:

(i) $\quad u_n = 3n - 2$
$$u_{n-1} = 3(n-1) - 2$$
$$= 3n - 3 - 2$$
$$= 3n - 5$$

(ii) $\quad u_n = n^2 - 2n + 5$
$$u_{n-1} = (n-1)^2 - 2(n-1) + 5$$
$$= n^2 - 2n + 1 - 2n + 2 + 5$$
$$= n^2 - 4n + 8$$

$$\begin{array}{cc} u_n & - & u_{n-1} \\ \downarrow & & \downarrow \end{array}$$

$= (3n-2)-(3n-5)$

$= 3n-2-3n+5$

$= 3 \quad$ (a constant)

$u_n - u_{n-1} =$ a constant

Thus, u_n is an arithmetic sequence.

$$\begin{array}{cc} u_n & - & u_{n+1} \\ \downarrow & & \downarrow \end{array}$$

$= (n^2-2n+5)-(n^2-4n+8)$

$= n^2-2n+5-n^2+4n-8$

$= 2n-3 \quad$ (not a constant)

$u_n - u_{n-1} \neq$ a constant

Thus, u_n is not an arithmetic sequence.

Alternative method for **(ii)**:

$u_1 = (1)^2 - 2(1) + 5$

$\quad = 1 - 2 + 5$

$\quad = 4$

$u_2 = (2)^2 - 2(2) + 5$

$\quad = 4 - 4 + 5$

$\quad = 5$

$u_3 = (3)^2 - 3(2) + 5$

$\quad = 9 - 6 + 5$

$\quad = 8$

$u_3 - u_2 = 8 - 5 = 3$

$u_2 - u_1 = 5 - 4 = 1$

$u_3 - u_2 \neq u_2 - u_1$

Thus, u_n is not an arithmetic sequence.

Example ▼

The sum of the first n terms of an arithmetic series is given by $S_n = 4n - n^2$.
Find: **(i)** u_n **(ii)** u_{18}.
(iii) If $S_n = -60$, find the value of n.

Solution:

(i) $\quad S_n = 4n - n^2$

$S_{n-1} = 4(n-1)-(n-1)^2$

$\quad = 4(n-1)-(n^2-2n+1)$

$\quad = 4n-4-n^2+2n-1$

$\quad = -n^2+6n-5$

$u_n = S_n - S_{n-1}$

$\quad = (4n-n^2)-(-n^2+6n-5)$

$\quad = 4n-n^2+n^2-6n+5$

$\quad = 5-2n$

(ii) $\quad u_n = 5-2n$

$u_{18} = 5 - 2(18)$

$\quad = 5 - 36$

$\quad = -31$

(iii) Given: $\qquad S_n = -60$

$\therefore \quad 4n - n^2 = -60$

$n^2 - 4n - 60 = 0$

$(n+6)(n-10) = 0$

$n = -6 \quad$ or $\quad n = 10$

$\therefore \qquad n = 10$, as $n \in \mathbf{N}$.

If we need to find three consecutive terms of an arithmetic sequence, we let the numbers be:

$$a-d, \quad a, \quad a+d.$$

If we need to find five consecutive terms of an arithmetic sequence, we let the numbers be:

$$a-2d, \quad a-d, \quad a, \quad a+d, \quad a+2d.$$

Keep 'a' in the middle of the sequence.

Three numbers are in arithmetic sequence. Their sum is 24 and their product is 494.
Find the three numbers.

Solution:

Let the three terms be $(a-d)$, a, $(a+d)$, which are in arithmetic sequence.

Given: Sum of the three terms $= 24$

$\therefore$ $(a-d)+a+(a+d)=24$

$$a-d+a+a+d=24$$

$$3a=24$$

$$a=8$$

Given: Product of the three terms $= 494$

$\therefore$ $(a-d)(a)(a+d)=494$

$$(8-d)(8)(8+d)=494 \qquad \text{(put in } a=8)$$

$$8(8-d)(8+d)=494$$

$$8(64-d^2)=494$$

$$512-8d^2=494$$

$$-8d^2=-18$$

$$8d^2=18$$

$$4d^2=9$$

$$d^2=\frac{9}{4}$$

$$d=\pm\sqrt{\frac{9}{4}}=\pm\frac{\sqrt{9}}{\sqrt{4}}=\pm\frac{3}{2}$$

$$a=8$$

$$a-d=8-\frac{3}{2}=\frac{13}{2}$$

$$a+d=8+\frac{3}{2}=\frac{19}{2}$$

Thus, the three terms are $\frac{13}{2}$, 8, $\frac{19}{2}$.

Exercise 7.3 ▼

1. The nth term of an arithmetic sequence is given by $u_n=5n-3$.
Write down the first three terms.

2. The first three terms of an arithmetic series are $3+7+11+\cdots$
Find: **(i)** u_{20} **(ii)** S_{10}.

3. The first three terms of an arithmetic series are $3 + 5 + 7 + \cdots$
   (i) Find, in terms of n, an expression for: (a) u_n (b) S_n.
   (ii) Find: (a) u_{40} (b) S_{20}.
   (iii) If $u_n = 189$, find the value of n.
   (iv) If $S_n = 80$, find the value of n.

4. If $u_1 = 4$ and $u_7 = 22$ are two terms of an arithmetic sequence, find:
   (i) the common difference, d
   (ii) in terms of n: (a) u_n (b) S_n
   (iii) (a) u_{24} (b) S_{25}.

5. The third term of an arithmetic series is 22 and the seventh term is 46.
   (i) Find the first term, a, and the common difference, d.
   (ii) Find, in terms of n: (a) u_n (b) S_n.
   (iii) Find: (a) u_{10} (b) S_{10}.

6. In an arithmetic sequence, $u_8 = 2u_3$ and $\frac{1}{2}u_{20} = 55$.
   (i) Find the first term, a, and the common difference, d.
   (ii) Express, in terms of n: (a) u_n (b) S_n.
   (iii) Find: (a) u_5 (b) S_8.
   (iv) If $S_n = 165$, find the value of n.

7. In an arithmetic series, the sixth term, u_6, is -8 and the sum of the first six terms is -3.
   (i) Find the first term, a, and the common difference, d.
   (ii) Find, in terms of n: (a) u_n (b) S_n.
   (iii) Find: (a) u_{20} (b) S_{20}.

8. In an arithmetic series, $S_{10} = 95$ and $S_{20} = 290$.
   Find the first term, a, and the common difference, d.

9. In an arithmetic sequence, $u_3 : u_5 = 5 : 8$ and $S_4 = 34$.
   (i) Find the first term, a, and the common difference, d.
   (ii) Find: (a) u_{10} (b) S_{10}.

10. In an arithmetic series, $u_1 = 38$ and $u_{10} = 2$.
    If $S_n = 72$, find the two possible values of n. Explain why there are two answers.

11. The four numbers -2, a, b and 28 are in arithmetic sequence. Find the values of a and b.

12. The five numbers 3, p, q, r and 31 are in arithmetic sequence. Find the values of p, q and r.

13. The six numbers A_1, A_2, 4, A_3, -2 and A_4 are in arithmetic sequence. Find the values of A_1, A_2, A_3 and A_4.

14. The four angles of a quadrilateral are in arithmetic sequence. Given that the value of the largest angle is three times the value of the smallest angle, find the values of all four angles.

15. How many terms are there in the arithmetic sequence $2, 5, 8, \ldots 59$?

16. Find the sum of the series: $-5 - 1 + 3 + \cdots + 151$.

17. Each of the following represents the first three terms of an arithmetic sequence.
In each case find the values of x, $x \in \mathbf{R}$.
(i) $x + 2, 11, 4x$ (ii) $2x - 1, 2x + 1, 3x$ (iii) $x + 1, 2x - 1, 5x + 3$
(iv) $5x - 1, 1, x + 1$ (v) $5x + 2, x^2, 3x - 2$ (vi) $3 - 5x, x^2, 3x + 1$

18. (a) If $4x + 5, x^2, 2x - 5$ and y are four consecutive terms in an arithmetic sequence, find the values of x and y, $x, y \in \mathbf{R}$, and write down the four terms.

(b) The nth term of a sequence is $u_n = n^2 + 3n - 2$. Verify that the sequence is **not** arithmetic.

19. The sum of the first n terms, S_n, of some series is given below.
In each case, find u_n and verify that the series is arithmetic:
(i) $S_n = n^2 + 2n$ (ii) $S_n = n^2 - n$ (iii) $S_n = 2n^2 + 5n$ (iv) $S_n = 3n - 2n^2$

20. The sum of the first n terms of an arithmetic series is given by $S_n = 2n^2 - 3n$.
Find: (i) S_{20} (ii) u_n (iii) u_{20}.
(iv) If $S_n = 77$, find the value of n.

21. The nth term of an arithmetic sequence is given by $u_n = pn + q$.
(i) If $u_2 = -1$ and $u_5 = 17$, find the value of p and the value of q.
(ii) If $S_n = an^2 + bn$, find the value of a and the value of b.

22. Evaluate: (i) $\displaystyle\sum_{r=1}^{50}(2r + 1)$ (ii) $\displaystyle\sum_{r=1}^{60}(3r - 2)$.

23. The sum of the first n terms of an arithmetic series is given by $S_n = \dfrac{n}{2}(n + 1)$.
Evaluate: $\sqrt{S_{n+1} + S_n - u_n}$.

24. An arithmetic series has a common difference d, where $d > 0$.
Three consecutive terms of the series, $a - d$, a and $a + d$, have a sum of 24 and a product of 120.
Calculate the value of d.

25. Three numbers are in arithmetic sequence. Their sum is 24 and their product is 312.
Find two possible sets of values for these terms.

26. Three numbers are in arithmetic sequence. The middle number is 6.
The sum of their squares is 120.5. Find the other two numbers.

27. Five numbers are in arithmetic sequence. Their sum is 50. The product of the least and the greatest term is 64. Find the five numbers.

28. In an arithmetic series, $u_1 = \cos x$, $u_2 = 2 \sin x$, and $u_3 = 2 \cos x$, where $0 < x < \frac{\pi}{2}$.
Find x and hence the common difference, d, and the first term, a.

29. The nth term of a series is given by $u_n = \ln[2^{n-1}(x)]$.
(i) Write down the first three terms.
(ii) Verify that the series is arithmetic.

Geometric Sequences and Series

Consider the sequence of numbers 4, 12, 36, 108, ...
Each term, after the first, can be found by multiplying the previous term by 3.
This is an example of a geometric sequence.

> A sequence in which each term, after the first, is found by multiplying the previous term by a constant number is called a **geometric sequence**.

The first term in a geometric sequence is denoted by a.
The constant number, by which each term is multiplied, is called the **common ratio** and is denoted by r.

Note: $r \neq -1, 0, 1$

Consider the geometric series 3, 6, 12, 24, . . .

$$a = 3 \quad \text{and} \quad r = 2$$

Each term, after the first, is found by multiplying the previous term by 2.

Consider the geometric series 27, 9, 3, 1, . . .

$$a = 27 \quad \text{and} \quad r = \tfrac{1}{3}$$

Each term, after the first, is found by multiplying the previous term by $\tfrac{1}{3}$.

Note: Multiplying by $\tfrac{1}{3}$ is the same as dividing by 3.

In a geometric sequence, the common ratio, r, between any two consecutive terms is always the same.

$$\frac{\text{Any term}}{\text{Previous term}} = \frac{u_n}{u_{n-1}} = \text{constant} = r.$$

> If three terms, u_n, u_{n+1}, u_{n+2} are in geometric sequence, then:
>
> $$\frac{u_{n+2}}{u_{n+1}} = \frac{u_{n+1}}{u_n}.$$

General Term of a Geometric Sequence

In a geometric sequence, a is the first term and r is the common ratio.
Thus, in a geometric sequence:

$$
\begin{aligned}
u_1 &= a &&= a \\
u_2 &= ar &&= ar \\
u_3 &= (ar)r &&= ar^2 \\
u_4 &= (ar^2)r &&= ar^3 \quad \text{and so on.}
\end{aligned}
$$

Notice that the power of r is always **one less** than the term number.
Thus, the general term of a geometric sequence is given by:

$$u_n = ar^{n-1}$$

For example, $u_6 = ar^5, \qquad u_{10} = ar^9.$

Note: If $u_n = pq^n$, where p and q are constants, the sequence is geometric.

Geometric Series

If the sequence $u_1, u_2, u_3, \ldots, u_n$ is geometric, then the corresponding series
$S_n = u_1 + u_2 + u_3 + \cdots + u_n$ is a geometric series.
The formula for S_n of a geometric series can be written in terms of the first term, a, and the common ratio, r.

If $S_n = u_1 + u_2 + u_3 + \cdots + u_n$ is a geometric series, then:
$$S_n = \frac{a(1-r^n)}{1-r} \text{ when } |r| < 1 \quad \text{or} \quad S_n = \frac{a(r^n-1)}{r-1} \text{ when } |r| > 1.$$

Note: In practice it does not matter which form is used.
To derive this result:

$$S_n = a + ar + ar^2 + \cdots + ar^{n-1}$$
$$rS_n = \quad ar + ar^2 + \cdots + ar^{n-1} + ar^n$$
$$\overline{S_n - rS_n = a \qquad\qquad\qquad\qquad - ar^n} \quad \text{(subtract)}$$
$$(1-r)S_n = a - ar^n$$
$$(1-r)S_n = a(1-r^n)$$
$$S_n = \frac{a(1-r^n)}{1-r} \qquad (r \neq \pm 1)$$

Once we find the first term, a, and the common ratio, r, we can answer any question about a geometric sequence or series.
If we need to find three unknown consecutive terms in geometric sequence, we let the terms be:

$$\frac{a}{r}, a, ar.$$

The nth term of a geometric sequence is $u_n = \left(\frac{2}{3}\right)^n$.

(i) Find the first three terms.　　**(ii)** Find S_5, the sum of the first five terms.

Solution:

(i)

$$u_n = \left(\frac{2}{3}\right)^n$$

$$u_1 = \left(\frac{2}{3}\right)^1 = \frac{2}{3}$$

$$u_2 = \left(\frac{2}{3}\right)^2 = \frac{4}{9}$$

$$u_3 = \left(\frac{2}{3}\right)^3 = \frac{8}{27}$$

Thus, the first three terms are:
$$\frac{2}{3}, \frac{4}{9}, \frac{8}{27}.$$

(ii)

$$S_n = \frac{a(1-r^n)}{1-r}$$

$$S_5 = \frac{\frac{2}{3}\left[1 - \left(\frac{2}{3}\right)^5\right]}{1 - \frac{2}{3}}$$

$$= \frac{\frac{2}{3}\left[1 - \frac{32}{243}\right]}{\frac{1}{3}}$$

$$= \frac{\frac{2}{3}\left(\frac{211}{243}\right)}{\frac{1}{3}} = \frac{422}{243}$$

2, 6, 18, . . . , 1458 is a geometric sequence.

Find: **(i)** the nth term　　**(ii)** the number of terms in the sequence.

Solution:

(i) $a = 2$ (given)

$$r = \frac{u_2}{u_1} = \frac{6}{2} = 3$$

$$u_n = ar^{n-1}$$

$$u_n = 2(3)^{n-1}$$

We know that $a = 2$ and $r = 3$.
We need to find n, the number of terms.

(ii) Given:
$$u_n = 1458$$
$$\therefore \quad 2(3)^{n-1} = 1458$$
$$3^{n-1} = 729$$
$$3^{n-1} = 3^6$$
$$n - 1 = 6$$
$$n = 7$$

Thus, there are 7 terms in the sequence.

Example ▼

Three terms in geometric sequence are $x - 3$, x, $3x + 4$, where $x \in \mathbf{R}$.
Find two possible values of x.

Solution:

We use the fact that in a geometric sequence, any term divided by the previous term is always a constant.

Thus,

$$\frac{u_{n+2}}{u_{n+1}} = \frac{u_{n+1}}{u_n} \qquad \text{[common ratio]}$$

$$\frac{3x+4}{x} = \frac{x}{x-3} \qquad \text{[put in given values]}$$

$$(3x+4)(x-3) = (x)(x) \qquad \text{[multiply both sides by } (x)(x-3)]$$

$$3x^2 - 5x - 12 = x^2$$

$$2x^2 - 5x - 12 = 0$$

$$(2x+3)(x-4) = 0$$

$$2x + 3 = 0 \qquad \text{or} \quad x - 4 = 0$$

$$x = -\frac{3}{2} \qquad \text{or} \qquad x = 4$$

To verify that a sequence is geometric, we must show the following:

$$\frac{u_n}{u_{n-1}} = \text{constant.}$$

Note: To show that a sequence is **not geometric**, it is necessary only to show that the ratio of any two consecutive terms is not the same. In practice, this usually involves showing that $u_3 \div u_2 \neq u_2 \div u_1$ or similar.

Example ▼

Write down the first four terms of the sequence $u_n = 8\left(\frac{3}{4}\right)^n$ and show that the sequence is geometric.

Solution:

$$u_n = 8\left(\frac{3}{4}\right)^n$$

$$u_1 = 8\left(\frac{3}{4}\right)^1 = 8\left(\frac{3}{4}\right) = 6$$

$$u_2 = 8\left(\frac{3}{4}\right)^2 = 8\left(\frac{9}{16}\right) = \frac{9}{2}$$

$$u_3 = 8\left(\frac{3}{4}\right)^3 = 8\left(\frac{27}{64}\right) = \frac{27}{8}$$

$$u_4 = 8\left(\frac{3}{4}\right)^4 = 8\left(\frac{81}{256}\right) = \frac{81}{32}$$

Thus, the first four terms are $6, \dfrac{9}{2}, \dfrac{27}{8}, \dfrac{81}{32}$.

$$u_n = 8\left(\frac{3}{4}\right)^n \qquad\qquad u_{n-1} = 8\left(\frac{3}{4}\right)^{n-1}$$

$$\frac{u_n}{u_{n-1}} = \frac{8\left(\frac{3}{4}\right)^n}{8\left(\frac{3}{4}\right)^{n-1}} = \frac{\left(\frac{3}{4}\right)^n}{\left(\frac{3}{4}\right)^{n-1}} = \left(\frac{3}{4}\right)^{n-(n-1)} = \left(\frac{3}{4}\right)^{n-n+1} = \left(\frac{3}{4}\right)^1 = \frac{3}{4} \qquad \text{(a constant)}$$

$$\frac{u_n}{u_{n-1}} = \text{a constant.}$$

Thus, u_n is a geometric sequence.

Example ▼

(i) In a geometric sequence, the second term is 8 and the fifth term is 64.
Find the first term, a, and the common ratio, r.

(ii) In a geometric sequence, the sum of the first and third terms is $\frac{20}{3}$ and the sum of the second and fourth terms is $\frac{20}{9}$.
Find the first term, a, and the common ratio, r.

Solution:

(i) $\hspace{4cm} u_n = ar^{n-1}$

Given: $\quad u_2 = 8$	**Given:** $\qquad u_5 = 64$
$\therefore \qquad ar = 8 \quad ①$	$\therefore \qquad ar^4 = 64 \quad ②$

We now divide ② by ① to eliminate a and find r.

② ÷ ① gives:	Put $r = 2$ into ① or ② to find a:
$\dfrac{ar^4}{ar} = \dfrac{64}{8}$	$ar = 8 \quad ①$
$r^3 = 8$	$a(2) = 8$
$r = 2$	$2a = 8$
	$a = 4$

Thus, the first term is $a = 4$ and the common ratio is $r = 2$.

Note: If the index of r is even, we get two values for r, one positive and the other negative.

(ii)

$$S_n = a + ar + ar^2 + ar^3 + \cdots + ar^{n-1}$$

Given: $u_1 + u_3 = \dfrac{20}{3}$ 　　　　　　　**Given:** $u_2 + u_4 = \dfrac{20}{9}$

$\therefore$ 　$a + ar^2 = \dfrac{20}{3}$ 　　　　　　　$\therefore$ 　$ar + ar^3 = \dfrac{20}{9}$

　$a(1 + r^2) = \dfrac{20}{3}$ 　①　　　　　　　$ar(1 + r^2) = \dfrac{20}{9}$ 　②

We now divide ② by ① to eliminate a and find r.

②÷① gives:　　　　　　　　　$a(1 + r^2) = \dfrac{20}{3}$

$$\frac{ar(1 + r^2)}{a(1 + r^2)} = \frac{\frac{20}{9}}{\frac{20}{3}}$$
　　　　　　　　　　　　　　　$a\left(1 + \dfrac{1}{9}\right) = \dfrac{20}{3}$

$$r = \frac{1}{3}$$
　　　　　　　　　　　　　　　$a\left(\dfrac{10}{9}\right) = \dfrac{20}{3}$

Put $r = \dfrac{1}{3}$ into ① or ② to find a.
　　　　　　　　　　　　　　　$\dfrac{10}{9}a = \dfrac{20}{3}$

　　　　　　　　　　　　　　　$10a = 60$

　　　　　　　　　　　　　　　(multiply both sides by 9)

　　　　　　　　　　　　　　　$a = 6$

Thus, the first term is $a = 6$ and the common ratio is $r = \frac{1}{3}$.

Example ▼

In an arithmetic sequence, the sum of the first term and the third term is 15. The first, third and seventh terms of the arithmetic sequence are the first three terms of a geometric sequence.

(i) Find the first term and the common difference of the arithmetic sequence, where the common difference is positive.

(ii) Find the first three terms and the common ratio of the geometric sequence.

Solution:

(i) For the arithmetic sequence, 　$u_n = a + (n-1)d$

　　$u_1 = a$ 　　　　　　$u_3 = a + 2d$ 　　　　　　$u_7 = a + 6d$

Given: 　　　　　$u_1 + u_3 = 15$

$\therefore$ 　　　　　$(a) + (a + 2d) = 15$

　　　　　　　　$a + a + 2d = 15$

　　　　　　　　$2a + 2d = 15$ 　①

Given: u_1, u_3 and u_7 are the first three terms in a geometric sequence.

$\therefore$
$$\frac{u_7}{u_3} = \frac{u_3}{u_1} \qquad \text{[common ratio]}$$

$$\frac{a+6d}{a+2d} = \frac{a+2d}{a}$$

$$a(a+6d) = (a+2d)(a+2d) \qquad \text{[multiply both sides by } a(a+2d)\text{]}$$

$$a^2 + 6ad = a^2 + 4ad + 4d^2$$

$$6ad = 4ad + 4d^2$$

$$2ad - 4d^2 = 0$$

$$ad - 2d^2 = 0$$

$$d(a - 2d) = 0$$

$$d = 0 \quad \text{or} \quad a - 2d = 0$$

$$d = 0 \quad \text{or} \quad a = 2d$$

Thus, $a = 2d$ ② (we are given $d > 0$)

We now solve between the simultaneous equations ① and ②.

$2a + 2d = 15$ ①	$2d = a$ ②
$2a + a = 15$ $(a = 2d)$	$2d = 5$
$3a = 15$	$d = \dfrac{5}{2}$
$a = 5$	

(ii) For the geometric sequence:

$$u_1 = a = 5$$

$$u_2 = a + 2d = 5 + 2\left(\frac{5}{2}\right) = 5 + 5 = 10$$

$$u_3 = a + 6d = 5 + 6\left(\frac{5}{2}\right) = 5 + 15 = 20$$

$$r = \frac{u_2}{u_1} = \frac{10}{5} = 2$$

Thus, the first three terms of the geometric sequence are 5, 10 and 20 and the common ratio is 2.

Exercise 7.4 ▼

1. The first three terms of a geometric series are $2 + 6 + 18 + \cdots$.
   - **(i)** Express, in terms of n: **(a)** u_n **(b)** S_n.
   - **(ii)** Find: **(a)** u_8 and **(b)** S_8.

2. The first three terms of a geometric series are $64 - 32 + 16$.
   - **(i)** Find, in terms of n: **(a)** u_n **(b)** S_n.
   - **(ii)** Find: **(a)** u_{10} and **(b)** S_{10}.

For each of the following geometric sequences, find u_n, the nth term:

3. 5, 10, 20, . . . **4.** 4, 12, 36, . . . **5.** 27, 18, 12, . . .

6. 50, −20, 8, . . . **7.** 1, $2a$, $4a^2$, . . . **8.** $\dfrac{5}{a}, \dfrac{10}{a^2}, \dfrac{20}{a^3}, \cdots$

9. Verify that the sequence $u_n = 5^n$ is geometric.

10. Verify that the sequence $u_n = 2(3)^{n+1}$ is geometric.

11. Verify that the sequence $u_n = n^2 - 3$ is not geometric.

12. The sum to n terms of a series is given by $3(2^n - 1)$.
    (i) Find u_n, the nth term.   **(ii)** Verify that the series is geometric.

Find, in terms of n, the sum of the first n terms of the geometric series:

13. $6 + 12 + 24 + \cdots$ **14.** $6 + 4 + \dfrac{8}{3} + \cdots$ **15.** $63 - 21 + 7 - \cdots$

16. Find, in terms of n, the sum of the first n terms of the geometric series $18 + 12 + 8 + \cdots$.
    If $S_n = \frac{1330}{27}$, find the value of n.

17. If $\displaystyle\sum_{r=1}^{n} 2^{n+1} = 508$, find the value of n.

18. A geometric series has 6 terms, a common ratio of $\frac{1}{2}$ and a sum of $\frac{189}{8}$.

    Find: **(i)** the first term   **(ii)** the nth term.

19. The lengths of the sides of a triangle are in geometric sequence. The length of the shortest side is 4 cm and the perimeter of the triangle is 19 cm. Find the lengths of the other sides.

Each of the following represents the first three terms of a geometric sequence.
In each case find the value(s) of x, $x \in \mathbf{R}$:

20. $x - 2, x, x + 3$ **21.** $x - 1, 2x + 1, 4x + 17$

22. $4x + 36, 2x + 6, x$ **23.** $x - 6, 2x, 8x + 20$

24. $x + 1, x + 4, 3x + 2$ **25.** $3x - 5, x - 1, x - 2$

26. $x + 1, x - 1$ and $2x - 5$ are the first three terms of a geometric series.
    (i) Find two values for x.
    (ii) Write down the first four terms of the two resulting series.

27. Four terms in geometric sequence are: 6, a, b, $\frac{3}{4}$. Find the values of a and b.

28. The third term, u_3, of a geometric sequence is −63. The fourth term, u_4, is 189.
    Find: **(i)** the common ratio   **(ii)** the first term.
    Express, in terms of n: **(iii)** u_n **(iv)** S_n.

29. In a geometric series, the fourth term is 12 and the seventh term is 324.
    Find: **(i)** the nth term   **(ii)** S_7, the sum of the first seven terms.

30. $S_n = a + ar + ar^2 + ar^3 + \cdots + ar^{n-1}$ is a geometric series.

$u_3 - u_2 = 5$ and $u_4 - u_3 = 6$.

Find the common ratio, r, and the first term, a.

31. A geometric series has a common ratio r.

The first three terms of the series are $\dfrac{a}{r}$, a and ar.

The product of the three terms is 216 and the sum of the three terms is 21.

Find: **(i)** the value of a **(ii)** the values of r.

(iii) Write down the first three terms.

32. The product of the first three terms of a geometric series is 27 and the sum of these terms is 13. Find the first four terms of the series.

33. Three terms, a, b and $a + b$, are in arithmetic sequence.

Three terms, a, b and ab, are in geometric sequence.

Find the value of a and the value of b, where $a, b \in \mathbf{R}$ and $a, b \neq 0$.

34. p, 10 and q are consecutive terms of an arithmetic sequence.

1, p and q are consecutive terms of a geometric sequence.

Find the value of p and the value of q, $p, q \in \mathbf{R}$.

35. The first, fifth and seventeenth terms of an arithmetic series are the first three terms of a geometric series. The sum of the first four terms of the arithmetic series is 28. Find the common difference of the arithmetic series and the common ratio of the geometric series.

36. The first, fifth and twenty-first terms of an arithmetic sequence are the first three terms of a geometric sequence. Find the common ratio of the geometric sequence.

37. p, m and q are three consecutive terms of an arithmetic sequence.

p, n and q are three consecutive terms of a geometric sequence, where $p, q, n > 0$.

Show that $m \geqslant n$.

Infinite Geometric Series

When a series has an infinite number of terms, it is called an **infinite series** and the sum of the series is called the **sum to infinity** of the series.

Let us consider the value of a proper fraction (less than 1) if we keep multiplying it by itself. Take for example, $\frac{1}{4}$, and keep multiplying it by itself, i.e. $(\frac{1}{4})^n$, as n increases indefinitely. We can represent this situation in a table using a calculator.

n	1	2	3	$\cdots$	10
$(\frac{1}{4})^n$	0.25	0.0625	0.015625	$\cdots$	0.0000009537

From the table we can see that the bigger the value of n, the nearer $(\frac{1}{4})^n$ gets to 0.
(This will happen for any proper fraction, positive or negative.)
We say that the limit of $(\frac{1}{4})^n$, as n approaches infinity, is 0.

Symbolically:

$$\lim_{n \to \infty} (\text{proper fraction})^n = 0$$

$n \to \infty$ means 'as n approaches infinity'.
lim is short for limit.
In general, for the infinite geometric series:

$$a + ar + ar^2 + ar^3 + \cdots$$

if r is a proper fraction, then the terms will get closer to zero.
For r to be a proper fraction it must be between -1 and 1, i.e., $-1 < r < 1$.

$$\therefore \qquad \text{If } -1 < r < 1$$

$$\text{then} \quad \lim_{n \to \infty} r^n = 0$$

Notes: If $r > 1$ or $r < -1$, then $\lim_{n \to \infty} r^n$ does not exist.

The sum to infinity, S_∞, of a series is denoted by $\lim_{n \to \infty} S_n$.

If $\lim_{n \to \infty} S_n$ exists, the series is said to be **convergent**.

If $\lim_{n \to \infty} S_n$ does **not** exist, the series is said to be **divergent**.

Let us now develop the general formula for the sum to infinity of a geometric series in which $-1 < r < 1$.

$$S_n = \frac{a(1 - r^n)}{1 - r}$$

The only part of this formula that changes as n increases is r^n.
As, $n \to \infty$, $r^n \to 0$, because r is a proper fraction.

$$\therefore \quad S_\infty = \frac{a(1 - 0)}{1 - r} = \frac{a}{1 - r}$$

> **Sum to infinity of a geometric series**
>
> $$S_\infty = \frac{a}{1 - r} = \frac{\text{first term}}{1 - \text{common ratio}}$$
>
> $$\text{if } -1 < r < 1.$$

Note: $-1 < r < 1$ is often written $|r| < 1$.

(i) Find the sum to infinity of the geometric series: $1 + \left(\dfrac{2}{5}\right) + \left(\dfrac{2}{5}\right)^2 + \left(\dfrac{2}{5}\right)^3 + \cdots$.

(ii) Evaluate $\displaystyle\sum_{n=0}^{\infty}\left(\dfrac{5}{2x+1}\right)^n$, in terms of x, where $x > 2$.

Solution:

(i) $1 + \left(\dfrac{2}{5}\right) + \left(\dfrac{2}{5}\right)^2 + \left(\dfrac{2}{5}\right)^3 + \cdots$

This is an infinite geometric series with first term $a = 1$ and common ratio $r = \dfrac{2}{5}$.

$$S_\infty = \frac{a}{1-r} = \frac{1}{1-\frac{2}{5}} = \frac{5}{5-2} = \frac{5}{3}$$

(ii) $\displaystyle\sum_{n=0}^{\infty}\left(\dfrac{5}{2x+1}\right)^n = 1 + \left(\dfrac{5}{2x+1}\right) + \left(\dfrac{5}{2x+1}\right)^2 + \left(\dfrac{5}{2x+1}\right)^3 + \cdots$

This is an infinite geometric series with first term $a = 1$ and common ratio $r = \dfrac{5}{2x+1}$.

$$S_\infty = \frac{a}{1-r} = \frac{1}{1-\dfrac{5}{2x+1}} = \frac{2x+1}{2x+1-5} = \frac{2x+1}{2x-4}$$

$\displaystyle\sum_{n=0}^{\infty}(2x-3)^n = 1 + (2x-3) + (2x-3)^2 + (2x-3)^3 + \cdots$ is a geometric series.

(i) Find, in terms of x, the sum to infinity.

(ii) If the sum to infinity is $\dfrac{5}{4}$, find the value of x.

(ii) Find the range of values of x for which the sum to infinity exists.

Solution:

This is an infinite geometric series with first term $a = 1$ and common ratio $r = (2x-3)$.

(i) $S_\infty = \dfrac{a}{1-r}$

$\qquad = \dfrac{1}{1-(2x-3)}$

$\qquad = \dfrac{1}{1-2x+3}$

$\qquad = \dfrac{1}{4-2x}$

(ii) Given: $S_\infty = \dfrac{5}{4}$

$\therefore \quad \dfrac{1}{4-2x} = \dfrac{5}{4}$

$\qquad\qquad 4 = 20 - 10x$

$\qquad\qquad 10x = 16$

$\qquad\qquad 5x = 8$

$\qquad\qquad x = \dfrac{8}{5}$

(iii) S_∞ exists if $\quad -1 < r < 1$ $\qquad\qquad$ (i.e. $|r| < 1$)

$$-1 < r < 1$$

$$-1 < 2x - 3 < 1 \qquad\qquad (r = 2x - 3)$$

$$2 < 2x < 4 \qquad\qquad \text{(add 3 to each part)}$$

$$1 < x < 2 \qquad\qquad \text{(divide each part by 2)}$$

Thus, the sum to infinity exists for $1 < x < 2$.

Example ▼

The sum to infinity of a geometric series is 36 and the second term of the series is 8.
Find two possible series.

Solution:

Let the series be $a + ar + ar^2 + \cdots$

Given: $\qquad S_\infty = 36$

$\therefore \qquad \dfrac{a}{1-r} = 36$

$$a = 36(1 - r) \quad ①$$

We now solve between ① and ②:

$$ar = 8 \quad ②$$

$$36(1 - r)r = 8$$

[replace a with $36(1-r)$]

$$(36 - 36r)r = 8$$

$$36r - 36r^2 = 8$$

$$-36r^2 + 36r - 8 = 0$$

$$36r^2 - 36r + 8 = 0$$

$$9r^2 - 9r + 2 = 0$$

$$(3r - 2)(3r - 1) = 0$$

$$3r - 2 = 0 \quad \text{or} \quad 3r - 1 = 0$$

$$3r = 2 \quad \text{or} \qquad 3r = 1$$

$$r = \tfrac{2}{3} \quad \text{or} \qquad r = \tfrac{1}{3}$$

Given: $\qquad u_2 = 8$

$\therefore \quad ar = 8 \qquad ②$

Put $r = \tfrac{2}{3}$ and $r = \tfrac{1}{3}$ into ① or ②
to find the value of a.

$$a = 36(1 - r) \quad ①$$

$r = \tfrac{2}{3}$	$r = \tfrac{1}{3}$
$a = 36\left(1 - \tfrac{2}{3}\right)$	$a = 36\left(1 - \tfrac{1}{3}\right)$
$a = 36\left(\tfrac{1}{3}\right)$	$a = 36\left(\tfrac{2}{3}\right)$
$a = 12$	$a = 24$

Thus, we have two series which obey the two given conditions:

(i) $a = 12$, $r = \tfrac{2}{3}$, the series is $12 + 8 + 5\tfrac{1}{3} + \cdots$

(ii) $a = 24$, $r = \tfrac{1}{3}$, the series is $24 + 8 + 2\tfrac{2}{3} + \cdots$.

Recurring Decimals

An application of the sum of infinite geometric series is expressing non-terminating, recurring decimals as rational numbers.

Note: The first five letters in the word 'rational' spell 'ratio'. In other words, a rational number is any number that can be written as a ratio (i.e. a fraction).

Recurring decimals can be expressed neatly by placing a dot over the first and last figures which repeat.
This is called the **dot notation**. For example:

1. $0.\dot{4} = 0.44444\ldots = \frac{4}{9}$

2. $0.1\dot{6} = 0.166666\ldots = \frac{1}{6}$

3. $1.\dot{2}\dot{5} = 1.252525\ldots = 1 + \frac{25}{99} = \frac{124}{99}$

4. $0.\dot{1}8\dot{5} = 0.185185185\ldots = \frac{5}{27}$

Example ▼

Express the recurring decimal $0.7\dot{3}$ in the form $\frac{a}{b}$, where $a, b \in \mathbf{N}$.

Solution:

$$0.7\dot{3} = 0.733333\ldots$$
$$= 0.7 + 0.03 + 0.003 + 0.0003 + \cdots$$
$$\downarrow \qquad \downarrow \qquad \downarrow \qquad \downarrow$$
$$= \frac{7}{10} + \left[\frac{3}{100} + \frac{3}{1,000} + \frac{3}{10,000} + \cdots \right]$$

The series in the brackets is an infinite geometric series, with $a = \dfrac{3}{100}$ and $r = \dfrac{1}{10}$.

$$S_\infty = \frac{a}{1-r} = \frac{\frac{3}{100}}{1 - \frac{1}{10}} = \frac{3}{100 - 10} = \frac{3}{90} = \frac{1}{30}$$

Thus, $0.7\dot{3} = \dfrac{7}{10} + \dfrac{1}{30} = \dfrac{22}{30} = \dfrac{11}{15}$.

Exercise 7.5 ▼

Find the sum to infinity of each of the following geometric series:

1. $1 + \dfrac{1}{2} + \dfrac{1}{4} + \cdots$

2. $2 + \dfrac{2}{3} + \dfrac{2}{9} + \cdots$

3. $5 + 1 + \dfrac{1}{5} + \cdots$

4. $2 + 1.8 + 1.62 + \cdots$

5. $3 - \dfrac{3}{2} + \dfrac{3}{4} - \cdots$

6. $\dfrac{3}{2} - \dfrac{1}{4} + \dfrac{1}{24} - \cdots$

7. $0.2 - 0.1 + 0.05 - \cdots$

8. $1 + x + x^2 + \cdots$

9. $2 + \dfrac{2a}{3} + \dfrac{2a^2}{9} + \cdots$

10. Evaluate: **(i)** $\sum_{n=0}^{\infty} \left(\frac{1}{3}\right)^n$ **(ii)** $\sum_{n=0}^{\infty} 3\left(\frac{1}{2}\right)^n$ **(iii)** $\sum_{n=0}^{\infty} x(1-x)^n$.

11. Find the sum to infinity of the geometric series $\frac{5}{10} + \frac{5}{100} + \frac{5}{1,000} + \cdots$.
Using this series, show that $1.\dot{5} = \frac{14}{9}$.

Express each of the following recurring decimals in the form $\dfrac{a}{b}$, where $a, b \in \mathbf{N}$:

12. $0.\dot{4}$ **13.** $2.\dot{2}$ **14.** $0.\dot{7}\dot{2}$ **15.** $0.2\dot{7}$ **16.** $0.1\dot{2}$ **17.** $1.8\dot{3}$

18. The sum to infinity of a geometric series is 20 and the common ratio is $\frac{2}{5}$. Find the first term.

19. The sum to infinity of a geometric series is 4 and the first term is 6. Find the common ratio.

20. The sum to infinity of a geometric series is 5. The common ratio and the first term of the series are equal. Find the common ratio.

21. If the sum to infinity of a geometric series is five times the first term, find the common ratio.

22. $24x - 5$, $6x - 1$ and x are the first three terms of a geometric series.
Find two values for: **(i)** x **(ii)** the common ratio   **(iii)** the sum to infinity.

23. In a geometric series, $u_1 = a$ and $u_2 = a^2 - 2a$, $a \neq 0$.
  (i) Write down, in terms of a, the common ratio of the series.
  (ii) If the sum to infinity is 5, find the value of a.
  (iii) Find the range of values of $a \in \mathbf{R}$ for which the series has a sum to infinity.

24. $\sum_{n=0}^{\infty} x^2 \left(\frac{1}{1-x}\right)^n = x^2 + \frac{x^2}{1-x} + \frac{x^2}{(1-x)^2} + \frac{x^2}{(1-x)^3} + \cdots$ is an infinite geometric series.

  (i) Find, in terms of x: **(a)** the common ratio   **(b)** the sum to infinity.
  (ii) If the sum to infinity is 30, find the values of x.

25. **(i)** Factorise $1 - r^2$.
  (ii) $a + ar + ar^2 + ar^3 + \cdots$ is an infinite geometric series with $|r| < 1$.
    The sum to infinity is 8 and the sum to infinity of the even terms is 2.
    Find the value of the common ratio.

26. The sum to infinity of a geometric series is 27 and the second term of the series is 6.
Find two possible series.

27. The sum to infinity of a geometric series is 2. When the terms of this geometric sequence are squared a new geometric sequence is obtained whose sum to infinity is 12.
Find the first term, a, and the common ratio, r, where $|r| < 1$.

Series of the Form $\displaystyle\sum_{n=0}^{\infty} nx^n$

A series can be formed by multiplying, term by term, the terms of an arithmetic series and a geometric series, called '**Arithmetic–geometric**' series.

Consider the series: $1 + 3x + 5x^2 + 7x^3 + \cdots$

Each term consists of two parts:

1. A coefficient: $1, 3, 5, 7, \ldots$, which are in arithmetic sequence.

2. A power: $1, x, x^2, x^3, \ldots$, which are in geometric sequence.

To find a formula for S_n for an arithmetic–geometric series, do the following:

---

1. Write down S_n.
2. Write down rS_n (multiply by the common ratio for the powers).
3. Subtract.
4. Use the formula for the sum of the first n terms of a geometric series, $\dfrac{a(1-r^n)}{1-r}$.
5. Divide both sides by $(1-r)$.

Example ▼

$S_n = \displaystyle\sum_{r=1}^{n} (r+3)x^{r-1}$, where $|x| < 1$.

(i) Write S_n in terms of n. **(ii)** Find: $\displaystyle\sum_{r=1}^{\infty} (r+3)x^{r-1}$.

(iii) Evaluate: $\displaystyle\sum_{r=1}^{\infty} (r+3)\left(\tfrac{1}{3}\right)^{r-1}$.

Solution:

$S_n = \displaystyle\sum_{r=1}^{n} (r+3)x^{r-1} = 4 + 5x + 6x^2 + 7x^3 + \cdots + (n+3)x^{n-1}$

(i)

[Multiply S_n by x, the common ratio of the geometric series]

$$S_n = 4 + 5x + 6x^2 + 7x^3 + \cdots + (n+3)x^{n-1}$$
$$xS_n = \qquad 4x + 5x^2 + 6x^3 + \cdots + (n+2)x^{n-1} + (n+3)x^n$$
$$(1-x)S_n = 4 + (x + x^2 + x^3 + \cdots + \qquad x^{n-1}) - (n+3)x^n \qquad \text{(subtract)}$$

> The series in the brackets is a geometric series with $a = x$, $r = x$ and $(n-1)$ terms.
> Thus, S_n for this series $= \dfrac{a(1-r^{n-1})}{1-r} = \dfrac{x(1-x^{n-1})}{1-x}$.

$$(1-x)S_n = 4 + (x + x^2 + x^3 + \cdots + x^{n-1}) - (n+3)x^n$$

$$\therefore \quad (1-x)S_n = 4 + \frac{x(1-x^{n-1})}{1-x} - (n+3)x^n$$

$$S_n = \frac{4}{(1-x)} + \frac{x(1-x^{n-1})}{(1-x)^2} - \frac{(n+3)x^n}{(1-x)}$$

(ii) If $|x| < 1$, then $\displaystyle\lim_{n \to \infty} x^n = 0$ and $\displaystyle\lim_{n \to \infty} x^{n-1} = 0$.

$$\sum_{r=1}^{\infty} (r+3)x^{r-1} = \lim_{n \to \infty} S_n$$

$$S_n = \frac{4}{(1-x)} + \frac{x(1-x^{n-1})}{(1-x)^2} - \frac{(n+3)x^n}{(1-x)}$$

$$\text{Thus, } \lim_{n \to \infty} S_n = \frac{4}{(1-x)} + \frac{x(1-0)}{(1-x)^2} - \frac{(n+3)(0)}{(1-x)}$$

$$= \frac{4}{(1-x)} + \frac{x}{(1-x)^2} = \frac{4(1-x)+x}{(1-x)^2} = \frac{4-3x}{(1-x)^2}$$

(iii) $\displaystyle\sum_{r=1}^{\infty} (r+3)\left(\tfrac{1}{3}\right)^{r-1} = 4 + 5\left(\tfrac{1}{3}\right) + 6\left(\tfrac{1}{3}\right)^2 + 7\left(\tfrac{1}{3}\right)^3 + \cdots + (r+3)\left(\tfrac{1}{3}\right)^{r-1} + \cdots$

This is exactly the same as the original series with $x = \tfrac{1}{3}$.

$$\text{But } \sum_{r=1}^{\infty} (r+3)x^{r-1} = \frac{4-3x}{(1-x)^2}$$

$$\therefore \quad \sum_{r=1}^{\infty} (r+3)\left(\tfrac{1}{3}\right)^{r-1} = \frac{4 - 3\left(\tfrac{1}{3}\right)}{\left(1 - \tfrac{1}{3}\right)^2} \qquad \left[\text{put in } x = \tfrac{1}{3} \text{ into } \frac{4-3x}{(1-x)^2} \right]$$

$$= \frac{4-1}{\tfrac{4}{9}} = \frac{36-9}{4} = \frac{27}{4}$$

Sometimes u_n is not given.

Example ▼

For the series $1 \cdot 1 + 3 \cdot 2 + 5 \cdot 2^2 + 7 \cdot 2^3 + \cdots$, find, in terms of n:

(i) u_n, the nth term   **(ii)** S_n, the sum of the first n terms.

Hence, evaluate S_{10}.

Solution:

(i) $1 \cdot 1 + 3 \cdot 2 + 5 \cdot 2^2 + 7 \cdot 2^3 + \cdots$

This series is a combination of an arithmetic series and a geometric series.
Thus, we need to find u_n separately for each of these series and combine the results.

213

Arithmetic series: $1+3+5+7+\cdots$

$u_n = a+(n-1)d$

$\quad = 1+(n-1)2$

$\quad = 2n-1$

Geometric series: $1+2+2^2+2^3+\cdots$

$u_n = ar^{n-1}$

$\quad = 1 \cdot 2^{n-1}$

$\quad = 2^{n-1}$

Thus, the nth term of the series is given by $u_n = (2n-1)2^{n-1}$.

(ii) [Multiply S_n by 2, the common ratio of the geometric series]

$S_n = 1 \cdot 1 + 3 \cdot 2 + 5 \cdot 2^2 + 7 \cdot 2^3 + \cdots + (2n-1)2^{n-1}$

$2S_n = \qquad 1 \cdot 2 + 3 \cdot 2^2 + 5 \cdot 2^3 + \cdots + (2n-3)2^{n-1} + (2n-1)2^n$

$-S_n = 1 + 2 \cdot 2 + 2 \cdot 2^2 + 2 \cdot 2^3 + \cdots + \quad 2 \cdot 2^{n-1} - (2n-1)2^n$

$-S_n = 1 + 2(2 + 2^2 + 2^3 + \cdots + 2^{n-1}) - (2n-1)2^n$

$\left[\begin{array}{l}\text{The series in the brackets is a geometric series with } a=2 \ r=2, \text{ and } (n-1) \text{ terms.}\\[4pt]\text{Thus, } S_n \text{ for this series} = \dfrac{a(r^{n-1}-1)}{r-1} = \dfrac{2(2^{n-1}-1)}{2-1} = 2^n - 2.\end{array}\right]$

$-S_n = 1 + 2(2 + 2^2 + 2^3 + \cdots + 2^{n-1}) - (2n-1)2^n$

$-S_n = 1 + 2(2^n - 2) - (2n-1)2^n$

$S_n = (2n-1)2^n - 2(2^n - 2) - 1$

$\quad = (2n-1)2^n - 2 \cdot 2^n + 4 - 1$

$\quad = (2n-1-2)2^n + 3$

$\quad = (2n-3)2^n + 3$

Exercise 7.6 ▼

1. (i) Find S_n, the sum to n terms of the series $1 + x + x^2 + x^3 + \cdots + x^{n-1}$.

(ii) Complete the following table:

$S_n = 1 + 2x + 3x^2 + 4x^3 + \cdots + nx^{n-1}$
$xS_n =$
$(1-x)S_n =$
$S_n =$
$\lim\limits_{n\to\infty} S_n =$
$1 + 2\left(\tfrac{1}{5}\right) + 3\left(\tfrac{1}{5}\right)^2 + 4\left(\tfrac{1}{5}\right)^3 + \cdots + n\left(\tfrac{1}{5}\right)^{n-1} + \cdots = \boxed{}$

(iii) Write down the first four terms of the series: $\sum\limits_{r=1}^{n} rx^{2r-2}$.

Hence find, in terms of x, an expression for $\sum\limits_{r=1}^{\infty} rx^{2r-2}$.

2. For the series $2x + 3x^2 + 4x^3 + \cdots + (n+1)x^n$, where $-1 < x < 1$:

(i) write S_n, in terms of n **(ii)** find $\sum\limits_{r=1}^{\infty}(r+1)x^r$

(iii) evaluate $\sum\limits_{r=1}^{\infty}(r+1)\left(\tfrac{1}{2}\right)^r$.

3. If $S_n = 3 + 5x + 7x^2 + \cdots + (2n+1)x^{n-1}$:

(i) show that $S_n = \dfrac{3 - (2n+1)x^n}{1-x} + \dfrac{2x(1-x^{n-1})}{(1-x)^2}$

(ii) if $|x| < 1$, find $\sum\limits_{n=1}^{\infty}(2n+1)x^{n-1}$ and evaluate $\sum\limits_{n=1}^{\infty}(2n+1)\left(\tfrac{1}{3}\right)^{n-1}$.

4. Find an expression for S_n of the series:

$2 + 5x + 8x^2 + \cdots + (3n-1)x^{n-1}$.

If $|x| < 1$, find $\lim\limits_{n\to\infty} S_n$. If $\sum\limits_{n=1}^{\infty}(3n-1)x^{n-1} = 4$, find the value of x.

5. Let $f(x) = \sum\limits_{n=1}^{\infty}(2n-1)x^{n-1} = 1 + 3x + 5x^2 + 7x^3 + \cdots$ for $-1 < x < 1$.

Show that $f(x) = \dfrac{1+x}{(1-x)^2}.$ Evaluate $\sum\limits_{n=1}^{\infty}(2n-1)\left(\tfrac{1}{4}\right)^{n-1}$.

6. Let $f(x) = \sum\limits_{n=1}^{\infty}(4n-3)x^{n-1}$, where $|x| < 1$.

(i) Show that $f(x) = \dfrac{1+3x}{(1-x)^2}.$ **(ii)** Evaluate $\sum\limits_{n=1}^{\infty}(4n-3)\left(\tfrac{4}{5}\right)^{n-1}$.

7. For the series $2.2 + 3.2^2 + 4.2^3 + \cdots + (n+1)2^n$, find:

(i) S_n, the sum of the first n terms   **(ii)** S_9, the sum of the first nine terms.

8. Write out the first four terms of the series $\sum\limits_{r=1}^{n} r2^{r-1}$.

Show that: $\sum\limits_{r=1}^{n} r2^{r-1} = (n-1)2^n + 1$. Evaluate $\sum\limits_{r=1}^{8} r2^{r-1}$.

9. For the series $2.1 + 3.3 + 4.3^2 + 5.3^3 + \cdots$, show that $S_n = \dfrac{(2n+1)3^n - 1}{4}.$

10. Evaluate $\sum\limits_{n=1}^{\infty} n\left(\tfrac{1}{3}\right)^n$.

Limits of Sequences

Consider the sequence given by $u_n = \dfrac{4n-1}{3n+2}$.

The terms are $\dfrac{3}{5}, \dfrac{7}{8}, \dfrac{11}{11}, \dfrac{15}{14}, \dfrac{19}{17}, \dfrac{23}{20}, \dfrac{27}{23}, \dfrac{31}{26}, \ldots$.

$$u_{20} = \frac{79}{62} \qquad\qquad u_{100} = \frac{399}{302} \qquad\qquad u_{1000} = \frac{3999}{3002}$$

As n gets larger, the sequence approaches $\frac{4}{3}$.

We say that the sequence has a limit of $\frac{4}{3}$ and is **convergent**.

Mathematically this is written:

$$\lim_{n\to\infty} u_n = \lim_{n\to\infty} \frac{4n-1}{3n+2} = \frac{4}{3}$$

Notes: Not all sequences have limits. A sequence which does not have a limit is said to be **divergent**.
'lim' is the abbreviation for limit.

The phrase 'n tends to infinity', written '$n \to \infty$', means that n can be made as large as we please.

Let us consider the value of the expression $\dfrac{1}{n}$ as $n \to \infty$.

n	$\dfrac{1}{n}$
10	0.1
100	0.01
1000	0.001
1,000,000	0.000001
1,000,000,000	0.000000001

The table indicates that as

$$n \to \infty, \; \frac{1}{n} \to 0.$$

This is written:

$$\lim_{n\to\infty} \frac{1}{n} = 0$$

This limit can be extended:

$$\lim_{n\to\infty} \frac{c}{n^p} = 0, \text{ for } p > 0, \, c \text{ a constant.}$$

To evaluate the limit, $\lim\limits_{x\to\infty} \dfrac{f(x)}{g(x)}$ do the following:

Divide the top and bottom by the dominant term and use the limit above.

The dominant term is the largest term as $n \to$ infinity.
In this section the dominant term is the highest power of n.

Example ▼

Find $\lim\limits_{n\to\infty} u_n$ if: **(i)** $u_n = \dfrac{n^2+5}{2n^2-3}$ **(ii)** $u_n = \dfrac{1}{4} - \dfrac{2}{n+5}$.

Solution:

(i) $\qquad u_n = \dfrac{n^2+5}{2n^2-3}$

$\qquad \lim\limits_{n\to\infty} u_n = \lim\limits_{n\to\infty} \dfrac{n^2+5}{2n^2-3}$

$\qquad = \lim\limits_{n\to\infty} \dfrac{1 + \dfrac{5}{n^2}}{2 - \dfrac{3}{n^2}}$

$\qquad \left(\begin{array}{c}\text{divide top and bottom by } n^2, \text{ the} \\ \text{dominant term}\end{array}\right)$

$\qquad = \dfrac{1+0}{2-0} = \dfrac{1}{2}$

(ii) $\qquad u_n = \dfrac{1}{4} - \dfrac{2}{n+5}$

$\qquad \lim\limits_{n\to\infty} u_n = \lim \left(\dfrac{1}{4} - \dfrac{2}{n+5}\right)$

$\qquad = \lim \left(\dfrac{1}{4} - \dfrac{\frac{2}{n}}{1+\frac{5}{n}}\right)$

$\qquad \left(\begin{array}{c}\text{divide top and bottom by } n, \text{ the} \\ \text{dominant term}\end{array}\right)$

$\qquad = \dfrac{1}{4} - \dfrac{0}{1+0} = \dfrac{1}{4} - 0 = \dfrac{1}{4}$

Sometimes we have to deal with limits that involve square roots.

For example: If $u_n = \dfrac{\sqrt{2n^2+3}}{n}$, evaluate $\lim\limits_{n\to\infty} u_n$.

In these cases, we write the total expression under one square root and then take the square root outside the limit.

Mathematically speaking: $\lim\limits_{n\to\infty} \sqrt{u_n} = \sqrt{\lim\limits_{n\to\infty} u_n}$

Taking the square root outside makes no difference, as $n\to\infty$.

Example ▼

$u_n = \dfrac{\sqrt{n^2-3n+2}}{4n+1}$. Find $\lim\limits_{n\to\infty} u_n$.

Solution:

$\qquad u_n = \dfrac{\sqrt{n^2-3n+2}}{4n+1} = \dfrac{\sqrt{n^2-3n+2}}{\sqrt{(4n+1)^2}} = \dfrac{\sqrt{n^2-3n+2}}{\sqrt{16n^2+8n+1}} = \sqrt{\dfrac{n^2-3n+2}{16n^2+8n+1}}$

$\qquad \lim\limits_{n\to\infty} u_n = \lim\limits_{n\to\infty} \dfrac{\sqrt{n^2-3n+2}}{4n+1} \qquad (\sqrt{(4n+1)^2} = 4n+1)$

$\qquad = \lim\limits_{n\to\infty} \sqrt{\dfrac{n^2-3n+2}{16n^2+8n+1}}$

$\qquad = \sqrt{\lim\limits_{n\to\infty} \dfrac{n^2-3n+2}{16n^2+8n+1}} \qquad \left(\begin{array}{c}\text{take } \sqrt{\ } \text{ outside; makes} \\ \text{no difference as } n\to\infty\end{array}\right)$

$$= \sqrt{\lim_{n \to \infty} \frac{1 - \frac{3}{n} + \frac{2}{n^2}}{16 + \frac{8}{n} + \frac{1}{n^2}}} \qquad \left(\begin{array}{c} \text{divide top and bottom by } n^2, \\ \text{the dominant term} \end{array} \right)$$

$$= \sqrt{\frac{1 - 0 + 0}{16 + 0 + 0}} = \sqrt{\frac{1}{16}} = \frac{\sqrt{1}}{\sqrt{16}} = \frac{1}{4}.$$

Exercise 7.7 ▼

In each of the following, find $\lim_{n \to \infty} u_n$ if:

1. $u_n = \dfrac{2n - 1}{n + 1}$

2. $u_n = \dfrac{4n + 1}{3n - 2}$

3. $u_n = \dfrac{2n + 1}{3n + 5}$

4. $u_n = \dfrac{4n^2 + 2n}{5n^2 - 3}$

5. $u_n = \dfrac{3n^2 - 4n}{7n^2 + 2n}$

6. $u_n = \dfrac{4}{3n + 1}$

7. $u_n = \dfrac{n}{n + 2}$

8. $u_n = \dfrac{1}{5} - \dfrac{1}{n + 1}$

9. $u_n = \dfrac{3}{4} - \dfrac{5}{n + 2}$

10. $u_n = \dfrac{1}{2} - \dfrac{1}{2(2n + 1)}$

11. $u_n = \dfrac{3}{2} - \dfrac{1}{n + 1} - \dfrac{1}{n + 2}$

12. $u_n = \dfrac{4}{5} - \dfrac{1}{n} - \dfrac{1}{n + 3}$

13. $u_n = \sqrt{\dfrac{25n + 2}{n - 3}}$

14. $u_n = \dfrac{\sqrt{n - 1}}{\sqrt{9n + 4}}$

15. $u_n = \dfrac{\sqrt{4n^2 - 1}}{n + 3}$

16. $u_n = \dfrac{1}{\sqrt{n^2 + 2}}$

17. $u_n = \dfrac{\sqrt{2n^2 + 3}}{n}$

18. $u_n = \dfrac{\sqrt{3n^2 - 1}}{2n + 3}$

19. (i) $1 + 3 + 5 + 7 + \cdots$ is an arithmetic series.
Find, in terms of n: **(a)** u_n **(b)** S_n.

(ii) Evaluate: $\displaystyle\lim_{n \to \infty} \frac{\sqrt{1 + 3 + 5 + 7 + \cdots + u_n}}{2n}$.

Series of the Form $\displaystyle\sum_{r=1}^{n} \frac{1}{r(r + 2)}$ and $\displaystyle\sum_{r=1}^{n} \frac{1}{(r + 1)(r + 3)}$

....

Infinite Series

Consider the infinite series $u_1 + u_2 + u_3 + \cdots$

This series can be written using the sigma notation:

$$\sum_{n=1}^{\infty} u_n = u_1 + u_2 + u_3 + \cdots$$

218

The sum to infinity of a series is denoted by $\lim\limits_{n\to\infty} S_n$, or simply S_∞.

Thus, we have the following:

$$\sum_{n=1}^{\infty} u_n = u_1 + u_2 + u_3 + \cdots = \lim_{n\to\infty} S_n$$

In this section we will show how to find a concise formula for S_n, the sum to n terms and, hence, evaluate $\lim\limits_{n\to\infty} S_n$, the sum to infinity, of series of the forms

$$\sum_{r=1}^{n} \frac{1}{r(r+2)} \quad \text{and} \quad \sum_{r=1}^{n} \frac{1}{(r+1)(r+3)}, \quad \text{which are neither arithmetic nor geometric.}$$

As with infinite geometric series:

if $\lim\limits_{n\to\infty} S_n$ exists, the series is said to be **convergent**;

if $\lim\limits_{n\to\infty} S_n$ does **not** exist, the series is said to be **divergent**.

Note: On this part of our course the series will be confined to those for which $\lim\limits_{n\to\infty} S_n$ exists (i.e. the sum of the series can be found).

The sum of an infinite convergent series is found with the following steps:

1. Find a concise expression for S_n.	**2.** Evaluate $\lim\limits_{n\to\infty} S_n$.

Partial Fractions and Telescoping the Series

By algebraic addition, $\dfrac{1}{n+1} - \dfrac{1}{n+2} = \dfrac{1}{(n+1)(n+2)}$.

The reverse process of showing that $\dfrac{1}{(n+1)(n+2)} = \dfrac{1}{n+1} - \dfrac{1}{n+2}$

is called resolving into **partial fractions**.

Partial fractions enable us to find a concise expression for S_n for a series of the form

$$\sum_{r=1}^{n} \frac{1}{(r+1)(r+2)} \quad \text{or} \quad \sum_{r=1}^{n} \frac{1}{r(r+2)}, \quad \text{using the following steps:}$$

1. Express the nth term in the form $u_r = v_r - v_{r+1}$ (or similar).
2. List the terms vertically.
3. Add the terms (most will cancel).

This will leave us with a concise expression for S_n (as most of the terms will cancel).
The process which enables us to find S_n of a series through cancellation is called **telescoping** a series (the series 'folds in' on itself).

(i) If $u_k = \dfrac{1}{(k+2)(k+3)} = \dfrac{A}{k+2} + \dfrac{B}{k+3}$, for all $k \in \mathbf{R}$,

   find the value of A and the value of B, $A, B \in \mathbf{R}$.

(ii) **(a)** Find, in terms of n: $\displaystyle\sum_{k=1}^{n} u_k$.   **(b)** Evaluate: $\displaystyle\sum_{k=1}^{100} u_k$.

(iii) Evaluate: $\displaystyle\sum_{k=1}^{\infty} u_k$.

(iv) Find the value of n such that $\displaystyle\sum_{k=1}^{n} u_k = \tfrac{24}{25} \sum_{k=1}^{\infty} u_k$.

Solution:

(i) $\dfrac{1}{(k+2)(k+3)} = \dfrac{A}{(k+2)} + \dfrac{B}{(k+3)}$

$$1 = A(k+3) + B(k+2) \qquad \text{[multiply both sides by } (k+2)(k+3)]$$

What we do next is choose two values for k and substitute these into the equation.
The two most suitable values are ones that make the coefficient of $B = 0$ and the coefficient of $A = 0$.

The values of k where $(k+2)$ and $(k+3)$ are zero are used as follows:

$$1 = A(k+3) + B(k+2)$$

Let $k = -2$:
$$1 = A(-2+3) + B(-2+2)$$
$$1 = A(1) + B(0)$$
$$1 = A$$

Let $k = -3$:
$$1 = A(-3+3) + B(-3+2)$$
$$1 = A(0) + B(-1)$$
$$1 = -B$$
$$-1 = B$$

$$\therefore \quad \dfrac{1}{(k+2)(k+3)} = \dfrac{1}{k+2} - \dfrac{1}{k+3}$$

Note: There are two other methods for finding the value of A and the value of B.

1. Substitute any two values for k to obtain two equations in A and B.
   Solve these simultaneous equations. (If the question says $k \in \mathbf{N}$, then you can use only positive whole numbers.)
2. Remove the brackets and equate the coefficients of like terms to obtain two equations in A and B. Solve these simultaneous equations.

(ii) (a) $\displaystyle\sum_{k=1}^{n} u_k = \sum_{k=1}^{n}\frac{1}{(k+2)(k+3)} = \sum_{k=1}^{n}\left(\frac{1}{k+2}-\frac{1}{k+3}\right) = S_n$

What we do next is telescope the series by listing the terms vertically and cancelling terms which are the same but of opposite signs. It is good practice to write down enough terms to see the terms that cancel. It always happens that the same number of terms remain at the top and the bottom.

$$u_k = \frac{1}{k+2}-\frac{1}{k+3}$$

(one term remaining) $\longrightarrow$ $\quad u_1 = \dfrac{1}{3} - \dfrac{1}{4}$

$$u_2 = \frac{1}{4} - \frac{1}{5}$$

$$u_3 = \frac{1}{5} - \frac{1}{6}$$

$$\vdots \qquad \vdots \qquad \vdots$$

$$\vdots \qquad \vdots \qquad \vdots$$

$$\vdots \qquad \vdots \qquad \vdots$$

$$u_{n-2} = \frac{1}{n} - \frac{1}{n+1}$$

$$u_{n-1} = \frac{1}{n+1} - \frac{1}{n+2}$$

$$u_n = \frac{1}{n+2} - \frac{1}{n+3} \qquad \longleftarrow \text{(one term remaining)}$$

$$S_n = \frac{1}{3} - \frac{1}{n+3} \qquad \text{(adding)}$$

(b) $\displaystyle\sum_{k=1}^{100} u_k = S_{100}$

$$S_n = \frac{1}{3} - \frac{1}{n+3}$$

$$S_{100} = \frac{1}{3} - \frac{1}{100+3} \qquad \text{[put in } n=100\text{]}$$

$$= \frac{1}{3} - \frac{1}{103} = \frac{100}{309}$$

(iii) $\displaystyle\sum_{k=1}^{\infty} u_k = \lim_{n\to\infty} S_n$

$$= \lim_{n\to\infty}\left(\frac{1}{3} - \frac{1}{n+3}\right)$$

$$= \lim_{n\to\infty}\left(\frac{1}{3} - \frac{\frac{1}{n}}{1+\frac{3}{n}}\right) \qquad \begin{bmatrix}\text{divide top and}\\ \text{bottom by } n\end{bmatrix}$$

$$= \frac{1}{3} - \frac{0}{1+0} = \frac{1}{3} - 0 = \frac{1}{3}$$

(iv) $\displaystyle\sum_{k=1}^{n} u_k = \frac{24}{25}\sum_{k=1}^{\infty} u_k$

$\therefore \qquad S_n = \frac{24}{25}\lim_{n\to\infty} S_n$

$$\frac{1}{3} - \frac{1}{n+3} = \frac{24}{25}\left(\frac{1}{3}\right) \qquad \left[S_n = \frac{1}{3} - \frac{1}{n+3} \text{ and } \lim_{n\to\infty} S_n = \frac{1}{3}\right]$$

$$\frac{1}{3} - \frac{1}{n+3} = \frac{8}{25}$$

$$25(n+3) - 75 = 24(n+3) \qquad \text{[multiply both sides by } 75(n+3)]$$

$$25n + 75 - 75 = 24n + 72$$

$$n = 72$$

Exercise 7.8 ▼

1. (i) Show that $\dfrac{1}{r(r+1)} = \dfrac{1}{r} - \dfrac{1}{r+1}$.

   (ii) Show that: **(a)** $\displaystyle\sum_{r=1}^{n} \frac{1}{r(r+1)} = \frac{n}{n+1}$ **(b)** $\displaystyle\sum_{r=1}^{\infty} \frac{1}{r(r+1)} = 1$.

2. (i) Show that $\dfrac{1}{(k+1)(k+2)} = \dfrac{1}{k+1} - \dfrac{1}{k+2}$.

   (ii) Evaluate, in terms of n: $\displaystyle\sum_{k=1}^{n} \frac{1}{(k+1)(k+2)}$.   **(iii)** Evaluate $\displaystyle\sum_{k=1}^{\infty} \frac{1}{(k+1)(k+2)}$.

3. (i) Show that $\dfrac{1}{(r+2)(r+3)} = \dfrac{1}{r+2} - \dfrac{1}{r+3}$.   **(ii)** Evaluate, in terms of n: $\displaystyle\sum_{r=1}^{n} \frac{1}{(r+2)(r+3)}$.

(iii) Evaluate $\displaystyle\sum_{r=1}^{\infty} \frac{1}{(r+2)(r+3)}$.   **(iv)** Evaluate $\displaystyle\sum_{r=1}^{72} \frac{1}{(r+2)(r+3)}$.

(v) If $\displaystyle\sum_{r=1}^{n} \frac{1}{(r+2)(r+3)} = \frac{13}{14}\sum_{r=1}^{\infty} \frac{1}{(r+2)(r+3)}$, find the value of n.

4. Show that $\displaystyle \frac{1}{r(r-1)} = \frac{1}{r-1} - \frac{1}{r}$.

(i) Let $u_r = \dfrac{1}{r(r-1)}$. Evaluate $\displaystyle\sum_{r=2}^{\infty} \frac{1}{r(r-1)}$.

(ii) Find the value of n, where $n \in \mathbf{N}$, such that:

$$\sum_{r=2}^{n} u_r = \frac{23}{24}\sum_{r=2}^{\infty} u_r$$

5. If $\displaystyle \frac{1}{(3n-2)(3n+1)} = \frac{A}{3n-2} + \frac{B}{3n+1}$, find the values of A and B, $A, B \in \mathbf{R}$.

6. If $\displaystyle \frac{1}{(k+1)(k+3)} = \frac{A}{k+1} - \frac{B}{k+3}$, find the values of A and B, $A, B \in \mathbf{R}$.

(i) Find, in terms of n: $\displaystyle\sum_{k=1}^{n} \frac{1}{(k+1)(k+3)}$.

(ii) Evaluate: **(a)** $\displaystyle\sum_{k=1}^{7} \frac{1}{(k+1)(k+3)}$ **(b)** $\displaystyle\sum_{k=1}^{\infty} \frac{1}{(k+1)(k+3)}$.

7. If $u_r = \dfrac{1}{r(r+2)} = \dfrac{A}{r} + \dfrac{B}{r+2}$, find the values of A and B, $A, B \in \mathbf{R}$.

(i) Find, in terms of n: $\displaystyle\sum_{r=1}^{n} u_r$.   **(ii)** Evaluate $\displaystyle\sum_{r=1}^{\infty} u_r$.

8. Show that $\displaystyle \frac{1}{(2k+1)(2k+3)} = \frac{1}{2}\left[\frac{1}{2k+1} - \frac{1}{2k+3}\right]$.

Let $u_k = \dfrac{1}{(2k+1)(2k+3)}$.

(i) Evaluate, in terms of n: $\displaystyle\sum_{k=1}^{n} u_k$.   **(ii)** Evaluate $\displaystyle\sum_{k=1}^{\infty} u_k$.

(iii) Find the least value of n, $n \in \mathbf{N}$, such that:

$$\sum_{k=1}^{n} u_k \geqslant \frac{19}{20}\sum_{k=1}^{\infty} u_k$$

9. (i) Find u_n of the series:

(a) $1+3+5+7+\cdots$ **(b)** $3+5+7+9+\cdots$.

(ii) (a) Find u_r of the series: $\displaystyle \frac{1}{1.3} + \frac{1}{3.5} + \frac{1}{5.7} + \frac{1}{7.9} + \cdots$.

(b) Find, in terms of n: $\displaystyle\sum_{r=1}^{n} u_r$.   **(c)** Evaluate $\displaystyle\sum_{r=1}^{\infty} u_r$.   **(d)** Evaluate $\displaystyle\sum_{r=1}^{100} u_r$.

223

10. (i) Explain why $\sqrt{a}\sqrt{a+1} = \sqrt{a^2+a}$.

(ii) Show that $\dfrac{\sqrt{k+1}-\sqrt{k}}{\sqrt{k^2+k}} = \dfrac{1}{\sqrt{k}} - \dfrac{1}{\sqrt{k+1}}$.

(iii) If $u_k = \dfrac{\sqrt{k+1}-\sqrt{k}}{\sqrt{k^2+k}}$, express, in terms of n: $\displaystyle\sum_{k=1}^{n} u_k$.

(iv) Evaluate: **(a)** $\displaystyle\sum_{k=1}^{80} u_n$ **(b)** $\displaystyle\sum_{k=1}^{\infty} u_n$.

11. If $u_r = \ln\left(\dfrac{r+1}{r}\right)$, express, in terms of n: $\displaystyle\sum_{r=1}^{n} u_r$.

(Hint: $\ln\dfrac{a}{b} = \ln a - \ln b$, and telescope the series.)

Evaluate $\displaystyle\sum_{r=1}^{53} u_r$, correct to two significant figures.

12. Show that $\dfrac{k}{(k+1)!} = \dfrac{1}{k!} - \dfrac{1}{(k+1)!}$.

If $u_k = \dfrac{k}{(k+1)!}$, express in terms of n: $\displaystyle\sum_{k=1}^{n} u_k$.

Series of Powers of Natural Numbers

There are three series on our course involving series of powers of natural numbers.

> **1.** $\displaystyle\sum_{r=1}^{n} k = k + k + k + \cdots + k = nk$
>
> **2.** $\displaystyle\sum_{r=1}^{n} r = 1 + 2 + 3 + \cdots + n = \dfrac{n}{2}(n+1)$
>
> **3.** $\displaystyle\sum_{r=1}^{n} r^2 = 1^2 + 2^2 + 3^2 + \cdots + n^2 = \dfrac{n}{6}(n+1)(2n+1)$
>
> We use these to find an expression for S_n if $u_n = an^2 + bn + c$, where $a, b, c \in \mathbf{R}$.

Notes: (i) $\displaystyle\sum_{r=1}^{n} 1 = \underset{\longleftarrow\; n\text{ times}\;\longrightarrow}{(1+1+1+\cdots+1)} = n$ (since a 1 is required for each $r = 1, 2, 3, \ldots n$).

(ii) Each of these formulae can be proved using induction.
(1 and 2 are arithmetic series and can be proved using the sum to n terms, $S_n = \dfrac{n}{2}[2a + (n-1)d]$.)

(iii) $\displaystyle\sum_{r=1}^{n}(u_r + v_r) = \sum_{r=1}^{n} u_r + \sum_{r=1}^{n} v_r$ and $\displaystyle\sum_{r=1}^{n} k u_r = k\sum_{r=1}^{n} u_r$.

Example ▼

(i) Write $\dfrac{n^3+1}{n+1}$ in the form an^2+bn+c, where $a, b, c \in \mathbf{R}$.

(ii) Hence, evaluate $\displaystyle\sum_{n=1}^{24} \dfrac{n^3+1}{n+1}$.

Solution:

(i) Method 1 (using factors):

$$\dfrac{n^3+1}{n+1}$$

$$=\dfrac{(n)^3+(1)^3}{n+1} \qquad \left(\begin{array}{l}\text{sum of two}\\\text{cubes on top}\end{array}\right)$$

$$=\dfrac{(n+1)(n^2-n+1)}{(n+1)}$$

$$=n^2-n+1$$

(i) Method 2 (using long division):

$$\begin{array}{r} n^2-n+1 \\ n+1\overline{\smash{\big)}\,n^3+0n^2+0n+1} \\ \underline{n^3+n^2} \\ -n^2+0n \\ \underline{-n^2-n} \\ n+1 \\ \underline{n+1} \\ 0+0 \end{array}$$

Thus, $\dfrac{n^3+1}{n+1}=n^2-n+1$.

(ii) $\displaystyle\sum_{n=1}^{24} \dfrac{n^3+1}{n+1}$

$$=\sum_{n=1}^{24}(n^2-n+1)$$

$$=\sum_{n=1}^{24}n^2-\sum_{n=1}^{24}n+\sum_{n=1}^{24}1$$

$$\left(\sum_{r=1}^{n}r^2=\dfrac{n}{6}(n+1)(2n+1); \quad \sum_{r=1}^{n}r=\dfrac{n}{2}(n+1); \quad \sum_{r=1}^{n}1=n\right)$$

$$=\dfrac{24}{6}(24+1)(48+1)-\dfrac{24}{2}(24+1)+24 \qquad \text{(put in } n=24)$$

$$=4(25)(49)-12(25)+24$$

$$=4,900-300+24$$

$$=4,624$$

$$\sum_{r=1}^{n}(3r-1)(2r+4) = 2.6+5.8+8.10+\cdots+(3n-1)(2n+4)$$

Find, in terms of n, an expression for $\sum_{r=1}^{n}(3r-1)(2r+4)$.

Solution:

$$u_r = (3r-1)(2r+4) = 6r^2 + 10r - 4$$

$$\therefore \quad \sum_{r=1}^{n}(3r-1)(2r+4)$$

$$= \sum_{r=1}^{n}(6r^2 + 10r - 4)$$

$$= \sum_{r=1}^{n}6r^2 \quad + \quad \sum_{r=1}^{n}10r \quad - \quad \sum_{r=1}^{n}4$$

$$= 6\sum_{r=1}^{n}r^2 \quad + \quad 10\sum_{r=1}^{n}r \quad - \quad 4\sum_{r=1}^{n}1$$

$$= 6\left[\frac{n}{6}(n+1)(2n+1)\right] + 10\left[\frac{n}{2}(n+1)\right] - 4[n]$$

$$= n(n+1)(2n+1) + 5n(n+1) - 4n$$

$$= n[(n+1)(2n+1) + 5(n+1) - 4] \qquad \text{(factor out } n\text{)}$$

$$= n(2n^2 + 3n + 1 + 5n + 5 - 4)$$

$$= n(2n^2 + 8n + 2)$$

$$= 2n(n^2 + 4n + 1)$$

Some sequences are a combination of powers of natural numbers and a geometric sequence.
For example, $u_n = 2n^2 + 3n + 5^n$.
These sequences can be split and summed separately.

Find, in terms of n, $\sum_{r=1}^{n}(2r-1+3^r)$. Hence, evaluate $\sum_{n=1}^{8}(2n-1+3^n)$

Solution:

u_n is made up of a 'sum of powers of natural numbers' part, $2r-1$, and a 'geometric' part, 3^r.
We sum these parts separately and combine the results.

Sum of the powers of natural numbers part:

$$\sum_{r=1}^{n}(2r-1)$$

$$=\sum_{r=1}^{n}2r-\sum_{r=1}^{n}1$$

$$=2\sum_{r=1}^{n}r-\sum_{r=1}^{n}1$$

$$=2\cdot\frac{n}{2}(n+1)-n$$

$$=n(n+1)-n$$

$$=n^2+n-n$$

$$=n^2$$

Sum of the geometric part:

$$\sum_{r=1}^{n}3^r$$

$$=\frac{a(r^n-1)}{r-1}$$

$$=\frac{3(3^n-1)}{3-1}$$

$$=\frac{3(3^n-1)}{2}$$

Thus, $\sum_{r=1}^{n}(2r-1+3^r)=n^2+\dfrac{3(3^n-1)}{2}$.

$$\sum_{n=1}^{8}(2n-1+3^n)=(8)^2+\frac{3(3^8-1)}{2} \qquad \text{(put in } n=8)$$

$$=64+\frac{3(6{,}561-1)}{2}$$

$$=64+9{,}840=9{,}904$$

Note: $\sum_{r=1}^{n}(2r-1)$ is the arithmetic series $1+3+5+\cdots+(2r-1)$.

This part could have been summed using the formula $S_n=\dfrac{n}{2}[2a+(n-1)d]$.

Exercise 7.9 ▼

Show that:

1. $1+3+5+7+\cdots+(2n-1)=n^2$

2. $1+5+9+13+\cdots+(4n-3)=2n^2-n$

3. $2\cdot 2+4\cdot 5+6\cdot 8+\cdots+2n(3n-1)=2n^2(n+1)$

4. $2\cdot 4+5\cdot 6+8\cdot 8+\cdots+(3n-1)(2n+2)=n(2n^2+5n+1)$

5. $3\cdot 7+5\cdot 13+7\cdot 19+\cdots+(2n+1)(6n+1)=n(4n^2+10n+7)$

6. Evaluate: (i) $\sum_{n=1}^{20}(2n+3)$ (ii) $\sum_{n=1}^{20}n(2n+1)$.

7. $\sum_{r=1}^{n}2r(3r-1)=an^2(n+b)$. Find the value of a and the value of b.

Hence, or otherwise, evaluate $\sum_{n=1}^{9}2n(3n-1)$.

8. (i) Express $(2r-1)^2$ in the form $ar^2 + br + c$, where $a, b, c \in \mathbf{Z}$.

(ii) Show that $\displaystyle\sum_{r=1}^{n} 3(2r-1)^2 = n(2n-1)(2n+1)$.

(iii) Hence, evaluate $\displaystyle\sum_{n=1}^{10} 3(2n-1)^2$.

9. (i) Express $\dfrac{n^2 + 6n + 5}{n+1}$ in the form $an + b$, where $a, b \in \mathbf{R}$.

(ii) Hence, evaluate $\displaystyle\sum_{n=1}^{100} \dfrac{n^2 + 6n + 5}{n+1}$.

10. (i) Express $\dfrac{n^3 + 64}{n+4}$ in the form $an^2 + bn + c$, where $a, b, c \in \mathbf{R}$.

(ii) Hence, evaluate $\displaystyle\sum_{n=1}^{21} \dfrac{n^3 + 64}{n+4}$.

11. Show that $\displaystyle\sum_{r=1}^{n} (3r^2 + r - 2) = n(n^2 + 2n - 1)$. Hence, evaluate $\displaystyle\sum_{n=1}^{20} (3n^2 + n - 2)$.

Evaluate each of the following:

12. $\displaystyle\sum_{n=1}^{6} (2 + 3^n)$ **13.** $\displaystyle\sum_{n=1}^{12} (5n + 3 + 2^n)$ **14.** $\displaystyle\sum_{n=1}^{10} (2^n - n^2 + 1)$

15. (i) Express $\displaystyle\sum_{r=1}^{n} (r+1)(2r+1)$ in the form $\dfrac{n}{6}(an^2 + bn + c)$, where $a, b, c \in \mathbf{N}$.

(ii) Hence, evaluate: $2 . 3 + 3 . 5 + 4 . 7 + \cdots + 11 . 21$.

16. For a certain sequence, $u_n = an^2 + bn + c$, where $a, b, c \in \mathbf{Z}$.
If $u_1 = 4$, $u_2 = 15$ and $u_3 = 2u_2$, find the values of a, b and c.
Hence, evaluate $\displaystyle\sum_{n=1}^{12} an^2 + bn + c$.

17. $\displaystyle\sum_{r=1}^{n} r = 1 + 2 + 3 + \cdots + n$. Show that $\displaystyle\sum_{r=1}^{n} r = \dfrac{n}{2}(n+1)$.
Evaluate: $1 + (1+2) + (1+2+3) + \cdots + (1+2+3+\cdots+20)$.

FURTHER CALCULUS AND SERIES

Maximum and Minimum Problems

The technique of finding the local maximum or local minimum of a function can be applied to many real and practical problems. For example, manufacturers wanting to maximise profits, farmers trying to minimise costs, speculators attempting to minimise risk, etc. These types of problem often require the construction of an appropriate function. We can then use our knowledge of differentiation to find the maximum, or minimum.

Maximum and minimum problems can be solved with the following steps:

1. Draw a diagram (if necessary). Label the diagram with the variables and constants.
2. Write down an equation in terms of the variables in the diagram for the quantity to be maximised or minimised. (If the quantity to be maximised or minimised is expressed in terms of one variable, go to step 5.)
3. If the quantity to be maximised or minimised is expressed in terms of two variables (for example, $P = 2l + 2b$, $A = \pi r^2 + 2\pi h$, $V = \pi r^2 h$), then read the question again to find the **constant** expression **linking** the two variables. From this constant expression write one variable in terms of the other.
4. Using a substitution from step 3, write the quantity to be maximised or minimised in terms of one variable.
5. Differentiate the quantity to be maximised or minimised, with respect to the single variable in step 4. Put this derivative equal to zero and solve the equation.
6. Reject values that don't make sense. Check, if necessary, that the value gives a maximum or minimum, by using the second derivative.

   (i) $\dfrac{d^2y}{dx^2} < 0$ for a maximum value   **(ii)** $\dfrac{d^2y}{dx^2} > 0$ for a minimum value.
7. Answer the question (for example, find the radius, calculate the volume, etc.).

Example ▼

A rectangular area is enclosed by a three-sided fence with 100 metres of fencing, using a ditch as the fourth side. Find the dimensions of the rectangle if the area is to be a maximum, and find the maximum area.

Solution:

1.

Let the dimensions be x m and y m and let the area be A m^2.

2.   Maximise the area, A:

$$A = xy$$

(two variables, x and y)

Thus we need a link between x and y.

3. Link between x and y:

Given: Length of fence is constant $= 100$ m

Link: $2x + y = 100$

$$y = (100 - 2x)$$

4. Area in terms of one variable:

$$A = xy$$
$$A = x(100 - 2x)$$
$$A = 100x - 2x^2$$

5. $A = 100x - 2x^2$

$$\frac{dA}{dx} = 100 - 4x = 0 \qquad \text{(max/min)}$$
$$-4x = -100$$
$$x = 25$$

6. $\dfrac{dA}{dx} = 100 - 4x$

$$\frac{d^2A}{dx^2} = -4 < 0$$

$\therefore$ a maximum value.

7. The dimensions:

$$x = 25$$
$$y = 100 - 2x = 100 - 50 = 50$$

Thus, $x = 25$ m and $y = 50$ m are the required dimensions.

$$A_{max} = xy$$
$$= 25 \times 50 = 1250$$

Thus, the maximum area is 1250 m^2.

Example ▼

A rectangular sheet of cardboard is 24 cm by 15 cm. Four equal squares are cut from each corner and the flaps are turned up to form an open box. Find the length of the side of the square that makes the volume of the box as large as possible. Find this largest volume.

Solution:

1. Let the length of the side of each square be x cm, and let V cm^3 be the volume of the box.

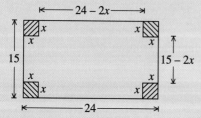
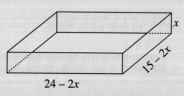

2. Maximise the volume, V:

$$V = l \times b \times h$$
$$V = (24 - 2x)(15 - 2x)(x)$$
$$V = 4x^3 - 78x^2 + 360x$$

(one variable, $\therefore$ skip steps 3 and 4)

5. $V = 4x^3 - 78x^2 + 360x$

$$\frac{dV}{dx} = 12x^2 - 156x + 360 = 0 \quad \text{(max/min)}$$
$$x^2 - 13x + 30 = 0$$
$$(x - 3)(x - 10) = 0$$
$$x = 3 \quad \text{or} \quad x = 10$$

$x = 10$ is rejected, as the length of the side of the square must be less than half the breadth of the rectangle.

6. $\dfrac{dV}{dx} = 12x^2 - 156x + 360$

$\dfrac{d^2V}{dx^2} = 24x - 156$

$\dfrac{d^2V}{dx^2}\bigg|_{x=3} = 24(3) - 156 = -84 < 0$

∴ a maximum value.

Thus, $x = 3$ is the solution.

7. Maximum volume of the box:

height $= h = x = 3$

length $= l = (24 - 2x) = 24 - 6 = 18$

breadth $= b = (15 - 2x) = 15 - 6 = 9$

$V_{max} = l \times b \times h$

$= 18 \times 9 \times 3$

$= 486 \text{ cm}^3$

Example ▼

A closed cylindrical can is made so that its volume is $128\pi \text{ cm}^3$. Find the dimensions of the can if the surface area is to be a minimum.

Solution:

1. Let the radius be r cm, the height be h cm and the surface area be A cm^2.

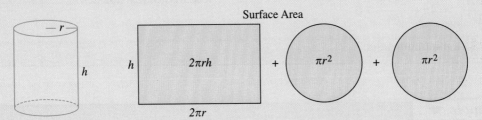

Surface Area

$2\pi rh$ $+$ πr^2 $+$ πr^2

2. Minimise the surface area, A:

$A = 2\pi r^2 + 2\pi rh$

(two variables, r and h)

Thus we need a **link** between r and h.

3. Link between r and h:

Given: Volume is constant $= 128\pi \text{ cm}^3$

Link: $\pi r^2 h = V$

$\pi r^2 h = 128\pi$

$r^2 h = 128$

$h = \dfrac{128}{r^2}$

4. Surface area in terms of one variable:

$A = 2\pi r^2 + 2\pi rh$

$A = 2\pi r^2 + 2\pi r\left(\dfrac{128}{r^2}\right)$

$A = 2\pi r^2 + \dfrac{256\pi}{r}$

$A = 2\pi r^2 + 256\pi r^{-1}$

$\left(\text{put in } h = \dfrac{128}{r^2}\right)$

$\left(\dfrac{1}{r} = r^{-1}\right)$

231

5. $A = 2\pi r^2 + 256\pi r^{-1}$

$$\frac{dA}{dr} = 4\pi r - 256\pi r^{-2} = 0 \qquad \text{(max/min)}$$

$$4\pi r - \frac{256\pi}{r^2} = 0$$

$$4\pi r^3 - 256\pi = 0 \qquad \text{(multiply both sides by } r^2)$$

$$r^3 - 64 = 0$$

$$r^3 = 64$$

$$r = 4$$

6. $\dfrac{dA}{dr} = 4\pi r - 256\pi r^{-2}$

$$\frac{d^2A}{dr^2} = 4\pi + 512\pi r^{-3}$$

$$\frac{d^2A}{dr^2} = 4\pi + \frac{512\pi}{r^3}$$

$$\left.\frac{d^2A}{dr^2}\right|_{r=4} = 4\pi + \frac{512\pi}{64} > 0$$

$\therefore$ a minimum value.

7. $r = 4$

$$h = \frac{128}{r^2}$$

$$h = \frac{128}{16} = 8$$

Thus, $r = 4$ cm and $h = 8$ cm are the required dimensions.

Example ▼

a is the point $(0, 1)$.

$p(x, y)$ is a point on the curve $y = x^2$, where $x > 0$.

(i) Express $|ap|$ in terms of x.

(ii) Given that there is only one value of x for which $|ap|$ is a minimum, find this value of x.

(iii) Hence, find the minimum value of $|ap|$.

Solution:

(i) $|ap|$ is the distance between the points $a(0, 1)$ and $p(x, y)$.

$$|ap| = \sqrt{(x-0)^2 + (y-1)^2}$$

$$= \sqrt{(x-0)^2 + (x^2-1)^2} \qquad [y = x^2]$$

$$= \sqrt{x^2 + x^4 - 2x^2 + 1}$$

$$= \sqrt{x^4 - x^2 + 1}$$

$$= (x^4 - x^2 + 1)^{1/2}$$

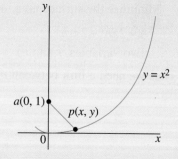

(ii) Let $|ap| = l$.

$$l = (x^4 - x^2 + 1)^{1/2} \qquad \text{[apply the chain rule]}$$

$$\frac{dl}{dx} = \tfrac{1}{2}(x^4 - x^2 + 1)^{-1/2}(4x^3 - 2x) = 0 \qquad \text{[max/min]}$$

$$\frac{4x^3 - 2x}{2(x^4 - x^2 + 1)} = 0$$

$$4x^3 - 2x = 0 \qquad \text{[multiply both sides by } 2(x^4 - x^2 + 1)]$$

$$2x^2 - 1 = 0 \qquad [x > 0]$$

$$2x^2 = 1$$

$$x^2 = \frac{1}{2}$$

$$x = \frac{1}{\sqrt{2}}$$

(iii)

$$|ap| = \sqrt{x^4 - x^2 + 1}$$

$$|ap|_{\min} = \sqrt{\left(\frac{1}{\sqrt{2}}\right)^4 - \left(\frac{1}{\sqrt{2}}\right)^2 + 1} \qquad \left[\text{put in } x = \frac{1}{\sqrt{2}}\right]$$

$$= \sqrt{\frac{1}{4} - \frac{1}{2} + 1}$$

$$= \sqrt{\frac{3}{4}} = \frac{\sqrt{3}}{\sqrt{4}} = \frac{\sqrt{3}}{2}$$

Example ▼

Find the area of the rectangle of maximum area that can be drawn inside a circle of radius r. (There is no need to test for a maximum.)

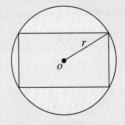

Solution:

1. Let the dimensions of the rectangle be $2x$ and $2y$ and let the area of the rectangle be A.

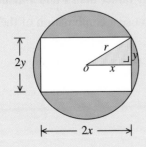

2. Maximise the area, A:

$$A = 2x \times 2y$$

$$A = 4xy$$

(two variables, x and y)

Thus we need a link between x and y.

233

3. Link between x and y:

Given: radius of circle is constant $= r$

Link: $x^2 + y^2 = r^2$ (Pythagoras's theorem)

$$y^2 = r^2 - x^2$$
$$y = \sqrt{r^2 - x^2}$$

4. Area in terms of one variable:

$$A = 4xy$$
$$A = 4x\sqrt{r^2 - x^2}$$
$$A = \sqrt{16x^2}\,\sqrt{r^2 - x^2}$$
$$A = \sqrt{16x^2\,(r^2 - x^2)}$$
$$A = \sqrt{16r^2x^2 - 16x^4}$$

5. $\quad A = \sqrt{16r^2x^2 - 16x^4}$

$$A = (16r^2x^2 - 16x^4)^{1/2}$$

$\qquad\qquad\qquad\qquad\qquad\qquad$ [apply the chain rule]

$$\frac{dA}{dx} = \tfrac{1}{2}(16r^2x^2 - 16x^4)^{-1/2}\,(32r^2x - 64x^3) = 0 \qquad \text{[max/min]}$$

$$\frac{32r^2x - 64x^3}{2(16r^2x^2 - 16x^4)^{1/2}} = 0$$

$$32r^2x - 64x^3 = 0 \qquad \text{[multiply both sides by } 2(16r^2x^2 - 16x^4)^{1/2}]$$

$$64x^3 = 32xr^2$$

$$2x^2 = r^2 \qquad [x > 0]$$

$$x^2 = \frac{r^2}{2}$$

$$x^2 = \frac{r}{\sqrt{2}}$$

(No need for step 6.)

7. $\quad x = \dfrac{r}{\sqrt{2}}$

$$y = \sqrt{r^2 - x^2} = \sqrt{r^2 - \frac{r^2}{2}} = \sqrt{\frac{r^2}{2}} = \frac{r}{\sqrt{2}}$$

$$A_{\max} = 4xy = 4 \times \frac{r}{\sqrt{2}} \times \frac{r}{\sqrt{2}} = 4\frac{r^2}{2} = 2r^2$$

Notes: 1. Letting the dimensions of the rectangle be $2x$ and $2y$ rather than x and y avoids fractions.

2. Writing $4x\sqrt{r^2 - x^2} = \sqrt{16x^2(r^2 - x^2)}$ avoids having to use a combination of the product and chain rule when differentiating.

1. $x + y = 10$. Express y in terms of x. If $A = xy$, find the maximum value of A, and the values of x and y which give this maximum.

2. $x + y = 6$. If $A = x^2 + y^2$, calculate the minimum value of A.

3. The length of a rectangle is $(x + 6)$ m and its width is $(18 - x)$ m. Calculate the value of x that gives the rectangle of maximum area. What is this maximum area?

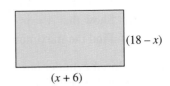

$(18 - x)$

$(x + 6)$

4. The cost of running a machine is given by $C = 17V(V - 5) + 80$, where $C =$ cent per hour and V is the number of revolutions per second. Find the number of revolutions per second that will minimise the cost.

5. At a speed of x km/h, a motorbike can cover y km on 1 litre of petrol, where

$$y = 5 + \frac{1}{2}x + \frac{1}{30}x^2 - \frac{1}{450}x^3$$

Calculate the maximum distance that the motorbike can travel on 16 litres of petrol.

6. A box has a square base, x cm by x cm, and a height h cm, where $h + x = 12$.
   (i) Express h in terms of x.
   (ii) Find the maximum volume of the box.

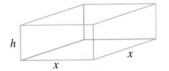

7. A closed rectangular box is made of metal of negligible thickness. Its length is three times its width. The volume of the box is 288 cm^3. If its width is x cm,

   show that its surface area, A, is given by $A = \left(\dfrac{768}{x} + 6x^2\right)$ cm^2.

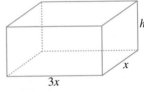

   If the surface area of the box is to be a minimum, find the dimensions of the box.

8. A farmer wishes to fence in a rectangular enclosure of 162 m^2. One part of the enclosure is formed by a wall. The length of the rectangle is y m and the width is x m.
   (i) Express y in terms of x.
   (ii) What is the least possible length of fencing required for the other three sides?

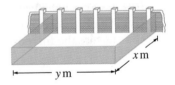

9. The width and length of a page in a book are x cm and y cm, respectively.
   (i) If the area of the page is 96 cm^2, express y in terms of x.
   (ii) It is necessary to leave a margin of 2 cm at each side of the text and 3 cm at the top and bottom (as shown).
      (a) Express, in terms of x and y, the area of the page available for text.
      (b) Express, in terms of x, the area of the page available for text.
      (c) Find the dimensions of the page, if the area available for text is a maximum.

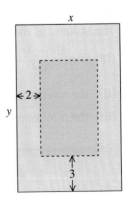

10. A rectangular sheet of cardboard measures 16 cm by 10 cm. Four equal squares are cut from each corner and the flaps are turned up to form an open box. Find the length of the side of the square which makes the volume of the box as large as possible. Find this largest volume.

11. The diagram shows a minor sector oab of a circle of radius r cm.
The perimeter of the sector is 12 cm and the area of the sector is A cm^2.

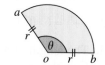

  (i) Express θ in terms of r.

  (ii) Show that $A = 6r - r^2$.

  (iii) Find the maximum value of A and the corresponding value of θ.

12. A closed cylinder has a base radius of r cm and a perpendicular height of h cm. Its total surface area is 96π cm^2.

  (i) Express h in terms of r.

  (ii) If the volume of the cylinder is to be a maximum, find the dimensions of the cylinder.

  (iii) Find the maximum volume in terms of π.

13. An open cylindrical can, with no lid, has a base radius of r cm and a height of h cm. The total surface area of the can is 300π cm^2.

  (i) Express h in terms of r.

  (ii) Show that the volume V cm^3 is given by:
$$V = 150\pi r - \tfrac{1}{2}\pi r^3.$$

  (iii) Find the dimensions of the can that gives a maximum volume. Calculate this maximum volume.

14. Closed cylindrical tins are to have a volume of one litre (1,000 cm^3). The curved surface area (the walls of the tin) are to be made from rectangular sheets of length $2\pi r$ cm and width h cm, without any waste. However, stamping out each circular end of πr^2 cm^2 requires a square piece of tin of length $2r$ cm and some tin is wasted.

  (i) Express h in terms of r.

  (ii) Express the area of the tin used in terms of r and h.

  (iii) Express the area of the tin in terms of r.

  (iv) Tinplate costs €0.03 per cm^2. Find the radius, height and cost of the tin which will manufacture the tin most cheaply.

15. A fuel storage tank is in the shape of a cylinder with a hemisphere at each end, as shown. The cylindrical part has a length of h m and the hemispheres each have an exterior radius of r m.

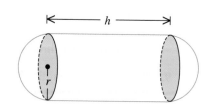

The volume of the tank is 36π m^3. Show that:

  (i) $h = \dfrac{108 - 4r^3}{3r^2}$

  (ii) the total exterior surface area is given by $A = \dfrac{4}{3}\pi r^2 + \dfrac{72\pi}{r}$

  (iii) the minimum value of A is 36π m^2.

16. $(-2, 4)$, (x, x^2) and $(4, 16)$ are three points on the curve $y = x^2$.
If these three points are the vertices of a triangle as shown,
calculate the value of x so that the area enclosed by the triangle
is a maximum, where $-2 < x < 4$, and find this maximum area.

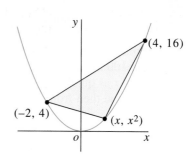

17. o is the origin, $(0, 0)$.
$p(x, y)$ is a point on the curve $y = \dfrac{4}{x}$, where $x > 0$.

$|op|$ is the distance from the origin to p.

(i) Express $|op|$ in terms of x.
(ii) Given that there is one value of x for which $|op|$ is a
minimum, find this value of x.
(iii) Hence, find the minimum value of $|op|$.

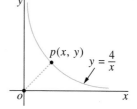

18. A rectangle is bounded by the positive x-axis, the positive y-axis
and the line with equation

$$y = mx + c.$$

Find, in terms of m and c, the area of the rectangle of largest possible
area.

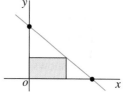

19. A right circular cone with a base radius of r cm and a
perpendicular height of h cm has a slant height of $10\sqrt{3}$ cm.
(i) Express r^2 in term of h^2.
(ii) If the volume of the cone is to be a maximum, find:
(a) the perpendicular height   (b) the radius.

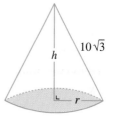

20. The slant height of a right circular cone is 12 cm. Find the
maximum volume of the cone in terms of π.

21. A cylinder is inscribed within a sphere of radius 3.
The cylinder has a radius r and a height $2h$.
(i) Express r^2 in terms of h.
(ii) Find the value of r when the volume of the cylinder is a
maximum.

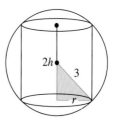

22. Prove that a cylinder of fixed volume has a minimum surface area when the height of the cylinder
is equal to the diameter of the cylinder.

23. *pqrs* is a rectangular field 155 m long and 60 m wide. *pq* is a path and the field has recently been ploughed. A woman can run at an average speed of 260 m per minute along the path and 100 m per minute on the field. She wants to reach the point *r* as quickly as possible. She runs to a point *u* along the path and then from *u* to *r*. If $|uq| = x$ m, express, in terms of *x*:

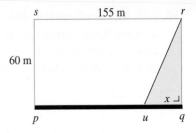

   (i) $|pu|$ **(ii)** $|ur|$

   (iii) the time taken to reach *r*.

   Find the value of *x* for which the time is a minimum and calculate this time in seconds.

24. Two cars, *P* and *Q*, are approaching an intersection, *o*, as shown. At the same instant, *P* is 100 m from *o* and travelling east at a steady speed of 10 m/s, while *Q* is 300 m from *o* and travelling north at a steady speed of 20 m/s.

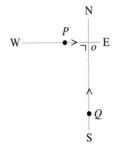

   (i) Write down, in terms of *t*, the distances that *P* and *Q* will each have travelled after *t* seconds.

   (ii) Write down, in terms of *t*, the distances that *P* and *Q* will be from *o* after *t* seconds.

   (iii) Show that the distance between *P* and *Q* after *t* seconds is given by:

   $$d = 10\sqrt{5t^2 - 140t + 1000}.$$

   (iv) Hence, or otherwise, find after how many seconds *P* will be closest to *Q*.

25. The diagram shows a right circular cone of base radius 4 cm and perpendicular height 12 cm. A cylinder of base radius *r* cm and perpendicular height *h* cm stands inside the cone such that the cylinder touches the curved surface of the cone, as shown. The cylinder has a volume of V cm^3.

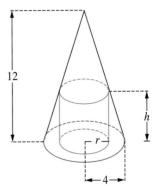

   (i) Using similar triangles, or otherwise, show that $h = 12 - 3r$.

   (ii) Show that $V = 12\pi r^2 - 3\pi r^3$.

   (iii) Find the maximum value of *V*.

Integration by Parts (Integration of Products)

Integration by Parts Formula

$$\int u \, dv = uv - \int v \, du + c$$ (see page 42 in the tables)

This is known as the formula for integration by parts, based on the product rule for differentiation. It is used to integrate products where neither function is related to the derivative of the other (i.e. substitution will not work), for example $\int x \, e^{2x} \, dx$. Our aim is to go from the given integral, $\int u \, dv$, to a new integral, $\int v \, du$, that is simpler.

We apply the formula with the following steps:

> **1.** Let u = one part and dv = the other part.
> **2.** Differentiate u and integrate dv.
> **3.** Substitute into the formula.
> **4.** Integrate the second part on the right-hand side.

Note: The constant of integration, c, appears only on the last integral. When obtaining v from dv, we do not include the constant of integration.

Order of Priority for u

One of the difficulties when using the formula for integration by parts is in deciding which part of the integral to let u be equal to (then let dv equal the other part).

The order of priority for u is:

Type	Examples	Memory Aid
1. Logs	$\ln x$, $(\ln x)^2$	L
2. Inverse trigonometric	$\sin^{-1} x$, $\tan^{-1} x$	IT
3. Algebraic	x^2, $\dfrac{1}{x^2}$, θ	A
4. Exponential	e^x, e^{-x}, e^{3x}	E
5. Trigonometric	$\sin x$, $\cos 2\theta$	T

Whichever one of these we meet first, let this equal u and the other part equal dv.

Note: The order of 4 and 5, exponential and trigonometric, is not important, but if we have to integrate twice we must keep the order we started with.

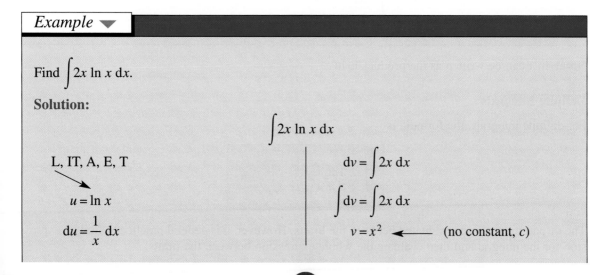

Example ▼

Find $\displaystyle\int 2x \ln x \, dx$.

Solution:

$$\int 2x \ln x \, dx$$

L, IT, A, E, T

$u = \ln x$

$du = \dfrac{1}{x} dx$

$dv = \displaystyle\int 2x \, dx$

$\displaystyle\int dv = \int 2x \, dx$

$v = x^2 \quad\longleftarrow\quad$ (no constant, c)

$$\int u \, dv = uv - \int v \, du$$

$$\int 2x \ln x \, dx = (\ln x)(x^2) - \int x^2 \left(\frac{1}{x}\right) dx$$

$$= x^2 \ln x - \int x \, dx$$

$$= x^2 \ln x - \left(\frac{x^2}{2}\right) + c \qquad \longleftarrow \qquad \text{(constant } c \text{ now put in)}$$

$$= x^2 \ln x - \tfrac{1}{2} x^2 + c$$

Example ▼

Find $\int \ln x \, dx$.

Solution:

L, IT, A, E, T

$u = \ln x$

$du = \dfrac{1}{x} dx$

$dv = dx$

$\int dv = \int dx$

$v = x$

$$\int u \, dv = uv - \int v \, du$$

$$\int \ln x \, dx = (\ln x)(x) - \int x \cdot \frac{1}{x} \, dx$$

$$= x \ln x - \int 1 \, dx$$

$$= x \ln x - x + c$$

Note: $\ln x$ can be written as the product $1. \ln x$.

Definite Integrals

For definite integrals, the formula is:

$$\int_a^b u \, dv = \Big[uv \Big]_a^b - \int_a^b v \, du$$

The uv part must also be evaluated between the limits. However, it is general practice to find an expression for the integral and then evaluate the whole expression between the limits.

Evaluate $\displaystyle\int_0^{\pi/2} \theta \sin 2\theta \, d\theta$.

Solution:

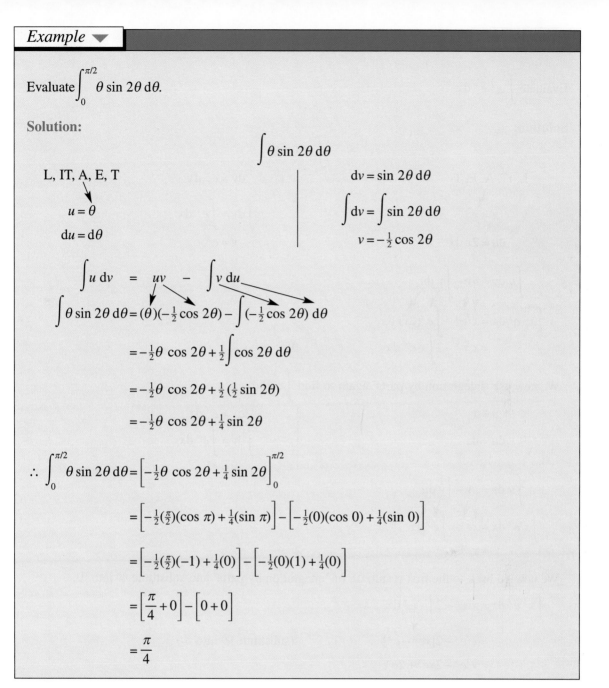

$$\int \theta \sin 2\theta \, d\theta$$

L, IT, A, E, T

$u = \theta$

$du = d\theta$

$dv = \sin 2\theta \, d\theta$

$\int dv = \int \sin 2\theta \, d\theta$

$v = -\tfrac{1}{2}\cos 2\theta$

$$\int u \, dv = uv - \int v \, du$$

$$\int \theta \sin 2\theta \, d\theta = (\theta)(-\tfrac{1}{2}\cos 2\theta) - \int (-\tfrac{1}{2}\cos 2\theta)\, d\theta$$

$$= -\tfrac{1}{2}\theta \cos 2\theta + \tfrac{1}{2}\int \cos 2\theta \, d\theta$$

$$= -\tfrac{1}{2}\theta \cos 2\theta + \tfrac{1}{2}\left(\tfrac{1}{2}\sin 2\theta\right)$$

$$= -\tfrac{1}{2}\theta \cos 2\theta + \tfrac{1}{4}\sin 2\theta$$

$$\therefore \int_0^{\pi/2} \theta \sin 2\theta \, d\theta = \left[-\tfrac{1}{2}\theta \cos 2\theta + \tfrac{1}{4}\sin 2\theta\right]_0^{\pi/2}$$

$$= \left[-\tfrac{1}{2}\left(\tfrac{\pi}{2}\right)(\cos \pi) + \tfrac{1}{4}(\sin \pi)\right] - \left[-\tfrac{1}{2}(0)(\cos 0) + \tfrac{1}{4}(\sin 0)\right]$$

$$= \left[-\tfrac{1}{2}\left(\tfrac{\pi}{2}\right)(-1) + \tfrac{1}{4}(0)\right] - \left[-\tfrac{1}{2}(0)(1) + \tfrac{1}{4}(0)\right]$$

$$= \left[\frac{\pi}{4} + 0\right] - \left[0 + 0\right]$$

$$= \frac{\pi}{4}$$

Sometimes we have to use 'integration by parts' twice.

Evaluate $\displaystyle\int_0^1 x^2\, e^x\, dx.$

Solution:

$$\int x^2\, e^x\, dx$$

L, IT, A, E, T
$$\downarrow$$
$$u = x^2 \qquad\qquad\qquad\qquad dv = e^x\, dx$$
$$\qquad\qquad\qquad\qquad \int dv = \int e^x\, dx$$
$$du = 2x\, dx \qquad\qquad\qquad\qquad v = e^x$$

$$\int u\, dv = uv - \int v\, du$$
$$\int x^2\, e^x\, dx = x^2 e^x - \int e^x(2x)\, dx$$
$$= x^2 e^x - 2\int x\, e^x\, dx \qquad\qquad ①$$

We now use 'integration by parts' again to find $\displaystyle\int x\, e^x\, dx$.

$$u = x \qquad\qquad\qquad\qquad dv = e^x\, dx$$
$$\qquad\qquad\qquad\qquad \int dv = \int e^x\, dx$$
$$du = dx \qquad\qquad\qquad\qquad v = e^x$$

$$\int u\, dv = uv - \int v\, du$$
$$\int x\, e^x\, dx = xe^x - \int e^x\, dx$$
$$= xe^x - e^x \qquad\qquad\qquad ②$$

We now go back to the first result, ①, of 'integration by parts' and substitute ② into ①:

$$\int x^2\, e^x\, dx = x^2 e^x - 2\int x\, e^x\, dx \quad ①$$
$$= x^2 e^x - 2[xe^x - e^x] \qquad\qquad \text{(substitute ② into ①)}$$
$$= x^2 e^x - 2xe^x + 2e^x$$

$$\therefore \int_0^1 x^2\, e^x\, dx = \left[x^2 e^x - 2xe^x + 2e^x \right]_0^1$$
$$= [(1)^2(e^1) - 2(1)(e^1) + 2(e^1)] - [(0)^2(e^0) - 2(0)(e^0) + 2(e^0)]$$
$$= (e - 2e + 2e) - (0 - 0 + 2)$$
$$= e - 2$$

In some special cases, when we integrate twice we end up with the **original** integral on **both** sides. When this happens we use algebra to get the required result.

Find $\displaystyle\int e^{-x}\cos x \, dx$.

Solution:

$$\int e^{-x}\cos x \, dx$$

L, IT, A, E, T

$$u = e^{-x}$$

$$du = -e^{-x}\,dx$$

$$dv = \cos x \, dx$$

$$\int dv = \int \cos x \, dx$$

$$v = \sin x$$

$$\int u \, dv \quad = \quad uv \quad - \quad \int v \, du$$

$$\int e^{-x}\cos x \, dx = e^{-x}\sin x - \int \sin x(-e^{-x}) \, dx$$

$$\int e^{-x}\cos x \, dx = e^{-x}\sin x + \int e^{-x}\sin x \, dx \qquad \text{①}$$

We now use 'integration by parts' again to find $\displaystyle\int e^{-x}\sin x \, dx$:

$$u = e^{-x}$$

$$du = -e^{-x}\,dx$$

$$dv = \sin x \, dx$$

$$\int dv = \int \sin x \, dx$$

$$v = -\cos x$$

$$\int u \, dv \quad = \quad uv \quad - \quad \int v \, du$$

$$\int e^{-x}\sin x \, dx = e^{-x}(-\cos x) - \int -\cos x(-e^{-x}) \, dx$$

$$= -e^{-x}\cos x - \int e^{-x}\cos x \, dx \qquad \text{②}$$

(back to where we started)

We now go back to the first result, ①, of 'integration by parts' and substitute ② into ①.

$$\int e^{-x}\cos x \, dx = e^{-x}\sin x + \int e^{-x}\sin x \, dx \qquad \text{①}$$

$$\int e^{-x}\cos x \, dx = e^{-x}\sin x + \left[-e^{-x}\cos x - \int e^{-x}\cos x \, dx\right]$$

$$\int e^{-x}\cos x \, dx = e^{-x}\sin x - e^{-x}\cos x - \int e^{-x}\cos x \, dx$$

$$\left[\int e^{-x}\cos x \, dx \text{ on both sides}\right]$$

$$2\int e^{-x}\cos x \, dx = e^{-x}\sin x - e^{-x}\cos x$$

$$2\int e^{-x}\cos x \, dx = e^{-x}(\sin x - \cos x)$$

$$\int e^{-x}\cos x \, dx = \tfrac{1}{2}e^{-x}(\sin x - \cos x) + c$$

Find:

1. $\int x\,e^x\,dx$

2. $\int x\cos x\,dx$

3. $\int (2x+1)e^x\,dx$

4. $\int x\,e^{3x}\,dx$

5. $\int x\cos 2x\,dx$

6. $\int x\ln 2x\,dx$

7. $\int x^3\ln x\,dx$

8. $\int 3x\,e^{-x}\,dx$

9. $\int \dfrac{\ln x}{x^2}\,dx$

Evaluate each of the following:

10. $\int_0^1 (x+1)\,e^x\,dx$

11. $\int_0^\pi x\sin x\,dx$

12. $\int_1^e x\ln x\,dx$

13. $\int_0^{\pi/4} x\sin 2x\,dx$

14. $\int_0^1 x\,e^{-x}\,dx$

15. $\int_0^{\pi/4} \theta\cos 2\theta\,d\theta$

Find:

16. $\int x^2\cos x\,dx$

17. $\int x^2\,e^{2x}\,dx$

18. $\int x^2\,e^{-x}\,dx$

Evaluate:

19. $\int_0^{\pi/2} x^2\sin x\,dx$

20. $\int_0^1 x^2\,e^x\,dx$

21. $\int_1^e x\,(\ln x)^2\,dx$

22. Find $\int e^x\cos x\,dx$ and, hence or otherwise, evaluate $\int_0^{\pi/2} e^x\cos x\,dx$.

Find:

23. $\int e^{-x}\sin x\,dx$

24. $\int e^{2x}\cos x\,dx$

25. $\int e^x\cos 2x\,dx$

Evaluate:

26. $\int_0^{\pi/2} e^{2x}\sin x\,dx$

27. $\int_0^{\pi/2} e^{-2x}\cos 2x\,dx$

28. $\int_0^{\pi/6} e^x\sin 3x\,dx$

29. The diagram shows part of the graph of the function $f: x \rightarrow (2x+1)\sin 2x$.
Find the area of the shaded region.

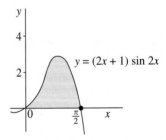

30. Show that: $\int \tan^{-1} x\, dx = x \tan^{-1} x - \frac{1}{2}\ln(1+x^2) + c.$

Hence, evaluate $\int_0^1 \tan^{-1} x\, dx.$

31. Evaluate $\int_0^1 \sin^{-1} x\, dx.$

Ratio Test

Consider the infinite series $\sum_{n=0}^{\infty} u_n = u_0 + u_1 + u_2 + u_3 + \cdots$

The series is said to be **convergent** if it has a limit (has a finite sum).

The series is said to be **divergent** if it doesn't have a limit (does not have a finite sum).

1. Consider the infinite geometric series $\sum_{n=0}^{\infty} \frac{2}{5^n} = 2 + \frac{2}{5} + \frac{2}{25} + \frac{2}{125} + \cdots.$

This series has a limit of $2\frac{1}{2}$ $\left(\text{given by } \frac{a}{1-r} = \frac{2}{1-\frac{1}{5}} = \frac{2}{\frac{4}{5}} = 2\frac{1}{2} \right).$

Thus this series is said to be convergent.

2. Consider the infinite geometric series $\sum_{n=1}^{\infty} (2n-1) = 1 + 3 + 5 + 7 + \cdots.$

This series has no limit. Therefore this series is said to be divergent.

Note: It makes no difference to the theory of convergence if we start off with $n=0$ or $n=1$. All infinite arithmetic series have no limit.

There are many infinite series which are not geometric or arithmetic, and it is not always as clear-cut as above as to whether the series is convergent or divergent. The test we use to determine whether or not an infinite series is convergent is called the **Ratio Test**.

Ratio Test

Suppose $\sum_{n=0}^{\infty} u_n = u_0 + u_1 + u_2 + u_3 + \cdots$ is a series such that:

$$\lim_{n \to \infty} \left| \frac{u_{n+1}}{u_n} \right| = R$$

Then:

1. If $R < 1$, the series is **convergent**.
2. If $R > 1$, the series is **divergent**.
3. If $R = 1$, the series is **inconclusive**.

Note: The Ratio Test does not give the actual limit of the series. If R is undefined, then by the Ratio Test the series is divergent.

Use the Ratio Test to show that $\displaystyle\sum_{n=1}^{\infty} \frac{n}{5^n}$ is convergent.

Solution:

[replace n with $(n+1)$]

$$u_n = \frac{n}{5^n} \qquad \Rightarrow \qquad u_{n+1} = \frac{n+1}{5^{n+1}}$$

$$\frac{u_{n+1}}{u_n} = \frac{\dfrac{n+1}{5^{n+1}}}{\dfrac{n}{5^n}} = \frac{n+1}{5^{n+1}} \cdot \frac{5^n}{n} = \frac{5^n}{5^{n+1}} \cdot \frac{n+1}{n} = \frac{1}{5} \cdot \frac{n+1}{n}$$

$$R = \lim_{n \to \infty} \left| \frac{u_{n+1}}{u_n} \right| \qquad\qquad \text{(divide each part by } n \text{, the dominant term)}$$

$$= \lim_{n \to \infty} \left| \frac{1}{5} \cdot \frac{n+1}{n} \right| = \frac{1}{5} \lim_{n \to \infty} \left| \frac{n+1}{n} \right| = \frac{1}{5} \lim_{n \to \infty} \left| \frac{1 + \frac{1}{n}}{1} \right| = \frac{1}{5} \left(\frac{1+0}{1} \right) = \frac{1}{5}(1) = \frac{1}{5}$$

$R < 1$, therefore by the Ratio Test the series $\displaystyle\sum_{n=1}^{\infty} \frac{n}{5^n}$ is convergent.

Note: $\displaystyle\sum_{n=1}^{\infty} \frac{n}{5^n} = \sum_{n=1}^{\infty} n \left(\frac{1}{5} \right)^n$

Use the Ratio Test to show that the series $\displaystyle\sum_{n=1}^{\infty} \frac{(n+1)!}{2^{n+1}}$ is divergent.

Solution:

[replace n with $(n+1)$]

$$u_n = \frac{(n+1)!}{2^{n+1}} \qquad \Rightarrow \qquad u_{n+1} = \frac{[(n+1)+1]!}{2^{(n+1)+1}} = \frac{(n+2)!}{2^{n+2}}$$

$$\frac{u_{n+1}}{u_n} = \frac{\dfrac{(n+2)!}{2^{n+2}}}{\dfrac{(n+1)!}{2^{n+1}}} = \frac{(n+2)!}{2^{n+2}} \cdot \frac{2^{n+1}}{(n+1)!} = \frac{2^{n+1}}{2^{n+2}} \cdot \frac{(n+2)!}{(n+1)!} = \frac{1}{2} \cdot \frac{(n+2)(n+1)!}{(n+1)!} = \frac{(n+2)}{2}$$

$$R = \lim_{n \to \infty} \left| \frac{u_{n+1}}{u_n} \right| \qquad \text{(divide top and bottom by } n \text{, the dominant term)}$$

$$= \lim_{n \to \infty} \left| \frac{n+2}{2} \right| = \lim_{n \to \infty} \left| \frac{1 + \frac{2}{n}}{\frac{2}{n}} \right| = \frac{1+0}{0} = \frac{1}{0} \qquad \text{(undefined)}$$

R is undefined, therefore by the Ratio Test the series $\displaystyle\sum_{n=1}^{\infty} \frac{(n+1)!}{2^{n+1}}$ is divergent.

Power Series

A power series is a series of the form:

$$\sum_{n=0}^{\infty} a_n x^n = a_0 + a_1 x + a_2 x^2 + a_3 x^3 + \cdots$$

The coefficients $a_0, a_1, a_2, a_3, \cdots$ are independent of x and the powers of x are ascending. It is essential to know something of the convergent, or non-convergent, properties of any series we may use and to appreciate the conditions under which a series is valid. In the next section on Maclaurin series we will see that we can represent many functions as a power series. We should use only the values of x for which a power series is convergent.

In general, a power series will be convergent for a given interval of the form $-k < x < k$. This interval is called the **interval of convergence** and the number k is called the **radius of convergence**.

To find the interval of convergence, solve the equation $R < 1$.

1. If $R = 0$, the series is convergent for all values of x.

2. If R is undefined, the series is convergent only for $x = 0$.

Note: Sometimes one or both of the end points $x = \pm k$ are included in the interval of convergence. However, the ratio test fails to tell us if any endpoints are included.

Expressions in x can be taken outside the limit, since x is not affected as $n \to \infty$.

Example ▼

Use the Ratio Test to determine the range of values of x for which the series

$$\sum_{n=1}^{\infty} \frac{x^n}{(n+1)3^n} \quad \text{is:} \quad \textbf{(i)} \text{ convergent} \qquad \textbf{(ii)} \text{ divergent.}$$

Solution:

[replace n with $(n+1)$]

$$u_n = \frac{x^n}{(n+1)3^n} \qquad \Rightarrow \qquad u_{n+1} = \frac{x^{n+1}}{(n+2)3^{n+1}}$$

$$\frac{u_{n+1}}{u_n} = \frac{\dfrac{x^{n+1}}{(n+2)3^{n+1}}}{\dfrac{x^n}{(n+1)3^n}} = \frac{x^{n+1}}{(n+2)3^{n+1}} \cdot \frac{(n+1)3^n}{x^n} = \frac{x^{n+1}}{x^n} \cdot \frac{3^n}{3^{n+1}} \cdot \frac{n+1}{n+2} = \frac{x}{3} \cdot \frac{n+1}{n+2}$$

$$R = \lim_{n \to \infty} \left| \frac{u_{n+1}}{u_n} \right| \qquad \text{(divide top and bottom by } n\text{, the dominant term)}$$

$$= \lim_{n \to \infty} \left| \frac{x}{3} \cdot \frac{n+1}{n+2} \right| = \left| \frac{x}{3} \right| \lim_{n \to \infty} \left| \frac{n+1}{n+2} \right| = \left| \frac{x}{3} \right| \lim_{n \to \infty} \left| \frac{1 + \dfrac{1}{n}}{1 + \dfrac{2}{n}} \right| = \left| \frac{x}{3} \right| \left(\frac{1+0}{1+0} \right) = \left| \frac{x}{3} \right| (1) = \left| \frac{x}{3} \right|$$

By the Ratio Test, the series is convergent for $R < 1$.	By the Ratio Test, the series is divergent for $R > 1$.
Thus, $\left\| \dfrac{x}{3} \right\| < 1$	Thus, $\left\| \dfrac{x}{3} \right\| > 1$
$\Rightarrow \quad -1 < \dfrac{x}{3} < 1$	$\Rightarrow \quad \dfrac{x}{3} < -1 \quad \text{or} \quad \dfrac{x}{3} > 1$
$\Rightarrow \quad -3 < x < 3$	$\Rightarrow \quad x < -3 \quad \text{or} \quad x > 3$
Thus, the series is convergent for $-3 < x < 3$.	Thus, the series is divergent for $x < -3 \quad \text{or} \quad x > 3$.

When $x = \pm 3$, $R = 1$ and the Ratio Test is inconclusive.

Exercise 8.3 ▼

Use the Ratio Test to determine which of the following series are convergent or divergent:

1. $\displaystyle\sum_{n=1}^{\infty} \frac{2^n}{n}$

2. $\displaystyle\sum_{n=0}^{\infty} \frac{n+1}{3^n}$

3. $\displaystyle\sum_{n=1}^{\infty} n \left(\frac{1}{4} \right)^n$

4. $\displaystyle\sum_{n=1}^{\infty} \frac{2^{n+1}}{n+1}$

5. $\displaystyle\sum_{n=1}^{\infty} \frac{3^n}{n4^n}$

6. $\displaystyle\sum_{n=1}^{\infty} \frac{2^n}{2n-1}$

7. $\displaystyle\sum_{n=1}^{\infty} \frac{1-n}{n2^n}$

8. $\displaystyle\sum_{n=1}^{\infty} \frac{n^2}{4^n}$

9. $\displaystyle\sum_{n=1}^{\infty} \frac{2^n}{n!}$

10. $\displaystyle\sum_{n=0}^{\infty} \frac{n!}{(n+1)\,2^n}$

11. $\displaystyle\sum_{n=1}^{\infty} \frac{\sqrt{n}}{3^n}$

12. $\displaystyle\sum_{n=1}^{\infty} \frac{\sqrt{n+1}}{5^n}$

13. Use the Ratio Test to show that $\displaystyle\sum_{n=1}^{\infty} \frac{(n+1)!}{2^{n+1}}$ is divergent.

14. Use the Ratio Test to show that $\displaystyle\sum_{n=0}^{\infty} \frac{(-1)^n}{(n+4)4^n}$ is convergent.

Use the Ratio Test to find the range of values of $x \in \mathbf{R}$ for which each of the following series is convergent:

15. $\displaystyle\sum_{n=1}^{\infty} (3x)^n n$

16. $\displaystyle\sum_{n=1}^{\infty} \frac{x^n}{2^{n+1}}$

17. $\displaystyle\sum_{n=0}^{\infty} \frac{x^n}{n+1}$

18. $\displaystyle\sum_{n=1}^{\infty} \frac{(x-2)^n}{n}$

19. $\displaystyle\sum_{n=1}^{\infty} \frac{2^n x^n}{n3^n}$

20. $\displaystyle\sum_{n=1}^{\infty} \frac{x^{2n}}{n+1}$

21. Show that the series $\displaystyle\sum_{n=1}^{\infty} \frac{x^n}{n!}$ is convergent for all values of $x \in \mathbf{R}$.

22. Show that the series $\displaystyle\sum_{n=1}^{\infty} \frac{(n+2)! \, x^n}{2^{n+2}}$ is convergent only for $x = 0$.

23. Use the Ratio Test to determine the range of values of x for which the series

$\displaystyle\sum_{n=1}^{\infty} \frac{x^n}{n4^n}$ is: **(i)** convergent **(ii)** divergent.

Maclaurin Series

Higher Derivatives

The notation $f^{(n)}(x)$ is used to represent the nth derivative of the function $f(x)$.

For example,

$$f^{(2)}(x) = \frac{d^2 y}{dx^2}, \qquad f^{(4)}(x) = \frac{d^4 y}{dx^4}, \qquad f^{(7)}(x) = \frac{d^7 y}{dx^7}, \quad \text{etc.}$$

In particular, $f^{(0)}(x) = f(x)$ and $f^{(1)}(x) = \dfrac{dy}{dx}$

Power Series

In the previous section we said that a power series is a series of the form:

$$\sum_{n=0}^{\infty} a_n x^n = a_0 + a_1 x + a_2 x^2 + a_3 x^3 + \cdots$$

It turns out that many functions can be expressed as a power series.
In other words, the function can be written as an infinite series composed of terms of the form $a_n x^n$.
On our course we use the **Maclaurin series** to represent a function $f(x)$ by a power series.

Maclaurin Series

$$f(x) = f(0) + f^{(1)}(0)\, x + \frac{f^{(2)}(0)}{2!}\, x^2 + \frac{f^{(3)}(0)}{3!}\, x^3 + \frac{f^{(4)}(0)}{4!}\, x^4 + \cdots$$

In short: $f(x) = \sum_{n=0}^{\infty} \frac{f^{(n)}(0)}{n!}\, x^n$

$f^{(n)}(0)$ represents the nth derivative of $f(x)$ evaluated at $x = 0$.

Our task is to calculate the constants $\dfrac{f^{(n)}(0)}{n!}$ for $n = 0, 1, 2, 3, \ldots$

Method:

1. Substitute $x = 0$ on both sides to find $f(0)$.

To find $f^{(1)}(0), f^{(2)}(0), f^{(3)}(0), f^{(4)}(0), \ldots, f^{(n)}(0), \ldots$

2. Differentiate both sides with respect to x.

3. Then substitute $x = 0$ on both sides.

Repeat steps 2 and 3 for the required number of terms.

Derivation of the Maclaurin Series

Let the function $f(x)$ be represented by the power series:

$$f(x) = a_0 + a_1 x + a_2 x^2 + a_3 x^3 + a_4 x^4 + \cdots$$

$f(0) = a_0$	$\therefore\ a_0 = f(0)$
$f^{(1)}(x) = a_1 + 2a_2 x + 3a_3 x^2 + 4a_4 x^3 + 5a_5 x^4 + 6a_6 x^5 + \cdots$ $f^{(1)}(0) = a_1$	$\therefore\ a_1 = f^{(1)}(0)$
$f^{(2)}(x) = 2a_2 + 6a_3 x + 12a_4 x^2 + 20a_5 x^3 + 30a_6 x^4 + \cdots$ $f^{(2)}(0) = 2a_2 = 2!a_2$	$\therefore\ a_2 = \dfrac{f^{(2)}(0)}{2!}$
$f^{(3)}(x) = 6a_3 + 24a_4 x + 60a_5 x^2 + 120a_6 x^3 + \cdots$ $f^{(3)}(0) = 6a_3 = 3!a_3$	$\therefore\ a_3 = \dfrac{f^{(3)}(0)}{3!}$
$f^{(4)}(x) = 24a_4 + 120a_5 x + 360a_6 x^2 + \cdots$ $f^{(4)}(0) = 24a_4 = 4!a_4$	$\therefore\ a_4 = \dfrac{f^{(4)}(0)}{4!}$
$f^{(5)}(x) = 120a_5 + 720a_6 x + \cdots$ $f^{(5)}(0) = 120a_5 = 5!a_5$	$\therefore\ a_5 = \dfrac{f^{(5)}(0)}{5!}$

Continuing this process, we can show that:

$$a_n = \frac{f^{(n)}(0)}{n!}$$

By comparing with our original series:

$$f(x) = a_0 + a_1 x + a_2 x^2 + a_3 x^3 + a_4 x^4 + a_5 x^5 + \cdots$$

$$f(x) = f(0) + f^{(1)}(0)x + \frac{f^{(2)}(0)}{2!}x^2 + \frac{f^{(3)}(0)}{3!}x^3 + \frac{f^{(4)}(0)}{4!}x^4 + \frac{f^{(5)}(0)}{5!}x^5 + \cdots$$

This is known as **Maclaurin's Theorem** and the series is called the Maclaurin expansion of $f(x)$.
Notice how tidy each term is:

The constant term is $f(0)$.

The term with x is multiplied by $f^{(1)}(0)$.

The term with x^2 is multiplied by $f^{(2)}(0)$ and divided by 2!

The term with x^3 is multiplied by $f^{(3)}(0)$ and divided by 3!

The term with x^4 is multiplied by $f^{(4)}(0)$ and divided by 4!

The term with x^5 is multiplied by $f^{(5)}(0)$ and divided by 5!

The term with x^{n-1} is multiplied by $f^{(n-1)}(0)$ and divided by $(n-1)!$

The term with x^n is multiplied by $f^{(n)}(0)$ and divided by $n!$

For such a power series to exist, the function $f(x)$ must be capable of being infinitely differentiable to find $f^{(1)}(x), f^{(2)}(x), f^{(3)}(x)$ and higher derivatives and these derivatives must be defined at $x = 0$. The values of x for which the Maclaurin series is a valid expansion of the function $f(x)$ are those values for which the series is convergent. These values may be found by using the Ratio Test.

Note: Sometimes the derivatives of $f(x)$ evaluated at $x = 0$ are indicated with primes, i.e.

$$f(x) = f(0) + f'(0)x + \frac{f''(0)}{2!}x^2 + \frac{f'''(0)}{3!}x^3 + \cdots$$

On our course there are only six basic functions for which we have to be able to find the Maclaurin series and its general term and determine the values of x for which the series is valid, using the Ratio Test.

Six basic functions:

1. **Exponential:**	$f(x) = e^x$	2. **Logarithmic:**	$f(x) = \ln(1 + x)$
3. **Sine:**	$f(x) = \sin x$	4. **Cosine:**	$f(x) = \cos x$
5. **Binomial:**	$f(x) = (1 + x)^n$	6. **Inverse tan:**	$f(x) = \tan^{-1} x$

When a Maclaurin series has been found for one of the six basic functions it can be used to derive a Maclaurin series for a related function.

For example, having found a Maclaurin series for $\ln(1 + x)$, we can use it to find a Maclaurin series for $\ln(1 - x)$ by substituting $(-x)$ for each x.

Note: When you are asked to derive a Maclaurin series, you must show each $f^{(n)}(x)$ and its corresponding $f^{(n)}(0)$ up to the number of terms required.

251

Maclaurin Series for the first four basic Functions: e^x, $\ln(1+x)$, $\sin x$ and $\cos x$

....

(i) Derive the Maclaurin series for $f(x) = e^x$ up to and including the term containing x^4.

(ii) Write down the general term and use the Ratio Test to show that the series is convergent for all $x \in \mathbf{R}$.

(iii) Write down the first five terms in the Maclaurin series for: **(a)** e^{-x} **(b)** e^{3x} **(c)** $(1+x)e^x$.

(iv) Use the first five terms to find an approximate value for e.

Write your answer in the form $\dfrac{a}{b}$, where $a, b \in \mathbf{N}$.

Solution:

Let $f(x) = e^x = f(0) + f^{(1)}(0)x + \dfrac{f^{(2)}(0)}{2!}x^2 + \dfrac{f^{(3)}(0)}{3!}x^3 + \dfrac{f^{(4)}(0)}{4!}x^4 + \cdots$

(i)

$$f(x) = e^x \qquad\qquad\qquad f(0) = e^0 = 1$$
$$f^{(1)}(x) = e^x \qquad\qquad\qquad f^{(1)}(0) = e^0 = 1$$
$$f^{(2)}(x) = e^x \qquad\qquad\qquad f^{(2)}(0) = e^0 = 1$$
$$f^{(3)}(x) = e^x \qquad\qquad\qquad f^{(3)}(0) = e^0 = 1$$
$$f^{(4)}(x) = e^x \qquad\qquad\qquad f^{(4)}(0) = e^0 = 1$$

(**Note:** In general $f''(x) = e^x \qquad \therefore \quad f''(0) = e^0 = 1$)

$f(x) = e^x = f(0) + f^{(1)}(0)x + \dfrac{f^{(2)}(0)}{2!}x^2 + \dfrac{f^{(3)}(0)}{3!}x^3 + \dfrac{f^{(4)}(0)}{4!} + \cdots$

$\therefore \quad e^x = 1 + 1x + \dfrac{1}{2!}x^2 + \dfrac{1}{3!}x^3 + \dfrac{1}{4!}x^4 \qquad$ (up to x^4)

$\therefore \quad e^x = 1 + x + \dfrac{x^2}{2!} + \dfrac{x^3}{3!} + \dfrac{x^4}{4!}$

(ii) Starting with $n = 0$,

$$u_0 = 1, \qquad u_1 = x, \qquad u_2 = \dfrac{x^2}{2!}, \qquad u_3 = \dfrac{x^3}{3!}, \qquad u_4 = \dfrac{x^4}{4!}$$

Thus, the general term is given by $u_n = \dfrac{x^n}{n!}$

and the series is given by $e^x = \displaystyle\sum_{n=0}^{\infty} \dfrac{x^n}{n!}$.

$$u_n = \frac{x^n}{n!} \quad \Rightarrow \quad u_{n+1} = \frac{x^{n+1}}{(n+1)!}$$

$$\frac{u_{n+1}}{u_n} = \frac{\frac{x^{n+1}}{(n+1)!}}{\frac{x^n}{n!}} = \frac{x^{n+1}}{(n+1)!} \cdot \frac{n!}{x^n} = \frac{x^{n+1}}{x^n} \cdot \frac{n!}{(n+1)!} = x \frac{1}{n+1}$$

$$\left[\text{Note: } \frac{n!}{(n+1)!} = \frac{n!}{(n+1)n!} = \frac{1}{n+1} \right]$$

$$R = \lim_{n \to \infty} \left| \frac{u_{n+1}}{u_n} \right|$$

$\left(\begin{array}{c} \text{divide top and bottom by } n, \\ \text{the dominant term} \end{array} \right)$

$$= \lim_{n \to \infty} \left| x \frac{1}{n+1} \right| = |x| \lim_{n \to \infty} \left| \frac{1}{n+1} \right| = |x| \lim_{n \to \infty} \left| \frac{\frac{1}{n}}{1 + \frac{1}{n}} \right| = |x| \left| \frac{0}{1+0} \right| = |x| (0) = 0$$

$R = 0$, therefore by the Ratio Test the series is convergent for all $x \in \mathbf{R}$.

(iii) (a) $e^x = 1 + x + \dfrac{x^2}{2!} + \dfrac{x^3}{3!} + \dfrac{x^4}{4!}$ (first five terms)

$e^{-x} = 1 + (-x) + \dfrac{(-x)^2}{2!} + \dfrac{(-x)^3}{3!} + \dfrac{(-x)^4}{4!}$ (put in $(-x)$ for x)

$e^{-x} = 1 - x + \dfrac{x^2}{2!} - \dfrac{x^3}{3!} + \dfrac{x^4}{4!}$ (odd powers are $-$, even powers are $+$)

(b) $e^x = 1 + x + \dfrac{x^2}{2!} + \dfrac{x^3}{3!} + \dfrac{x^4}{4!}$ (first five terms)

$e^{3x} = 1 + (3x) + \dfrac{(3x)^2}{2!} + \dfrac{(3x)^3}{3!} + \dfrac{(3x)^4}{4!}$ (put in $(3x)$ for x)

$e^{3x} = 1 + 3x + \dfrac{9x^2}{2!} + \dfrac{27x^3}{3!} + \dfrac{81x^4}{4!}$

(c) $(1+x)e^x$

$= (1+x)\left(1 + x + \dfrac{x^2}{2!} + \dfrac{x^3}{3!} + \dfrac{x^4}{4!} \right)$

$= (1+x)\left(1 + x + \tfrac{1}{2}x^2 + \tfrac{1}{6}x^3 + \tfrac{1}{24}x^4 \right)$

$= 1\left(1 + x + \tfrac{1}{2}x^2 + \tfrac{1}{6}x^3 + \tfrac{1}{24}x^4 \right) + x\left(1 + x + \tfrac{1}{2}x^2 + \tfrac{1}{6}x^3 + \tfrac{1}{24}x^4 \right)$

$= 1 + x + \tfrac{1}{2}x^2 + \tfrac{1}{6}x^3 + \tfrac{1}{24}x^4 + x + x^2 + \tfrac{1}{2}x^3 + \tfrac{1}{6}x^4 + \tfrac{1}{24}x^5$

$= 1 + x + x + \tfrac{1}{2}x^2 + x^2 + \tfrac{1}{6}x^3 + \tfrac{1}{2}x^3 + \tfrac{1}{24}x^4 + \tfrac{1}{6}x^4 + \tfrac{1}{24}x^5$

$= 1 + 2x + \tfrac{3}{2}x^2 + \tfrac{2}{3}x^3 + \tfrac{5}{24}x^4$ (first five terms)

(iv) $e = e^1$, therefore to approximate e, put in 1 for x.

$$e^x = 1 + x + \frac{x^2}{2!} + \frac{x^3}{3!} + \frac{x^4}{4!} \qquad \text{(first five terms)}$$

$$e^1 = 1 + 1 + \frac{1}{2} + \frac{1}{6} + \frac{1}{24} \qquad \text{(put in 1 for } x)$$

$$e = \frac{65}{24} \qquad \text{(using the first five terms)}.$$

The function $f(x) = \ln x$ is not defined for $x = 0$, because $f(0) = \ln 0$ is not defined and therefore has no Maclaurin series.

However, we can obtain a Maclaurin series for $\ln(1 + x)$.

Example ▼

(i) Derive the Maclaurin series for $f(x) = \ln(1 + x)$ up to and including the term containing x^5.

(ii) Write down the general term and use the Ratio Test to show that the series converges for $-1 < x \leqslant 1$, given that it is convergent for $x = 1$ and divergent for $x = -1$.

(iii) Deduce a Maclaurin series for $\ln(1 - x)$ and hence write down the first 3 non-zero terms in the expansion of $\ln\left(\dfrac{1+x}{1-x}\right)$.

(iv) Use these 3 terms to find an approximate value for $\ln 3$, correct to three decimal places.

Solution:

$$\text{Let } f(x) = \ln(1+x) = f(0) + f^{(1)}(0)x + \frac{f^{(2)}(0)}{2!}x^2 + \frac{f^{(3)}(0)}{3!}x^3 + \frac{f^{(4)}(0)}{4!}x^4 + \frac{f^{(5)}(0)}{5!}x^5 + \cdots$$

$f(x) = \ln(1+x)$ $\qquad\qquad\qquad\qquad$ $f(0) = \ln(1) = 0$

$f^{(1)}(x) = \dfrac{1}{1+x} = (1+x)^{-1}$ $\qquad\qquad$ $f^{(1)}(0) = \dfrac{1}{1} = 1$

$f^{(2)}(x) = -(1+x)^{-2}$ $\qquad\qquad\qquad$ $f^{(2)}(0) = -(1)^{-2} = -1$

$f^{(3)}(x) = 2(1+x)^{-3}$ $\qquad\qquad\qquad$ $f^{(3)}(0) = 2(1)^{-3} = 2 = 2!$

$f^{(4)}(x) = -6(1+x)^{-4}$ $\qquad\qquad\quad$ $f^{(4)}(0) = -6(1)^{-4} = -6 = -3!$

$f^{(5)}(x) = 24(1+x)^{-5}$ $\qquad\qquad\quad$ $f^{(5)}(0) = 24(1)^{-5} = 24 = 4!$

$$f(x) = \ln(1+x) = f(0) + f^{(1)}(0)x + \frac{f^{(2)}(0)}{2!}x^2 + \frac{f^{(3)}(0)}{3!}x^3 + \frac{f^{(4)}(0)}{4!}x^4 + \frac{f^{(5)}(0)}{5!}x^5 + \cdots$$

$$\therefore \quad \ln(1+x) = 0 + 1x + \frac{(-1)}{2!}x^2 + \frac{2!}{3!}x^3 + \frac{(-3!)}{4!}x^4 + \frac{4!}{5!}x^5 + \cdots$$

$$\therefore \quad \ln(1+x) = x - \frac{x^2}{2} + \frac{x^3}{3} - \frac{x^4}{4} + \frac{x^5}{5} \qquad \text{(up to } x^5)$$

$$\left[\text{Note: } \frac{2!}{3!} = \frac{2!}{3.2!} = \frac{1}{3}, \qquad \frac{3!}{4!} = \frac{3!}{4.3!} = \frac{1}{4}, \qquad \frac{4!}{5!} = \frac{4!}{5.4!} = \frac{1}{5} \right]$$

254

(ii) Starting with $n = 1$,

$$u_1 = x, \qquad u_2 = -\frac{x^2}{2}, \qquad u_3 = \frac{x^3}{3}, \qquad u_4 = -\frac{x^4}{4}, \qquad u_5 = \frac{x^5}{5}$$

Thus, the general term is given by $u_n = \dfrac{(-1)^{n+1}x^n}{n}$

and the series is given by $\ln(1 + x) = \displaystyle\sum_{n=1}^{\infty} \dfrac{(-1)^{n+1}x^n}{n}$.

Note: As the signs alternate, the general term will contain $(-1)^n$ or $(-1)^{n+1}$. You can decide which to use by inspection.

$$u_n = \frac{(-1)^{n+1}x^n}{n} \qquad \Rightarrow \qquad u_{n+1} = \frac{(-1)^{n+2}x^{n+1}}{n+1}$$

$$\frac{u_{n+1}}{u_n} = \frac{\dfrac{(-1)^{n+2}x^{n+1}}{n+1}}{\dfrac{(-1)^{n+1}x^n}{n}} = \frac{(-1)^{n+2}x^{n+1}}{n+1} \cdot \frac{n}{(-1)^{n+1}x^n} = \frac{(-1)^{n+2}}{(-1)^{n+1}} \cdot \frac{x^{n+1}}{x^n} \cdot \frac{n}{n+1} = -x\frac{n}{n+1}$$

$$R = \lim_{n \to \infty} \left| \frac{u_{n+1}}{u_n} \right| \qquad \text{(divide top and bottom by } n \text{, the dominant term)}$$

$$= \lim_{n \to \infty} \left| -x\frac{n}{n+1} \right| = |-x| \lim_{n \to \infty} \left| \frac{n}{n+1} \right| = |-x| \lim_{n \to \infty} \left| \frac{1}{1 + \dfrac{1}{n}} \right| = |x| \left| \frac{1}{1 + 0} \right| = |-x|\,(1) = |-x|$$

By the Ratio Test, the series is convergent for $R < 1$.

Thus, $\qquad\qquad |-x| < 1$

$\therefore \qquad\qquad -1 < -x < 1$

$\therefore \qquad\qquad -1 < x < 1$

Thus the series is convergent for

$$-1 < x \leqslant 1$$

as we are given that it is convergent for $x = 1$ and divergent for $x = -1$.

(iii) To find the Maclaurin series for $\ln(1 - x)$, replace x with $(-x)$:

$$\ln(1 + x) = x - \frac{x^2}{2} + \frac{x^3}{3} - \frac{x^4}{4} + \frac{x^5}{5} \qquad \text{(up to the term containing } x^5\text{)}$$

$$\ln(1 - x) = (-x) - \frac{(-x)^2}{2} + \frac{(-x)^3}{3} - \frac{(-x)^4}{4} + \frac{(-x)^5}{5} \qquad \text{(put in } (-x) \text{ for } x\text{)}$$

$$\ln(1 - x) = -x - \frac{x^2}{2} - \frac{x^3}{3} - \frac{x^4}{4} - \frac{x^5}{5}$$

$$\ln\left(\frac{1+x}{1-x}\right) = \ln(1 + x) - \ln(1 - x)$$

$$= \left(x - \frac{x^2}{2} + \frac{x^3}{3} - \frac{x^4}{4} + \frac{x^5}{5} \right) - \left(-x - \frac{x^2}{2} - \frac{x^3}{3} - \frac{x^4}{4} - \frac{x^5}{5} \right)$$

$$= x - \frac{x^2}{2} + \frac{x^3}{3} - \frac{x^4}{4} + \frac{x^5}{5} + x + \frac{x^2}{2} + \frac{x^3}{3} + \frac{x^4}{4} + \frac{x^5}{5}$$

$$= 2x + \tfrac{2}{3}x^3 + \tfrac{2}{5}x^5$$

(iv)

Let $\ln\left(\dfrac{1+x}{1-x}\right) = \ln 3$

$\therefore \qquad \dfrac{1+x}{1-x} = 3$

$1 + x = 3 - 3x$

$4x = 2$

$x = \dfrac{1}{2}$

$\left(\text{i.e. } \ln\left(\dfrac{1+x}{1-x}\right) = \ln 3 \text{ when } x = \dfrac{1}{2}\right)$

To approximate $\ln 3$, replace x with $\frac{1}{2}$ in the first three terms of $\ln\left(\dfrac{1+x}{1-x}\right)$.

$\ln\left(\dfrac{1+x}{1-x}\right) = 2x + \tfrac{2}{3}x^3 + \tfrac{2}{5}x^5$

$\therefore \quad \ln 3 = 2\left(\tfrac{1}{2}\right) + \tfrac{2}{3}\left(\tfrac{1}{2}\right)^3 + \tfrac{2}{5}\left(\tfrac{1}{2}\right)^5$

$\left(\text{let } x = \tfrac{1}{2} \text{ on both sides}\right)$

$\ln 3 = 1.0958333$

$\ln 3 = 1.096$

(correct to three decimal places).

Example ▼

(i) Derive the Maclaurin series for $f(x) = \sin x$ up to and including the term containing x^7 and write down the general term of the series.

(ii) Hence, or otherwise, write down the first four non-zero terms of the Maclaurin series for $f(x) = \cos x$ and write down the general term of the series. Use these four terms to find $\cos 0.4$, correct to two decimal places.

(iii) Write down the first four non-zero terms of $\cos \dfrac{x}{2}$.

Solution:

Let $f(x) = \sin x = f(0) + f^{(1)}(0)x + \dfrac{f^{(2)}(0)}{2!}x^2 + \dfrac{f^{(3)}(0)}{3!}x^3 + \cdots$

(i)
$f(x) = \sin x$	$f(0) = \sin 0 = 0$
$f^{(1)}(x) = \cos x$	$f^{(1)}(0) = \cos 0 = 1$
$f^{(2)}(x) = -\sin x$	$f^{(2)}(0) = -\sin 0 = 0$
$f^{(3)}(x) = -\cos x$	$f^{(3)}(0) = -\cos 0 = -1$
$f^{(4)}(x) = \sin x$	$f^{(4)}(0) = \sin 0 = 0$
$f^{(5)}(x) = \cos x$	$f^{(5)}(0) = \cos 0 = 1$
$f^{(6)}(x) = -\sin x$	$f^{(6)}(0) = -\sin 0 = 0$
$f^{(7)}(x) = -\cos x$	$f^{(7)}(0) = -\cos 0 = -1$

$f(x) = \sin x = f(0) + f^{(1)}(0)x + \dfrac{f^{(2)}(0)}{2!}x^2 + \dfrac{f^{(3)}(0)}{3!}x^3 + \cdots$

$$\therefore \quad \sin x = \cancel{0} + 1(x) + \frac{\cancel{0}}{2!}x^2 + \frac{(-1)}{3!}x^3 + \frac{\cancel{0}}{4!}x^4 + \frac{(1)}{5!}x^5 + \frac{\cancel{0}}{6!}x^6 + \frac{(-1)}{7!}x^7 + \cdots$$

$$\therefore \quad \sin x = x - \frac{x^3}{3!} + \frac{x^5}{5!} - \frac{x^7}{7!} \qquad \text{(up to } x^7)$$

Starting with $n = 1$:

$$u_1 = x \qquad u_2 = -\frac{x^3}{3!} \qquad u_3 = \frac{x^5}{5!} \qquad u_4 = -\frac{x^7}{7!}$$

Thus, the general term is given by $u_n = \dfrac{(-1)^{n+1}x^{2n-1}}{(2n-1)!}$.

Alternatively, we could start at $n = 0$:

$$u_0 = x \qquad u_1 = -\frac{x^3}{3!} \qquad u_2 = \frac{x^5}{5!} \qquad u_3 = -\frac{x^7}{7!}$$

Thus, the general term is given by $u_n = \dfrac{(-1)^{n}x^{2n+1}}{(2n+1)!}$.

This shows that there can be a number of different ways of writing u_n.

(ii) The question says 'hence or otherwise', so there is more than one method for finding the Maclaurin series for $\cos x$.

We could find the Maclaurin series for $\cos x$ using the same method as for $\sin x$.

However, we can also use our knowledge of differentiation.

$$\sin x = x - \frac{x^3}{3!} + \frac{x^5}{5!} - \frac{x^7}{7!} \qquad \text{(from (i))}$$

$$\cos x = 1 - \frac{3x^2}{3!} + \frac{5x^4}{5!} - \frac{7x^6}{7!} \qquad \text{(differentiate both sides w.r.t. } x)$$

$$\cos x = 1 - \frac{x^2}{2!} + \frac{x^4}{4!} - \frac{x^6}{6!}$$

$$\left[\text{Note: } \frac{3}{3!} = \frac{3}{3.2!} = \frac{1}{2!}, \qquad \frac{5}{5!} = \frac{5}{5.4!} = \frac{1}{4!}, \qquad \frac{7}{7!} = \frac{7}{7.6!} = \frac{1}{6!} \right]$$

Starting with $n = 0$,

$$u_0 = 1, \qquad u_1 = -\frac{x^2}{2!}, \qquad u_2 = \frac{x^4}{4!}, \qquad u_3 = \frac{x^6}{6!}$$

Thus, the general term is given by $u_n = \dfrac{(-1)^{n}x^{2n}}{(2n)!}$.

$$\cos x = 1 - \frac{x^2}{2!} + \frac{x^4}{4!} - \frac{x^6}{6!}$$

$$\therefore \quad \cos 0.4 = 1 - \frac{(0.4)^2}{2!} + \frac{(0.4)^4}{4!} - \frac{(0.4)^6}{6!} \qquad \text{(put in 0.4 for } x)$$

$$\cos 0.4 = 0.921060977778$$

$$\cos 0.4 = 0.921 \qquad \text{(correct to two decimal places)}$$

(iii) $\cos x = 1 - \dfrac{x^2}{2!} + \dfrac{x^4}{4!} - \dfrac{x^6}{6!}$

$\cos \dfrac{x}{2} = 1 - \dfrac{\left(\frac{x}{2}\right)^2}{2} + \dfrac{\left(\frac{x}{2}\right)^4}{24} - \dfrac{\left(\frac{x}{2}\right)^6}{720}$ (put in $\left(\dfrac{x}{2}\right)$ for x)

$\cos \dfrac{x}{2} = 1 - \dfrac{\frac{x^2}{4}}{2} + \dfrac{\frac{x^4}{16}}{24} - \dfrac{\frac{x^6}{64}}{720}$

$\cos \dfrac{x}{2} = 1 - \dfrac{x^2}{8} + \dfrac{x^4}{384} - \dfrac{x^6}{46{,}080}$

Note: In the Maclaurin series expansions for $\cos x$ and $\sin x$, x is measured in radians.

Exercise 8.4 ▼

1. Derive the first four non-zero terms in the Maclaurin series expansion for each of the following:

   (i) e^x **(ii)** $\ln(1+x)$ **(iii)** $\sin x$ **(iv)** $\cos x$

   In each case write down the general term and use the Ratio Test to find the values of x for which the series is valid.

Use the series expansions from question 1 to answer each of the following.
Find the first four non-zero terms of each of the following:

2. e^{-x} 3. e^{2x} 4. e^{-2x} 5. e^{x^2}

6. $e^{x/2}$ 7. $(1+2x)e^x$ 8. $(1-x^2)e^{2x}$ 9. $\ln(1-x)$

10. $\ln(1+2x)$ 11. $\ln(1-3x)$ 12. $\ln\left(\dfrac{1+2x}{1-3x}\right)$ 13. $\sin 2x$

14. $\cos 3x$ 15. $\sin 2x + \cos 3x$ 16. $e^{2x} + e^{-2x} + e^{-x}$

Use the series expansions from question 1 to approximate, correct to three decimal places:

17. $e^{0.2}$ 18. $e^{1.7}$ 19. $\ln 1.1$ 20. $\ln 1.9$ 21. $\sin 0.2$ 22. $\cos 1.5$

23. **(i)** Write down the first four terms of the Maclaurin series for $\ln(1+x)$.

   (ii) Deduce the first four terms of the Maclaurin series for $\ln(1-2x)$.

   (iii) Find the value of x for which $\ln(1-2x) = \ln(0.98)$.

   (iv) Use the four terms to find an approximation for $\ln(0.98)$, correct to two decimal places.

   (v) Show that the first four non-zero terms of $\ln\left(\dfrac{1+x}{1-2x}\right) = 3x + \dfrac{3}{2}x^2 + 3x^3 + \dfrac{15}{4}x^4$.

   (vi) Find the value of x for which $\ln\left(\dfrac{1+x}{1-2x}\right) = \ln 2$.

   (vii) Use these four non-zero terms to find an approximate value for $\ln 2$.

24. The first three non-zero terms in the series expansion of $e^x + e^{2x}$ are $a + bx + cx^2$, $a, b, c \in \mathbf{R}$. Find the value of a, the value of b and the value of c.

25. Write down the first three terms of the series expansion for e^{-2x}.
Find the value of a and b if the first two terms of the series expansion of $(a+bx)e^{-2x}$ are $1-2x^2$, where $a, b, \in \mathbf{N}$.

26. Write down the first four terms of the Maclaurin series for e^x.

Hence, evaluate $\lim\limits_{x\to 0}\left(\dfrac{e^x-1}{x}\right)$.

27. Consider the following Maclaurin series:

$$e^x = 1 + x + \frac{x^2}{2!} + \frac{x^3}{3!} + \frac{x^4}{4!} + \frac{x^5}{5!} + \frac{x^6}{6!} + \frac{x^7}{7!} + \cdots + \frac{x^n}{n!} + \cdots$$

$$\cos x = 1 - \frac{x^2}{2!} + \frac{x^4}{4!} - \frac{x^6}{6!} + \frac{x^8}{8!} - \frac{x^{10}}{10!} + \cdots + \frac{(-1)^n x^{2n}}{(2n)!} + \cdots$$

$$\sin x = x - \frac{x^3}{3!} + \frac{x^5}{5!} - \frac{x^7}{7!} + \frac{x^9}{9!} - \frac{x^{11}}{11!} + \cdots + \frac{(-1)^{n+1} x^{2n-1}}{(2n-1)!} + \cdots$$

We know that every integer power of i is a member of the set $\{1, -1, i, -i\}$.

$$i = \sqrt{-1}, \qquad i^2 = -1, \qquad i^3 = -i, \qquad i^4 = 1, \qquad i^5 = i, \qquad i^6 = -1, \qquad i^7 = -i, \qquad i^8 = 1, \text{ etc.}$$

Write down the first eight terms of the series expansions for $e^{i\theta}$.
Write down the first eight terms of the series $\cos\theta + i\sin\theta$, grouping the real and imaginary parts together.
Hence show that $e^{i\theta} = \cos\theta + i\sin\theta$ and, hence, $e^{i\pi} = -1$.
This is known as Euler's Formula, after whom e is named.

Note: Euler is pronounced 'Oil-er'.

Binomial Series

In this section we will derive the Maclaurin series for the binomial function:

$$f(x) = (1+x)^n$$

where $n \in \mathbf{Q}$ (i.e. n is a rational number (fraction)).

Consider the binomial coefficients:

$$\binom{n}{0} = 1 \qquad\qquad \binom{n}{1} = n \qquad\qquad \binom{n}{2} = \frac{n(n-1)}{2!} \qquad\qquad \binom{n}{3} = \frac{n(n-1)(n-2)}{3!}$$

The general binomial coefficient is $\binom{n}{r} = \dfrac{n(n-1)(n-2)\ldots(n-r+1)}{r!}$.

For example:

$$\binom{8}{4} = \frac{8(8-1)(8-2)\overset{(n-r+1)}{(8-4+1)}}{4!} = \frac{8(7)(6)(5)}{4!}$$

$$\binom{12}{5} = \frac{12(12-1)(12-2)(12-3)(12-5+1)}{5!} = \frac{12(11)(10)(9)(8)}{5!}$$

with $(n-r+1)$ pointing to the factor $(12-5+1)$.

By the Binomial Theorem, if n is a positive integer (positive whole number), $\quad n \in \mathbf{N}_0$:

$$(1+x)^n = \binom{n}{0} + \binom{n}{1}x + \binom{n}{2}x^2 + \binom{n}{3}x^3 + \cdots + \binom{n}{n}x^n$$

$$(1+x)^n = 1 + nx + \frac{n(n-1)}{2!}x^2 + \frac{n(n-1)(n-2)}{3!}x^3 + \cdots + 1x^n$$

When $n \in \mathbf{N}_0$, the series $(1+x)^n$ consists of a finite number of terms.

This result can be extended to other values of n, in particular, $\quad n \in \mathbf{Q/N}$:

$$(1+x)^n = 1 + nx + \frac{n(n-1)}{2!}x^2 + \frac{n(n-1)(n-2)}{3!}x^3 + \cdots + \frac{n(n-1)(n-2)\cdots(n-r+1)}{r!}x^n + \cdots$$

When $n \in \mathbf{Q/N}$, the expansion produces an **infinite** series called the **Binomial Series**.
The Ratio Test can be used to show that the series is a valid expansion of $(1+x)^n$
when $|x| < 1$, i.e. when $-1 < x < 1$.

Notes: **1.** $n \in \mathbf{Q/N}$ means n can be a positive or negative fraction or a negative whole number,

for example, $\quad \dfrac{3}{2}, -\dfrac{1}{2}, -3$ (but **not** a positive whole number).

2. When $n \in \mathbf{Q/N}$, the definition $\dbinom{n}{r} = \dfrac{n!}{n!(n-r)!}$ has nothing to do with combinations and

cannot be used.

For example $\dbinom{-5}{3}$ makes no sense, i.e.,

$\dbinom{-5}{3}$ = the number of ways of choosing 3 objects from -5 objects, which is absurd.

Also, when $n = -4$, what is $(-4)!$?

We will now use the Maclaurin series to derive the **same** expansion for $(1+x)^n$.

Example ▼

(i) Derive the first four terms in the Maclaurin series for $f(x) = (1+x)^n$.

(ii) Write down the $(r+1)$th term (the general term) and use the Ratio Test to find the range of values of $x \in \mathbf{R}$ for which the series is convergent.

Solution:

Let $f(x) = (1+x)^n = f(0) + f^{(1)}(0)x + \dfrac{f^{(2)}(0)}{2!}x^2 + \dfrac{f^{(3)}(0)}{3!}x^3 + \cdots$

(i)
$$f(x) = (1+x)^n \qquad\qquad f(0) = 1$$
$$f^{(1)}(x) = n(1+x)^{n-1} \qquad\qquad f^{(1)}(0) = n$$
$$f^{(2)}(x) = n(n-1)(1+x)^{n-2} \qquad\qquad f^{(2)}(0) = n(n-1)$$
$$f^{(3)}(x) = n(n-1)(n-2)(1+x)^{n-3} \qquad\qquad f^{(3)}(0) = n(n-1)(n-2)$$

$$f(x) = (1+x)^n = f(0) + f^{(1)}(0)x + \dfrac{f^{(2)}(0)}{2!}x^2 + \dfrac{f^{(3)}(0)}{3!}x^3 + \cdots$$

$\therefore \quad (1+x)^n = 1 + nx + \dfrac{n(n-1)}{2!}x^2 + \dfrac{n(n-1)(n-2)}{3!}x^3$ (first four terms).

Note: From the question, we had to use the Maclaurin series.

(ii) $u_1 = 1 \qquad u_2 = nx \qquad u_3 = \dfrac{n(n-1)}{2!}x^2 \qquad u_4 = \dfrac{n(n-1)(n-2)}{3!}x^3$

Thus, $u_{r+1} = \dbinom{n}{r}x^r = \dfrac{n(n-1)(n-2)\,\ldots\,(n-r+2)(n-r+1)}{r!}x^r$

$\therefore \quad u_r = \dbinom{n}{r-1}x^{r-1} = \dfrac{n(n-1)(n-2)\,\ldots\,(n-r+2)}{(r-1)!}x^{r-1}$

$$\dfrac{u_{r+1}}{u_r} = \dfrac{\dfrac{n(n-1)(n-2)\,\ldots\,(n-r+2)(n-r+1)}{r!}x^r}{\dfrac{n(n-1)(n-2)\,\ldots\,(n-r+2)}{(r-1)!}x^{r-1}}$$

$$= \dfrac{n(n-1)(n-2)\,\ldots\,(n-r+2)(n-r+1)x^r}{r!} \times \dfrac{(r-1)!}{n(n-1)(n-2)\,\ldots\,(n-r+2)x^{r-1}}$$

$$= \dfrac{n-r+1}{r}x \qquad \left(\dfrac{(r-1)!}{r!} = \dfrac{(r-1)!}{r(r-1)!} = \dfrac{1}{r}\right)$$

$$R = \lim_{r\to\infty}\left|\dfrac{u_{r+1}}{u_r}\right|$$

$$= \lim_{r\to\infty}\left|\dfrac{n-r+1}{r}x\right| = |x|\lim_{r\to\infty}\left|\dfrac{n-r+1}{r}\right| = |x|\lim_{r\to\infty}\left|\dfrac{\dfrac{n}{r}-1+\dfrac{1}{r}}{1}\right| = |x|.|-1| = |x|(1) = |x|$$

The series is convergent for $|x| < 1$, i.e. $-1 < x < 1$.

We could also be asked to derive a number of terms of the Maclaurin series for $(1+x)^n$ for some value of $n \in \mathbf{Q}/\mathbf{N}$ and to use the corresponding series to approximate some number.

Example ▼

(i) Derive the first four terms of the Maclaurin series for $f(x) = \sqrt{1+x}$.

(ii) Deduce the first four terms of the series expansion of $\sqrt{1-2x}$.
Write down the values of x for which this expansion is valid.

(iii) Use these four terms to evaluate $\sqrt{96}$, correct to two places of decimals.

Solution:

Let $f(x) = \sqrt{1+x} = (1+x)^{1/2} = f(0) + f^{(1)}(0)x + \dfrac{f^{(2)}(0)}{2!}x^2 + \dfrac{f^{(3)}(0)}{3!}x^3 + \cdots$

(i)

$$f(x) = (1+x)^{1/2} \qquad\qquad\qquad f(0) = 1$$

$$f^{(1)}(x) = \tfrac{1}{2}(1+x)^{-1/2} \qquad\qquad f^{(1)}(0) = \tfrac{1}{2}$$

$$f^{(2)}(x) = -\tfrac{1}{4}(1+x)^{-3/2} \qquad\qquad f^{(2)}(0) = -\tfrac{1}{4}$$

$$f^{(3)}(x) = \tfrac{3}{8}(1+x)^{-5/2} \qquad\qquad f^{(3)}(0) = \tfrac{3}{8}$$

$$f(x) = (1+x)^{1/2} = f(0) + f^{(1)}(0)x + \dfrac{f^{(2)}(0)}{2!}x^2 + \dfrac{f^{(3)}(0)}{3!}x^3 + \cdots$$

$$\therefore \quad \sqrt{1+x} = 1 + \tfrac{1}{2}x + \dfrac{-\tfrac{1}{4}}{2!}x^2 + \dfrac{\tfrac{3}{8}}{3!}x^3 \qquad\qquad \text{(first four terms)}$$

$$\sqrt{1+x} = 1 + \tfrac{1}{2}x + \dfrac{-\tfrac{1}{4}}{2}x^2 + \dfrac{\tfrac{3}{8}}{6}x^3$$

$$\sqrt{1+x} = 1 + \tfrac{1}{2}x - \tfrac{1}{8}x^2 + \tfrac{1}{16}x^3$$

(ii) To find the first four terms of the Maclaurin series for $\sqrt{1-2x}$,
replace x with $(-2x)$.

$$\sqrt{1+x} = 1 + \tfrac{1}{2}x - \tfrac{1}{8}x^2 + \tfrac{1}{16}x^3$$

$$\sqrt{1-2x} = \sqrt{1+(-2x)} = 1 + \tfrac{1}{2}(-2x) - \tfrac{1}{8}(-2x)^2 + \tfrac{1}{16}(-2x)^3 \qquad \text{(put in } (-2x) \text{ for } x)$$

$$= 1 + \tfrac{1}{2}(-2x) - \tfrac{1}{8}(4x^2) + \tfrac{1}{16}(-8x^3)$$

$$= 1 - x - \tfrac{1}{2}x^2 - \tfrac{1}{2}x^3$$

In the expansion of $\sqrt{1+x}$, the series is valid for $|x| < 1$, i.e., $-1 < x < 1$.

In the expansion of $\sqrt{1-2x}$, the series is valid for $|-2x| < 1$, or $|2x| < 1$,

i.e. $\quad -1 < 2x < 1 \quad \Rightarrow \quad -\tfrac{1}{2} < x < \tfrac{1}{2}$.

(iii) To use the expansion of $\sqrt{1-2x}$ to evaluate $\sqrt{96}$, then $\sqrt{96}$ must be written in the form

$$a\sqrt{1-\frac{b}{c}}, \text{ where } -\frac{1}{2} < \frac{b}{c} < \frac{1}{2}.$$

$$\sqrt{96} = \sqrt{100-4} = \sqrt{100\left(1-\frac{4}{100}\right)} = \sqrt{100(1-0.04)} = \sqrt{100}\sqrt{1-0.04} = 10\sqrt{1-0.04}$$

Then $\sqrt{1-2x} = 10\sqrt{1-0.04}$ when $2x = 0.04$, i.e., when $x = 0.02$.

Thus $\sqrt{96} = 10\sqrt{1-2x}$ when $x = 0.02$

$$\therefore \quad \sqrt{96} = 10[1 - x - \tfrac{1}{2}x^2 - \tfrac{1}{2}x^3] \qquad\qquad \text{when } x = 0.02$$

$$= 10[1 - (0.02) - \tfrac{1}{2}(0.02)^2 - \tfrac{1}{2}(0.02)^3] \quad \text{(put in } x = 0.02)$$

$$= 10(0.979796)$$

$$= 9.79796$$

$$= 9.80 \qquad \text{(correct to two places of decimals)}.$$

Exercise 8.5 ▼

1. (i) Derive the first four terms of the Maclaurin series for $\dfrac{1}{1+x}$.

(ii) Deduce the first four terms of the series expansions of:

     (a) $\dfrac{1}{1-x}$ **(b)** $\dfrac{1}{1-2x}$ **(c)** $\dfrac{1}{1+x^2}$.

(iii) Write down the general term in the series expansion of $(1+x)^{-1}$ and use the Ratio Test to show that the series is convergent for $-1 < x < 1$.

2. (i) Derive the first four terms of the Maclaurin series of $\dfrac{1}{(1+x)^2}$ and write down the general term.

(ii) Use the Ratio Test to find the range of values for which the series is convergent.

(iii) Deduce the first four terms of the series expansion of $\dfrac{1}{(1+x^2)^2}$.

3. (i) Derive the first four terms of the Maclaurin series of $\sqrt{1+x}$.

(ii) Deduce the first four terms in the series expansion of $\sqrt{1-x}$.

     Use these four terms to approximate $\sqrt{99}$, correct to two decimal places.

4. (i) Derive the first four terms of the Maclaurin series for $\dfrac{1}{\sqrt{1+x}}$.

(ii) Deduce the first four terms of the series expansion for $\dfrac{1}{\sqrt{1-x}}$.

     Use these four terms to evaluate $\dfrac{1}{\sqrt{0.99}}$, correct to three decimal places.

(iii) Deduce the first four terms of the series expansion for $\dfrac{1}{\sqrt{1-2x}}$.

Use these four terms to evaluate $(0.94)^{-1/2}$, correct to two decimal places.

(iv) Write down the first three terms of the series expansion for $\sqrt{1+x}$.

(v) Hence, write down the first three terms of the series expansion of $\sqrt{\dfrac{1+x}{1-x}}$.

By letting $x = \dfrac{1}{10}$, use these three terms to find an approximate value of $\sqrt{11}$, correct to three decimal places.

5. Derive the first three terms of the Maclaurin series of $(1+x)^{-1/3}$.

By letting $x = \dfrac{1}{8}$, use these three terms to find an approximate value of $(9)^{-1/3}$, writing your answer in the form $\dfrac{a}{b}$, $a, b \in \mathbb{N}$.

6. Show that the first four terms of the Maclaurin series of $(1+x)^n$ are:

$$(1+x)^n = 1 + nx + \frac{n(n-1)}{2!}x^2 + \frac{n(n-1)(n-2)}{3!}x^3$$

Hence, or otherwise, find the first four terms of the series expansion of:

(i) $(1+x)^{-2}$ **(ii)** $(1-3x)^{-2}$ **(iii)** $(1+x^2)^{-3}$ **(iv)** $(1-3x)^{1/3}$

Approximating π

We can use the Maclaurin series expansion of $\tan^{-1} x$ to find an approximate value for π.

Example ▼

Derive the first two non-zero terms of the Maclaurin series for $\tan^{-1} x$.

Solution:

Let $f(x) = \tan^{-1} x = f(0) + f^{(1)}(0)x + \dfrac{f^{(2)}(0)}{2!}x^2 + \dfrac{f^{(3)}(0)}{3!}x^3 + \cdots$.

$$f(x) = \tan^{-1} x \qquad\qquad\qquad\qquad\qquad f(0) = 0$$

$$f^{(1)}(x) = \frac{1}{1+x^2} = (1+x^2)^{-1} \qquad\qquad f^{(1)}(0) = 1$$

$$f^{(2)}(x) = -1(1+x^2)^{-2}(2x) = \frac{-2x}{(1+x^2)^2} \qquad f^{(2)}(0) = 0$$

$$f^{(3)}(x) = \frac{(1+x^2)^2(-2) - (-2x)(2)(1+x^2)(2x)}{(1+x^2)^4} \qquad f^{(3)}(0) = -2$$

$$f(x) = \tan^{-1} x = f(0) + f^{(1)}(0)x + \frac{f^{(2)}(0)}{2!}x^2 + \frac{f^{(3)}(0)}{3!}x^3 + \cdots$$

$$\therefore \quad \tan^{-1} x = 0 + 1x + \tfrac{0}{2}x^2 + \tfrac{-2}{6}x^3 + \cdots$$

$$\tan^{-1} x = x - \tfrac{1}{3}x^3 \qquad \text{(first two terms)}$$

The Maclaurin series for $\tan^{-1} x$ is given by:

$$\tan^{-1} x = x - \frac{x^3}{3} + \frac{x^5}{5} - \frac{x^7}{7} + \frac{x^9}{9} - \frac{x^{11}}{11} + \cdots = \sum_{n=0}^{\infty} \frac{(-1)^n x^{2n+1}}{2n+1}$$

The series is valid for $-1 \leqslant x \leqslant 1$.

As can be seen from the example above, the calculation of the higher derivatives in deriving the Maclaurin series for $\tan^{-1} x$ becomes very awkward and unwieldy. To overcome this problem we look to easier methods to find a Maclaurin series for $\tan^{-1} x$.

1. Using an infinite geometric series

Consider the infinite geometric series:

$$\sum_{n=0}^{\infty}(-1)^n x^{2n} = 1 - x^2 + x^4 - x^6 + x^8 - x^{10} + \cdots \qquad \text{for } -1 < x < 1.$$

For this series, $a = 1$ and $r = -x^2$.

$$S_{\infty} = \frac{a}{1-r} = \frac{1}{1-(-x^2)} = \frac{1}{1+x^2}$$

$$\therefore \quad \frac{1}{1+x^2} = 1 - x^2 + x^4 - x^6 + x^8 - x^{10} + \cdots$$

Note: This can also be shown by using long division.

From our work on differentiation,

$$\tan^{-1} x = \int \frac{1}{1+x^2}\, dx$$

$$\tan^{-1} x = \int (1 - x^2 + x^4 - x^6 + x^8 - x^{10} + \cdots)\, dx$$

Thus, $\tan^{-1} x = x - \dfrac{x^3}{3} + \dfrac{x^5}{5} - \dfrac{x^7}{7} + \dfrac{x^9}{9} - \dfrac{x^{11}}{11} + \cdots$

2. Using a previous Maclaurin series

Consider the Binomial Series:

$$\frac{1}{1+x} = (1+x)^{-1} = 1 - x + x^2 - x^3 + x^4 - x^5 + \cdots$$

Replace x with x^2 on both sides:

$$\frac{1}{1+x^2} = 1 - x^2 + x^4 - x^6 + x^8 - x^{10} + \cdots$$

$$\therefore \quad \int \frac{1}{1+x^2} \, dx = \int (1 - x^2 + x^4 - x^6 + x^8 - x^{10} + \cdots) \, dx$$

Integrate both sides with respect to x.

Thus, $\tan^{-1} x = x - \dfrac{x^3}{3} + \dfrac{x^5}{5} - \dfrac{x^7}{7} + \dfrac{x^9}{9} - \dfrac{x^{11}}{11} + \cdots$

This series can be shown to be valid for $-1 \leqslant x \leqslant 1$.

The Maclaurin series for $\tan^{-1} x$ can be used to find an approximation for π.
Consider the first eight terms of the Maclaurin series for $\tan^{-1} x$:

$$\tan^{-1} x = x - \frac{x^3}{3} + \frac{x^5}{5} - \frac{x^7}{7} + \frac{x^9}{9} - \frac{x^{11}}{11} + \frac{x^{13}}{13} - \frac{x^{15}}{15}$$

Let $x = 1$ on both sides.

$$\tan^{-1} 1 = 1 - \frac{1}{3} + \frac{1}{5} - \frac{1}{7} + \frac{1}{9} - \frac{1}{11} + \frac{1}{13} - \frac{1}{15}$$

$\dfrac{\pi}{4} = 0.7542679543$ (using a calculator)

$\pi = 4(0.7542679543)$ $\left(\tan^{-1} 1 = \dfrac{\pi}{4} \right)$

$\pi = 3.0170718172$ (multiply both sides by 4)

This is not a good approximation for π after using eight terms. In fact it would take thousands of terms to get a good approximation by letting $x = 1$ on both sides. Thus, while valid, it is not very efficient. To overcome this problem we use a series that converges far more quickly. We use the following result:

$$\tan^{-1} a + \tan^{-1} b = \tan^{-1} \frac{a+b}{1-ab}, \text{ for } ab < 1.$$

The basic idea is to find two fractions a and b such that

$$\tan^{-1} a + \tan^{-1} b = \tan^{-1} 1 = \frac{\pi}{4}$$

and by combining two series into one we will get a series that converges far more rapidly. The condition, $ab < 1$, is to ensure that we are dealing with the principal values for each $\tan^{-1} x$.

Proof:

Let $p = \tan^{-1} a$ and $q = \tan^{-1} b$

$\therefore \quad \tan p = a$ and $\tan q = b$

$$\tan(p+q) = \frac{\tan p + \tan q}{1 - \tan p \tan q}$$

$$\tan(p+q) = \frac{a+b}{1-ab}$$

$$p + q = \tan^{-1}\left(\frac{a+b}{1-ab}\right)$$

$$\tan^{-1} a + \tan^{-1} b = \tan^{-1}\left(\frac{a+b}{1-ab}\right)$$

Example ▼

Find the value of $a \in \mathbf{R}$ for which $\tan^{-1} a + \tan^{-1} \dfrac{3}{7} = \dfrac{\pi}{4}$.

Solution:

$$\tan^{-1} a + \tan^{-1} \frac{3}{7} = \frac{\pi}{4}$$

$$\tan^{-1}\left(\frac{a + \frac{3}{7}}{1 - \frac{3}{7}a}\right) = \frac{\pi}{4}$$

$$\frac{a + \frac{3}{7}}{1 - \frac{3}{7}a} = \tan \frac{\pi}{4}$$

$$\frac{7a + 3}{7 - 3a} = 1 \qquad \left(\begin{array}{c}\text{multiply each part on the}\\ \text{left-hand side by 7}\end{array}\right)$$

$$7a + 3 = 7 - 3a$$

$$10a = 4$$

$$a = \frac{4}{10}$$

$$a = \frac{2}{5}$$

The Maclaurin series for $\tan^{-1} x = x - \dfrac{x^3}{3} + \dfrac{x^5}{5} - \dfrac{x^7}{7} + \cdots$

The series is convergent for $-1 \leqslant x \leqslant 1$.

(i) Write down the first four terms in the series expansion for: **(a)** $\tan^{-1} \dfrac{1}{2}$ **(b)** $\tan^{-1} \dfrac{1}{3}$.

(ii) Verify that: $\tan^{-1} \dfrac{1}{2} + \tan^{-1} \dfrac{1}{3} = \dfrac{\pi}{4}$.

Use this fact to deduce a series expansion for π up to the seventh powers.

(iii) Use these terms to find an approximation for π, giving your answer correct to four decimal places.

Solution:

(i)
$$\tan^{-1} x = x - \frac{x^3}{3} + \frac{x^5}{5} - \frac{x^7}{7} + \cdots$$

(a)
$$\tan^{-1}\left(\frac{1}{2}\right) = \frac{1}{2} - \frac{\left(\frac{1}{2}\right)^3}{3} + \frac{\left(\frac{1}{2}\right)^5}{5} - \frac{\left(\frac{1}{2}\right)^7}{7}$$
$$= \frac{1}{2} - \frac{\frac{1}{8}}{3} + \frac{\frac{1}{32}}{5} - \frac{\frac{1}{128}}{7}$$
$$= \frac{1}{2} - \frac{1}{24} + \frac{1}{160} - \frac{1}{896}$$

(b)
$$\tan^{-1}\left(\frac{1}{3}\right) = \frac{1}{3} - \frac{\left(\frac{1}{3}\right)^3}{3} + \frac{\left(\frac{1}{3}\right)^5}{5} - \frac{\left(\frac{1}{3}\right)^7}{7}$$
$$= \frac{1}{3} - \frac{\frac{1}{27}}{3} + \frac{\frac{1}{243}}{5} - \frac{\frac{1}{2187}}{7}$$
$$= \frac{1}{3} - \frac{1}{81} + \frac{1}{1215} - \frac{1}{15309}$$

(ii)
$$\tan^{-1} \frac{1}{2} + \tan^{-1} \frac{1}{3} = \tan^{-1}\left(\frac{\frac{1}{2} + \frac{1}{3}}{1 - \frac{1}{2} \times \frac{1}{3}}\right)$$
$$= \tan^{-1}\left(\frac{\frac{1}{2} + \frac{1}{3}}{1 - \frac{1}{6}}\right)$$
$$= \tan^{-1}\left(\frac{3 + 2}{6 - 1}\right) \qquad \text{(multiply each part by 6)}$$
$$= \tan^{-1}\left(\frac{5}{5}\right)$$
$$= \tan^{-1} 1 = \frac{\pi}{4}$$

(iii)
$$\frac{\pi}{4} = \tan^{-1} \frac{1}{2} + \tan^{-1} \frac{1}{3}$$
$$\pi = 4\left[\tan^{-1} \frac{1}{2} + \tan^{-1} \frac{1}{3}\right]$$
$$\pi = 4\left[\frac{1}{2} - \frac{1}{24} + \frac{1}{160} - \frac{1}{896} + \frac{1}{3} - \frac{1}{81} + \frac{1}{1215} - \frac{1}{15309}\right]$$
$$\pi = 4[0.78521264044] \qquad \text{(using a calculator)}$$
$$\pi = 3.1409 \qquad \text{(correct to four decimal places)}$$

1. Show that: **(i)** $\tan^{-1}\dfrac{1}{4}+\tan^{-1}\dfrac{3}{5}=\dfrac{\pi}{4}$ **(ii)** $\tan^{-1}\dfrac{5}{11}+\tan^{-1}\dfrac{3}{8}=\dfrac{\pi}{4}.$

2. Find the value of $k \in \mathbf{R}$ if:

(i) $\tan^{-1}k+\tan^{-1}\dfrac{1}{5}=\dfrac{\pi}{4}$ **(ii)** $\tan^{-1}\dfrac{3}{4}+\tan^{-1}k=\tan^{-1}1.$

3. Find the value of x for which $\tan^{-1}\dfrac{1}{4}+\tan^{-1}(2x)=\dfrac{\pi}{4},\quad 0<x<1.$

4. $\tan^{-1}\dfrac{1}{3}+\tan^{-1}\dfrac{1}{5}=\tan^{-1}a$ and $\tan^{-1}\dfrac{1}{7}+\tan^{-1}\dfrac{1}{8}=\tan^{-1}b.$

  (i) Find the value of a and the value of b.
  (ii) Evaluate $\tan^{-1}a+\tan^{-1}b.$

5. Show that: **(i)** $\tan^{-1}\dfrac{1}{2}+\tan^{-1}\dfrac{1}{5}+\tan^{-1}\dfrac{1}{8}=\dfrac{\pi}{4}$ **(ii)** $2\tan^{-1}\dfrac{1}{3}+\tan^{-1}\dfrac{1}{7}=\dfrac{\pi}{4}.$

6. If $\tan^{-1}\dfrac{1}{2}+\tan^{-1}\dfrac{1}{3}=\tan^{-1}\dfrac{5}{6}+\tan^{-1}k,$ find the value of $k,\quad k \in \mathbf{R}.$

7. (i) If $\displaystyle\int_0^x\frac{dt}{1+t^2}=\int_0^x(1-t^2+t^4-t^6+\cdots)\,dt,$ show that:

$\tan^{-1}x=x-\dfrac{x^3}{3}+\dfrac{x^5}{5}-\dfrac{x^7}{7}+\cdots$ and write down the general term.

(ii) If the series is convergent for $x=\pm1$, use the Ratio Test to show that the series is convergent for $-1\leqslant x\leqslant1.$

By letting $x=1$ on both sides, show that $\dfrac{\pi}{4}=1-\dfrac{1}{3}+\dfrac{1}{5}-\dfrac{1}{7}+\cdots$

(iii) Hence, use the first four terms to approximate π, writing your answer in the form $\dfrac{a}{b}$, where $a,b \in \mathbf{N}.$

8. The Maclaurin series for $\tan^{-1}x=x-\dfrac{x^3}{3}+\dfrac{x^5}{5}-\dfrac{x^7}{7}+\cdots$

The series is convergent for $-1\leqslant x\leqslant1.$

(i) Show that $\tan^{-1}\dfrac{1}{5}+\tan^{-1}\dfrac{2}{3}=\dfrac{\pi}{4}.$

(ii) Write down the first three terms in the series expansion for: **(a)** $\tan^{-1}\dfrac{1}{5}$ **(b)** $\tan^{-1}\dfrac{2}{3}.$

Hence, use these terms to find an approximation for π, correct to two decimal places.

9. The Maclaurin series for $\tan^{-1} x = x - \dfrac{x^3}{3} + \dfrac{x^5}{5} - \dfrac{x^7}{7} + \cdots$

The series is convergent for $-1 \leqslant x \leqslant 1$.

(i) Show that $\tan^{-1} \dfrac{2}{5} + \tan^{-1} \dfrac{3}{7} = \dfrac{\pi}{4}$

(ii) Write down the first three terms in the series expansion for: **(a)** $\tan^{-1} \dfrac{2}{5}$ **(b)** $\tan^{-1} \dfrac{3}{7}$.

Hence, use these terms to find an approximation for π, correct to four decimal places.

10. The Maclaurin series for $\tan^{-1} x = x - \dfrac{x^3}{3} + \dfrac{x^5}{5} - \dfrac{x^7}{7} + \cdots$

The series is convergent for $-1 \leqslant x \leqslant 1$.

(i) Show that $\tan^{-1} \dfrac{1}{2} + \tan^{-1} \dfrac{1}{3} = \dfrac{\pi}{4}$.

(ii) Deduce an infinite series for π, indicating the first few terms with non-zero coefficients.

(iii) Find the general term.

(iv) Use the first four terms to find an approximation for π, correct to four decimal places.

PROOFS

Coordinate Geometry of the Circle

Equation of a Tangent to the Circle $x^2 + y^2 = r^2$ at the Point (x_1, y_1) on the Circle

> The equation of the tangent to the circle $x^2 + y^2 = r^2$ at the point (x_1, y_1) on the circle is:
> $$x_1 x + y_1 y = r^2.$$

Proof:

From the diagram:

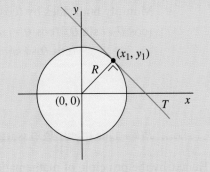

Slope of radius $R = \dfrac{y_1 - 0}{x_1 - 0} = \dfrac{y_1}{x_1}$

Thus, slope of the tangent T is $\quad -\dfrac{x_1}{y_1}, \quad$ as $R \perp T$.

Equation of the tangent, T:

$$(y - y_1) = m(x - x_1)$$

$$(y - y_1) = -\frac{x_1}{y_1}(x - x_1) \qquad \left(m = -\frac{x_1}{y_1}\right)$$

$$y_1 y - y_1^2 = -x_1 x + x_1^2$$

$$x_1 x + y_1 y = x_1^2 + y_1^2$$

$$x_1 x + y_1 y = r^2 \qquad \text{(since (x_1, y_1) is on the circle, $x_1^2 + y_1^2 = r^2$)}$$

Thus, the equation of the tangent T is $x_1 x + y_1 y = r^2$.

Complex Numbers

De Moivre's Theorem:
$(\cos\,\theta + i\,\sin\,\theta)^n = \cos\,n\theta + i\,\sin\,n\theta$

$$(\cos\,\theta + i\,\sin\,\theta)^n = \cos\,n\theta + i\,\sin\,n\theta$$

Proof: (for $n \in \mathbf{N}$)

$P(n)$: $(\cos\,\theta + i\,\sin\,\theta)^n = \cos\,n\theta + i\,\sin\,n\theta, \quad n \in \mathbf{N}$

Step 1: $P(0)$: $(\cos\,\theta + i\,\sin\,\theta)^0 = \cos\,0(\theta) + i\,\sin\,0(\theta)$

$$1 = \cos\,0 + i\,\sin\,0$$
$$1 = 1 \qquad \text{which is true}$$

$\therefore \quad P(0)$ is true.

Step 2: Assume $P(k)$ is true, i.e. $(\cos\,\theta + i\,\sin\,\theta)^k = \cos\,k\theta + i\,\sin\,k\theta$

Test $P(k+1)$:

Multiply both sides by $(\cos\,\theta + i\,\sin\,\theta)$:

$(\cos\,\theta + i\,\sin\,\theta)^k(\cos\,\theta + i\,\sin\,\theta) = (\cos\,k\theta + i\,\sin\,k\theta)(\cos\,\theta + i\,\sin\,\theta)$

$(\cos\,\theta + i\,\sin\,\theta)^{k+1} = (\cos\,k\theta\,\cos\,\theta - \sin\,k\theta\,\sin\,\theta)$
$$+ i(\sin\,k\theta\,\cos\,\theta + \cos\,k\theta\,\sin\,\theta)$$
$$= \cos(k\theta + \theta) + i\,\sin(k\theta + \theta)$$
$$= \cos(k+1)\theta + i\,\sin(k+1)\theta$$

i.e. $P(k+1)$ is true if $P(k)$ is true.

Hence, by the principle of mathematical induction, $P(n)$ is true.

Proof: (for $n \in \mathbf{Z}/\mathbf{N}$)

Consider $(\cos\theta + i\sin\theta)^{-n}, \quad n \in \mathbf{N}_0$

$(\cos\theta + i\sin\theta)^{-n}$

$= \dfrac{1}{(\cos\theta + i\sin\theta)^n}$

$= \dfrac{1}{\cos n\theta + i\sin n\theta}$ $\qquad$ [as $n \in \mathbf{N}_0$]

$= \dfrac{1}{\cos n\theta + i\sin n\theta} \cdot \dfrac{\cos n\theta - i\sin n\theta}{\cos n\theta - i\sin n\theta}$ $\qquad \left[\begin{array}{l}\text{multiply top and bottom by}\\ \text{the conjugate of the bottom}\end{array}\right]$

$= \dfrac{\cos n\theta - i\sin n\theta}{\cos^2 n\theta + \sin^2 n\theta}$

$= \cos n\theta - i\sin n\theta$ $\qquad$ [$\cos^2 n\theta + \sin^2 n\theta = 1$]

$= \cos(-n\theta) + i\sin(-n\theta)$

$\therefore \quad (\cos\theta + i\sin n\theta)^{-n} = \cos(-n\theta) + i\sin(-n\theta)$

Therefore De Moivre's Theorem is true for all $n \in \mathbf{Z}$.

Difference Equations: Theorem

> If α and β are the roots of the quadratic equation
>
> $$px^2 + qx + r = 0 \text{ and}$$
>
> $$u_n = l\alpha^n + m\beta^n \text{ for all } n, \text{ then:}$$
>
> $$pu_{n+2} + qu_{n+1} + ru_n = 0 \text{ for all } n.$$

Proof:

$$u_n = l\alpha^n + m\beta^n$$

$$u_{n+1} = l\alpha^{n+1} + m\beta^{n+1} = \alpha l\alpha^n + \beta m\beta^n$$

$$u_{n+2} = l\alpha^{n+2} + m\beta^{n+2} = \alpha^2 l\alpha^n + \beta^2 m\beta^n$$

If α and β are the roots of $px^2 + qx + r = 0$, then:

$$p\alpha^2 + q\alpha + r = 0 \quad \text{and} \quad p\beta^2 + q\beta + r = 0$$

Thus, $pu_{n+2} + qu_{n+1} + ru_n$

$$= p(\alpha^2 l\alpha^n + \beta^2 m\beta^n) + q(\alpha l\alpha^n + \beta m\beta^n) + r(l\alpha^n + m\beta^n)$$

$$= p\alpha^2 l\alpha^n + p\beta^2 m\beta^n + q\alpha l\alpha^n + q\beta m\beta^n + rl\alpha^n + rm\beta^n$$

$$= l\alpha^n(p\alpha^2 + q\alpha + r) + m\beta^n(p\beta^2 + q\beta + r)$$

$$= l\alpha^n(0) + m\beta^n(0)$$

$$= 0$$

REVISION EXERCISE I   COMPLEX NUMBERS AND MATRICES

Paper I, Question 3

This revision exercise covers Chapters 2 and 3.

1. $M = \begin{pmatrix} 2 & 1 \\ 2 & 3 \end{pmatrix}$. Show that $M^2 - 5M + 4I = 0$.

2. $A = \begin{pmatrix} 5 & 7 \\ 2 & 3 \end{pmatrix}$; $M = \begin{pmatrix} 2 & -1 \\ 0 & 4 \end{pmatrix}$. Find $A^{-1} + 3M$.

3. If $A = \begin{pmatrix} 3 & 2 \\ 4 & 3 \end{pmatrix}$ and $B = \begin{pmatrix} 3 & 2 \\ -2 & 1 \end{pmatrix}$, find a matrix M such that $M = BA^{-1}$.

4. Given the matrices $A = \begin{pmatrix} 1 & -2 \\ -1 & 3 \end{pmatrix}$ and $B = \begin{pmatrix} 2 & 1 \\ 3 & 3 \end{pmatrix}$,

    (i) find A^{-1}

    (ii) hence, find the matrix X such that $XA = B$.

5. Let $u = \dfrac{1 + 3i}{3 + i}$, where $i^2 = -1$.

    (i) Express u in the form $a + ib$, where $a, b \in \mathbf{R}$.

    (ii) Evaluate $|u|$.

6. $z = \dfrac{6 + 2i}{1 + 2i}$. Plot, on an Argand diagram: **(i)** z **(ii)** z^2.

7. Find the two real numbers a and b such that: $a(1 + 2i) - b(3 + 4i) = 5$.

8. If $|-7 + ki| = |20 + 15i|$, find the two values of k, $k \in \mathbf{R}$.

9. The complex number $u = 4 + 3i$, where $i^2 = -1$.

    (i) Find the complex number $v = p + qi$, $p, q \in \mathbf{R}$, where $uv = 10 - 5i$,

    (ii) Verify that $|u + v + 3 - 5i| = 4\sqrt{5}$.

10. If $-2+3i$ is a root of the equation $z^2+pz+q=0$, $\quad p, q \in \mathbf{R}$, write down the other root and, hence, find the value of p and the value of q.

11. Express $-1+\sqrt{3}i$ in the form $r(\cos\theta+i\sin\theta)$, where $i^2=-1$.

12. $M = \begin{pmatrix} \lambda-2 & 1 \\ 2 & \lambda-3 \end{pmatrix}$, $\quad \lambda \in \mathbf{R}$.

If the determinant of M is zero (i.e. M is singular), find the values of λ.

13. Find the real part of $\dfrac{1}{(1-2i)^2}$.

14. If $\dfrac{2-\sqrt{2}i}{2+\sqrt{2}i}=p+qi$, find the values of p and q and, hence, evaluate p^2+q^2.

15. Let $z=-1+\sqrt{3}i$, where $i^2=-1$. Express z^2 in the form $x+yi$, $\quad x, y \in \mathbf{R}$.
Find the real value of k such that z^2+kz is: **(i)** real **(ii)** a multiple of i.

16. Express $i^{30}-2i^{11}$ in the form $a+bi$, $\quad a, b \in \mathbf{R}$, $i=\sqrt{-1}$.

17. The matrix $A = \begin{pmatrix} 2 & i \\ -i & 0 \end{pmatrix}$ and the matrix $B = \begin{pmatrix} i & -1 \\ 3 & 4i \end{pmatrix}$. Find AB.

18. If $M = \begin{pmatrix} 3 & 5 \\ 2 & 3 \end{pmatrix}$ and $N = \begin{pmatrix} -1 & 3 \\ -1 & 2 \end{pmatrix}$, verify that $(MN)^{-1}=N^{-1}M^{-1}$.

19. (i) Let $M = \begin{pmatrix} 1 & 6 \\ 1 & 1 \end{pmatrix}$. Find M^{-1}.

(ii) If $M^{-1}AM = \begin{pmatrix} -2 & 0 \\ 0 & 3 \end{pmatrix}$, find the matrix A.

20. If $A = \begin{pmatrix} \cos\theta & \sin\theta \\ \sin\theta & -\cos\theta \end{pmatrix}$, show that $A^{-1}=A$ and, hence, evaluate A^2-I.

21. $M = \begin{pmatrix} x+2 & x+4 \\ x-2 & x-1 \end{pmatrix}$, $\quad x \in \mathbf{R}$. If $\det(M)=0$, find the value of x.

22. If $A = \begin{pmatrix} 3 & 2 \\ 5 & 4 \end{pmatrix}$ and $B = \begin{pmatrix} 1 & -2 \\ 3 & 4 \end{pmatrix}$, find the matrix C such that $C=A(A-B)$.

23. If $A = \begin{pmatrix} 3 & 1 \\ 2 & 1 \end{pmatrix}$ and $B = \begin{pmatrix} 1 & -1 \\ -2 & 3 \end{pmatrix}$, evaluate: **(i)** AB **(ii)** $(AB)^{10}$.

24. Evaluate $\left(\dfrac{-1+\sqrt{3}i}{\sqrt{3}+i}\right)^{98}$.

25. If $z = \cos\dfrac{\pi}{3}+i\sin\dfrac{\pi}{3}$, evaluate $|1+z|$, where $i=\sqrt{-1}$.

26. $z_1 = 3 + 2i$ and $z_2 = 1 - ki$, where $k \in \mathbf{R}$. If $|z_1 z_2| = \sqrt{65}$, find the possible values of k.

27. Write $(x \ \ y)\begin{pmatrix} 2 & 5 \\ 5 & 8 \end{pmatrix}\begin{pmatrix} x \\ y \end{pmatrix}$ in the form $ax^2 + bxy + cy^2$.

28. Evaluate: **(i)** $(1 \ \ -2)\begin{pmatrix} 3 & 0 \\ -5 & 1 \end{pmatrix}\begin{pmatrix} 1 \\ -2 \end{pmatrix}$ **(ii)** $(1 \ \ i)\begin{pmatrix} 3 & 2-i \\ 2+i & 3 \end{pmatrix}\begin{pmatrix} 1 \\ -i \end{pmatrix}$.

29. Find the coefficient of xy in the product $(x \ \ y)\begin{pmatrix} 3 & -1 \\ 2 & 4 \end{pmatrix}\begin{pmatrix} x \\ -2y \end{pmatrix}$.

30. If $(x \ \ 2)\begin{pmatrix} 1 & 5 \\ 2 & -1 \end{pmatrix}\begin{pmatrix} 3 \\ x \end{pmatrix} = 30$, find the values of x.

Exercise 1R.B ▼

1. $A = \begin{pmatrix} 4 & 3 \\ -1 & 7 \end{pmatrix}$, $B = \begin{pmatrix} 3 & 4 \\ 1 & 2 \end{pmatrix}$ and $C = \begin{pmatrix} -1 & 1 \\ 2 & -5 \end{pmatrix}$.

   Solve, for l and m: $lB + mC = A$, $l, m \in \mathbf{R}$.

2. Find the two roots of the equation: $z^2 - (1 + 2i)z + (-1 + i) = 0$.
   Explain why the roots do not occur in conjugate pairs.

3. (i) Simplify $\left(\dfrac{-2 + 3i}{3 + 2i}\right)$ and, hence, find the value of $\left(\dfrac{-2 + 3i}{3 + 2i}\right)^9$, where $i^2 = -1$.

   (ii) Find the two complex numbers $a + ib$ such that $(a + ib)^2 = 15 - 8i$, where $a, b \in \mathbf{R}$.

4. If $A = \begin{pmatrix} 5 & 4 \\ 1 & 2 \end{pmatrix}$ and $B = \begin{pmatrix} 4 & 1 \\ 1 & -1 \end{pmatrix}$, find AB.

   Show that $B^{-1}AB$ is of the form $\begin{pmatrix} p & 0 \\ 0 & q \end{pmatrix}$, where $p, q \in \mathbf{N}_0$.

5. Evaluate $\left(\dfrac{a + bi}{b - ai}\right)^4$.

6. (i) Find a quadratic equation whose roots are $3 + i$ and $3 - i$, where $i^2 = -1$.

   (ii) Let $P(z) = z^3 - kz^2 + 22z - 20$, $k \in \mathbf{R}$. $3 + i$ is a root of the equation $P(z) = 0$.

   (a) Find the value of k.   **(b)** Find the other two roots of the equation $P(z) = 0$.

7. If $M = \begin{pmatrix} 2 & 0 \\ 0 & 5 \end{pmatrix}$, find M^2, M^3 and write down an expression for M^{50}.

8. The complex number w is such that $(w + 1)(2 - i) = 3 - 4i$.

   (i) Express w in the form $p + qi$, where $p, q \in \mathbf{R}$.

   (ii) Calculate $|w|$, the modulus of w.

   (iii) w is a root of the equation $z^2 + az + b = 0$.
   Find the value of a and the value of b, where $a, b \in \mathbf{R}$.

9. (i) Find the values of h and k, if $2 - 3i$ is a root of the equation
$$z^3 + hz^2 + kz - 65 = 0, \text{ where } h, k \in \mathbf{R}.$$

(ii) Find the two other roots of this equation.

10. If $(2 + \sqrt{3}i)^2 = a + bi + 2(1 + i)$, express $2(b - 2a)$ in the form $p\sqrt{q}$, $p, q \in \mathbf{N}$ and q is prime.

11. $M = \begin{pmatrix} 5 & -3 \\ -2 & 1 \end{pmatrix}$ and $N = \begin{pmatrix} 1 & 1 \\ 3 & 4 \end{pmatrix}$.

Find the matrix A, if $MAN = \begin{pmatrix} 2 & 0 \\ 0 & 3 \end{pmatrix}$.

12. The matrix $M = \begin{pmatrix} \cos\theta & k\sin\theta \\ \frac{1}{k}\sin\theta & -\cos\theta \end{pmatrix}$. Evaluate $M^2 - I = 0$, where $I = \begin{pmatrix} 1 & 0 \\ 0 & 1 \end{pmatrix}$.

13. Express the equations $8x + 5y = 19$; $3x + 2y = 7$ in matrix form and, hence, use matrices to solve the resulting simultaneous equations.

14. Given that $\lambda M + \mu I = M^2$ and $M = \begin{pmatrix} 5 & -2 \\ 0 & 4 \end{pmatrix}$, find the value of λ and the value of μ, $\lambda, \mu \in \mathbf{R}$.

15. $z = \dfrac{a}{1+i}$ and $w = \dfrac{b}{1+2i}$.

If $z - w = 1$, find the value of a and the value of b, $a, b \in \mathbf{R}$.

16. Let $z = a + bi$, $a, b \in \mathbf{R}$ and $i^2 = -1$.

Solve: **(i)** $\dfrac{2z - 1 - i}{z} = 2 + i$ **(ii)** $\dfrac{1}{z} + \dfrac{2}{\bar{z}} = 1 + i$.

17. Solve for x and y: $\dfrac{5}{x + yi} + \dfrac{2}{1 + 3i} = 1$.

18. Solve $z^2 + (i - 2)z + 3 - i = 0$. Say why the roots do not occur in conjugate pairs.

19. Express the simultaneous equations $3(x - 2) - 7y = 0$ and $\dfrac{x}{3} - \dfrac{y}{2} = -\dfrac{1}{6}$
in matrix form and use matrix methods to solve them.

20. If $z = 4\left(\cos\dfrac{\pi}{3} + i\sin\dfrac{\pi}{3}\right)$ and $w = 2\left(\cos\dfrac{\pi}{6} + i\sin\dfrac{\pi}{6}\right)$,

show that: **(i)** $zw = 8i$ **(ii)** $\dfrac{z}{w} = \sqrt{3} + i$.

21. $f(z) = z^2 + (p + 2i)z + (1 + qi)$, $p, q \in \mathbf{R}$.
(i) If $f(-1 + i) = 0$, find the value of p and the value of q. **(ii)** Find the other root.

22. If the matrix $M = \begin{pmatrix} 2 & -1 \\ 1 & 3 \end{pmatrix}$, find M^2.

Given that $M^{-1}\begin{pmatrix} p & q \\ r & s \end{pmatrix} = M\begin{pmatrix} 1 & 2 \\ 1 & 3 \end{pmatrix}$, find the values of p, q, r and s.

23. Simplify: $\cos\theta\begin{pmatrix} \cos\theta & \sin\theta \\ -\sin\theta & \cos\theta \end{pmatrix} + \sin\theta\begin{pmatrix} \sin\theta & -\cos\theta \\ \cos\theta & \sin\theta \end{pmatrix}$.

24. Let $M = \begin{pmatrix} x & x \\ y & y+2 \end{pmatrix}$. Find M^{-1}.

If $M^{-1}\begin{pmatrix} 2 \\ 1 \end{pmatrix} = \begin{pmatrix} 2 \\ -1 \end{pmatrix}$, find the value of x and the value of y.

25. Show that: $\begin{pmatrix} 1 & \alpha \\ \dfrac{1}{\alpha} & 1 \end{pmatrix}\begin{pmatrix} 1 & -\alpha \\ -\dfrac{1}{\alpha} & 1 \end{pmatrix} = \begin{pmatrix} 0 & 0 \\ 0 & 0 \end{pmatrix}$.

26. Let $w = a + bi$ be a complex number, such that $w\overline{w} + w - \overline{w} = 13 + 4i$. Find the two possible values of w.

27. Find two complex numbers such that $2z\overline{z} + 3(z - \overline{z}) = 2(7 - 6i)$. Write your answers in the form $a + bi$, where $a, b \in \mathbf{R}$.

28. Given that $\dfrac{2}{z} = \dfrac{1}{u} + \dfrac{1}{v}$, where $u = 2 - i$, $v = 1 + 2i$, express z in the form $a + bi$ and, hence, evaluate $|z|$.

29. Evaluate $\left|\dfrac{z-1}{1-\overline{z}}\right|$, $z \in \mathbf{C}$.

30. If $M = \begin{pmatrix} 7 & 4 \\ 4 & 1 \end{pmatrix}$, find the slope of the line represented by $M\begin{pmatrix} x \\ y \end{pmatrix} = 9\begin{pmatrix} x \\ y \end{pmatrix}$.

31. $\dfrac{1 + 2i}{1 - i}$ is a root of the quadratic equation $az^2 + bz + 5 = 0$, where $a, b \in \mathbf{R}$ and $i^2 = -1$.

Verify that $a = b$.

32. (i) Given that $z = 2 - i\sqrt{3}$, find the real number t such that $z^2 + tz$ is real.

(ii) w is a complex number such that $w\overline{w} - 2iw = 7 - 4i$, where $\overline{w}$ is the complex conjugate of w. Find the two possible values of w. Express each in the form $p + qi$, where $p, q \in \mathbf{R}$.

33. (i) Given that $z = 2 - i$, calculate $|z^2 - z + 3|$, where $i^2 = -1$.

(ii) k is a real number such that $\dfrac{-1 + i\sqrt{3}}{-4\sqrt{3} - 4i} = ki$. Find k.

34. (i) Verify that $(2 + \sqrt{3}i)(2 - \sqrt{3}i) = 7$.

(ii) $2 + \sqrt{3}i$ is a root of the equation $x^3 - 6x^2 + 15x + a = 0$, where $a \in \mathbf{Z}$. Find the value of a and the other two roots of this equation.

35. Let $M = \begin{pmatrix} k & 1+k \\ 1-k & -k \end{pmatrix}$, where $k \in \mathbf{R}$. Find M^2 and M^{-1}.

Hence, find a matrix A such that $M^{17}A = \begin{pmatrix} 4 & -3 \\ -2 & 2 \end{pmatrix}$, for $k = 2$.

Find A^{10}.

36. Calculate: $\begin{pmatrix} 1 & 1 \\ 5 & -2 \end{pmatrix}\begin{pmatrix} 2 & 3 \\ 4 & -1 \end{pmatrix}$.

If $\begin{pmatrix} 2 & 3 \\ 4 & -1 \end{pmatrix}\begin{pmatrix} x \\ y \end{pmatrix} = \begin{pmatrix} a \\ b \end{pmatrix}$ and $\begin{pmatrix} 1 & 1 \\ 5 & -2 \end{pmatrix}\begin{pmatrix} a \\ b \end{pmatrix} = \begin{pmatrix} 14 \\ 21 \end{pmatrix}$, find the values of $x,\ y \in \mathbf{R}$.

37. Express $\dfrac{1+i\tan\theta}{1-i\tan\theta}$ in the form $\cos k\theta + i\sin k\theta, \quad k \in \mathbf{R}$.

38. **(i)** Write the simultaneous equations

$$x - \sqrt{3}y = -2$$
$$\sqrt{3}x + y = 2\sqrt{3}$$

in the form $A\begin{pmatrix} x \\ y \end{pmatrix} = \begin{pmatrix} -2 \\ 2\sqrt{3} \end{pmatrix}$, where A is a 2×2 matrix.

(ii) Then, find A^{-1} and use it to solve the equations for x and y.

39. $P(z) = (z-2)(z^2 - 10z + 28)$.

(i) Plot on an Argand diagram the solution set of $P(z) = 0$.

(ii) Verify that the three points form an equilateral triangle.

40. Let $P(z) = z^3 - (10+i)z^2 + (29+10i)z - 29i$, where $i^2 = -1$.

(i) Determine the real numbers a and b, if $P(z) = (z-i)(z^2 + az + b)$.

(ii) Plot on an Argand diagram the solution set of $P(z) = 0$.

Exercise 1R.C ▼

1. The following three statements are true whenever x and y are real numbers:

$$x + y = y + x$$
$$xy = yx$$

If $xy = 0$, then either $x = 0$ or $y = 0$.

Investigate whether the statements are also true when X is the matrix $\begin{pmatrix} 3 & -1 \\ -6 & 2 \end{pmatrix}$ and Y is the matrix $\begin{pmatrix} 2 & 3 \\ 6 & 9 \end{pmatrix}$.

2. Use De Moivre's theorem:

(i) to prove that $\cos 3\theta = 4\cos^3\theta - 3\cos\theta$

(ii) to express $(-\sqrt{3} - i)^{10}$ in the form $2^n(1 - i\sqrt{k})$, where $n,\ k \in \mathbf{N}$.

3. **(i)** $z_1 = 2\left(\cos\dfrac{\pi}{6} + i\sin\dfrac{\pi}{6}\right)$ and $z_2 = 3\left(\cos\dfrac{\pi}{3} + i\sin\dfrac{\pi}{3}\right)$, where $i^2 = -1$.

Calculate z_1z_2 in the form $x + iy$, where $x,\ y \in \mathbf{R}$.

(ii) $(2+3i)(a+ib) = -1 + 5i$. Express $a + ib$ in the form $r(\cos\theta + i\sin\theta)$ and, hence or otherwise, calculate $(a+ib)^{11}$.

4. (i) If $B = \begin{pmatrix} 3 & -1 \\ 1 & 3 \end{pmatrix}$ and $B^{-1}MB = \begin{pmatrix} 5 & 0 \\ 0 & -5 \end{pmatrix}$, find the matrix M.

(ii) Prove that $(B^{-1}MB)^3 = B^{-1}M^3B$ and, hence, find the value of M^3.

5. If z_1 and z_2 are complex numbers, solve the simultaneous equations:
$$4z_1 + 3z_2 = 5 + 13i$$
$$z_1 + iz_2 = -1$$

6. If $a + bi$ is a root of the equation $x^2 + px + q = 0$, where a, b, p, $q \in \mathbf{R}$,
show that: **(i)** $2a = -p$ **(ii)** $a^2 + b^2 = q$

7. (i) Express $\sqrt{-3 - 4i}$ in the form $a + bi$, where a, $b \in \mathbf{R}$.
(ii) Solve: $x^2 - 3x + (3 + i) = 0$.

8. Let $w_1 = -\dfrac{1}{2} + \dfrac{\sqrt{3}}{2}i$ and $w_2 = (w_1)^2$.
Verify that: $x^2 + xy + y^2 = (x - w_1 y)(x - w_2 y)$, where x, $y \in \mathbf{R}$.

9. Use De Moivre's Theorem to evaluate $(-1 + \sqrt{3}i)^6$.

10. (i) Express $-8i$ in the form: **(a)** $r(\cos\theta + i\sin\theta)$ **(b)** $r(\cos(\theta + 2n\pi) + i\sin(\theta + 2n\pi))$.
(ii) Use De Moivre's Theorem to find the three roots of the equation $z^3 = -8i$.
(iii) Hence, write down the three roots of the equation $(z - i)^3 = -8i$.

11. (i) Use De Moivre's theorem to evaluate: **(a)** $(-1 + i)^{10}$ **(b)** $(\sqrt{3} + i)^{12}$.

(ii) Write $\dfrac{1}{2} - \dfrac{\sqrt{3}}{2}i$ in polar form. Hence, or otherwise, express $\left(\dfrac{1}{2} - \dfrac{\sqrt{3}}{2}i\right)^{18}$ in the form $a + bi$,

where a, $b \in \mathbf{R}$.

12. (i) Let $M = \begin{pmatrix} 3 & 4 \\ -2 & -3 \end{pmatrix}$. Find λ_1, $\lambda_2 \in \mathbf{R}$ such that:

$$M\begin{pmatrix} 1 \\ -1 \end{pmatrix} = \lambda_1 \begin{pmatrix} 1 \\ -1 \end{pmatrix} \text{ and } M\begin{pmatrix} -2 \\ 1 \end{pmatrix} = \lambda_2 \begin{pmatrix} -2 \\ 1 \end{pmatrix}.$$

(ii) Let $A = \begin{pmatrix} 1 & -2 \\ -1 & 1 \end{pmatrix}$. Calculate $A^{-1}MA$. Show that $(A^{-1}MA)^2 = A^{-1}M^2A$.

(iii) Hence, or otherwise, calculate A^{100}.

13. (i) Find the value of λ for which $\dfrac{\sqrt{3} + \lambda i}{1 + \sqrt{3}i}$ is real, where $\lambda \in \mathbf{R}$.

(ii) Express $\dfrac{\sqrt{3} - i}{1 + \sqrt{3}i}$ in the form $r(\cos\theta + i\sin\theta)$ and, hence, evaluate $\left(\dfrac{\sqrt{3} - i}{1 + \sqrt{3}i}\right)^8$.

14. Evaluate $\sqrt{-2i}$, giving your answers in the form $\pm(a + bi)$.

Hence, solve: $z^2 - 3(1 + i)z + 5i = 0$.

15. Show that $z^2 - 16$ is a factor of $z^3 + (1+i)z^2 - 16z - 16(1+i)$ and, hence, find the three roots of $z^3 + (1+i)z^2 - 16z - 16(1+i) = 0$.

16. Using De Moivre's theorem, show that:

    (i) $\cos 3\theta = 4\cos^3\theta - 3\cos\theta$ **(ii)** $\sin 3\theta = 3\cos^2\theta\sin\theta - \sin^3\theta$.

    Hence, show that $\tan 3\theta = \dfrac{\tan\theta(3 - \tan^2\theta)}{1 - 3\tan^2\theta}$.

17. **(i)** Solve for w: $\sqrt{5}|w| + iw = 3 + i$. Write your answers in the form $u + iv$, $u, v \in \mathbf{R}$.

    (ii) Use De Moivre's theorem to find three roots of the equation: $z^6 - 1 = 0$.

18. Find $\sqrt{24 - 10i}$ in the form $a + bi$ and, hence, solve the quadratic equation: $z^2 + (1 - 3i)z + i - 8 = 0$.

19. **(i)** Verify that $3 - 4i$ is a root of $z^2 - (7 - 4i)z + 12 - 16i = 0$, and find the other root.

    (ii) Hence, or otherwise, deduce the roots of $z^4 - (7 - 4i)z^2 + 12 - 16i = 0$.

20. **(i)** Express $z = 1$ in the form $(\cos\theta + i\sin\theta)$.

    (ii) Use De Moivre's theorem to find the four roots of the equation: $z^4 - 1 = 0$.

    (iii) If $1, z_1, z_2$ and z_3 are the roots of the equation $z^4 - 1 = 0$, evaluate $(1 - z_1)(1 - z_2)(1 - z_3)$.

21. The complex number $w = (a + bi)(1 + 3i)$, where $a, b \in \mathbf{R}$ and $a > 0$.

    If $w = 10\sqrt{2}\left(\cos\dfrac{\pi}{4} + i\sin\dfrac{\pi}{4}\right)$, show that: **(i)** $a + 2b = 0$ **(ii)** $a = 4, b = -2$.

22. **(i)** $z_1 = 2\left(\cos\dfrac{\pi}{2} + i\sin\dfrac{\pi}{2}\right)$ and $z_2 = \cos\dfrac{\pi}{3} + i\sin\dfrac{\pi}{3}$, where $i^2 = -1$.

    Calculate $\dfrac{(z_1)^2}{z_2}$ in the form $x + iy$, where $x, y \in \mathbf{R}$.

    (ii) Calculate M^6 when $N^{-1}MN = \begin{pmatrix} 2 & 0 \\ 0 & 1 \end{pmatrix}$ and $N = \begin{pmatrix} 1 & 2 \\ -1 & -3 \end{pmatrix}$.

23. Let $z = \cos\theta + i\sin\theta$. Express $\dfrac{2}{1 + z}$ in the form $1 - i\tan(k\theta)$, $k \in \mathbf{Q}$ and $z \neq -1$.

24. Given that $N = \begin{pmatrix} 1 & 2 \\ -1 & -3 \end{pmatrix}$ and $A = \begin{pmatrix} a & b \\ -3 & -1 \end{pmatrix}$, find N^{-1}.

    If $N^{-1}AN = \begin{pmatrix} 2 & 0 \\ 0 & 1 \end{pmatrix}$, find: **(i)** the values of a and b, where $a, b \in \mathbf{N}$ **(ii)** A^5.

25. Let $M = \begin{pmatrix} a & k \\ k & -a \end{pmatrix}$.

    If $M^{-1} = M$, prove that $a^2 + k^2 = 1$ and then write out the matrix M, given that $a = \frac{3}{5}$ and $k > 0$.

26. Using De Moivre's Theorem, prove that:

    (i) $\cos 4\theta = 8\cos^4 \theta - 8\cos^2 \theta + 1$ **(ii)** $\sin 4\theta = 4\cos^3 \theta \sin \theta - 4\cos \theta \sin^3 \theta$.

    Express $\tan 4\theta$ in terms of $\tan \theta$.

27. (i) Determine real numbers s and t such that: $(s + it)^2 = -3 + 4i$.

    (ii) Hence, determine the two roots of the equation: $z^2 - (4 - 2i)z + 6 - 8i = 0$.

28. Determine the real numbers a and b such that: $\sqrt{15 - 8i} = a + ib$, where $i = \sqrt{-1}$.

    Hence, or otherwise, solve the equation: $(1 + i)z^2 + (-2 + 3i)z - 3 + 2i = 0$.

29. (i) Find two complex numbers w_1 and w_2 which satisfy the equation: $3w\overline{w} + 2(w - \overline{w}) = 12 + 4i$.

    (Hint: let $w = a + bi$.)

    (ii) Express w_1^{20} and w_2^{20} in the form $2^n(x + yi)$, where $n \in \mathbf{N}$ and $x, y \in \mathbf{R}$.

30. Express $z = \dfrac{\sqrt{3} + i}{\sqrt{3} - i}$ in the form: **(i)** $a + bi$ **(ii)** $\cos \theta + i \sin \theta$.

    Find the least positive value of $n \in \mathbf{N}$, such that z^n is a real number.

31. (i) Express in the form of $p + qi$, where $p, q \in \mathbf{R}$ and $i^2 = -1$:

$$\left(\cos \frac{\pi}{3} + i \sin \frac{\pi}{3}\right)^2 \left(\cos \frac{\pi}{6} + i \sin \frac{\pi}{6}\right).$$

    (ii) Use De Moivre's theorem to find the smallest integer n, where $n > 0$, such that

$$(\sqrt{3} + i)^n = (\sqrt{3} - i)^n.$$

32. (i) Express $-27i$ in the form $r(\cos \theta + i \sin \theta)$.

    (ii) Use De Moivre's Theorem to find the three roots of the equation: $z^3 + 27i = 0$.

33. p and q are the roots of $z^2 - 2z + 4 = 0$.

    Find the values of p and q and, hence, show that: $p^n + q^n = 2^{n+1}\cos \dfrac{n\pi}{3}$.

34. Express $\left(\dfrac{1}{2} - \dfrac{\sqrt{3}}{2}i\right)$ in the form: **(i)** $\cos \theta + i \sin \theta$ **(ii)** $\cos(\theta + 2n\pi) + i \sin(\theta + 2n\pi)$.

    Use De Moivre's Theorem to find the two roots of $\left(\dfrac{1}{2} - \dfrac{\sqrt{3}}{2}i\right)^{3/2}$.

35. (i) Express $2(1 - i\sqrt{3})$ in the form $r(\cos \theta + i \sin \theta)$.

    (ii) Using De Moivre's theorem, find values for $[2(1 - i\sqrt{3})]^{3/2}$, writing your answers in the form $p + qi$, $p, q \in \mathbf{R}$.

36. Express $4i$ in the form $r(\cos \theta + i \sin \theta)$.

    Hence, find two possible values of $(4i)^{3/2}$.

37. Express $z = \dfrac{1}{2} + \dfrac{\sqrt{3}}{2}i$ in the form $(\cos\theta + i\sin\theta)$, where $i^2 = -1$.

Hence, using De Moivre's theorem, find the two roots of $\sqrt{z}$.

38. Prove by induction that $(\cos\theta + i\sin\theta)^n = \cos n\theta + i\sin n\theta$, for $n \in \mathbf{N}_0$ and $i^2 = -1$.

Deduce that $(\cos\theta + i\sin\theta)^{-n} = \cos n\theta - i\sin n\theta$.

If $z = \cos\theta + i\sin\theta$, show that $\dfrac{1}{z} = \cos\theta - i\sin\theta$.

Show that:

(i) $z^n + \dfrac{1}{z^n} = 2\cos n\theta$ **(ii)** $z^n - \dfrac{1}{z^n} = 2i\sin n\theta$.

39. $A = \begin{pmatrix} 2 & 0 \\ 0 & 3 \end{pmatrix}$; prove by induction that $A^n = \begin{pmatrix} 2^n & 0 \\ 0 & 3^n \end{pmatrix}$, for $n \geqslant 2$, $n \in \mathbf{N}$.

40. (i) Use De Moivre's theorem to find the three roots of the equation: $z^3 - 1 = 0$.

   (ii) If w is one of the non-real roots, show that the roots can be written $1, w, w^2$.

   (iii) Show that:

      (a) $1 + w + w^2 = 0$ **(b)** $w^3 = 1$ **(c)** $(1 - w + w^2)(1 + w - w^2) = 4$ **(d)** $(1 + w^2)^6 = 1$.

   (iv) Evaluate: **(a)** $(1 + w)^6$ **(b)** $(1 - w - w^2)^5$.

   (v) If $x = a + b$, $y = aw + bw^2$ and $z = aw^2 + bw^4$, show that $x^2 + y^2 + z^2 = 6ab$.

REVISION EXERCISE 2 SEQUENCES AND SERIES

Paper I, Question 4

This revision exercise covers Chapter 7.

Exercise 2R.A ▼

1. Three consecutive terms in an arithmetic sequence are $k-1$, $2k+1$, $4k-1$, where $k \in \mathbf{R}$. Find the value of k.

2. The first three terms of a geometric sequence are $2x-4$, $x+1$, $x-3$. Find the two possible values of x.

3. Find the value of a, $a \in \mathbf{R}$, if a, $a+5$ and $7a+5$ are consecutive terms in:

   (i) an arithmetic sequence $\qquad$ **(ii)** a geometric sequence.

4. A sequence is defined by: $u_{n+1} = 1 - \dfrac{1}{u_n}$. If $u_1 = 2$, find u_2 and u_3.

5. In a sequence, $u_1 = 1$ and $u_{n+1} = \dfrac{1-u_n}{1+2u_n}$. Find u_2, u_3, u_4 and u_5.

   Evaluate $\displaystyle\sum_{n=1}^{200} u_n$.

6. Find the sum to infinity of the geometric series:

   (i) $1 + \left(\dfrac{2}{3}\right) + \left(\dfrac{2}{3}\right)^2 + \left(\dfrac{2}{3}\right)^3 + \cdots$ $\qquad$ **(ii)** $1 - \dfrac{1}{4} + \dfrac{1}{16} - \dfrac{1}{64} + \cdots$

7. Given that $12x-5$, $3x-1$ and $\dfrac{x}{2}$ are the first three terms of a geometric series, find the possible values of the sum to infinity of the series.

8. Find S_∞, the sum to infinity, of the geometric series:

   (i) $x + \dfrac{1}{2}x + \dfrac{1}{4}x + \dfrac{1}{8}x + \cdots$

   (ii) $1 + \dfrac{3}{2x+1} + \left(\dfrac{3}{2x+1}\right)^2 + \cdots + \left(\dfrac{3}{2x+1}\right)^{n-1} + \cdots$, where $x > 1$.

9. Find the range of values of x, $x \in \mathbf{R}$, for which the geometric series:

$1 + 2x + 4x^2 + 8x^3 + \cdots$ is convergent,

and find its sum to infinity.

10. The first term of a geometric series is two-thirds of the sum to infinity.
Find the common ratio.

11. Express the recurring decimal $0.252525\ldots$ in the form $\dfrac{p}{q}$, where $p, q \in \mathbf{N}$ and $q \neq 0$.

12. Express the recurring decimal $1.\dot{2}$ in the form $\dfrac{a}{b}$, where $a, b \in \mathbf{N}$ and $b \neq 0$.

13. Express the recurring decimal $2.3\dot{8}$ in the form $\dfrac{p}{q}$, where $p, q \in \mathbf{N}$ and $q \neq 0$.

14. Find the sum of the first 12 terms of the geometric sequence:

$$2, \ 2(3), \ 2(3)^2, \ 2(3)^3, \ \ldots$$

15. The nth term of an arithmetic series is given by $u_n = 52 - 4n$, for $n \in \mathbf{N}_0$.
Find: **(i)** the term which is zero

(ii) the sum of the positive terms.

(iii) If $S_n = 0$, find the value of n.

16. The sum of the first n terms of an arithmetic series is given by $S_n = 3n^2 - 4n$.
Use S_n to find: **(i)** the first term, u_1

(ii) the sum of the second term and the third term, $u_2 + u_3$.

17. The second term, u_2, of a geometric sequence is 21. The third term, u_3, is -63.
Find: **(i)** the common ratio **(ii)** the first term.

18. Find, in terms of n, the sum of the first n terms of the geometric series: $3 + \dfrac{3}{2} + \dfrac{3}{4} + \dfrac{3}{8} + \cdots$

19. Find S_n, the sum of n terms, of the geometric series: $2 + \dfrac{2}{3} + \dfrac{2}{3^2} + \cdots + \dfrac{2}{3^{n-1}}$.
If $S_n = \dfrac{242}{81}$, find the value of n.

20. How many terms of the arithmetic series $24 + 20 + 16 + \cdots$ must be added in order to give a total of 72?

21. Evaluate: **(i)** $\displaystyle\sum_{n=1}^{20} (2n - 1)$ **(ii)** $\displaystyle\sum_{n=1}^{6} 3(4)^{n-1}$.

22. Solve each of the following for $n \in \mathbf{N}$:

(i) $\dbinom{n+2}{2} = 36$ **(ii)** $\dbinom{n+4}{2} = 91$ **(iii)** $\dbinom{n-3}{2} = 36$.

23. A sequence is defined by: $u_1 = 1$, $u_2 = 2$, $u_3 = 0$. $u_{r+2} = 2u_{r+1} + u_r$ for all $r \in \mathbf{N}$.
Write out the first six terms.

24. A sequence is defined by: $u_1 = 2$, $u_{n+1} = 2^{u_{n-1}} + 1$, for all $n \in \mathbf{N}$.
Verify that: $u_5 - (u_2 u_3 u_4)^2 = 2^{3u_2}$.

25. A sequence $u_1, u_2, u_3, \ldots, u_r, \ldots$ is defined as follows:

$$u_1 = 0, \qquad u_2 = 1, \qquad u_{r+1} = \frac{u_r + \sqrt{u_r \cdot u_{r-1}}}{2}.$$

Find u_4, and express your answer in the form $\dfrac{1}{a} + \dfrac{1}{b\sqrt{b}}$, where $a, b \in \mathbf{N}$.

26. The first three terms of an arithmetic sequence are $6, -9$ and x.
The first three terms of a geometric sequence are $-9, x$ and y.
Find the value of x and the value of y.

Exercise 2R.B ▼

1. In an arithmetic series, $u_6 = 29$ and $S_4 - S_3 = 19$.
   (i) Find the first term, a, and the common difference, d.
   (ii) Find, in terms of n: **(a)** u_n **(b)** S_n.

2. In an arithmetic series, the sum of the second term and the fifth term is 18.
The sixth term is greater than the third term by 9.
   (i) Find the first term and the common difference.
   (ii) What is the smallest value of n such that $S_n > 600$, where S_n is the sum of the first n terms of the series?

3. If for all integers n, $u_n = 3 + n(n-1)^2$, show that $u_{n+1} - u_n = 3n^2 - n$.

4. If for all integers n, $u_n = (5n - 3)2^n$, verify that $u_{n+1} - 2u_n = 5(2^{n+1})$.

5. Given that $u_n = \dfrac{1}{2}(4^n - 2^n)$ for all integers n, show that $u_{n+1} = 2u_n + 4^n$.

6. If for all positive integers n, $u_n = \dfrac{n+1}{n^2}$, prove that $u_{n+1} < u_n$.

7. The nth term of a sequence is given by $u_n = 3^{n+1}$.
   (i) Prove that the sequence is geometric.
   (ii) Show that the sum of the first n terms is given by $S_n = \dfrac{1}{2}(3^{n+2} - 9)$.
   (iii) Find S_7.

8. The sum of the first n terms of an arithmetic sequence is given by $S_n = 4n - 3n^2$.
   (i) Find u_n. **(ii)** Find u_{15}.
   (iii) If $S_n = -160$, find the value of n, $n \in \mathbf{N}$.

9. In an arithmetic series, $u_{20} : u_{10} = 3 : 1$.
   (i) Express the first term, a, in terms of the common difference, d.
   (ii) If $S_{20} : S_{10} = p : q$, find the value of p and the value of q, $p, q \in \mathbf{N}$.

10. $a + ar + ar^2 + \cdots$ is a geometric series.
If $u_1 + u_2 = 24$ and the sum to infinity is 27:
   (i) show that $r = \pm\dfrac{1}{3}$ **(ii)** find two possible values for a.

11. (i) Factorise $1 + r^3$.

(ii) In a geometric series, $u_2 + u_3 = 48$ and $u_1 + u_4 = 112$.
Write down the first four terms of the two geometric series which satisfy these conditions.

12. A geometric series is defined by: $\displaystyle\sum_{n=1}^{\infty}\left(\frac{x}{1-x}\right)^n = \left(\frac{x}{1-x}\right) + \left(\frac{x}{1-x}\right)^2 + \left(\frac{x}{1-x}\right)^3 + \cdots$

(i) Write down, in terms of x: **(a)** the common ratio **(b)** the sum to infinity.

(ii) If the sum to infinity is $\dfrac{3}{2}$, find the value of x.

(iii) Find the values of x for which the sum to infinity exists.

13. The nth term of a sequence is defined by: $u_n = \dfrac{n}{2}(n+1)$, for all $n \in \mathbf{N}_0$.

(i) Find $(u_1 + u_2)$, $(u_2 + u_3)$ and $(u_3 + u_4)$.

(ii) By simplifying $(u_{n+1} + u_n)$, show that the sum of any two consecutive pairs is a perfect square.

14. In an arithmetic series, $u_1 = 2$, $u_2 = p - q$, $u_3 = 2p + q + 7$ and $u_4 = p - 3q$, where $p, q \in \mathbf{Z}$.

(i) Find the value of p and the value of q.

(ii) Express, in terms of n: **(a)** u_n **(b)** S_n.

(iii) Evaluate: **(a)** u_{10} **(b)** S_{10}.

15. An arithmetic sequence has seven terms. The middle term is 15 and the greatest term is 27.
Find S_7, the sum of the seven terms.

16. Three consecutive terms of a geometric series are $x + 3y$, 4 and $2x + 2y$.
Three consecutive terms of an arithmetic series are $x + 4y$, 4 and $x - 2y$.
Find the value of x and the value of y.

17. If $10a - 1$, a^2, $4a + 1$ and b are four consecutive terms in an arithmetic sequence, find the values of a and b, $a, b \in \mathbf{R}$.

18. Three consecutive terms of an arithmetic sequence are ab, b^2 and c^2.
Prove that b, c and $2b - a$ are three consecutive terms of a geometric sequence.

19. If a, b, c are three consecutive terms of both an arithmetic and a geometric sequence, prove that $a = b = c$.

20. Three terms, $\dfrac{1}{4}$, m and 9 are in geometric sequence.

Three terms, $\dfrac{1}{4}$, m and $9 - n$ are in arithmetic sequence.

Find the value of m and the value of n, where $m, n \in \mathbf{R}$, and $m, n > 0$.

21. In an arithmetic sequence, three consecutive terms have a sum of -9 and a product of 48.
Find the possible values of these terms.

22. When p is added to 6, 12 and 14, respectively, and the results are squared, the new sequence is arithmetic. Find the value of p.

23. $u_1 + u_2 + u_3 + \cdots$ is an arithmetic series.

$v - \dfrac{v}{2} + \dfrac{v}{4} - \cdots$ is a geometric series.

   (i) Write down the common ratio of the geometric series.

   (ii) if $u_1 = 2$, $u_5 = 30$ and $v - \dfrac{v}{2} = u_2$, find v.

24. (i) The nth term of an arithmetic series is $3n + 2$. Find S_n, the sum of the first n terms, in terms of n.

   (ii) Evaluate, in terms of n: $\displaystyle\sum_{k=1}^{n}\left(\dfrac{1}{k} - \dfrac{1}{k+1}\right)$.

25. (i) Show that $\dfrac{2}{k(k+2)} = \dfrac{1}{k} - \dfrac{1}{k+2}$, for all $k \in \mathbf{R}$, $k \neq 0, -2$.

   (ii) Evaluate, in terms of n: $\displaystyle\sum_{k=1}^{n}\dfrac{2}{k(k+2)}$.   (iii) Evaluate $\displaystyle\sum_{k=1}^{\infty}\dfrac{2}{k(k+2)}$.

26. (i) Show that: $\dfrac{1}{(n+2)(n+3)} = \dfrac{1}{n+2} - \dfrac{1}{n+3}$ for $n \in \mathbf{N}$.

   (ii) Hence, find $\displaystyle\sum_{n=1}^{k}\dfrac{1}{(n+2)(n+3)}$ and evaluate $\displaystyle\sum_{k=1}^{\infty}\dfrac{1}{(n+2)(n+3)}$.

27. (i) Show that $\dfrac{1}{\sqrt{n+1}+\sqrt{n}}$ is equal to $\sqrt{n+1} - \sqrt{n}$.

   (ii) If $u_n = \dfrac{1}{\sqrt{n+1}+\sqrt{n}}$, find an expression for the sum of the first n terms in terms of n.

   (iii) Evaluate $\displaystyle\sum_{n=1}^{24}\dfrac{1}{\sqrt{n+1}-\sqrt{n}}$.

   (iv) If $\displaystyle\sum_{n=1}^{k}\dfrac{1}{\sqrt{n+1}-\sqrt{n}} = 10$, find the value of k.

28. P, Q, R, S and T are consecutive terms of a geometric sequence. €21,100 is divided among five people in the ratio $P : Q : R : S : T$.

For every €100 the person with the lowest amount received, the person with the second highest amount received €337.50. How much did each person receive?

29. The sequence $u_1, u_2, u_3, u_4, \ldots$ is given by $u_n = 2n^2$.

   (i) Write down the value of u_1, u_2, u_3, u_4.

   (ii) Express $u_{n+1} - u_n$ in the form $pn + q$.

   (iii) The differences between consecutive terms, $u_{n+1} - u_n$, of the sequence themselves form an arithmetic sequence. For this arithmetic sequence, find the first term and the common difference.

30. (i) Factorise: $qp + q + 2pr + 2r$.

   (ii) By considering two separate series, find the sum of the first $2n$ terms of the series:

$$a + 2b + 2a + 4b + 3a + 6b + \cdots$$

31. Write out the first six terms of the series $\displaystyle\sum_{r=1}^{n}(-1)^{r}(2r-1)^{r}$.

Evaluate $\displaystyle\sum_{r=1}^{20}(-1)^{r}(2r-1)$.

32. $a_1, a_2, a_3, \ldots, a_n, \ldots$ is a sequence such that
$a_1 = 2$ and $S_n = 2S_{n-1} + 5$, for $n \in \mathbf{N}_0$ and $n \geqslant 2$. Find a_3.

In questions 33 – 38, we make use of the following: $\displaystyle\sum_{n=1}^{k}n = \frac{k}{2}(k+1); \quad \sum_{n=1}^{k}n^2 = \frac{k}{6}(k+1)(2k+1).$

33. Express, in terms of n: $\displaystyle\sum_{r=1}^{n}6r^2 + 2r$. Hence, evaluate $\displaystyle\sum_{r=1}^{20}3r^2 + 2r$.

34. Evaluate $\displaystyle\sum_{n=1}^{10}(n-2)(n+1)$.

35. (i) Simplify $\dfrac{n^2 + 4n + 3}{n+3}$. **(ii)** Evaluate $\displaystyle\sum_{n=1}^{12}\dfrac{n^2 + 4n + 3}{n+3}$.

36. $u_1, u_2, u_3, u_4, \ldots, u_n$ is a sequence, where $u_n = 1 + 3 + 7 + 13 + \cdots + (1 - n + n^2)$.

(i) Show that $u_n = \dfrac{n}{3}(n^2 + 2)$. **(ii)** Express $u_{n+1} - u_n$ in terms of n.

37. If $\displaystyle\sum_{n=1}^{k}n = 36$, find the value of $k \in \mathbf{N}$.

38. If $\displaystyle\sum_{n=1}^{k}(n+1) = 65$, find the value of $k \in \mathbf{N}$.

Exercise 2R.C ▼

1. The first three terms of an arithmetic sequence are 31, a and b.
The first three terms of a geometric sequence are b, 4 and a.
Find the value of a and the value of b, $a, b \in \mathbf{R}$.

2. a, x and b are three consecutive terms of an arithmetic sequence.
a, y and b are three consecutive terms of a geometric sequence, where $y > 0$.
Show that $x \geqslant y$.

3. $\displaystyle\sum_{n=0}^{\infty}\cos^{2n}\theta = 1 + \cos^2\theta + \cos^4\theta + \cdots$

If $0 < \theta < \dfrac{\pi}{2}$, show that $\displaystyle\sum_{n=0}^{\infty}\cos^{2n}\theta = \operatorname{cosec}^2\theta$.

4. (i) Write $\dfrac{n^3 + 8}{n+2}$ in the form $an^2 + bn + c$, where $a, b, c \in \mathbf{R}$. **(ii)** Hence, evaluate $\displaystyle\sum_{n=1}^{30}\dfrac{n^3 + 8}{n+2}$.

$$\left[\text{Note: } \sum_{n=1}^{k}n = \frac{k}{2}(k+1); \quad \sum_{n=1}^{k}n^2 = \frac{k}{6}(k+1)(2k+1). \right]$$

5. (i) Show that: $\dfrac{1}{4n^2-1} = \dfrac{1}{2}\left(\dfrac{1}{2n-1} - \dfrac{1}{2n+1}\right)$.

Let $u_n = \dfrac{1}{4n^2-1}$.

(ii) Find $\displaystyle\sum_{n=1}^{\infty} u_n$. **(iii)** Find the least value of r such that: $\displaystyle\sum_{n=1}^{r} u_n > \dfrac{99}{100}\sum_{n=1}^{\infty} u_n$, $\quad r \in \mathbf{N}$.

6. (i) Show that $\dfrac{2}{\sqrt{2n+1}+\sqrt{2n-1}} = \sqrt{2n+1} - \sqrt{2n-1}$, for all $n \in \mathbf{N_0}$.

(ii) Hence, find $\displaystyle\sum_{n=1}^{12} \dfrac{2}{\sqrt{2n+1}+\sqrt{2n-1}}$. **(iii)** If $\displaystyle\sum_{n=1}^{k} \dfrac{2}{\sqrt{2n+1}+\sqrt{2n-1}} = 6$, find the value of k.

7. (i) Show that $\dfrac{n}{(n+1)!} = \dfrac{1}{n!} - \dfrac{1}{(n+1)!}$. Hence, evaluate $\displaystyle\sum_{n=1}^{\infty} \dfrac{n}{(n+1)!}$.

(ii) $\displaystyle\sum_{n=1}^{n} 6(n+1)(2n-1) = an^3 + bn^2 + cn$, where a, b, $c \in \mathbf{Z}$.

Find the value of a, the value of b and the value of c.

8. $u_1, u_2, u_3, \ldots, u_n$ is a sequence, where $u_n = 1 + 2 + 3 + \cdots + n$.

(i) Show that $u_n = \dfrac{n}{2}(n+1)$. **(ii)** Express $u_n - u_{n-1}$ in terms of n.

(iii) Show that $u_n + u_{n-1} = n^2$. **(iv)** Find $u_n^2 - u_{n-1}^2$.

Hence, show that: $\displaystyle\sum_{1}^{n}\left(u_n^2 - u_{n-1}^2\right) = 1 + 2^3 + 3^3 + \cdots + n^3$, where $u_0 = 0$.

9. $a-d$, a, $a+d$ are three consecutive terms of an arithmetic sequence with a positive common difference. Three times the sum of their squares exceeds the square of their sum by 73.5. Find the common difference.

10. Three numbers are in arithmetic sequence. Their sum is 27 and their product is 704. Find the three numbers.

11. Three numbers are in arithmetic sequence. Their sum is 15 and the sum of their squares is 93. Find the three numbers.

12. In an arithmetic sequence, $u_4 = 5y$ and $u_9 = 10x$. Express, in terms of x and y:

(i) the first term, a **(ii)** the common difference, d

(iii) S_8, the sum of the first eight terms.

Express u_n, the nth term, in terms of n, x and y.

Hence, verify that: **(iv)** $u_4 = 5y$ and **(v)** $u_9 = 10x$.

13. For a certain sequence, $u_n = a + bn + c(2^n)$, where a, b and c are constants. Given that the first three terms are 9, 13 and 23 respectively, find:

(i) the values of a, b and c **(ii)** S_{10}.

14. (i) If for all integers n, $u_n = x^{n-1}$, find S_n, the sum of the first n terms, in terms of x and n.

(ii) Let $f(x) = \displaystyle\sum_{n=1}^{\infty} (4n-3)x^{n-1}$, where $|x| < 1$. Show that $f(x) = \dfrac{1+3x}{(1-x)^2}$.

15. Let $f(x) = \sum_{n=1}^{\infty} q^{n-1}x^n$, where $|x| < 1$ and $0 < q < 1$.

(i) Show that $f(x) = \dfrac{x}{1 - qx}$.

(ii) If $g(x) = \dfrac{1}{1 - (1 - q)f(x)}$, show that $g(x) = \dfrac{1 - qx}{1 - x}$.

16. $f(x) = 2x + 3x^2 + 4x^3 + \cdots + (n+1)x^n + \cdots$ for $-1 < x < 1$.

(i) Show that $f(x) = \dfrac{x(2 - x)}{(1 - x)^2}$.

(ii) Evaluate $2\left(\dfrac{1}{5}\right) + 3\left(\dfrac{1}{5}\right)^2 + 4\left(\dfrac{1}{5}\right)^3 + \cdots + (n+1)\left(\dfrac{1}{5}\right)^n + \cdots$

17. (i) Given that $g(x) = 1 + 2x + 3x^2 + 4x^3 \ldots$, where $-1 < x < 1$, show that: $g(x) = \dfrac{1}{(1 - x)^2}$.

(ii) $P(n) = u_1 u_2 u_3 u_4 \ldots u_n$, where $u_k = ar^{k-1}$, for $k = 1, 2, 3, \ldots, n$ and $a, r \in \mathbf{R}$.

Write $P(n)$ in the form $a^n r^{f(n)}$, where $f(n)$ is a quadratic expression in n.

18. (i) Find u_n for the series $\dfrac{1}{3.5} + \dfrac{1}{4.6} + \dfrac{1}{5.7} + \dfrac{1}{6.8} + \cdots$ **(ii)** Evaluate $\sum_{n=1}^{\infty} u_n$.

19. Find, for the series: $2 + 3 \cdot 2 + 4 \cdot 2^2 + 5 \cdot 2^3 + \cdots :$ **(i)** u_n **(ii)** S_n **(iii)** S_{10}.

20. $1 + 3 + 5 + 7 \ldots$ is an arithmetic series.

(i) Write, in terms of n: **(a)** u_n **(b)** u_n^2.

(ii) Show that: $1^2 + 3^2 + 5^2 + 7^2 + \cdots = \dfrac{n}{3}(2n - 1)(2n + 1)$.

(iii) Hence, evaluate: $1^2 + 3^2 + 5^2 + 7^2 + \cdots + 17^2$.

21. (i) Let $S_n = 1 + 2 + 3 + \cdots + n$.

Write down a formula for S_n and, hence, evaluate:
$1 + (1 + 2) + (1 + 2 + 3) + \cdots + (1 + 2 + 3 + \cdots + 24)$.

(ii) If $S_n = \dfrac{1}{n}\sqrt{1 + 2 + 3 + \cdots + n}$, find $\lim\limits_{n \to \infty} S_n$.

22. $\sum_{r=1}^{n} 2^{r-1} = 1 + 2 + 2^2 + 2^3 + \cdots + 2^{n-1}$.

(i) Show that: $\sum_{r=1}^{n} 2^{r-1} = 2^n - 1$.

(ii) Evaluate: $1 + (1 + 2) + (1 + 2 + 2^2) + (1 + 2 + 2^2 + 2^3) + \cdots + (1 + 2 + 2^2 + 2^3 + \cdots + 2^{19})$.
Write your answer in the form $a^m - n$.

(iii) If $u_{n+1} - u_n = 128$, find the value of n.

23. A sequence $u_1, u_2, u_3, \ldots, u_r \ldots$ is defined as follows:

$u_1 = \sin x$, $u_{r+1} = \dfrac{d}{dx}(u_r)$.

Write down u_2, u_3, u_4 and u_5. Evaluate $\sum_{r=1}^{15} u_r$ when $x = \dfrac{\pi}{3}$.

24. The positive integers, starting at 1, are grouped into sets containing 1, 2, 4, 8, . . . integers, as indicated below, so that the number of integers in each set after the first is twice the number of integers in the previous set.

$$\{1\}, \{2, 3\}, \{4, 5, 6, 7\}, \{8, 9, 10, 11, 12, 13, 14, 15\}, \ldots$$

Write down expressions, in terms of r, for:

(i)   the number of integers in the rth set

(ii) the first integer in the rth set

(iii) the last integer in the rth set.

25. An arithmetic series A and a convergent geometric series G have the same first term, 1. The sum of the first two terms of either series is equal to the sum of the first three terms of the other. Find the common ratio of G and also the sum to infinity of G.

Find also the integer n such that the sum of the first n terms of A is equal to the $(n + 1)$th term of A.

26. Given that $\dfrac{1}{b+c}, \dfrac{1}{c+a}, \dfrac{1}{a+b}$ are three consecutive terms of an arithmetic sequence,

show that a^2, b^2 and c^2 are also three consecutive terms of an arithmetic sequence.

27. The fifth, seventh and twelfth terms of an arithmetic sequence are consecutive terms for a geometric sequence. Find the common ratio, r, of the geometric sequence.

28. p, q, r and s are consecutive terms of a geometric sequence.
Prove that: $(q - r)^2 + (r - p)^2 + (s - q)^2 = (p - s)^2$.

29. (i) $u_1, u_2, u_3, u_4, u_5, \ldots$ is a sequence, where $u_1 = 2$ and $u_{n+1} = (-1)^n u_n + 3$.
Evaluate u_2, u_3, u_4, u_5 and u_{10}.

(ii) a, b, c, d are the first, second, third and fourth terms of a geometric sequence, respectively.
Prove that $a^2 - b^2 - c^2 + d^2 \geqslant 0$.

30. Consider the sum to n terms, S_n, of the following finite geometric series:

$$S_n = 1 + (1 + x) + (1 + x)^2 + (1 + x)^3 + \cdots + (1 + x)^{n-1} \text{ for } x > 0.$$

Show that the coefficient of x^2 in the above expression for S_n is:

$$\binom{2}{2} + \binom{3}{2} + \binom{4}{2} + \cdots + \binom{n-1}{2}.$$

By finding S_{25} in terms of x and by considering the coefficient of x^2 in S_{25}, find the value of p and the value of q for which:

$$\binom{2}{2} + \binom{3}{2} + \binom{4}{2} + \cdots + \binom{24}{2} = \binom{p}{q}, \text{ where } p, q \in \mathbf{N}.$$

31. The first three terms of an arithmetic progression are $\log_2 32, \log_2 p$ and $\log_2 q$.
The common difference is -3. Evaluate p and q.

32. Show that the nth term of the sequence 5, 55, 555, 5555, . . . can be written as the sum of n terms of a geometric series and has the value $\frac{5}{9}(10^n - 1)$.

Hence find the sum of the first n terms of the sequence.

REVISION EXERCISE 3   COORDINATE GEOMETRY OF THE CIRCLE

Paper 2, Question 1

This revision exercise covers Chapter 1.

Exercise 3R.A ▼

1. A circle with centre $(-3, 7)$ passes through the point $(5, -8)$. Find the equation of the circle.

2. $a(1, -4)$ and $b(5, 8)$ are the end points of a diameter of a circle S.
   (i) Calculate the centre of S.   (ii) Find the equation of S.

3. Find the equation of the circle containing the point $(5, -2)$ and which has the same centre as the circle $x^2 + y^2 - 8x + 6y + 5 = 0$.

4. The equation of a circle is $x^2 + y^2 = 130$. Find the slope of the tangent to the circle at the point $(-7, 9)$.

5. Find the equation of the tangent to the circle $x^2 + y^2 - 4x - 8y - 5 = 0$ at the point $(6, 7)$.

6. The equation of a circle is $(x + 7)(x + 3) + (y - 2)(y + 2) = 0$. Find the centre and radius length of the circle.

7. The equation of the circle K is $x^2 + y^2 - 6x + 4y - 16 = 0$. K intersects the x-axis at p and q. If $p < q$, find the coordinates of p and the coordinates of q.

8. The following parametric equations define a circle:
$$x = 4 + 3 \cos \theta, \quad y = -2 + 3 \sin \theta, \text{ where } \theta \in \mathbf{R}.$$
   What is the Cartesian equation of the circle?

9. The following parametric equations define a circle:
$$x = 5 + \tfrac{\sqrt{3}}{2} \cos \theta, \quad y = -3 + \tfrac{\sqrt{3}}{2} \sin \theta, \text{ where } \theta \in \mathbf{R}.$$
   What is the Cartesian equation of the circle?

10. The line $x - 2y + 5 = 0$ intersects the circle $x^2 + y^2 = 25$ at the points p and q. Find $|pq|$.

11. The circle $x^2 + y^2 - 6x - 4y + k = 0$ touches the x-axis at the point p. Find the coordinates of p and the value of k.

12. The line $x = k$ is a tangent to the circle $x^2 + y^2 - 2x + 4y - 4 = 0$. Find the values of k.

13. A line containing $p(5, 6)$ touches the circle $x^2 + y^2 - 4x - 4y + 4 = 0$ at k. Calculate $|pk|$.

14. (i) Show that the line $3x - 4y + 10 = 0$ is a tangent to the circle $y^2 = x(10 - x)$

    (ii) Investigate whether the line $x + 3y + 16 = 0$ is a tangent to the circle $y^2 + 2y - 3 = x(12 - x)$.

15. $p(k, 2)$ and $q(-6, -k)$ are the end points of a diameter of a circle S with centre $(3, -5)$.
Find the value of k.
Verify that the radius length of S is $\sqrt{130}$.

16. The following parametric equations define a circle:

$$x = \theta, \quad y = \sqrt{(2 - \theta)(2 + \theta)}, \text{ where } \theta \in \mathbf{R}.$$

What is the Cartesian equation of the circle?

17. For all values of $t \in \mathbf{R}$, the point $\left(\dfrac{3 - 3t^2}{1 + t^2}, \ \dfrac{6t}{1 + t^2} \right)$ lies on the circle $x^2 + y^2 = r^2$.
Find r, the radius of the circle.

18. The circle $(x + 1)^2 + (y - k)^2 = 10$ contains the origin $(0, 0)$. Find the possible values of k.

19. If the length of the tangent from the point $(1, -1)$ to the circle $x^2 + y^2 - 4x + 6y + k = 0$ is 2 units, find the value of k.

Exercise 3R.B ▼

1. K is the circle with equation $x^2 + y^2 = 100$.

    (i) Show, by calculation, that the point $a(12, -9)$ lies outside K.

    (ii) Find the equation of the line oa, where o is the origin.

    (iii) Find the coordinates of the points where oa intersects K.

2. The points $a(-2, 4)$, $b(0, -10)$ and $c(6, -2)$ are the vertices of a triangle.

    (i) Verify that the triangle is right-angled at c.

    (ii) Hence, or otherwise, find the equation of the circle that passes through the points a, b and c.

3. The equation of a circle is $(x + 1)^2 + (y - 8)^2 = 160$.
The line $x - 3y + 25 = 0$ intersects the circle at the points p and q.

    (i) Find the coordinates of p and the coordinates of q.

    (ii) Investigate whether $[pq]$ is a diameter of the circle.

4. Prove that the line $2x - y + 2 = 0$ intersects the circle $x^2 + y^2 - x - y - 2 = 0$ and find the length of the chord which the line makes with the circle.

5. L: $3x - 2y - 8 = 0$ is a line and S: $x^2 + y^2 + 2x - 2y - 11 = 0$ is a circle.
Verify that L is a tangent to S and find the coordinates of the point of contact.

6. (i) Find the equation of the circle C with centre $(3, 2)$ which touches the x-axis at one point only.

    (ii) T is a tangent to C and is parallel to the y-axis. Find the two possible equations for T.

7. Find the two values of c for which the line $x + 2y + c = 0$ is a tangent to the circle
$x^2 + y^2 - 6x - 4y + 8 = 0$.

8. The line $kx - y = 0$ is a tangent to the circle $x^2 + y^2 - 8x - 6y + 20 = 0$.
Find the two values of k.

9. The equation of a circle with radius length 7 is $x^2 + y^2 - 10kx + 6y + 60 = 0$, where $k > 0$.
   (i) Find the centre of the circle in terms of k.   **(ii)** Find the value of k.
   (iii) The line $3x + 4y + d = 0$ is a tangent to the circle, where $d \in \mathbf{Z}$.
   Show that one value for d is 17, and find the other value for d.

10. $p(0, -2)$ and $p(-2, -6)$ are points of a circle, centre $c(k, -2k)$.
Find k and write the equation of the circle.

11. Find the equation of the circle which touches the x-axis and contains the points $(-2, 8)$ and $(6, 8)$.

12. A circle S has centre $(-2, 3)$ and makes a chord of 8 units along the x-axis. Find the equation of S.

13. The point $(4, 1)$ is the midpoint of a chord of the circle $x^2 + y^2 - 6x + 2y - 15 = 0$.
Find the length of this chord.

14. Find the equations of the tangents to the circle $x^2 + y^2 + 2x + 4y - 3 = 0$ at the points where the circle crosses the x-axis. Prove that these two tangents are perpendicular to each other.

15. Prove that the equation of the tangent to the circle $x^2 + y^2 = r^2$ at the point (x_1, y_1) on the circle is $x_1 x + y_1 y = r^2$.

16. **(i)** State the centre and radius of the circle C: $x^2 + y^2 - 4x - 6y - 12 = 0$.
   (ii) Show that the point $p(5, 7)$ is on C and find the equation of the tangent T to C at p.
   (iii) Find the equation of K, the image of C under an axial symmetry in T.

17. S is the circle $x^2 + y^2 - 8x + 4y - 5 = 0$. A circle K touches S internally and passes through c, the centre of S. If $3x - 4y + 5 = 0$ is the tangent common to both circles, find the equation of K.

   H is the image of K under the central symmetry in c. Find the equation of H and of the common tangent to H and S.

18. Prove that the circles $x^2 + y^2 = 16$ and $x^2 + y^2 + 6x - 8y + 24 = 0$ touch externally.

19. S: $x^2 + y^2 - 16y + 32 = 0$ and K: $x^2 + y^2 - 18x + 2y + 32 = 0$ are two circles.
Show that the circles touch externally and find their point of contact.

20. **(i)** $x^2 + y^2 - 6x + 4y - 12 = 0$ is the equation of a circle. Write down the coordinates of its centre and the length of its radius.
   (ii) $x^2 + y^2 + 12x - 20y + k = 0$ is another circle, where $k \in \mathbf{R}$. The two circles touch externally. Find the value of k.

21. **(i)** Show that the circles $x^2 + y^2 + 2x - 6y + 9 = 0$ and $x^2 + y^2 + 8x - 6y + 9 = 0$ touch internally. Find the equation of their common tangent.

22. **(i)** The equation of the circle C is: $x^2 + y^2 - 6x + 4y - 7 = 0$. Find its centre and radius.
   (ii) A circle K, centred at $(-5, 2)$, touches the circle C at one point only.
   Find the two possible equations of the circle K.

23. S_1 and S_2 are two circles which touch externally.
The centre of S_1 is $(13, 3)$ and the equation of S_2 is $x^2 + y^2 - 2x + 4y - 11 = 0$.
Find the equation of: **(i)** S_1 **(ii)** the common tangent T at the point of contact.

24. $C_1: x^2 + y^2 + 2x - 2y - 23 = 0$ and

$C_2: x^2 + y^2 - 14x - 2y + 41 = 0$ are two circles.

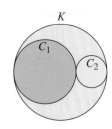

(i) Prove that C_1 and C_2 touch externally.

(ii) K is a third circle.
Both C_1 and C_2 touch K internally.
Find the equation of K.
(All three centres lie on a straight line.)

25. $S_1: x^2 + y^2 + 4x + 2y - 4 = 0$ is the equation of a circle.

Find the equations of the circles, S_2 and S_3, both with centre $(-5, 3)$, such that S_1 touches S_2 internally and S_1 touches S_3 externally.

26. Find the range of values of $k \in \mathbf{R}$ for which the equation $x^2 + y^2 + 2x - 6y + k = 0$ represents a circle with a radius greater than zero.

27. The equation of a circle is $x^2 + y^2 - 2x - 4y = 20$.

(i) Write down the coordinates of its centre and the length of its radius.

(ii) Find the equation of the chord of the circle whose midpoint is $(-1, 3)$.

(iii) Find the length of this chord, giving your answer in the form of $a\sqrt{5}$, where $a \in \mathbf{N}$.

28. $p(3, -1)$, $q(3, -4)$ and $r(x, y)$ are points such that $2|qr| = |pr|$.

Verify that r is on a circle. Find the centre and radius length of the circle.

29. $p(2, 6)$ and $q(-4, -2)$ are two points. Show that the locus of a point $r(x, y)$, such that $|\angle prq| = 90°$, is a circle. Write down its centre and radius.

30. Points $(1, -1)$, $(-6, -2)$ and $(3, -5)$ are on a circle C. Find the equation of C.

31. Find the equation of the circle passing through the points $(1, 2)$ and $(-3, 6)$ and whose centre is on the line $x - 3y + 9 = 0$.

32. The lines $3x - 4y - 3 = 0$ is a tangent to the circle C at the point $(5, 3)$.

The point $(-2, 4)$ is on the circle. Find the equation of the circle C.

33. Find two values of k for which the line $8x + 3y + k = 0$ is a tangent to the circle $x^2 + y^2 + 4x - 3y - 12 = 0$.

Exercise 3R.C ▼

1. Verify that the circles S_1 and S_2 touch externally if

$$S_1: x^2 + y^2 - 2x + 4y - 8 = 0$$

$$S_2: x^2 + y^2 + 6x - 8y + 12 = 0.$$

Verify that $2x - 3y + 5 = 0$ is a tangent to each of the circles at their point of contact.

2. The circles $x^2 + y^2 + 3x - y - 6 = 0$ and $x^2 + y^2 + 2y - 9 = 0$ intersect at the points a and b. Find $|ab|$.

3. The following parametric equations define a circle:

$$x = a + 4a \cos \theta, \quad y = -3a + 4a \sin \theta, \text{ where } a, \theta \in \mathbf{R}.$$

What is the Cartesian equation of the circle?

4. Find the two values of k for which the line $3x - 4y + k = 0$ is a tangent to the circle $x^2 + y^2 - 4x + 2y - 20 = 0$.

5. A tangent from the point $k(5, -4)$ touches the circle $x^2 + y^2 + 2kx + 2ky + 2(4 - k) = 0$ at the point t. Calculate $|kt|$.

6. The circle $x^2 + y^2 + 2gx + 2fy + c = 0$ passes through the points $(3, 3)$ and $(4, 1)$.
The line $3x - y - 6 = 0$ is a tangent to the circle at $(3, 3)$.

    (i) Find the real numbers g, f and c.

    (ii) Find the coordinates of the point on the circle at which the tangent parallel to $3x - y - 6 = 0$ touches the circle.

7. A circle of radius 5 units has its centre in the first quadrant, touches the x-axis and intercepts a chord of length 6 units on the y-axis. Find its equation.

8. S is the circle $x^2 + y^2 - 4x - 4y - 17 = 0$.

    (i) Find the length of the chord made by the line $4x - 3y + 18 = 0$ on the circle S.

    (ii) The line $3x + 4y + d = 0$ makes a chord 8 units long on the circle S. Find the two possible values of d.

9. **(i)** Verify that $x(x - p) + y(y - q) = \alpha(qx + py - pq)$ is the equation of a circle which contains the points $(p, 0)$ and $(0, q)$, where $\alpha \in \mathbf{R}$.

    (ii) Hence, or otherwise, find the equation of the circle which passes through the points $(1, 0)$ and $(0, 2)$ and has its centre on the line $x + 3y - 11 = 0$.

10. The line $y = mx + c$ is a tangent to the circle $x^2 + y^2 = r^2$.

Show that $c = \pm r\sqrt{m^2 + 1}$.

11. **(i)** Show that the line $y = mx - 5m$ contains the point $(5, 0)$.

    (ii) Find the equations of the two tangents from the point $(5, 0)$ to the circle $x^2 + y^2 = 5$.

12. Find the equations of the tangents to the circle $x^2 + y^2 - 5x - y + 4 = 0$ which have slope 3.

13. Find the equations of the two tangents from the point $(7, -1)$ to the circle $x^2 + y^2 - 8x + 4y + 12 = 0$.

14. The circle C has equation $x^2 + y^2 - 4x + 6y - 12 = 0$.
L intersects C at the points p and q.
M intersects C at the points t and s.
$|pq| = |ts| = 8$.

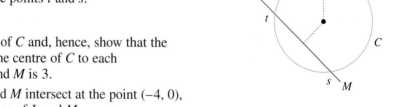

    (i) Find the radius of C and, hence, show that the distance from the centre of C to each of the lines L and M is 3.

    (ii) Given that L and M intersect at the point $(-4, 0)$, find the equations of L and M.

15. $x^2 + y^2 + 2x - 4y - 20 = 0$ is the equation of a circle. Two lines L and M intersect at $(2, -2)$.
The distance from the centre of the circle to each line is $2\sqrt{5}$.
Find the equation of L and the equation of M.

16. $x^2 + y^2 + 4x + 2y - 15 = 0$ is the equation of a circle. Two lines L and M intersect at $(3, 4)$. The distance from the centre of the circle to each line is $\sqrt{10}$.

   (i) Find the equations of L and M.

   (ii) Find the coordinates of the points where L and M meet the circle.

17. $S_1: x^2 + y^2 - 6x - 4y + 12 = 0$, $S_2: x^2 + y^2 + 10x + 4y + 20 = 0$ are two circles.

   (i) Find the coordinates of their centres p and q and the lengths of their radii r_1, r_2 respectively.

   (ii) Verify that the lines $L: y - 1 = 0$ and $M: 4x - 3y - 1 = 0$ are tangents to S_1.

   (iii) If w is the point of intersection of L and M and $w \in [pq]$, show that $|pw| : |wq| = r_1 : r_2$.

18. The line $ax + by = 0$ is a tangent to the circle $x^2 + y^2 - 12x + 6y + 9 = 0$, where $a, b \in \mathbf{R}$ and $b \neq 0$.

   (i) Show that $\dfrac{a}{b} = -\dfrac{3}{4}$.   **(ii)** Hence, or otherwise, find the coordinates of the point of contact.

19. **(i)** Find the condition that the circle $x^2 + y^2 + 2gx + 2fy + c = 0$:

      (a) contains the origin $(0, 0)$ **(b)** touches the x-axis   **(c)** touches the y-axis.

   (ii) The x-axis is a tangent to a circle K at the point $(3, 0)$. The point $(-1, 4) \in K$. Find the equation of K.

   (iii) Prove that the circle with equation $x^2 + y^2 - 2px - 2qy + q^2 = 0$ touches the y-axis.

      Hence, or otherwise, find the equations of the two circles which touch the y-axis and pass through the points $(2, 3)$ and $(1, 2)$.

20. Two circles intersect at the points $a(1, 2)$ and $b(7, -6)$. The line joining the centres of the circles is the perpendicular bisector of $[ab]$. The distance from the centre of each circle to the midpoint of $[ab]$ is 10.

   (i) Find the midpoint of $[ab]$ and the radius length of each circle.

   (ii) Find the equation of each circle.

21. A circle intersects a line at the points $a(-3, 0)$ and $b(5, -4)$.

   (i) The midpoint of $[ab]$ is m. Find the coordinates of m.

   (ii) The distance from the centre of the circle to m is $\sqrt{5}$.

      Find the equations of the two circles that satisfy these conditions.

22. A circle of radius length $\sqrt{20}$ contains the point $(-1, 3)$. Its centre lies on the line $x + y = 0$. Find the equations of the two circles that satisfy these conditions.

23. A line $2x - 3y + 1 = 0$ is a tangent to a circle K at the point $(1, 1)$. If the radius of K is $\sqrt{13}$, find two possible equations of K.

24. Find the equations of the two circles which contain the points $(-2, 4)$ and $(5, 3)$ and have a radius 5.

25. Find the equation of the circle which passes through $(1, 2)$ and $(-1, 4)$ and has a radius of $\sqrt{10}$.

26. Find the Cartesian equation of the circle: $x = \dfrac{3t}{1 + t^2}$, $y = \dfrac{3}{1 + t^2}$, $t \in \mathbf{R}$.

27. Find the equations of the circles which touch both axes, which contain the point $(3, 6)$ and whose centre lies in the first quadrant.

REVISION EXERCISE 4   VECTORS

Paper 2, Question 2

This revision exercise covers Chapter 4.

Exercise 4R.A ▼

1. $\vec{s} = 4\vec{i} - 3\vec{j}$ and $\vec{t} = 2\vec{i} - 5\vec{j}$. Find $|\vec{sk}|$.

2. $oabc$ is a parallelogram where o is the origin. d is the midpoint of $[cb]$.

   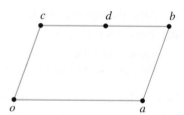

   (i) Express $\vec{b}$ in terms of $\vec{a}$ and $\vec{c}$.

   (ii) Express $\vec{d}$ in terms of $\vec{a}$ and $\vec{c}$.

3. $oabc$ is a parallelogram where o is the origin, $\vec{a} = 3\vec{i} - \vec{j}$ and $\vec{b} = 4\vec{i} + 3\vec{j}$.
   Express $\vec{c}$ in terms of $\vec{i}$ and $\vec{j}$.

4. $abcd$ is a parallelogram where $\vec{a} = 2\vec{i} - 7\vec{j}$, $\vec{b} = -6\vec{i} - 11\vec{j}$ and $\vec{c} = -8\vec{i} + 4\vec{j}$.
   Express $\vec{d}$ in terms of $\vec{i}$ and $\vec{j}$.

5. $\vec{p} = 3\vec{i} - 5\vec{j}$, $\vec{pq} = 10\vec{i} + 2\vec{j}$. Express $\vec{q}$ in terms of $\vec{i}$ and $\vec{j}$.

6. Let $\vec{p} = 3\vec{i} + k\vec{j}$, $\vec{q} = t\vec{i} + 3\vec{j}$. If $\vec{pq} = -5\vec{i} - 2\vec{j}$, find the values of k and t and, hence, calculate $\vec{p} \cdot \vec{q}$

7. $\vec{p} = 3\vec{i} + 2\vec{j}$, $\vec{q} = 5\vec{i} - 6\vec{j}$ and $\vec{p} = r\vec{q}$. Express $\vec{r}$ in terms of $\vec{i}$ and $\vec{j}$.

8. $\vec{a} = 2\vec{i} - 7\vec{j}$ and $\vec{b} = 14\vec{i} + 4\vec{j}$. Prove that $\vec{a} \perp \vec{b}$.

9. $\vec{p} = 3k\vec{i} - (k+1)\vec{j}$ and $\vec{q} = -k\vec{i} - (k+2)\vec{j}$.
   If $\vec{p} \perp \vec{q}$, find the two possible values of k.

10. $\vec{p} = 4\vec{i} + \vec{j}$ and $\vec{q} = \vec{i} - \vec{j}$. If $(\vec{p} + k\vec{q}) \perp \vec{pq}$, find the value of k, where $k \in \mathbf{R}$.

11. **(i)** $\vec{v} = t\vec{i} - 8\vec{j}$, where $t \in \mathbf{R}$. Find the two possible values of t for which $|\vec{v}| = 17$.

    (ii) If $|k\vec{i} + 10\vec{j}| = |2\vec{i} + 11\vec{j}|$, find two possible values of k, $k \in \mathbf{R}$.

12. $\vec{a} = k\vec{i} - 2\vec{j}$ and $\vec{b} = -\vec{i} + 2\vec{j}$. If $|\vec{ab}| = 5$, find the two values of k, $k \in \mathbf{R}$.

13. $\vec{r} = 7\vec{i} - 4\vec{j}$. If $m\vec{r} + n\vec{r}^{\perp} = 5\vec{i} - 40\vec{j}$, $m, n \in \mathbf{R}$, find the value of m and the value of n.

14. Let $\vec{u} = 3\vec{i} + 2\vec{j}$, $\vec{w} = -\vec{i} + 4\vec{j}$. The vector $t\vec{w} + \vec{u}$ is on the $\vec{j}$-axis; find the value of the scalar t.

15. oab is a triangle, o is the origin.
p, q are points on $[oa]$ and $[ab]$, respectively, such that:

$$|op| : |pa| = 2:1 \quad \text{and} \quad |bq| : |qa| = 2:3.$$

Express in terms of $\vec{a}$ and $\vec{b}$:

(i) $\vec{p}$　　**(ii)** $\vec{bq}$　　**(iii)** $\vec{q}$.

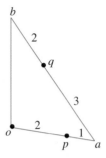

16. oab is a triangle where o is the origin.
p and q are points such that:

$$|oq| : |qb| = 2:1 = |bq| : |pa|.$$

If $\vec{a} = 6\vec{i} + 3\vec{j}$ and $\vec{b} = 9\vec{i} + 12\vec{j}$, express $\vec{p}$ and $\vec{q}$
in terms of $\vec{i}$ and $\vec{j}$ and find $h, k \in \mathbf{R}$, such that

$$h\vec{p} = k\vec{q} = 4\vec{i} + 12\vec{j}.$$

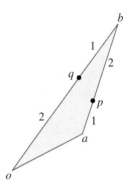

17. Find the unit vector in the direction $-20\vec{i} + 21\vec{j}$.

18. If $\vec{c} = 3\vec{i} - 2\vec{j}$ and $\vec{d} = 9\vec{i} + 6\vec{j}$, find a unit vector perpendicular to $\vec{cd}$.

19. In the diagram, $|\vec{a}| = 4$, $|\vec{b}| = 6$
and $|\angle aob| = \dfrac{\pi}{3}$, where o is the origin.

Evaluate $\vec{a} \cdot \vec{b}$

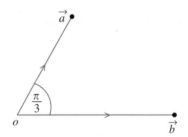

20. $\vec{p} = \vec{i} - 2\vec{j}$ and $\vec{q} = k\vec{i} + 2\vec{j}$. If $|\vec{pq}| = 5$, find two values of k, $k \in \mathbf{R}$.

Exercise 4R.B ▼

1. Let $\vec{h} = 6\vec{i} - 8\vec{j}$ and $\vec{k} = 4\vec{i} - 3\vec{j}$.

(i) If $ohkm$ is a parallelogram, o being the origin, express $\vec{m}$ in terms of $\vec{i}$ and $\vec{j}$.

(ii) If $\vec{p} = \vec{k} + a\vec{m}$, $a \in \mathbf{R}$, and $\vec{p}$ is a point on the $\vec{j}$-axis, calculate the value of a.
Express $\vec{p}$ in terms of $\vec{i}$ and $\vec{j}$ and calculate $|\vec{pm}|$.

2. $\vec{p} = 2\vec{i} + 3\vec{j},\quad \vec{q} = 3\vec{i} + 6\vec{j}\quad$ and $\quad \vec{r} = 6\vec{i} + 5\vec{j}.$

    (i) Express, in terms of $\vec{i}$ and $\vec{j}$:   **(a)** $\vec{qp}$ **(b)** $\vec{rp}$

    (ii) Show that $\vec{qp} \cdot \vec{rp} = 10.$

    (iii) Calculate $|\angle qpr|.$

3. If $\vec{a} = -\vec{i} + 3\vec{j},\quad \vec{b} = \vec{i} - 3\vec{j}\quad$ and $\quad \vec{c} = 8\vec{i} + 6\vec{j},$ calculate $|\angle bac|.$

4. $\vec{a} = -\vec{i} - 3\vec{j},\quad \vec{b} = \vec{i} + 5\vec{j}\quad$ and $\quad \vec{c} = -4\vec{i} - 7\vec{j}.$ Verify that:

    (i) $|\angle acb| = \cos^{-1}\dfrac{63}{65}$ **(ii)** the area of triangle $abc = 8.$

5. $\vec{a} = 2\vec{i} + (2k + 3)\vec{j}\quad$ and $\quad \vec{b} = k^2\vec{i} + 6\vec{j},\quad$ where $k \in \mathbf{Z},$ and $\vec{a}$ is perpendicular to $\vec{b}.$

    (i) Find the value of $k.$ **(ii)** Using your value for $k,$ write $\vec{a} + \vec{b}$ in terms of $\vec{i}$ and $\vec{j}.$

    (iii) Hence, find the measure of the angle between $\vec{a}$ and $\vec{a} + \vec{b},$ correct to the nearest degree.

6. $\vec{p} = 2\vec{i} + 3\vec{j}\quad$ and $\quad \vec{p}^{\perp}$ is its related vector $-3\vec{i} + 2\vec{j}.$
    Let $\vec{q} = \vec{p}^{\perp} - \vec{p}\quad$ and $\quad \vec{r} = \vec{q} + \vec{q}^{\perp}.$

    (i) Express $\vec{q}$ and $\vec{r}$ in terms of $\vec{i}$ and $\vec{j}.$ **(ii)** Find the measure of the angle between $\vec{q}$ and $\vec{r}.$

7. $\vec{p} = 9\vec{i} - 5\vec{j},\quad \vec{q} = 5\vec{i} + 3\vec{j}\quad$ and $\quad \vec{s} = -5\vec{i} - \frac{9}{2}\vec{j}.$

    Let $\vec{m} = \frac{1}{2}(\vec{p} + \vec{q})$ and $\vec{n} = \frac{2}{5}(\vec{sq}).$

    (i) Express $\vec{m}$ and $\vec{n}$ in terms of $\vec{i}$ and $\vec{j}.$ **(ii)** Find the measure of the angle between $\vec{m}$ and $\vec{n}.$

8. $\vec{p} = k\vec{i} + 2\vec{j}\quad$ and $\quad \vec{q} = 3\vec{i} + \vec{j},\quad$ where $k \in \mathbf{R}.$

    If $|\angle poq| = \dfrac{\pi}{4},$ where o is the origin, find two possible values of $k.$

9. $\vec{p} = 2\vec{i} + \vec{j},\quad \vec{q} = 3\vec{i} + k\vec{j}\quad$ and $\quad \vec{r} = 3\vec{i} + t\vec{j},$ where $k, t \in \mathbf{R}$ and o is the origin.

    (i) Given that $\vec{p} \perp \vec{q},$ calculate the value of $k.$

    (ii) Given that $|\angle por| = 45°,$ calculate the two possible values of $t.$

10. $\vec{a} = k\vec{i} + 4\vec{j}\quad$ and $\quad \vec{b} = \vec{i} - 2\vec{j}.$ If $\cos\angle aob = -\dfrac{1}{\sqrt{5}},$ find the value of $k,$ $k \in \mathbf{R},$

    where o is the origin and $0° < |\angle aob| < 180°.$

11. r is an internal point of $[pq]$ such that $|pr| = \frac{2}{3}|pq|.$

    (i) Express $\vec{r}$ in terms of $\vec{p}$ and $\vec{q}.$

    (ii) If $\vec{p}$ is $\vec{i} - \vec{j}\quad$ and $\quad \vec{q}$ is $4\vec{i} + 2\vec{j},\quad$ express $\vec{r}$ in terms of $\vec{i}$ and $\vec{j},$ these being the unit vectors along the horizontal and vertical directions, respectively.

    (iii) Show that the acute angle between $\vec{r}$ and $\vec{pr}$ is given by $\cos^{-1}\dfrac{2}{\sqrt{5}}.$

12. (i) *opqr* is a parallelogram, where *o* is the origin,
$\vec{p} = 2\vec{i} - 8\vec{j}$ and $\vec{q} = 11\vec{i} + \vec{j}$.
Express $\vec{r}$ in terms of $\vec{i}$ and $\vec{j}$.

(ii) $s \in [pq]$ and $|ps| : |sq| = 5 : 4$.
Express $\vec{s}$ in terms of $\vec{i}$ and $\vec{j}$.

(iii) If $\vec{w} = x\vec{i} - 4\vec{j}$ and $|\vec{ws}| = \sqrt{37}$, find two values for *x*.
Show that the larger value gives $\vec{ws} \perp \vec{rs}$.
Show that the smaller value gives an angle of
$\cos^{-1}\left(\dfrac{-12}{37}\right)$ between $\vec{ws}$ and $\vec{rs}$.

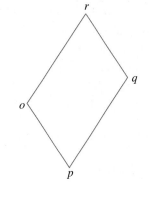

13. In the diagram, *a*, *p* and *b* are collinear and *o* is the origin.
If $|\vec{ap}| = t|\vec{ab}|$, $t \in \mathbf{R}$,
express $\vec{p}$ in terms of $\vec{a}$ and $\vec{b}$.

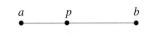

14. [*mr*] is divided into four line segments of equal length
by the points *n*, *p* and *q*.
Given that $\vec{m} = -2\vec{i} + 3\vec{j}$ and $\vec{q} = 7\vec{i} - 9\vec{j}$, express:

(i) $\vec{p}$ in terms of $\vec{i}$ and $\vec{j}$

(ii) $\vec{r}$ in terms of $\vec{i}$ and $\vec{j}$.

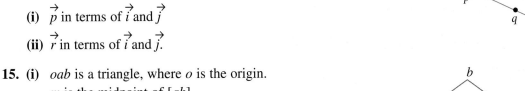

15. (i) *oab* is a triangle, where *o* is the origin.
m is the midpoint of [*ab*].
Express $\vec{m}$ in terms of $\vec{a}$ and $\vec{b}$.

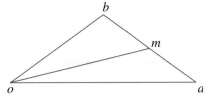

(ii) In the triangle *xyz*, *w* is the midpoint of
[*yz*], *g* is a point in [*xw*] such that
$|xg| = \frac{2}{3}|xw|$ and *o* is the origin.
Express $\vec{g}$ in terms of $\vec{x}$, $\vec{y}$ and $\vec{z}$.

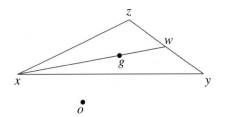

16. *p*, *q*, *r*, *s* are the midpoints of the sides of a
quadrilateral *abcd*.
Prove by vector methods that *pqrs* is a
parallelogram.

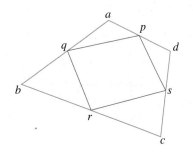

303

17. *oabc* is a parallelogram, where *o* is the origin.

$p \in [ab]$ such that $|ap|:|pb| = 3:1$.

q is the midpoint of $[oc]$.

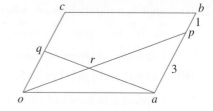

(i) Using equiangular triangles, or otherwise, find the ratio $|or|:|rp|$.

(ii) Express $\vec{p}$, and hence $\vec{r}$, in terms of $\vec{a}$ and $\vec{b}$.

18. $\vec{a} = p\vec{i} + q\vec{j}$ and $\vec{b} = r\vec{i} + s\vec{j}$. Investigate whether:

(i) $\vec{a}^{\perp} - \vec{b}^{\perp} = (\vec{a} - \vec{b})^{\perp}$ **(ii)** $\vec{a}^{\perp} \cdot \vec{b} = -\vec{b}^{\perp} \cdot \vec{a}$

19. $\vec{r}^{\perp} = -y\vec{i} + x\vec{j}$, where $\vec{r} = x\vec{i} + y\vec{j}$. Investigate whether:

(i) $(\vec{r} + \vec{s})^{\perp} = \vec{r}^{\perp} + \vec{s}^{\perp}$ **(ii)** $(\vec{r}^{\perp})^{\perp} = \vec{r}$

(iii) $(k\vec{r})^{\perp} = k(\vec{r}^{\perp})$ **(iv)** $\vec{r}^{\perp} \cdot \vec{s} = \vec{r} \cdot \vec{s}^{\perp}$

20. $\vec{a} = \vec{i} - 2\vec{j}$ and $\vec{b} = k\vec{i} + 2\vec{j}$, where $k \in \mathbf{N}$.

If $\vec{a} \cdot \vec{b} = \frac{2}{5}|\vec{a}|^2$, find the value of *k*.

21. $\vec{a} = \vec{i} + 4\vec{j}$ and $\vec{b} = x\vec{i} + y\vec{i}$. If $|\vec{b}| = \sqrt{85}$ and $\vec{a} \cdot \vec{b} = 17$, find $\vec{b}$.

22. $\vec{p}, \vec{q}$ and $\vec{r}$ are three vectors such that $\vec{p} \cdot \vec{r} = 3$ and $\vec{q} \cdot \vec{r} = 4$.

If $\vec{s} \perp \vec{r}$, where $\vec{s} = \vec{p} + \lambda\vec{q}$ and $\lambda \in \mathbf{R}$, find the value of λ.

23. $\vec{p} = 3\vec{i} + 4\vec{j}$ and $\vec{q} = a\vec{i} + b\vec{j}$, $a, b \in \mathbf{R}$.

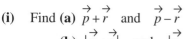

Exercise 4R.C ▼

---

1. *rst* is a triangle, where $\vec{r} = -\vec{i} + 2\vec{j}$, $\vec{s} = -4\vec{i} - 2\vec{j}$ and $\vec{t} = 3\vec{i} - \vec{j}$.

(i) Express $\vec{rs}$, $\vec{st}$ and $\vec{tr}$ in terms of $\vec{i}$ and $\vec{j}$.

(ii) Show that the triangle *rst* is right-angled at *r*.

(iii) Find the measure of $\angle rst$.

2. Vertices *p* and *r* of the parallelogram *opqr* are $\vec{p} = 4\vec{i} - \vec{j}$ and $\vec{r} = 2\vec{i} + 3\vec{j}$, where *o* is the origin.

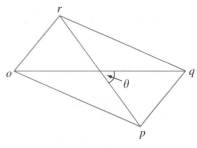

(i) Find **(a)** $\vec{p} + \vec{r}$ and $\vec{p} - \vec{r}$

        (b) $|\vec{p} + \vec{r}|$ and $|\vec{p} - \vec{r}|$.

(ii) Show that θ, the acute angle between $\vec{oq}$ and $\vec{rp}$, is given by $\cos^{-1} \dfrac{1}{5\sqrt{2}}$.

(iii) A point *d* in the plane is such that $\vec{d} = \vec{r} - k\vec{p}$, $k \in \mathbf{R}$ and $\vec{d} \perp \vec{p}$. Find the value of *k*.

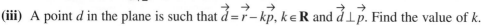

3. (i) $\vec{p} + \vec{q} = 5\vec{i} - 5\vec{j}$ and $\vec{pq} = 3\vec{i} + \vec{j}$. Express $\vec{p}$ and $\vec{q}$ in terms of $\vec{i}$ and $\vec{j}$.

(ii) Given that $\vec{r} = \dfrac{\vec{p} \cdot \vec{q}}{\vec{q} \cdot \vec{q}} \vec{q}$, express $\vec{r}$ in terms of $\vec{i}$ and $\vec{j}$.

(iii) Given that $\vec{s} = \frac{7}{2}\vec{i} + m\vec{j}$, $m \in \mathbf{Q}$, find the value of m for which the origin, r and s are collinear.

4. $\vec{x} = 3\vec{i} + 4\vec{j}$ and $\vec{y} = 5\vec{i} + \vec{j}$.

If $\vec{x} \cdot \left(\vec{y} - \dfrac{k\vec{x}}{|\vec{x}|} \right) = 0$, find the value of k, $k \in \mathbf{Q}$.

5. In the diagram, $\vec{a} = 4\vec{i} + 2\vec{j}$,
$|\vec{b}| = \sqrt{10} = |\vec{c}|$ and
$|\angle boa| = \dfrac{\pi}{4} = |\angle coa|$.

Express $\vec{b}$ and $\vec{c}$ in the form $x\vec{i} + y\vec{j}$.

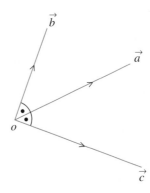

6. $\vec{x} = -3\vec{i} + 4\vec{j}$ and $\vec{y} = 5\vec{i} + 12\vec{j}$.

(i) Find $|\vec{x}|$ and $|\vec{y}|$.

(ii) If $\vec{r} = (1 - t)\vec{x} + t\vec{y}$, where $t = \dfrac{|\vec{x}|}{|\vec{x}| + |\vec{y}|}$, express $\vec{r}$ in terms of $\vec{i}$ and $\vec{j}$.

(iii) If $k\left(\dfrac{\vec{x}}{|\vec{x}|} + \dfrac{\vec{y}}{|\vec{y}|} \right) = 18\vec{r}$, find the value of k, $k \in \mathbf{N}$.

7. $oabc$ is a parallelogram, where o is the origin.
m is a point on $[ob]$ such that $|om| : |mb| = 3 : 1$ and
a, m and n are collinear.

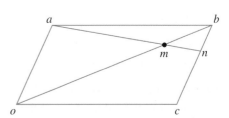

(i) Express $\vec{cb}$ in terms of $\vec{a}$.

(ii) Express in terms of $\vec{a}$ and $\vec{c}$:

(a) $\vec{b}$ **(b)** $\vec{m}$ **(c)** $\vec{am}$.

(iii) Given that $\vec{n} = \vec{a} + h\vec{am} = \vec{c} + k\vec{cb}$, $h, k \in \mathbf{R}$,
find the value of h and the value of k.

(iv) Write down the ratio $|nb| : |cn|$.

8. In the diagram, o is the origin, $op \parallel rq$ and $os \parallel pq$.
s is a point on $[pr]$ such that $|ps|:|sr| = 4:1$.

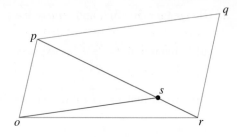

  (i) Express in terms of $\vec{p}$ and $\vec{r}$:

   (a) $\overrightarrow{pr}$ **(b)** $\overrightarrow{rs}$ **(c)** $\vec{s}$.

  (ii) $\overrightarrow{rq} = h\vec{p}, \quad h \in \mathbf{R}$.

   (a) Express $\overrightarrow{pq}$ in terms of h, $\vec{p}$ and $\vec{r}$.

   (b) Find the value of h.

9. oab is a triangle, where o is the origin.

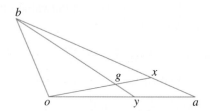

  (i) x is a point on $[ab]$ such that $|ax|:|xb| = 1:3$.
  Express $\vec{x}$ in terms of $\vec{a}$ and $\vec{b}$.

  (ii) y is a point on $[oa]$ such that $|oy|:|ya| = 2:1$.
  Express $\overrightarrow{by}$ in terms of $\vec{a}$ and $\vec{b}$.

  (iii) $[ox]$ and $[by]$ intersect at g.
  Given that $\vec{g} = m\vec{x}$ and $\overrightarrow{bg} = n\overrightarrow{by}$, where $m, n \in \mathbf{R}$,
  find the value of m and the value of n.

10. In the diagram, o is the origin,
p is the midpoint of $[oq]$ and
$|px|:|xr| = 1:3$.

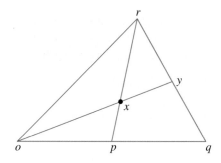

  (i) Express in terms of $\vec{p}$ and $\vec{r}$:

   (a) $\overrightarrow{rp}$ **(b)** $\overrightarrow{px}$ **(c)** $\vec{x}$.

  (ii) Taking $\vec{y} = h\vec{x}$, where $h \in \mathbf{R}$, find
  $\overrightarrow{qy}$ in terms of $\vec{p}$, $\vec{r}$ and h.
  Hence, find the ratio $|\overrightarrow{qy}|:|\overrightarrow{yr}|$.

11. oxy and omn are two triangles.
$|mt| = |tn|$ and $|oy|:|yn| = 4:1$.
$\overrightarrow{mx} = h\overrightarrow{hm}$ and $\overrightarrow{tx} = k\overrightarrow{yt}, \quad h, k \in \mathbf{R}$.
Express $\overrightarrow{tx}$ in terms of:

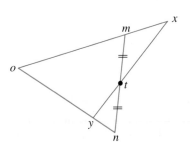

  (i) h, $\vec{m}$ and $\vec{n}$ **(ii)** k, $\vec{m}$ and $\vec{n}$.
  Hence, find the value of h and the value of k.

12. Let o be the origin and let oab be a triangle as shown.
p is a point on $[ab]$ such that $|ap| = 3|pb|$.
q is the midpoint of $[ob]$.

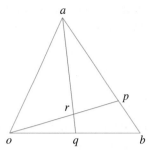

    (i) Express $\vec{p}$ and $\vec{q}$ in terms of $\vec{a}$ and $\vec{b}$.

    (ii) If $\vec{r} = x\vec{p}$ and $\vec{ar} = y\vec{aq}$, $x, y \in \mathbf{R}$,
        find values for x and y.

13. $\vec{k} = \vec{i} + 3\vec{j}$, $\vec{n} = 4\vec{i} - 2\vec{j}$, $\vec{u} = 2\vec{i} + \vec{j}$ and $\vec{v} = x\vec{i} + y\vec{j}$, where $x, y \in \mathbf{R}$.

    (i) Express the value of $\vec{kn} \cdot \vec{kv}$ in the form $ax + by + c$, where $a, b, c \in \mathbf{R}$.

    (ii) Prove that if $\vec{kn} \cdot \vec{kv} = \vec{kn} \cdot \vec{ku}$, and $\vec{u} \neq \vec{v}$, then $\vec{kn} \perp \vec{uv}$.

14. In the diagram, $|\angle por| = |\angle qor|$,
where o is the origin.

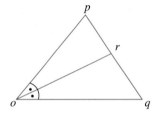

    Show that $\vec{r} = k\left(|\vec{q}|\vec{p} + |\vec{p}|\vec{q}\right)$,
    for some $k \in \mathbf{R}$.

    If $|pr| : |rq| = m : n$, express $\vec{r}$ in terms of $\vec{p}$, $\vec{q}$, m and n.
    Hence, show that $|\vec{p}| : |\vec{q}| = m : n$.

15. In the diagram, a and b are points on
triangle oxy, where o is the origin, such that:
$|xa| : |ay| = 1 : 2 = |yb| : |bo|$ and $|oa| = |ab|$.

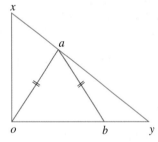

    Prove that $\vec{x} \perp \vec{y}$.

16. $\vec{a}$ is a vector parallel to $2\vec{i} + \vec{j}$, $\vec{b}$ is a vector parallel to $\vec{i} + \vec{j}$ and the vector $(\vec{a} + \vec{b})$ is parallel to $4\vec{i} + 3\vec{j}$.   If $|\vec{a} + \vec{b}| = 10$, find: **(i)** $\vec{a}$ **(ii)** $\vec{b}$.

17. **(i)** If $\vec{a} = 2\vec{i} + 3\vec{j}$ and $\vec{b} = -3\vec{i} + 4\vec{j}$,   verify that: $|\vec{a} + \vec{b}|^2 = (\vec{a} + \vec{b}) \cdot (\vec{a} + \vec{b})$

    (ii) If $\vec{x} = 4\vec{i} + 3\vec{j}$, $\vec{y} = -3\vec{i} + 5\vec{j}$ and $\vec{z} = 2\vec{i} + \vec{j}$,   verify that: $\vec{x} \cdot (\vec{y} + \vec{z}) = \vec{x} \cdot \vec{y} + \vec{x} \cdot \vec{z}$

18. **(i)** $\vec{o}$, $\vec{x}$ and $\vec{y}$ are non-collinear vectors, where o is the origin. Show that:

    (a) $\vec{x} \cdot \vec{x} = |\vec{x}|^2$ **(b)** $\vec{x} \perp \vec{y} \Leftrightarrow \vec{x} \cdot \vec{y} = 0$

    (c) $(\vec{x} + \vec{y}) \cdot (\vec{x} + \vec{y}) = |\vec{x}|^2 + |\vec{y}|^2 + 2\vec{x} \cdot \vec{y}$

    (d) if $|\vec{x} + \vec{y}| = |\vec{x} - \vec{y}|$, then $\vec{x} \perp \vec{y}$.

    (ii) If $|\vec{x}| = 9$, $|\vec{y}| = 8$ and $\vec{x} \cdot \vec{y} = 12$,

    calculate: **(a)** $(\vec{x} + \vec{y}) \cdot (\vec{x} + \vec{y})$ **(b)** $(\vec{x} - \vec{y}) \cdot (\vec{x} - \vec{y})$

    Hence, find: **(c)** $|\vec{x} + \vec{y}|$ **(d)** $|\vec{x} - \vec{y}|$

19. $\vec{a}$ and $\vec{b}$ are two vectors such that $|\vec{a}| > 0$ and $|\vec{b}| > 0$.

If $|\vec{a}| = 5$, $|\vec{b}| = 10$ and $\vec{a} \cdot \vec{b} = 22$,

calculate: **(i)** $|\vec{a} + \vec{b}|$ **(b)** $|\vec{a} - \vec{b}|$.

20. Show that: $|\vec{a} + \vec{b}|^2 + |\vec{a} - \vec{b}|^2 = 2|\vec{a}|^2 + 2|\vec{b}|^2$.

If $pqrs$ is a rectangle, show that: $|\vec{op}|^2 + |\vec{or}|^2 = |\vec{oq}|^2 + |\vec{os}|^2$.

21. $\vec{a}$ and $\vec{b}$ are two non-parallel vectors.

If $\vec{c} = \vec{b} - \left(\dfrac{\vec{a} \cdot \vec{b}}{|\vec{a}|^2} \right) \vec{a}$, show that $\vec{a} \perp \vec{c}$.

22. In the diagram, $\vec{o}$, the origin, is the centre of the circle.

$\vec{p}$ and $\vec{r}$ are the end points of a diameter and $\vec{q}$ is a point on the circumference of the circle.

Show that: $|\vec{q}|^2 = \vec{p} \cdot \vec{q} + \vec{r} \cdot (\vec{q} - \vec{p})$

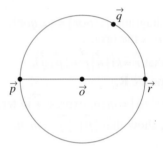

23. If $\vec{c} = |\vec{a}| \vec{b} + |\vec{b}| \vec{a}$, show that the angle between $\vec{a}$ and $\vec{c}$ is equal to the angle between $\vec{b}$ and $\vec{c}$.

24. o is the origin, $\vec{a} = 2\vec{i} + 2\vec{j}$, $\vec{b} = 4\vec{i} + 4\vec{j}$.

If $\vec{r} = \frac{1}{2}(\vec{a} + \vec{b}) + t(\vec{b} - \vec{a})^\perp$, $t \in \mathbf{R}$, express $\vec{r}$ in terms of $\vec{i}, \vec{j}$ and t.

Show that r lies on the perpendicular bisector of $[ab]$ for all $t \in \mathbf{R}$, i.e. show that $|\vec{ra}| = |\vec{rb}|$.

25. a, b and c are distinct points.

If $\vec{ad} = t\left(\dfrac{\vec{ab}^\perp}{|\vec{ab}|} - \dfrac{\vec{ac}^\perp}{|\vec{ac}|} \right)$, where $t \in \mathbf{R}$ and $t \neq 0$, show that $|\angle bad| = |\angle cad|$.

REVISION EXERCISE 5   DISCRETE MATHEMATICS

Paper 2, Questions 6 and 7

This revision exercise covers Chapters 5 and 6.

Exercise 5R.A ▼

1. In their Leaving Certificate, two students, A and B, obtained the following points:

Subject		Maths	Irish	English	Biology	French	Accounting
Points	A	100	40	20	60	80	40
	B	80	20	60	100	40	40

How many points had each student?

A university attached weights, 4, 3, 4, 2, 1, 1, respectively, to the six subjects as written above. If there was only one place left in the university, which student obtained the place?

2. A composite index number is constructed by taking the weighted mean.
The following table gives the index and weighting for each of four commodities:

Commodity	Food	Fuel	Mortgage	Clothing
Index	120	110	90	80
Weight	w	5	4	3

What weight, w, is attached to food if the composite index number is 105.5?

3. In the following grouped frequency distribution table the estimated value of the mean is 8.
Calculate the value of m.

Number	0 – 2	2 – 6	6 – 12	12 – 20	20 – 30
Frequency	$m + 1$	4	2	m	1

(**Note:** 0 – 2 means 0 is included but 2 is not, etc.)

4. **(i)** Show that the following arrays of numbers have the same standard deviation:

   (a) 3, 4, 6, 8, 9   **(b)** 7, 8, 10, 12, 13.

   (ii) The array of numbers, 1, 2, 4, 5, 8, 16 has a mean of $\bar{x}$ and a standard deviation of σ. Verify that $\bar{x} - \sigma = 1$.

5. 20 pupils were given a problem to solve, The following grouped frequency distribution table gives the number of pupils who solved the problem in the given time interval.

Time (minutes)	0 – 4	4 – 12	12 – 24	24 – 40
Frequency	3	8	7	2

Assuming the data can be taken at the mid-interval values, calculate:

(i) the mean   **(ii)** the standard deviation, correct to 2 places of decimals.

6. If p is the mean of the numbers a, b, c and d, express in terms of p and k the mean of the numbers $2a + k$, $2b + k$, $2c + k$ and $2d + k$.

7. Four numbers have a mean of p. Five numbers have a mean of x. These nine numbers have a mean of q. Express x in terms of p and q.

8. How many different five-digit numbers can be formed from the digits 1, 2, 3, 4 and 5 if:

   (i)   there are no restrictions on digits and repetitions are allowed

   (ii) the number is odd and no repetitions are allowed

   (iii) the number is even and repetitions are allowed

   (iv) the number is greater than 50,000 and no repetitions are allowed?

9. How many different four-digit numbers greater than 5,000 can be formed from the digits 2, 4, 5, 8, 9 if each digit can be used only once in any given number?
How many of these numbers are odd?

10. A bank gives each of its customers a four-digit personal identification number which is formed from the digits 0 to 9 inclusive. Examples are 2475, 0865 and 3422.

   (i) How many different personal identification numbers can the bank use?

   (ii) If the bank decides not to use personal identification numbers that begin with 0, how many different numbers can it then use?

11. **(i)** How many different four-letter arrangements can be made from the letters of the word *FRIDAY* if each letter is used no more than once in each arrangement?

   (ii) How many of the above arrangements begin with the letter D and also end with a vowel?

12. **(i)** In how many ways can the letters of the word *IRELAND* be arranged if each letter is used exactly once in each arrangement?

   (ii) In how many of these arrangements do the three vowels come together?

   (iii) In how many of these arrangements do the three vowels come not together?

13. Six discs of equal size are stacked one on top of the other. There are two identical red discs and one each of blue, yellow, green and white.

In how many different ways can the six discs be stacked so that the two red discs are either at the top or at the bottom?

14. Five cars enter a car park. There are exactly five vacant spaces in the car park.

    (i) In how many different ways can the five cars park in the vacant spaces?

    (ii) Two of the cars leave the car park without parking. In how many different ways can the remaining three cars park in the five vacant spaces?

15. How many different whole numbers can be formed from the digits 1, 2 and 3?

16. (i) How many different sets of three books or of four books can be selected from six different books?

    (ii) How many of the above sets contain one particular book?

17. Eight people, including Kieran and Anne, are available to form a committee.
Five people must be chosen for the committee.

    (i) In how many ways can the committee be formed if both Kieran and Anne must be chosen?

    (ii) In how many ways can the committee be formed if neither Kieran nor Anne can be chosen?

18. Ten distinct points are taken on the circumference of a circle (as shown).

    (i) Calculate the number of different chords that can be formed using these points as end points.

    (ii) How many different triangles can be formed using these points as vertices?

    (iii) Calculate the number of different quadrilaterals that can be formed using these points as vertices.

    (iv) Two of the ten points are labelled x and y respectively. How many of the above quadrilaterals have x and y as vertices?

    (v) How many of the quadrilaterals do not have x and y as vertices?

19. In how many ways can a group of four people be selected from three men and four women?
In how many of these groups are there more women then men?

20. In how many ways can a group of five be selected from ten people?
How many groups can be selected if two particular people from the ten cannot be in the same group?

21. A student committee of four is being selected from five boys and three girls, from which at least one boy and one girl must be selected.

In how many different ways can the student committee be selected?

22. Nine friends wish to travel in a car. Only two of them, John and Mary, have licences to drive. Only five people can fit in the car (i.e. the driver and four others).

In how many ways can the group of five people be selected if:

    (i) both John and Mary are included   **(ii)** either John or Mary is included, but not both?

Later, another one of the nine friends, Anne, gets a driving licence.

    (iii) The next time the journey is made, in how many ways can the group of five be chosen, given that at least one licensed driver must be included?

23. Two unbiased dice, each with faces numbered from 1 to 6, are thrown.

    (i) What is the probability of getting a total equal to 8?

    (ii) What is the probability of getting a total less than 8?

24. There are 40 people in a club, 24 male, 16 female. Four of the males and two of the females wear glasses.

When a person is selected at random what is the probability that the person:

(i) is a male?

(ii) is a female not wearing glasses?

(iii) is a female wearing glasses or a male not wearing glasses?

(iv) is a male, given that the person wears glasses?

(v) does not wear glasses, given that the person is a female?

25. A bag contained 8 red, 12 blue and an unknown number of green beads. In a random draw the probability of drawing a green bead was $\frac{1}{5}$. How many green beads were in the bag at the start?

26. Three cards are drawn, one after the other, without replacement, from a pack of 52 playing cards. Find the probability that the first is a king, the second is an ace, and the third is neither an ace nor a king.

27. There are three balls in a bag, one green, one red, one blue. When a fair die is rolled a ball is also taken from the bag at random. What is the probability of:

(i) a red ball and a six?   (ii) a green ball and an even number?

28. There are six balls in a bag, numbered as follows: 1, 1, 2, 2, 4, 5.
Two of the balls are selected, at random, from the bag and the scores are added.
What is the probability that the total will be 6 or more?

29. A bag contains 5 red and 3 yellow discs only. When a disc is drawn from the bag, it is returned before the next draw. What is the probability that two draws will yield:

(i) both discs yellow?   (ii) both discs the same colour?

30. Two dice are thrown, one red and the other blue. Calculate the probability that the sum of the outcomes is even, if the 5 on the red die and the 2 on the blue die are excluded when forming an even sum.

31. The probability that a woman will hit the target with a single shot at a rifle range is $\frac{2}{5}$.
Find the probability that she first hits the target with her third shot.

1. The table below shows the prices of various commodities in the year 2000, as a percentage of their prices in 1999. These are called *price relatives*. (For example, the price relative for *Food, drink & other goods* is 105, indicating that the cost of these items was 5% greater in 2000 than in 1999.)

   The table also shows the weight assigned to each commodity. The weight represents the importance of the commodity to the average consumer.

Commodity	Weight	Price in 2000 as % of price in 1999
Housing	8	110
Fuel and transport	19	108
Tobacco	5	116
Services	16	105
Clothing & durable goods	10	97
Food, drink & other goods	42	105

   (i) Calculate the weighted mean of the price relatives in the table.

   (ii) Calculate, correct to two decimal places, the change in the weighted mean if *Tobacco* is removed from consideration.

2. The numbers x, y, 10, 12 and 16 have a mean of 14.
   If the numbers are given weights of 1, 3, 2, 1 and 3, respectively, the weighted mean is 16.
   Find the value of x and the value of y.

3. In the following frequency distribution the mean is 2. Find a relationship between a and b.

x	1	2	3	4
f	a	6	b	2

   In the following frequency distribution the mean is 3.5.

   Find a relationship between a and b.

x	0	2	4	6	8
f	3	a	7	b	2

   Hence, calculate the value of a and the value of b, if the values of a and b in the first frequency distribution are the same as the values of a and b in the second frequency distribution.

4. A, B, C, D, E and F represent six students. In how many ways can they be seated in a row if:
   (i) there are no restrictions on the seating **(ii)** A and F must sit at each end of the row
   (iii) A and B must sit beside each other **(iv)** A and B must not sit beside each other
   (v) D, E and F must sit beside each other?

5. How many five-digit numbers can be formed in which the first and last digits are greater than 5, the three centre digits are identical and the last digit is odd?

6. (i) How many different three-digit numbers can be formed using the digits 0 to 9 inclusive, if no digit can be used more than once and zero cannot be the first digit?

(ii) If one of the digits must be 9, how many different numbers can be formed?

(iii) If the digits 3 and 9 cannot be used together, how many different numbers can be formed?

7.

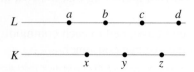

L and K are distinct parallel lines.

a, b, c and d are points on L such that $|ab| = |bc| = |cd| = 1$ cm.

x, y and z are points on K such that $|xy| = |yz| = 1$ cm.

(i) How many different triangles can be constructed using three of the named points as vertices?

(ii) How many different quadrilaterals can be constructed using four of the named points as vertices?

(iii) How many different parallelograms can be constructed using four of the named points as vertices?

(iv) If one quadrilateral is constructed at random, what is the probability that it is *not* a parallelogram?

8. How many bundles of 5 different books can be made from 8 Maths books and 6 Physics books, if the number of Maths books must always be greater than the number of Physics books?

9. A group of five is to be selected from 7 men and 4 women. How many groups can be formed? How many groups can be formed if the group must contain:

(i) no women   **(ii)** 3 men and 2 women   **(iii)** at least 3 women

(iv) at least one man and one woman?

10. A committee of 4 people is to be formed from a group of 7 men and 6 women.

(i) How many different committees can be formed?

(ii) On how many of these committees is there an equal number of men and of women?

(iii) On how many of these committees are there 2 or more women?

11. An examination has two sections, Section A containing 5 questions and Section B also containing 5 questions. A student must answer exactly 7 questions. Given that the student must answer at least 3 questions from Section A, find the number of ways in which the student may select the 7 questions.

12. Two balls are at the same time taken at random from a box containing three black, three red and three yellow balls.

Find the probability that:

(i) both balls are yellow   **(ii)** neither of the two balls is yellow

(iii) at least one of the two balls is yellow.

13. Two dice A and B are cast and the scores are added. What is the probability of getting:

(i) a total of two or a total of six?   **(ii)** a total greater than nine or a total which is prime?

(iii) a total which is three times as great as other possible totals?

14. Of five balls in a bag, one bears the number 1, another the number 3, two others the number 4 and one the number 6. Two balls are drawn together. If an outcome is the product of the numbers on the two balls, write out all the possible outcomes. Calculate the probability of an outcome of:

(i) 4   **(ii)** 6   **(iii)** 3 or 24.

15. To play a game, a player spins a wheel.

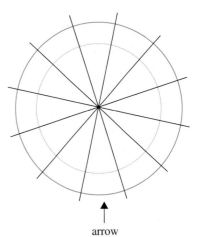

The wheel is fixed to a wall, and it spins freely around its centre point. Its rim is divided equally into twelve regions. Three of the regions are coloured red, four are coloured blue, and five are coloured green.

When the wheel stops an arrow fixed to the wall points to one of the regions. All the regions are equally likely to stop at the arrow. The colour of the region to which the arrow points is the outcome of the game.

When the game is played twice, calculate the probability that:

(i) both outcomes are green

(ii) both outcomes are the same colour

(iii) the first outcome is red and the second outcome is green

(iv) one outcome is green and the other outcome is blue.

arrow

16. Nine discs were each given a natural number from two to ten inclusive, each number different from the others. All nine were placed in a box.

(i) A disc was picked at random and replaced. A disc was then picked again. Find the probability that both discs showed prime numbers.

(ii) Three discs were picked at random. What is the probability that three odd-numbered discs or three even-numbered discs were picked?

17. A bag contains 20 marbles, 8 of which are white and the remainder black. Three marbles are removed at random, one at a time, without replacement. Find the probability that:

(i) all are black   **(ii)** at least one is white.

18. A bag contains 4 red and 2 blue discs only. When a disc is drawn from the bag, it is returned before the next draw. What is the probability that two draws will yield:

(i) boths discs red   **(ii)** both discs the same colour   **(iii)** discs with different colours?

19. There are seven white and four black beads in a bag. A bead is picked at random and not replaced. A second bead is then picked.

(i) Find the probability that both beads are the same colour.

The two beads are returned to the bag and three red beads are added. Three beads are then picked at random without replacement. Find the probability that:

(ii) all three beads are different in colour

(iii) at least two beads of the same colour are picked.

20. Three cards are drawn, at random and without replacement, from a pack of 52 playing cards. Find the probability that:

    (i) the three cards drawn are the Jack of clubs, the Queen of clubs and the King of clubs

    (ii) the three cards are aces

    (iii) two cards are black and one card is a diamond

    (iv) the three cards are of the same colour.

21. Sarah and Jim celebrate their birthdays in a particular week (Monday to Sunday inclusive). Assuming that the birthdays are equally likely to fall on any day of the week, what is the probability that:

    (i) Sarah's birthday is on Friday?

    (ii) Sarah's birthday and Jim's birthday are both on Friday?

22. Of the 100 tickets sold in a raffle, 40 were red, 30 were blue and 30 were green. The winning ticket is drawn at random.

    (i) Find the probability that: **(a)** it is red   **(b)** it is not blue.

    (ii) Every red ticket is even numbered, while every blue ticket is odd numbered; of the green tickets, 20 are even numbered and 10 are odd numbered. Find the probability that the winning ticket is: **(a)** green or even-numbered   **(b)** green, given that it is odd.

    (iii) A ticket is drawn and then replaced. If three such tickets are drawn, what is the probability that at least two are red?

23. A classroom contains 15 desks which are arranged in rows. The front row contains 3 desks. 15 students are seated at random in the classroom, 8 of whom are boys and 7 of whom are girls. Each desk seats only one student.

    What is the probability that:

    (i) three girls occupy the front row of desks?

    (ii) there are more boys than girls seated in the front row?

    (iii) there are two girls and one boy seated in the front row, with the two girls seated next to each other?

24. A box contains eleven balls numbered 1 to 11. Two balls are selected at random from the box. Given that the sum of the numbers of the two selected balls is even, find the probability that the numbers on each of the selected balls are both odd.

25. Solve the difference equation $2u_{n+2} - 11u_{n+1} + 5u_n = 0$, $n \geqslant 0$, if $u_0 = 2$ and $u_1 = -8$.

26. (i) Solve the difference equation $u_{n+2} - 4u_{n+1} + 3u_n = 0$, where $n \geqslant 0$, given that $u_0 = -2$ and $u_1 = 4$.

    (ii) Verify that the solution you have obtained in **(i)** satisfies the difference equation.

27. Solve the difference equation $4u_{n+2} - 25u_{n+1} - 29u_n = 0$, where $n \geqslant 0$, given that $u_0 = 0$ and $u_1 = 16.5$.

28. (i) Solve the difference equation $12u_{n+2} - 8u_{n+1} + u_n = 0$, where $n \geqslant 0$, given that $u_0 = \frac{1}{15}$ and $u_1 = \frac{7}{30}$.

    (ii) Hence, express u_3 in the form $\dfrac{p}{q}$, where $p, q \in \mathbf{N}$.

29. Solve the difference equation $u_{n+2} - 2u_{n+1} - 6u_n = 0$, where $n \geqslant 0$, given that $u_0 = 0$ and $u_1 = 14$.

30. Solve the difference equation $u_{n+2} - 4u_{n+1} + u_n = 0$, $n \geqslant 0$, where $u_0 = 4$ and $u_1 = 8$.

31. Solve the difference equation $u_{n+2} - 8u_{n+1} + 11u_n = 0$, where $n \geqslant 0$, given that $u_0 = 0$ and $u_1 = 2\sqrt{15}$.

32. Solve the difference equation $u_{n+1} - 2u_n - 53u_{n-1} = 0$, $n \geqslant 1$, where $u_0 = 0$ and $u_1 = 6$.

33. If the general solution of the difference equation $2u_{n+2} - ku_{n+1} + 5u_n = 0$ is $u_n = l(\frac{1}{2})^n - m(5)^n$, for $l, m \in \mathbf{R}$, find the value of $k \in \mathbf{R}$. Find the particular solution if $u_0 = 2$ and $u_1 = -8$.

34. The solution of the difference equation $u_{n+2} + hu_{n+1} + ku_n = 0$ is $p(3)^n + q(5)^n$.
    Find the value of h and the value of k.
    If $u_1 = 23$ and $u_2 = 49$, find the value of p and the value of q.

35. u_n is one solution of the difference equation $u_{n+2} - 2u_{n+1} + ku_n = 0$, for $n \geqslant 0$.
    (i) If $u_n = (1 + \sqrt{3})^n$, find the value of k.
    (ii) If $u_0 = 0$ and $u_1 = 10\sqrt{3}$, find the unique solution.

36. Verify that $u_n = 2(6)^n - 3(3)^n$ is a solution of the difference equation $u_{n+2} - 9u_{n+1} + 18u_n = 0$, for $n \geqslant 0$.
    If $u_5 = 3^p(2^q - 3)$, find the value of p and the value of q, $p, q \in \mathbf{N}$.

37. Show that $u_n = 3^n(pn + q)$, $p, q \in \mathbf{R}$, is a solution of the difference equation
    $$u_{n+2} - 6u_{n+1} + 9u_n = 0.$$

38. Prove that if α and β are the roots of the quadratic equation
    $$px^2 + qx + r = 0, \text{ and}$$
    $$u_n = l\alpha^n + m\beta^n \text{ for all } n, \text{ then:}$$
    $$pu_{n+2} + qu_{n+1} + ru_n = 0 \text{ for all } n.$$

39. The mean of the following frequency distribution is x, where $x \in \mathbf{N}$.

x	1	2	3	4
f	1	3	$x+1$	5

(i) Find the value of x.   (ii) Express the standard deviation in the form $\sqrt{\dfrac{a}{b}}$, $a, b \in \mathbf{N}$.

40. Verify that the mean, $\bar{x}$, of the following distribution is 4.

x	2	3	4	5	6
f	1	5	k	3	2

If the standard deviation, σ, is 1, find the value of k.

41. Show that the mean of the following distribution is independent of the value of x, and find the mean:

Number	1	2	3	4	5	6
Frequency	9	9	x	4	7	3

If the standard deviation is $\sqrt{2.6}$, find the value of x.

Exercise 5R.C ▼

1. A whole number between 100 and 1000 is to be formed so that one of the digits is 3, and no repetitions are allowed. How many numbers are possible?
(Note: If 3 is not the first digit, then the first digit cannot be 0.)

2. The following data give the age and gender of twenty-five pupils in a class on a given day:

	Boys	Girls
Number of pupils aged sixteen years	5	7
Number of pupils aged seventeen years	7	6

(i) One of the pupils is picked at random. What is the probability that a boy aged sixteen years or a girl aged seventeen years is picked?

(ii) Each pupil in the class is given his/her examination results. Only three pupils scored full marks. Determine the probability that these three pupils are of the same age and the same gender.

3. Nine discs were each given a natural number from 2 to 10 inclusive, each number different from the others. All nine were placed in a box.

(i) A disc was picked at random and replaced. A disc was then picked again. Find the probability that both discs showed prime numbers.

(ii) Three discs were picked at random. What was the probability that three odd-numbered discs or three even-numbered discs were picked?

4. A palindromic number is one that reads the same backwards as forwards, such as 727 or 38183.

(i) The year 2002 is a palindromic year. What will be the next palindromic year?

(ii) How many palindromic years are there from 1000 to 9999 inclusive?

(iii) A whole number, greater than 9 and less than 10,000, is selected at random. What is the probability that the number is palindromic?

5. Ten discs, each marked with a different whole number from 1 to 10, are placed in a box. Three of the discs are drawn at random (without replacement) from the box.

(i) What is the probability that the disc with the number 7 is drawn?

(ii) What is the probability that the three numbers on the discs drawn are odd?

(iii) What is the probability that the product of the three numbers on the discs drawn is even?

(iv) What is the probability that the smallest number on the discs drawn is 4?

6. There are seven white and four black beads in a bag. A bead is picked at random and not replaced. A second bead is then picked.

   (i) Find the probability that both beads are the same colour.

   The two beads are returned to the bag and three red beads are added. Three beads are then picked at random without replacement.

   Find the probability that:

   (ii) all three beads are different in colour

   (iii) at least two beads of the same colour are picked.

7. Six red discs, numbered from 1 to 6, and four green discs, numbered from 7 to 10, are placed in box A.

   Ten blue discs, numbered from 1 to 10, are placed in box B.

   Two discs are drawn from box A and two discs are drawn from box B. The four discs are drawn at random and without replacement.

   Find the probability that the discs drawn are:

   (i) two red discs and two even-numbered blue discs

   (ii) one red disc, one green disc and two blue discs with all four discs odd numbered

   (iii) one red disc, one green disc and two blue discs, with the total on the red and green discs equal to 10 and the total on the blue discs also equal to 10.

8. A bag contains ten discs, numbered from 1 to 10 inclusive. A disc is drawn from the bag and returned. A second disc is then drawn. What is the probability that the product of the two numbers on the discs is between 30 and 40?

9. There were 100 discs in a bag, each having one of the 100 natural numbers from 1 to 100 printed on it. There was a different number on each disc. Forty numbers were red. The rest were black. Twenty-six of the black numbers were even.

   (i) How many red discs had even numbers?

   (ii) If a disc was selected at random, what was the probability that its number was odd, given that it was red?

   (iii) A disc was drawn and replaced. Then a disc was drawn again. Find the probability that the first had a red number, given that it was odd, and that the second had an odd number, given that it was black.

10. A bag contains m red discs and n blue discs. If a disc is taken at random from the bag, the probability that it is red is $\frac{3}{7}$. Write down an equation in m and n.

   If there had been 5 more red discs in the bag, the probability that the disc selected was red would have been $\frac{1}{2}$. Find the value of m and the value of n.

11. Three students have their birthdays in the same week. What is the probability that:

   (i) none has their birthday on a Sunday **(ii)** all have their birthdays on a Tuesday or Wednesday

   (iii) all have their birthdays on the same day   **(iv)** all the birthdays fall on different days

   (v) at least two of them have their birthdays on the same day?

12. In a class of 24 students, there are 14 boys and 10 girls.

In a particular week (Monday to Sunday inclusive), three students celebrate their birthdays. Assume that the birthdays are equally likely to fall on any day of the week and that the birthdays are independent of each other:

What is the probability that these three students:

(i) are three boys or three girls

(ii) have birthdays falling on different days of the week or on the same day of the week other than Monday?

13. On an unbiased die, the numbers 1, 3 and 4 are coloured red and the numbers 2, 5 and 6 are coloured black.

(i) The die is thrown once. Find the probability of getting an even number or a red number.

(ii) The die is thrown three times with the following outcome:

the second throw shows a red number, and the sum of the numbers on the first and second throws is equal to the number on the third throw.

Find the probability of this outcome.

14. A student takes two tests, A and B. The probability of passing in test A is $\frac{1}{2}$ and the probability of passing in test B is $\frac{2}{3}$. The probability of passing in both tests is $\frac{1}{3}$. Find the probability of passing in at least one of the two tests.

15. A box contains four silver coins, two gold coins and x copper coins. Two coins are picked at random, and without replacement, from the box.

(i) Write down an expression in x for the probability that the two coins are copper.

If it is known that the probability of picking two copper coins is $\frac{4}{13}$:

(ii) how many coins are in the box

(iii) what is the probability that neither of the two coins picked is copper?

16. A drawer contains 5 red and x blue biros. One is drawn at random and not replaced. Another is then drawn at random. If the probability that both were blue was $\frac{1}{6}$, how many blue biros were in the drawer?

17. An unbiased coin is tossed five times. What is the probability that the outcome is:

(i) two heads and three tails   **(ii)** at least two heads?

18. Consider the numbers: 1, k, $3k-2$, 9, where $k \in \mathbf{Z}$.

The mean of these numbers is $\bar{x}$. The standard deviation is σ.

(i) Express $\bar{x}$ in terms of k.   **(ii)** Given that $\sigma = \sqrt{20}$, find the value of k.

19. 5, k, $3k-8$ and 15 are four numbers.

(i) Express the mean, $\bar{x}$, in terms of k.

(ii) If the standard deviation, σ, is $\sqrt{17}$, find the two values of k.

20. The real numbers 3, 4, 6, a and b have a mean of $\bar{x}$ and a standard deviation of σ.

(i) If $\bar{x} = 6$, express b in terms of a.

(ii) If $\sigma^2 = 6$, calculate the value of a and the value of b, $a < b$.

21. The data in the set $\{1, 2, 5, x, y\}$ have a mean of 5.

Express, in terms of x: **(i)** y **(ii)** σ, the standard deviation of the data.

If the standard deviation is $\sqrt{\dfrac{99}{10}}$, find the value of x and the value of y.

22. The mean of the real numbers a and b is $\bar{x}$. The standard deviation is σ.
     (i)   Express σ in terms of a, b and $\bar{x}$.   **(ii)** Hence, express σ in terms of a and b only.
     (iii) Show that $\bar{x}^2 - \sigma^2 = ab$.

23. The numbers a, b, c have a mean of $\bar{x}$ and a standard deviation of σ.
     (i) Express $\bar{x}$ in terms of a, b and c.   **(ii)** Show that: $\sigma^2 = \dfrac{1}{3}(a^2 + b^2 + c^2) - (\bar{x})^2$.

24. The three real numbers p, q and r have a mean of $\bar{x}$ and a standard deviation of σ.
     (i)   Express $\bar{x}$ in terms of p, q and r.

     (ii)   Show that: $\sigma^2 = \frac{1}{3}(p^2 + q^2 + r^2) - \frac{1}{9}(p + q + r)^2$.

     (iii) If $p = 1$, $q = 4$ and $\sigma^2 = 6$, find the value of r, $r > 0$.

25. The ten real numbers $a_1, a_2, a_3, \ldots, a_{10}$ have a mean of 3 and a standard deviation of σ.
If $a_1^2 + a_2^2 + a_3^2 + \cdots + a_{10}^2 = 100$, evaluate σ.

26. The numbers a, $3a$, b, $2b$ have a mean of $2b$ and a standard deviation of σ.
     (i)   Express b in terms of a.   **(ii)** Express σ in terms of a.
     (iii) Find the range of values of a for which $\sigma^2 < 18.5$.

27. The set of numbers a, b, c and d have a mean of $\bar{x}$ and a standard deviation of σ.
Show that the set of numbers $5a$, $5b$, $5c$ and $5d$ have:
     (i) a mean $= 5\bar{x}$ **(ii)** a standard deviation $= 5\sigma$.

28. The mean of the real numbers q, r, s and t is $\bar{x}$ and the standard deviation is σ.
Consider the numbers: $\beta q + \alpha$, $\beta r + \alpha$, $\beta s + \alpha$ and $\beta t + \alpha$, where β, $\alpha \in \mathbf{R}$ and $\beta > 0$.
     (i)   Show that the mean of these numbers is $\beta \bar{x} + \alpha$.
     (ii) Show that the standard deviation of these numbers is $\beta \sigma$.

29. Prove that if $\bar{x}_1$ and σ_1 are the mean and standard deviation of the set $\{x_1, x_2, x_3, \ldots, x_r\}$, and $\bar{x}_2$ and σ_2 are the mean and standard deviation of the set $\{kx_1, kx_2, kx_3, \ldots, kx_r\}$, then:
     (i) $\bar{x}_2 = k\bar{x}_1$ **(ii)** $\sigma_2 = k\sigma_1$.

30. A and B play a game which can result in a win for A, a win for B or a draw. The probability of a win for A is k and the probability of a win for B is $2k$.
     (i)   Find, in terms of k, the probability of a draw.
     (ii) The game is played twice.
         (a)   Show that the probability of the same outcome occurring in both games is $14k^2 - 6k + 1$.
         (b)   Given that the probability that A and B each wins one game is 0.36, find the value of k.

31. A bag contains four blue discs and three red discs. Three discs are selected at random. Find the probability that they are blue, given that all three are the same colour.

32. 4 books are selected at random from 3 history, 5 French and 2 art books. Find the probability that the 4 books chosen will contain at least one of each type.

33. Bag A contains three gold coins and two silver coins. Bag B contains four gold coins and five silver coins.

   (i) A coin is picked at random from each bag and then returned to the bag from which it was picked.

   What is the probability that one of the coins picked is gold and the other silver?

   (ii) A coin is picked at random from bag A and placed in bag B. A coin is then picked at random from bag B and placed in bag A.

   These two operations are performed again, in the same order. What is the probability that bag A now contains five gold coins?

34. Box A contains 2 red balls and 5 black balls. Box B contains 3 red balls and 2 black balls.

   A box is chosen at random. A ball is drawn from this box and placed in the other box, from which a ball is then drawn.

   Find the probability that:

   (i) the first ball drawn is red

   (ii) both balls drawn are the same colour, given that there is an equal probability of selecting box A or box B.

35. Two persons look at the letters in the word *DISCOVERY*. Independently of one another, each person writes down two of the letters from the word *DISCOVERY*.

   What is the probability that:

   (i) one person writes down two vowels and the other person two consonants

   (ii) the two persons write down different letters: that is, they have no letters in common?

36. When a biased die is thrown a score of 1 is twice as likely as a score of 2, and a score of 2 is twice as likely as a score of 3. Scores of 3, 4, 5 and 6 are equally likely.

   Find the probability of a score of: **(i)** 6   **(ii)** 1.

   If then a fair die is thrown simultaneously with the biased die, calculate the probability of a total score of 8.

37. A die is loaded so that the probability of a particular number being thrown is proportional to that number, so that $P(1) = k$, $P(2) = 2k$, $P(3) = 3k$, etc.

   Find the probability that: **(i)** 1 is thrown   **(ii)** 3 or 4 is thrown.

38. In the sequence 0, 1, 1, 2, 3, 5, 8, . . . u_n, u_{n+1}, u_{n+2}, . . . , each term is the sum of the two previous terms.

   (i) Write down the difference equation which represents the sequence.

   (ii) Solve the difference equation, given that $u_0 = 0$ and $u_1 = 1$.

39. In a game played between two players, A and B, the first and second rounds consist of each player drawing a ticket from a bag, and subsequent rounds consist of finding the average of the previous two scores for that player. The game continues until it becomes obvious that one or other player will have the higher eventual score. If A drew tickets 1 and 100 in the first and second rounds, respectively, and B drew tickets 90 and 51, express each score in round n, i.e. u_n, as a function of n and, hence, determine the winner.

40. (i) Solve the difference equation $6u_{n+2} - 5u_{n+1} - u_n = 0$, where $n \geqslant 0$, given that $u_0 = 5$ and $u_1 = 2$.

(ii) Find an expression in n for the sum of the terms $u_0 + u_1 + u_2 + \cdots + u_n$.
(Hint: it is the sum of two geometric series.)

(iii) Evaluate the sum to infinity of this series (that is: $\displaystyle\sum_{n=0}^{\infty} u_n$).

41. $\{x_1, x_2, x_3, x_4, \cdots, x_n\}$ is a set of numbers such that $x_1 < x_2 < x_3 < \cdots < x_n$.

Prove that $x_1 < \bar{x} < x_n$.

42. Real numbers x_1, x_2 and x_3 are each greater than a and less than b, as shown on the number line.

$$a \underset{\underset{\displaystyle a}{}}{\rule{0pt}{0pt}} \overset{\displaystyle x_1 \quad x_2 \qquad x_3}{\rule{5cm}{0.4pt}} \underset{}{} b$$

Prove that:

(i) $a < \bar{x} < b$, where $\bar{x}$ is the mean of x_1, x_2 and x_3.

(ii) $\sigma \leqslant b - a$, where σ is the standard deviation of x_1, x_2 and x_3.

43. Find $\sigma(x)$, the standard deviation of 0, x, 1.

Show that $\sigma(x) = \sigma(1 - x)$ for all $x \in \mathbf{R}$.

Show that in $0 \leqslant x \leqslant 1$, the minimum value of $\sigma(x)$ is $\dfrac{1}{\sqrt{6}}$.

REVISION EXERCISE 6   OPTION: FURTHER CALCULUS AND SERIES

Paper 2, Question 8

This revision exercise covers Chapter 8.

Exercise 6R.A ▼

1. Use the Ratio Test to show that $\displaystyle\sum_{n=1}^{\infty} \frac{n}{2^n}$ is convergent.

2. Use integration by parts to find $\displaystyle\int xe^x \, dx$.

3. $f(x) = f(0) + f^{(1)}(0)x + \dfrac{f^{(2)}(0)}{2!}x^2 + \dfrac{f^{(3)}(0)}{3!}x^3 + \cdots$ is the Maclaurin series.

   Write the Maclaurin series for $f(x) = e^x$ up to the term containing x^4. Hence, find an approximation for e correct to four decimal places.

4. Use integration by parts to find $\displaystyle\int x \ln x \, dx$.

5. Use the Ratio Test to show that $\displaystyle\sum_{n=1}^{\infty} \frac{(n+1)}{2^n}$ is convergent.

6. Use integration by parts to find $\displaystyle\int x \cos x \, dx$.

7. Use the Ratio Test to show that $\displaystyle\sum_{n=1}^{\infty} \frac{(n+2)!}{2^{n+2}}$ is divergent.

8. Use integration by parts to find the indefinite integral $\displaystyle\int xe^{2x} \, dx$.

9. Use the Ratio Test to show that $\displaystyle\sum_{n=1}^{\infty} \frac{x^n}{n!}$ is convergent for all $x \in \mathbf{R}$.

10. Use integration by parts to find $\displaystyle\int xe^{-x} \, dx$.

11. Use integration by parts to find $\displaystyle\int xe^{-5x} \, dx$.

12. Use integration by parts to evaluate $\displaystyle\int_0^{\pi/4} x \sin 2x \, dx$.

13. Show that $\displaystyle\int_1^e \frac{1}{x^2} \ln x \, dx = 1 - \frac{2}{e}$.

14. Find the range of values of x for which the series $\displaystyle\sum_{n=1}^{\infty} \frac{x^n}{n.3^n}$ is:

    (i) convergent   **(ii)** divergent.

15. If $x + y = 12$, find the maximum value of $x^2 + y^2 + 3xy$.

    Give a reason why your result is a maximum.

16. If $xy = 9$, find the minimum value of $x^2 + 6y + 5$.

17. A garden is to be L-shaped, as shown. Its perimeter is 36 m.

    (i) Express x in terms of y.

    (ii) Express the area of the garden in terms of y.

    (iii) Find the value of x and the value of y that
            maximise the area of the garden.

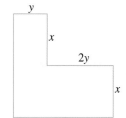

18. A piece of wire 32 cm long is bent into the shape of a rectangle. Show that for the rectangle to have maximum area, the rectangle will be a square.

19. If $f(x) = \dfrac{1}{x}$, find the expression $f^{(n)}(x)$, the nth derivative of $f(x)$.

20. Use the Ratio Test to show that the series $\displaystyle\sum_{n=0}^{\infty} n!(x-k)^n$ is convergent only for $x = k$.

21. Let $f(x) = 1 - x + \dfrac{x^2}{2!} - \dfrac{x^3}{3!} + \dfrac{x^4}{4!} + \cdots + (-1)^n \dfrac{x^n}{n!} + \cdots$

    Show that $\dfrac{df(x)}{dx} = af(x)$, $a \in \mathbf{R}$. Find the value of a.

    Express $f(x)$ in a simpler form.

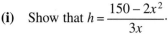

Exercise 6R.B ▼

1. Show that: **(i)** $\displaystyle\int_1^e x \ln x \, dx = \tfrac{1}{4}(e^2 + 1)$ **(ii)** $\displaystyle\int_0^1 x^2 e^{2x} \, dx = \tfrac{1}{4}(e^2 - 1)$.

2. The diagram shows a block with a
base measuring $2x$ cm by x cm and a height of h cm.
The total surface area of the block is 300 cm^2.

    (i) Show that $h = \dfrac{150 - 2x^2}{3x}$.

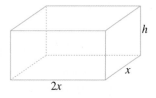

    (ii) Express the volume of the block in terms of x.

    (iii) Find the value of x that gives the block of maximum
            volume, and calculate this maximum volume.

3. $f(x) = f(0) + f^{(1)}(0)x + \dfrac{f^{(2)}(0)}{2!}x^2 + \dfrac{f^{(3)}(0)}{3!}x^3 + \cdots$ is the Maclaurin series.

(i) Derive the Maclaurin series for $f(x) = \sin x$, up to and including the term containing x^7.

(ii) Write down the general term and use the Ratio Test to show that the series converges for all $x \in \mathbf{R}$.

4. Evaluate $\displaystyle\int_0^\pi e^x \sin x \, dx$.

5. A rectangular sheet of cardboard measures 40 cm by 25 cm. Four equal squares are cut from each corner and the flaps are turned up to form an open box. Find the length of the side of the square which makes the volume of the box as large as possible. Find this largest volume.

6. $f(x) = f(0) + f^{(1)}(0)x + \dfrac{f^{(2)}(0)}{2!}x^2 + \dfrac{f^{(3)}(0)}{3!}x^3 + \cdots$ is the Maclaurin series.

(i) Derive the Maclaurin series for $f(x) = e^x$, up to the term containing x^3.

(ii) Write down the first four non-zero terms of the series expansions of:

(a) e^{-x} **(b)** e^{2x} **(c)** e^{-2x} **(d)** $(1+2x)e^{2x}$.

(iii) Write down the first three non-zero terms in the series expansions for:

(a) $e^x - (1+x)$ **(b)** $e^x - e^{-x}$ **(c)** $\frac{1}{4}(e^{2x} - e^{-2x})$.

(iv) Evaluate $\displaystyle\lim_{x \to 0} \dfrac{x^2}{e^x - (1+x)}$.

7. Evaluate $\displaystyle\int_0^{\pi/2} x^2 \cos x \, dx$.

8. The slant length of a right circular cone is 10 cm, as shown in the diagram.

Find the maximum volume of the cone, in terms of π.

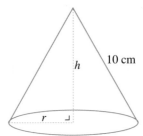

9. $f(x) = f(0) + f^{(1)}(0)x + \dfrac{f^{(2)}(0)}{2!}x^2 + \dfrac{f^{(3)}(0)}{3!}x^3 + \cdots$ is the Maclaurin series.

(i) Derive the Maclaurin series for $f(x) = \cos x$, up to and including the term containing x^6.

(ii) Write down the first four non-zero terms in the series expansions for:

(a) $\cos 2x$ **(b)** $9x \cos 2x$.

(iii) Hence, write down the general term of the Maclaurin series for $f(x) = \cos x$.

(iv) Use the Ratio Test to show that the series converges for all $x \in \mathbf{R}$.

10. The perimeter of a sector of a circle of radius r is 8 metres.

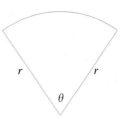

   (i) Express θ in terms of r, where θ is the angle of
     the sector in radians, as shown in the diagram.

   (ii) Hence, show that the area of the sector, in square metres,
     is $4r - r^2$.

   (iii) Find the maximum possible area of the sector.

11. A closed rectangular box is made of thin metal. The length of the box is three times its width. The volume of the box is 36 cm^3 and its width is x cm.

Show that the surface area is $\left(6x^2 + \dfrac{96}{x}\right)$ cm^2.

Find the dimensions of the box with the least surface area.

12. A cylinder with an open top has a capacity of 512π cm^3.

   (i) Find the total surface area in terms of r.

   (ii) If the surface area is to be a minimum, what will be the dimensions of the cylinder?

13. In the diagram $ab \perp bc$.
The lengths of the sides can vary
but, in every case, $ab \perp bc$
and $|ab| + |bc| = 20$ cm. Find
the maximum area of the triangle.
(You do not need to test for a maximum.)

14. (i) Use integration by parts to find $\displaystyle\int e^{-x}\cos x \, \mathrm{d}x$.

   (ii) The diagram shows part of the graph of the
     curve $y = e^{-x}\cos x$.
     Calculate the area of the shaded region.

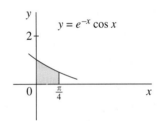

15. (i) Use integration by parts to find $\displaystyle\int e^{2x}\cos x \, \mathrm{d}x$.

   (ii) Given that $\displaystyle\int_0^{\pi/2} e^{2x}\cos x \, \mathrm{d}x = \dfrac{1}{n}(e^{\pi} - 2)$, find the value of n, where $n \in \mathbf{N}$.

16. (i) Write down the first four non-zero terms in the series expansion for $\ln(1 + x)$.

   (ii) Deduce the first four non-zero terms of the series expansion of $\ln(1 - 3x)$.

   (iii) Find the first three non-zero terms of $\ln(1 + x)(1 - 3x)$.
     (Hint: $\ln AB = \ln A + \ln B$.)

1. Use the Ratio Test to find the values of x for which the series

   $$\sum_{n=1}^{\infty} \frac{(x+3)^n 2^{n+1}}{5^n . n^2} \quad \text{converges,} \quad x \in \mathbf{R}.$$

2. If $f(n) = \int x^n e^x \, dx$, prove that $f(n) = x^n e^x - nf(n-1)$. Hence, or otherwise, evaluate $\int_0^1 x^3 e^x \, dx$.

3. **(i)** Find the value of x for which $\ln\left(\frac{1+x}{1-x}\right) = \ln \frac{3}{2}$.

   (ii) $f(x) = f(0) + f^{(1)}(0)x + \frac{f^{(2)}(0)}{2!}x^2 + \frac{f^{(3)}(0)}{3!}x^3 + \cdots$ is the Maclaurin series.

   Derive the Maclaurin series for $\ln(1+x)$, up to the term containing x^5.

   (iii) Write down the Maclaurin series for $\ln(1-x)$, up to the term containing x^5, and write down

   the first three non-zero terms in the series expansion of $\ln\left(\frac{1+x}{1-x}\right)$. Use these three terms to

   find an approximate value of $\ln \frac{3}{2}$, correct to two decimal places.

4. A closed cylindrical can of radius r and height h
   has a constant volume, V.
   (i) Express h in terms of V and r.

   (ii) Show that the surface area, A, is given by

   $$A = \frac{2V}{r} + 2\pi r^2.$$

   (iii) Find the ratio $r:h$ for which the surface
   area is a minimum.

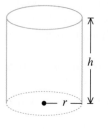

5. The diagram shows part of the graph of the curve
   $y = x \sin 2x$. The graph meets the x-axis at the
   origin, 0, and at a.
   (i) Find the coordinates of the point a.
   (ii) Find the area of the shaded region.

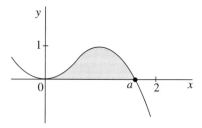

6. $f(x) = f(0) + f^{(1)}(0)x + \frac{f^{(2)}(0)}{2!}x^2 + \frac{f^{(3)}(0)}{3!}x^3 + \cdots$ is the Maclaurin series.

   (i) Derive the Maclaurin series for $f(x) = \frac{1}{(1-x)^2}$, up to the term containing x^3.

   (ii) Hence, write down the general term of the Maclaurin series for $f(x) = \frac{1}{(1-x)^2}$.

   (iii) Use the Ratio Test to find the values of x for which the series is convergent.

7. A cylindrical can is made so that the sum of its height and the circumference of its base is 45π cm.
   Find the radius of the base of the cylinder if the volume of the can is to be a maximum.

8. The diagram shows a minor sector *opq* of a circle of radius *r* cm. The perimeter of the sector is 100 cm and the area of the sector is A cm^2.

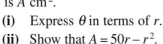

(i) Express θ in terms of *r*.

(ii) Show that $A = 50r - r^2$.

Find:

(iii) the value of *r* for which A is a maximum

(iv) the value of θ, in radians, for this maximum value of A

(v) the maximum area of the sector *opq*.

9. $f(x) = f(0) + f^{(1)}(0)x + \dfrac{f^{(2)}(0)}{2!}x^2 + \dfrac{f^{(3)}(0)}{3!}x^3 + \cdots$ is the Maclaurin series.

(i) **(a)** Write the first four terms of the Maclaurin series for $f(x) = \sqrt{1+x}$.

(b) Write down the values of *x* for which the series converges.

(ii) Write out the first 4 terms of the Maclaurin expansion for $\sqrt{1-2x}$. Use the result to estimate $\sqrt{0.98}$ correct to five decimal places.

(iii) Use the first four terms of the Maclaurin series for $f(x) = \sqrt{1+x}$ to evaluate $\sqrt{10}$, correct to one place of decimals.

10. A manufacturer determines that the total cost of producing *q* units of a certain product is given by: $C = \frac{1}{4}q^2 + 3q + 400$.

(i) Express, in terms of *q*, the average cost of the product per unit.

(ii) Find the value of *q* for which the average cost per unit will be a minimum.

11. Find the area of the largest isosceles triangle that can be drawn above the *x*-axis, with one vertex at the origin and with another on the curve $y = 27 - x^2$ and with a side parallel to the *x*-axis.

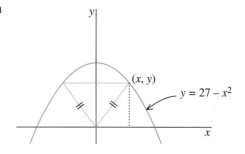

12. $f(x) = f(0) + f^{(1)}(0)x + \dfrac{f^{(2)}(0)}{2!}x^2 + \dfrac{f^{(3)}(0)}{3!}x^3 + \cdots$ is the Maclaurin series.

(i) Derive the Maclaurin series for e^x, as far as the term containing x^3.

(ii) Hence, find the first four terms of the series expansion of e^{-2x}.

(iii) Find the values of *a*, *b* and *c* if the first three terms of the series expansion of $(a + bx)e^{-2x}$ are $2 - 7x + cx^3$, $a, b, c \in \mathbf{Z}$.

13. The cost of a trip is €800 per student for a group consisting of exactly 50 students. If fewer than 50 people wish to travel, the trip will be cancelled. However, for each additional reservation over 50, the cost will be decreased by €10 for every student. How many reservations will result in the largest revenue?

14. The Maclaurin series for $\tan^{-1} x$ is $x - \dfrac{x^3}{3} + \dfrac{x^5}{5} - \dfrac{x^7}{7} + \cdots$

The series is convergent when $|x| < 1$.

(i) Write down the first four terms in the series expansion for $\tan^{-1} \dfrac{1}{2}$.

(ii) Use the fact that $\tan^{-1} \dfrac{1}{2} + \tan^{-1} \dfrac{1}{3} = \dfrac{\pi}{4}$ to derive a series expansion for π,

giving the terms up to and including seventh powers.

(iii) Use these terms to find an approximation for π.
Give your answer correct to four decimal places.

15. The shape of a playing field is a rectangle with semi-circular ends.
The rectangle has dimensions of x m by $2r$ m.

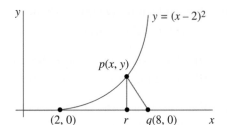

(i) If the area of the rectangle is $3{,}200\,\pi$ m^2, express r in terms of x.

(ii) Show that the perimeter, P m, is given by:

$$P = 2x + \frac{3200\pi^2}{x}$$

(iii) Find the minimum value of P.

16. $p(x, y)$ is a point on the curve $y = (x - 2)^2$ in the domain $2 < x < 8$.
q is the point $(8, 0)$ and $pr \perp rq$.

(i) Express, in terms of x, the area of the triangle prq.

(ii) What value of x maximises the area of triangle prq?

(iii) Find the maximum area of triangle prq.

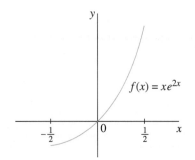

17. (i) Write down, in ascending powers of x, the first three non-zero terms of the Maclaurin series of: **(a)** e^x **(b)** $\sin x$ **(c)** $\ln(1 - x)$.

(ii) The first two non-zero terms of $[e^x + \ln(1 - x)]$ are $a + bx^3$, $a, b \in \mathbf{R}$.
Find the value of a and the value of b.

(iii) Find, in ascending powers of x, the first three non-zero terms in the Maclaurin series expansion

of $e^x \sin x$. Use these three terms to approximate $\displaystyle\int_0^1 e^x \sin x \, dx$, writing your answer as a fraction.

18. The diagram shows the graph of $f(x) = xe^{2x}$

in the domain $-\dfrac{1}{2} \leqslant x \leqslant \dfrac{1}{2}$.

(i) Find $\displaystyle\int xe^{2x} \, dx$.

(ii) $\displaystyle\int_{-1/2}^{0} xe^{2x} \, dx = A_1$ and $\displaystyle\int_{0}^{1/2} xe^{2x} \, dx = A_2$.

Find the value of A_1 and the value of A_2.

(iii) Show that $A_1 : A_2 = (2 - e) : e$.

19. A line, L, contains the point $(-1, 2)$ and has a slope of m, where $m > 0$.

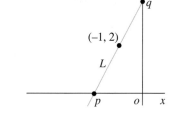

    (i) Write the equation of L in the form $ax + by + c = 0$.

    (ii) L intercepts the x-axis at p and the y-axis at q. Find, in terms of m, the coordinates of p and q.

    (iii) Show that the area of triangle opq is given by $A = \dfrac{(m+2)^2}{2m}$, where o is the origin.

    (iv) Find the minimum value of A.

20. A rectangle is bounded by the semi-circle with equation $y = \sqrt{50 - x^2}$, where $-5\sqrt{2} \leqslant x \leqslant 5\sqrt{2}$, and the x-axis.

Find the dimensions of the rectangle having the largest area and write down this maximum area.

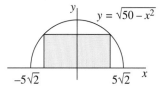

21. o is the origin, $(0, 0)$.

$p(x, y)$ is a point on the curve $y = \dfrac{9}{x}$, where $x > 0$.

$|op|$ is the distance from the origin to p.

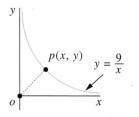

    (i) Express $|op|$ in terms of x.

    (ii) Given that there is one value of x for which $|op|$ is a minimum, find this value of x.

    (iii) Hence, find the minimum value of $|op|$.

22. Find $f(0), f^{(1)}(0), f^{(2)}(0), f^{(3)}(0)$ for $f(x) = (1+x)^m$.

Hence, write the first four terms and the $(r+1)$th term of the Maclaurin series for $f(x) = (1+x)^m$. Test the series for convergence when $m \in \mathbf{Q} \backslash \mathbf{N}$.

23. A cone, radius r and height h, is inscribed in a sphere, radius R.

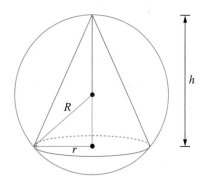

    (i) Find the height of the cone of maximum volume which can be inscribed in the sphere.

    (ii) If $R = 9$ cm, find the maximum volume of the cone in terms of π.

24. A tank with a base is made from thin, uniform metal. The tank, standing on level ground, is in the shape of an upright circular cylinder and hemispherical top with radius of length r metres. The height of the cylinder is h metres.

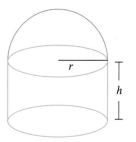

    (i) If the total surface area of the tank is $45\pi \,\mathrm{m}^2$, express h in terms of r.

    (ii) Find the value of h and of r for which the tank has maximum volume.

25. K is a circle with centre o.

a, b, c and d are points on K such that $abcd$ is a rectangle.

$|oa| = r$ cm; $|ab| = 2x$ cm and $|ad| = 2y$ cm.

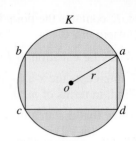

   (i) Express y in terms of x and r.

   (ii) Hence, or otherwise, show that the maximum area of $abcd$ is $2r^2$ cm^2.

26. Find the dimensions of the cylinder of maximum volume that can be inscribed in a sphere of fixed radius, a.

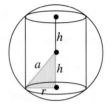

27. A window is in the shape of a rectangle surmounted by a semi-circle (called a 'roman arc'). The perimeter of the window is $(12 + 3\pi)$ metres. What width should the window be in order to maximise the area of the window?

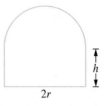

28. The point p is 4 km due east of the point o.

At noon, A leaves o and travels north at a steady speed of 12 km/h. At the same time, B leaves p and travels towards o at a steady speed of 6 km/h.

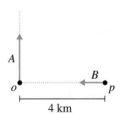

   (i) Write down expressions in x for the distances that A and B will each have travelled at x minutes after noon.

   (ii) Find an expression in x for the distance that B will be from A at x minutes after noon.

   (iii) At how many minutes after noon will B be closed to A?

29. A rectangle is inscribed in an ellipse, of centre $(0, 0)$, whose equation is:

$$\frac{x^2}{a^2} + \frac{y^2}{b^2} = 1.$$

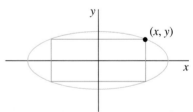

   (i) Show that the area of the rectangle is given by:

$$A = 4xy = \frac{4b}{a}\sqrt{a^2x^2 - x^4}.$$

   (ii) Hence, show that the maximum area of the rectangle is $2ab$.

30. A closed tin is to be constructed as shown. It is made up of a cylinder of base radius r and height h which is surmounted by a hemispherical cap.

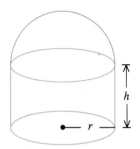

   (i) Find, in terms of r and h, an expression for:

      (a) its volume, V **(b)** its surface area, A.

   (ii) Given that $V = \pi k^2$, where $k \in \mathbf{R}$ and $k > 0$,

      show that $A = \dfrac{2\pi k^2}{r} + \dfrac{5\pi}{3}r^2.$

   (iii) If A is to be a minimum, find the ratio $r : h$.

31. A right circular cone 11 cm in height and of base diameter 8 cm is to enclose a cylinder (see two-dimensional diagram).

Express the height, h, of the cylinder in terms of its radius, r.

Find the maximum volume of the cylinder in terms of π.

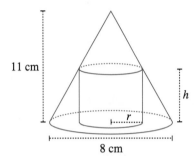

11 cm

h

8 cm

ANSWERS

1. $x^2+y^2=4$ **2.** $x^2+y^2=16$ **3.** $x^2+y^2=25$ **4.** $x^2+y^2=13$

5. $x^2+y^2=2$ **6.** $x^2+y^2=12$ **7.** $4x^2+4y^2=1$ **8.** $2x^2+2y^2=5$

9. $x^2+y^2=25$ **10.** $x^2+y^2=169$ **11.** $x^2+y^2=26$ **12.** $x^2+y^2=9$

13. $x^2+y^2=2$ **14.** $x^2+y^2=29$ **15.** 4   **16.** 10   **17.** 1   **18.** $\sqrt{13}$

19. $\sqrt{5}$ **20.** $\sqrt{29}$ **21.** $\frac{3}{2}$ **22.** $\frac{5}{3}$ **23.** $\frac{1}{4}$ **24.** $x^2+y^2=25$ **25.** $x^2+y^2=37$

26. $(-6, 3)$ **27.** 40π **28.** $x^2+y^2=5$ **29.** $x^2+y^2=17$ **30.** $x^2+y^2=10$

31. $x^2+y^2=26$ **32.** $x^2+y^2=8$ **33.** $x^2+y^2=20$

1. $(x-2)^2+(y-3)^2=16$ **2.** $(x+2)^2+(y+4)^2=25$ **3.** $(x+3)^2+(y-2)^2=10$

4. $(x+3)^2+y^2=13$ **5.** $4x^2+4(y-2)^2=9$ **6.** $4(x+1)^2+4(y-7)^2=25$

7. $(x-1)^2+(y-2)^2=10$ **8.** $(x-2)^2+(y+1)^2=41$ **9.** $(x+1)^2+(y-3)^2=5$

10. $(x+1)^2+(y+3)^2=25$ **11.** $(x+2)^2+(y+5)^2=45$ **12.** $(x-4)^2+(y+2)^2=20$

13. $(2, 3)$; 5   **14.** $(-1, 2)$; 3   **15.** $(5, -7)$; 1   **16.** $(-5, -7)$; 2

17. $(0, 5)$; $\sqrt{10}$ **18.** $(4, 0)$; $\sqrt{13}$ **19.** $(x-3)^2+(y-3)^2=5$ **20.** $(x+1)^2+(y-2)^2=13$

21. $(x-2)^2+(y-9)^2=25$ **22.** $(x-1)^2+(y-3)^2=25$ **23.** $(x+6)^2+(y-1)^2=8$

1. $x^2+y^2-2x-4y-4=0$ **2.** $x^2+y^2+4x-6y-12=0$ **3.** $x^2+y^2+6x+10y+17=0$

4. $x^2+y^2-4x-6=0$ **5.** $x^2+y^2+6y+1=0$ **6.** $2x^2+2y^2-2x+2y-9=0$

7. $x^2+y^2+2x-6y-10=0$ **8.** $x^2+y^2+6x+4y-12=0$ **9.** $(3, 4)$; 6   **10.** $(2, 3)$; 4

11. $(1, -2)$; 3   **12.** $(5, -1)$; $\sqrt{20}$ **13.** $(-4, 3)$; 5   **14.** $(-1, 5)$; 6

15. $(-3, 0)$; 4   **16.** $(0, 2)$; $\sqrt{8}$ **17.** $(\frac{1}{2}, \frac{3}{2})$; 3   **18.** $(\frac{1}{3}, -3)$; 2

19. $(-1, 3)$; 4   **20.** $(0, -4)$; $\sqrt{13}$ **21.** on   **22.** inside   **23.** outside

24. inside   **25.** on   **26.** outside   **27.** -6; 4   **28.** 1, 7   **29.** 6

30. (i) $(k, -2)$; $\sqrt{k^2 + 11}$ **(ii)** ± 5 **31.** ± 3 **32.** 11; $\sqrt{117}$

33. (i) (a) $5k^2 + 8k + 4$ **(b)** $5k^2 - 28k + 40$ **(ii)** $k = 1$; $x^2 + y^2 - 4x - 2y - 12 = 0$

Exercise 1.4 ▼

1. (i) (a) $\dfrac{y-5}{x-1}$ **(b)** $\dfrac{y+3}{x+5}$ **(ii)** $x^2 + y^2 + 4x - 2y - 20 = 0$

2. $x^2 + y^2 - 10x + 21 = 0$; centre $= (5, 0)$; radius $= 2$

3. $x^2 + y^2 + 4x + 2y - 11 = 0$; centre $= (-2, -1)$; radius $= 4$

4. $x^2 + y^2 - 2x + 6y + 1 = 0$; centre $= (1, -3)$; radius $= 3$

Exercise 1.5 ▼

1. $x^2 + y^2 = 4$ **2.** $x^2 + y^2 = 3$ **3.** $x^2 + y^2 - 2x - 4y + 4 = 0$

4. $x^2 + y^2 + 6x - 8y + 24 = 0$ **5.** $x^2 + y^2 - 6x - 10y + 30 = 0$ **6.** $x^2 + y^2 + 4x + 10y + 20 = 0$

7. $x^2 + y^2 - 2x + 4y - 11 = 0$ **8.** $x^2 + y^2 + 10x - 6y + 9 = 0$ **9.** $x^2 + y^2 - 6x + 10y + 32 = 0$

10. $x^2 + y^2 + 4x - 2y - 3 = 0$ **11.** $4x^2 + 4y^2 + 24x + 8y + 39 = 0$ **12.** $4x^2 + 4y^2 - 24x + 16y + 49 = 0$

13. $x^2 + y^2 = 9$; $r = 3$ **14.** $x^2 + y^2 = 4$; $r = 2$ **15.** $x^2 + y^2 = 16$; $r = 4$

16. $x^2 + y^2 = 4$; $r = 2$ **17.** $x^2 + y^2 = 1$; $r = 1$ **18.** $x^2 + y^2 = 9$; $r = 3$

19. $x^2 + y^2 - 2ax + 4ay - 4a^2 = 0$; centre $= (a, -2a)$; radius $= 3a$ **20.** $x^2 + y^2 = a^2$; radius $= a$

21. $x^2 + y^2 - 4x + 3 = 0$; $(2, 0)$; 1 **22.** $x^2 + y^2 - x = 0$; $(\frac{1}{2}, 0)$; $\frac{1}{2}$

Exercise 1.6 ▼

1. $(3, 1)$, $(-3, -1)$; no   **2.** $(3, 1)$, $(-1, 3)$; no   **3.** $(-1, 2)$, $(2, 1)$; no

4. $(4, -1)$; yes   **5.** $(1, 0)$, $(2, 1)$; no   **6.** $(-1, -1)$, $(3, 1)$; no

7. $(-4, 0)$; yes   **8.** $(-2, 1)$, $(7, 4)$; no   **9.** $(3, 2)$; yes

10. $(-2, -2)$; yes   **11.** $(4, 1)$, $(1, -4)$; no   **12.** $(6, 1)$; yes

13. $4\sqrt{5}$ **14. (i)** $a(-1, 0)$, $b(5, 2)$ **(ii)** yes

Exercise 1.7 ▼

1. $x^2 + y^2 - 6x - 10y + 24 = 0$ **2.** $x^2 + y^2 - 4x - 2y - 45 = 0$ **3.** $x^2 + y^2 - 4x + 8y = 0$

4. $x^2 + y^2 - 12x - 10y - 4 = 0$ **5.** $x^2 + y^2 - 2x - 9 = 0$ **6.** $x^2 + y^2 + 2x + 6y + 5 = 0$

1. $x^2+y^2-4x-6y+3=0$ **2.** $x^2+y^2+2x+4y-20=0$ **3.** $g=-2,\ f=1,\ c=-15$

4. $x^2+y^2-2x-4y-15=0$ **5.** $x^2+y^2-4x-4y-2=0$ **6.** $g=-2,\ f=3,\ c=-7$

1. $x^2+y^2-2x-2y-2=0;\ x^2+y^2-2x+6y-6=0$ **2.** $x^2+y^2+8x-8y+12=0;\ x^2+y^2-4x+4y-12=0$

3. $x^2+y^2+12x-6y+35=0;\ x^2+y^2+4x-2y-5=0$ **4.** $x^2+y^2+4x-6y=0;\ x^2+y^2-4x+6y=0$

5. (i) $(2,1),\ x-2y=0$ **(ii)** 5   **(iii)** $x^2+y^2-12x-6y+20=0;\ x^2+y^2+4x+2y-20=0$

6. $x^2+y^2+4x-2y-5=0;\ x^2+y^2-4x-10y+19=0$

1. $3x+y-10=0$ **2.** $2x-5y+29=0$ **3.** $7x+y+50=0$ **4.** $8x-6y-25=0$

5. $3x-y-25=0$ **6.** $5x-2y-19=0$ **7.** $2x+3y+22=0$ **8.** $x+2y-7=0$

9. $3x+4y-43=0$ **10.** $x+y-2=0$ **17.** 10   **18.** 8   **19.** 4   **20.** 5

21. $2\sqrt{5}$ **22.** $5\sqrt{2}$ **23.** 31

1. ±5 **2.** $-12,8$ **3. (i)** $-2,-12$ **(ii)** $\frac{1}{9},3$ **4.** $-2,\frac{1}{2}$ **5.** ±4

6. $4x-3y+25=0,\ 4x-3y-25=0$ **7.** $3x-y+10=0,\ 3x-y-10=0$

8. $2x-y-4=0,\ 2x-y+6=0$ **9.** $x+4y+22=0,\ x+4y-12=0$

10. $3x-4y+38=0,\ 3x-4y-12=0$ **11.** $-7,1$ **12.** $x-2y-5=0,\ x+2y-5=0$

13. $x-2y-10=0,\ 2x-y+10=0$ **14.** $y=0,\ 4x-3y=0$

15. $2x+y-4=0,\ x+2y+1=0$ **16.** $x-y+1=0,\ x+y-1=0$

17. $x-3y+5=0,\ 3x-y-1=0$ **18.** $(\frac{6}{5},\frac{8}{5})$

1. $x^2+y^2-4x-10y+4=0$ **2.** $x^2+y^2+6x-8y+16=0$ **4.** $x^2+y^2-10x-8y+25=0$

5. $x^2+y^2-10x-4y+4=0$ **6.** $x^2+y^2-4x-4y+4=0$

7. $x^2+y^2-6x-6y+9=0,\ x^2+y^2-30x-30y+225=0$

8. $x^2+y^2-2x-2y+1=0,\ x^2+y^2-10x-10y+25=0$

Exercise 1.13 ▼

1. $3 + 2 = 5$ **2.** $8 + 5 = 13$ **3.** $11 - 1 = 10$ **4.** $4\sqrt{5} - \sqrt{5} = \sqrt{45} = 3\sqrt{5}$

5. $5 + 5 = 10$; $(5, 5)$ **6.** $10 + 5 = 15$; $(-1, -3)$ **7.** $\sqrt{2} + 4\sqrt{2} = \sqrt{50} = 5\sqrt{2}$; $(2, -1)$

8. $4\sqrt{2} - \sqrt{2} = \sqrt{18} = 3\sqrt{2}$; $(2, 1)$ **9.** $2\sqrt{2} + \sqrt{2} = \sqrt{18} = 3\sqrt{2}$; $(-2, 2)$

10. $x^2 + y^2 - 24x - 10y + 88 = 0$ **11.** -19 **12.** $x^2 + y^2 - 10x - 4y - 7 = 0$

12. (i) $(7, 2)$ **(ii)** $x^2 + y^2 - 10x - 4y - 7 = 0$

Exercise 1.14 ▼

1. (i) $(-2, 0)$ and $(8, 0)$ **(ii)** $(0, 2)$ and $(0, -8)$ **2.** 6 **3.** 8 **4.** $x + y - 1 = 0$, $x - y + 3 = 0$

5. $x - y + 1 = 0$ **6.** $x + 3y + 2 = 0$ **7.** $x - 2y = 0$; $a(4, 2)$, $b(8, 4)$

8. $x - y + 7 = 0$; $a(-5, 2)$, $b(-3, 4)$ **9.** $(-3, 2)$ **10.** $h = -15$, $k = 45$

11. $x^2 + y^2 - 10x - 6y + 5 = 0$ **12.** $x^2 + y^2 - 4x - 9 = 0$ **13.** $x^2 + y^2 - 8x - 10y + 16 = 0$

14. $x^2 + y^2 - 8x - 4y + 4 = 0$ **15. (i)** $\sqrt{50}$ **(ii)** -10 **16.** $(-2, 1)$ **(i)** $3\sqrt{2}$ **(ii)** $\sqrt{26}$; $k = -21$

17. $x^2 + y^2 - 8x - 2y + 9 = 0$

Exercise 2.1 ▼

1. $2i$ **2.** $5i$ **3.** $7i$ **4.** $10i$ **5.** $4i$ **6.** $12i$ **7.** $3i$ **8.** $11i$

9. $20i$ **10.** $14i$ **11.** $13i$ **12.** $17i$ **13.** $2\sqrt{2}i$ **14.** $2\sqrt{3}i$ **15.** $3\sqrt{2}i$ **16.** $5\sqrt{2}i$

17. $4\sqrt{5}i$ **18.** $3\sqrt{7}i$ **19.** -1 **20.** $-i$ **21.** 1 **22.** i **23.** 1 **24.** -1

25. $-i$ **26.** -1 **27.** i **28.** -1 **29.** $-i$ **30.** 1 **32.** $-7 + 10i$

33. $-2 + 15i$ **34.** $-18 - i$ **35.** $-1 - 17i$ **36.** $-5 + 5i$ **37.** $0 - 12i$ **38.** $17 + 17i$

39. $8 - 64i$ **40.** $-13 + 10i$ **41.** 1 **42.** $-11 + 3i$

43. (i) $-16 - 11i$ **(ii)** $-5 + 12i$ **(iii)** $2 + 5i$ **(iv)** $11 - 16i$ **45.** $\frac{2}{3}$ **46.** $-\frac{5}{2}$

47. -2 **48. (i)** -2 **(ii)** 1 **49. (i)** -1 **(ii)** 4

Exercise 2.2 ▼

1. $2 + i$ **2.** $2 + 3i$ **3.** $1 + i$ **4.** $2 - 3i$ **5.** $\frac{1}{2} + \frac{1}{2}i$

6. $\frac{4}{5} - \frac{3}{5}i$ **7.** $\frac{4}{13} - \frac{7}{13}i$ **8.** $-\frac{1}{2} + \frac{7}{2}i$ **9.** $a = 3, b = 1$ **10.** 1

11. $1 + i$ **12. (i)** $-3 - 4i$ **(ii)** $-\frac{3}{25}$ **13.** $-\frac{1}{2}$ **14.** 1

15. (i) i **(ii)** 1 **(iii)** –1 **(iv)** i **(v)** $-i$ **16.** 64 **17.** 256

18. $\frac{1}{81}$ **19.** –1 **20.** $k = -\frac{1}{5}$

Exercise 2.3 ▼

1. $x = 2,\ y = 1$ **2.** $x = 3,\ y = 2$ **3.** $x = 15,\ y = -21$ **4.** $x = -5,\ y = 5$

5. $h = 3,\ k = 2$ **6.** $p = 4,\ q = -1$ **7.** $t = \frac{3}{5},\ k = 7$ **8.** $t = 10,\ k = 2$

9. $a = -\frac{4}{3},\ b = \frac{4}{3}$ **10.** $l = -2,\ k = -3$ **11.** $l = -2,\ p = 7$ **12.** $4 + 2i$

13. $4 - 3i$ **14.** $4 + 3i,\ 4 - 3i$ **15.** $5 - 5i,\ 5 + 2i$ **16.** $3 + 2i,\ 3 - i$

17. $a = 1,\ b = -3$ **18.** $a = 1,\ b = 4,$ or $a = -1,\ b = -4$

Exercise 2.4 ▼

11. $\sqrt{2}$ **12. (i)** 13 **(ii)** $\sqrt{34}$ **(iii)** $\sqrt{3}$ **(iv)** 2 **(v)** 4 **(vi)** $\frac{5}{2}$

(vii) 1 **(viii)** $\frac{1}{2}$ **13. (i)** $\frac{6}{5} - \frac{8}{5}i$ **(ii)** 2 **14. (i)** $\frac{1}{5}$ **(ii)** 1

15. $3 - 4i;\ h = 2,\ k = -\frac{2}{5}$ **16.** $k = \pm 6$ **17.** $a = \pm 5$

18. $k = 11,$ or $k = -9$ **19.** $15 + 8i$ or $-15 + 8i$ **20.** $w = \sqrt{2} + i$

Exercise 2.5 ▼

1. $1 \pm i$ **2.** $1 \pm 2i$ **3.** $-5 \pm 3i$ **4.** $\frac{1}{2} \pm \frac{1}{2}i$ **5.** $-\frac{3}{2} \pm \frac{1}{2}i$

6. $\frac{1}{5} \pm \frac{7}{5}i$ **7.** $2 + 2i,\ -1 + 2i$ **8.** $3 - i;\ -i$ **9.** $1 + 3i,\ 1 + 2i$

10. $1 + 3i,\ 1 - i$ **11.** $z^2 + 4z + 5 = 0$ **12.** $z^2 - 6z + 13 = 0$ **13.** $z^2 + 2z + 26 = 0$

14. $z^2 + 9 = 0$ **15.** $z^2 + 2z + 3 = 0$ **16.** $z^2 - 4z + 9 = 0$ **17.** $2z^2 + 2z + 1 = 0$

18. $9z^2 + 6z + 5 = 0$ **19.** $p = -6,\ q = 34$ **20.** $-2 + i,\ -2 - i$ **21.** $3 + 5i$

22. $a = -4,\ b = 13$ **23.** $a = 5,\ b = 2;\ 5 - i,\ 5 - 5i$ **24.** $1 + 2i$

25. $k = -4$ **26.** $p = 5,\ q = 7;\ 1 + 2i$ **27.** $p = -1,\ q = -13;\ -3 - 2i$

28. $a = 3,\ b = 5;\ 1 + 3i$ **29. (i)** $2 - 2i$ **(ii)** $4 - 2i$ **(iii)** $-8 - 4i;\ z^2 - 2z + 5 = 0$

Exercise 2.6 ▼

1. $1 + 4i,\ -1 - 4i$ **2.** $1 - 2i,\ -1 + 2i$ **3.** $3 - i,\ -3 + i$ **4.** $2 + 3i,\ -2 - 3i$

5. $4 - i,\ -4 + i$ **6.** $2 + 5i,\ -2 - 5i$ **7.** $3 - 4i,\ -3 + 4i$ **8.** $4 - 5i,\ -4 + 5i$

9. $1 + i,\ -1 - i$ **10.** $1 + 2i,\ -1 - 2i;\ 2 + i,\ 1 - i$ **11.** $1 + 5i,\ -1 - 5i;\ 2 + 4i,\ 1 - i$

12. $4+i$, $-4-i$; 1, $-3-i$ **13.** $2+i$, $-2-i$; -2, i

14. $x=3$, $y=-2$ or $x=-3$, $y=2$; **(i)** $-2+i$, $1-i$ **(ii)** $3+4i$, $-1-2i$

15. $\sqrt{3}-i$, $-\sqrt{3}+i$

Exercise 2.7 ▼

1. $1-2i$, -4 **2.** $-2-3i$, 5 **3.** $3+5i$, $3-5i$ **4. (i) (a)** $2i$ **(b)** $-2+2i$ **(ii)** $1-i$, 3

5. $1-3i$, 5 **6.** $-2-2i$, 1 **7.** $2+i$, -4 **8.** $2-3i$, $\frac{1}{2}$

9. ± 3 **10. (i) (a)** $-2i$ **(b)** $-2-2i$ **(ii)** $k=-4$; $1+i$, 2

11. $k=-3$; $1+2i$, 1 **12.** $a=-4$, $b=6$ **13.** $p=-6$, $q=34$

14. $a=-2$, $b=2$ **15.** $a=4$, $b=5$ **16. (i)** $(z-3)(z-2)$ **(iii)** $2, 3, -1-i$

17. (i) $(z-2)(z+2)$; $2, -2$ **(ii)** $2, -2, -3-i$ **18.** $k=\pm 3$; $3i$, $-3i$, $\frac{1}{2}$

Exercise 2.8 ▼

1. $\sqrt{2}\left(\cos\dfrac{\pi}{4}+i\sin\dfrac{\pi}{4}\right)$ **2.** $2\left(\cos\dfrac{\pi}{6}+i\sin\dfrac{\pi}{6}\right)$ **3.** $5(\cos\pi+i\sin\pi)$

4. $3\left(\cos\dfrac{\pi}{2}+i\sin\dfrac{\pi}{2}\right)$ **5.** $2\left(\cos\dfrac{3\pi}{2}+i\sin\dfrac{3\pi}{2}\right)$ **6.** $2\left(\cos\dfrac{4\pi}{3}+i\sin\dfrac{4\pi}{3}\right)$

7. $\sqrt{2}\left(\cos\dfrac{7\pi}{4}+i\sin\dfrac{7\pi}{4}\right)$ **8.** $2\sqrt{2}\left(\cos\dfrac{7\pi}{4}+i\sin\dfrac{7\pi}{4}\right)$ **9.** $2\left(\cos\dfrac{5\pi}{4}+i\sin\dfrac{5\pi}{4}\right)$

10. $2\sqrt{3}\left(\cos\dfrac{5\pi}{6}+i\sin\dfrac{5\pi}{6}\right)$ **11.** $\cos\dfrac{5\pi}{3}+i\sin\dfrac{5\pi}{3}$ **12.** $\cos\dfrac{3\pi}{4}+i\sin\dfrac{3\pi}{4}$

13. $0+i$ **14.** $1+i$ **15.** $-3+3\sqrt{3}$ **16.** $-2+2i$ **17.** $-5\sqrt{3}+5i$

18. $-1-\sqrt{3}i$ **19.** $2\left(\cos\dfrac{\pi}{2}+i\sin\dfrac{\pi}{2}\right)$ **20.** $\sqrt{2}\left(\cos\dfrac{\pi}{4}+i\sin\dfrac{\pi}{4}\right)$

21. $2\left(\cos\dfrac{11\pi}{6}+i\sin\dfrac{11\pi}{6}\right)$ **22.** $\dfrac{1}{2}\left(\cos\dfrac{\pi}{2}+i\sin\dfrac{\pi}{2}\right)$ **23.** $0-10i$

24. $4-4i$ **25.** 2 **26.** $1+\sqrt{3}i$ **27.** $\sqrt{2}\left(\cos\dfrac{7\pi}{4}+i\sin\dfrac{7\pi}{4}\right)$

Exercise 2.9 ▼

1. $1+0i$,   **2.** $-1+0i$ **3.** $0+i$ **4.** $0-i$ **5.** $64+0i$ **6.** $0-8i$

7. $-\frac{1}{2}+\frac{\sqrt{3}}{2}i$ **8.** $-\frac{\sqrt{3}}{2}-\frac{1}{2}i$ **9.** $2\left(\cos\dfrac{\pi}{6}+i\sin\dfrac{\pi}{6}\right)$; $0+8i$ **10.** $16+0i$

11. $-4+0i$ **12.** $0-8i$ **13.** $128+128i$ **14.** $0+64i$ **15.** $-128+128\sqrt{3}i$

16. $0 - i$ **17.** $-\frac{1}{2} - \frac{\sqrt{3}}{2}i$ **19.** $-\frac{1}{2} - \frac{\sqrt{3}}{2}i$ **20.** $\sqrt{2}\left(\cos\frac{\pi}{4} + i\sin\frac{\pi}{4}\right)$; $32i$

22. $\left(\cos\frac{11\pi}{6} + i\sin\frac{11\pi}{6}\right)$; -1

Exercise 2.10 ▼

1. $\dfrac{2\tan\theta}{1 - \tan^2\theta}$ **2.** $\dfrac{3\tan\theta - \tan^3\theta}{1 - 3\tan^2\theta}$ **3.** $\dfrac{4\tan\theta - 4\tan^3\theta}{1 - 6\tan^2\theta + \tan^4\theta}$

Exercise 2.11 ▼

1. $\cos\pi + i\sin\pi$; -1, $\frac{1}{2} + \frac{\sqrt{3}}{2}i$, $\frac{1}{2} - \frac{\sqrt{3}}{2}$ **2.** $8\left(\cos\frac{3\pi}{2} + i\sin\frac{3\pi}{2}\right)$; $2i$, $\sqrt{3} - i$, $-\sqrt{3} - i$

3. $-\sqrt{2} + \sqrt{2}i$, $\sqrt{2} - \sqrt{2}i$ **4.** $\sqrt{3} - i$, $-\sqrt{3} + i$ **5.** -2, $1 + \sqrt{3}i$, $1 - \sqrt{3}i$

6. $1, -1, i, -i$ **7.** $4i$, $2\sqrt{3} - 2i$, $-2\sqrt{3} - 2i$ **8.** $-3i$, $\frac{3\sqrt{3}}{2} + \frac{3}{2}i$, $-\frac{3\sqrt{3}}{2} + \frac{3}{2}i$

9. $\pm 2i$, $\pm(\sqrt{3} + i)$, $\pm(-\sqrt{3} + i)$ **10.** $16\left(\cos\frac{4\pi}{3} + i\sin\frac{4\pi}{3}\right)$; $\pm(1 + \sqrt{3}i)$, $\pm(\sqrt{3} - i)$

11. $\cos\frac{5\pi}{3} + i\sin\frac{5\pi}{3}$; $\pm i$ **12.** $4\left(\cos\frac{2\pi}{3} + i\sin\frac{2\pi}{3}\right)$; ± 8

13. $4\left(\cos\frac{\pi}{2} + i\sin\frac{\pi}{2}\right)$; $\pm(16\sqrt{2} + 16\sqrt{2}i)$

Exercise 3.1 ▼

1. (i) $\begin{pmatrix} 5 & 5 \\ 7 & 12 \end{pmatrix}$ (ii) $\begin{pmatrix} 1 & -3 \\ 1 & -2 \end{pmatrix}$ (iii) $\begin{pmatrix} 6 & 2 \\ 8 & 10 \end{pmatrix}$ (iv) $\begin{pmatrix} 6 & 12 \\ 9 & 21 \end{pmatrix}$ (v) $\begin{pmatrix} 0 & 10 \\ 1 & 11 \end{pmatrix}$

2. (i) $\begin{pmatrix} -2 & -1 \\ 1 & 2 \end{pmatrix}$ (ii) $\begin{pmatrix} 15 & -3 \\ -8 & 18 \end{pmatrix}$ (iii) $\begin{pmatrix} 5 & -8 \\ -5 & 20 \end{pmatrix}$

3. (i) $\begin{pmatrix} 2 & 9 \\ 0 & 12 \end{pmatrix}$ (ii) $\begin{pmatrix} 2 & 3 \\ -8 & 8 \end{pmatrix}$ (iii) $\begin{pmatrix} -2 & -15 \\ -8 & -16 \end{pmatrix}$ (iv) $\begin{pmatrix} 4 & 21 \\ 4 & 26 \end{pmatrix}$; $\begin{pmatrix} 1 & 6 \\ 2 & 7 \end{pmatrix}$ **4.** $\begin{pmatrix} 8 & 1 \\ 6 & -1 \end{pmatrix}$

5. $\begin{pmatrix} 6 & 5 \\ -5 & 8 \end{pmatrix}$ **6.** $p = -5$, $q = -2$, $r = -6$, $s = -13$ **7.** $a = -3$, $b = 5$, $c = 2$, $d = -6$

8. $x = 4$, $y = 3$ **9.** $x = 5$, $y = -1$ **10.** $x = 3$, $y = -4$ **11.** $x = 4$, $y = -7$

12. $a = 4$, $b = 3$ or $a = -4$, $b = 11$ **13.** $a = 5$, $b = -2$ **14.** $x = 4$, $y = -2$, $p = -6$, $q = 8$

15. $l = 1$, $m = -1$ **16.** $a = 3$, $b = -2$

1. (i) $\begin{pmatrix} 6 & 10 \\ 23 & 36 \end{pmatrix}$ (ii) $\begin{pmatrix} -25 & -1 \\ 34 & -7 \end{pmatrix}$ (iii) $\begin{pmatrix} 5 \\ -11 \end{pmatrix}$ (iv) 1 **2.** (i) $\begin{pmatrix} 2 & -5 \\ 6 & 0 \end{pmatrix}$ (ii) $\begin{pmatrix} 6 & 9 \\ -6 & -4 \end{pmatrix}$

(iii) $\begin{pmatrix} 3 & 2 \\ 4 & 11 \end{pmatrix}$ (iv) $\begin{pmatrix} 6 & -6 \\ -4 & 10 \end{pmatrix}$ **3.** (i) $\begin{pmatrix} 4 \\ 18 \end{pmatrix}$ (ii) 3 (iii) 4

4. (i) $\begin{pmatrix} 1 & 10 \\ -1 & 25 \end{pmatrix}$ (ii) $\begin{pmatrix} 9 & -1 \\ 11 & 6 \end{pmatrix}$ (iii) $\begin{pmatrix} 1 & -13 \\ 18 & 13 \end{pmatrix}$ (iv) $\begin{pmatrix} -17 & -24 \\ 19 & -16 \end{pmatrix}$ **8.** $k = 5$

9. $p = 1; q = -3$ **10.** $x = 2, y = 5$ **11.** $x = 4, y = 3$

12. (i) $\begin{pmatrix} 1 & 0 \\ 0 & 1 \end{pmatrix}$ (ii) $\begin{pmatrix} 1 & 0 \\ 0 & 1 \end{pmatrix}$ **13.** $\lambda = 1$ **14.** $x = 4, y = -2$

15. $x = -2, y = 7$ **16.** $x = \pm 4$ **17.** $5x^2 + 16xy + 13y^2$ **18.** (i) 11 (ii) 4

19. (i) 2 (ii) -2 **20.** $\begin{pmatrix} 1 & 0 \\ 0 & 1 \end{pmatrix}$

1. 2; $\frac{1}{2}\begin{pmatrix} 4 & -5 \\ -2 & 3 \end{pmatrix}$ **2.** 5; $\frac{1}{5}\begin{pmatrix} 2 & -3 \\ -1 & 4 \end{pmatrix}$ **3.** 11; $\frac{1}{11}\begin{pmatrix} 5 & -2 \\ -2 & 3 \end{pmatrix}$

4. $-4; -\frac{1}{4}\begin{pmatrix} 2 & -6 \\ -1 & 1 \end{pmatrix}$ **5.** 5; $\frac{1}{5}\begin{pmatrix} 1 & 1 \\ -2 & 3 \end{pmatrix}$ **6.** 1; $\begin{pmatrix} 2 & 5 \\ 1 & 3 \end{pmatrix}$

7. 20; $\frac{1}{20}\begin{pmatrix} 4 & 2 \\ 0 & 5 \end{pmatrix}$ **8.** 5; $\frac{1}{5}\begin{pmatrix} -1 & 2 \\ -3 & 1 \end{pmatrix}$ **9.** $\begin{pmatrix} 2 & -1 \\ 5 & -3 \end{pmatrix}$

10. $\frac{1}{5}\begin{pmatrix} 1 & -2 \\ 1 & 3 \end{pmatrix}$ **11.** (i) $\frac{1}{2}\begin{pmatrix} 2 & -1 \\ -4 & 3 \end{pmatrix}$ (ii) $\frac{1}{3}\begin{pmatrix} 2 & 1 \\ 5 & 4 \end{pmatrix}$ **12.** $\begin{pmatrix} 1 & 2 \\ 2 & -1 \end{pmatrix}$

13. $\frac{1}{2}B$ **14.** $\begin{pmatrix} -3 & 2 \\ -1 & 3 \end{pmatrix}$ **15.** (i) $X = A^{-1}B$ (ii) $\begin{pmatrix} 11 & -18 \\ -28 & 46 \end{pmatrix}$

16. $a = 15, b = 9, c = -9, d = 24$ **17.** (i) $\begin{pmatrix} 3 & 2 \\ -1 & -1 \end{pmatrix}$ (ii) $p = 4, q = 2$

18. (i) $\begin{pmatrix} 4 & 1 \\ 1 & 0 \end{pmatrix}$ (ii) $\begin{pmatrix} 7 & 1 \\ 1 & 3 \end{pmatrix}$ **19.** (i) $\begin{pmatrix} -4 & -7 \\ 3 & 4 \end{pmatrix}$ (ii) $\begin{pmatrix} -2 & -7 \\ 3 & 6 \end{pmatrix}$

20. $k = -4$ **21.** $x = 1$ **22.** (i) $\begin{pmatrix} 3 & 5 \\ 1 & 2 \end{pmatrix}\begin{pmatrix} x \\ y \end{pmatrix} = \begin{pmatrix} 27 \\ 10 \end{pmatrix}$ (ii) $\begin{pmatrix} 2 & -5 \\ -1 & 3 \end{pmatrix}$ (iii) $x = 4, y = 3$

23. (i) $\begin{pmatrix} 3 & -2 \\ 5 & -4 \end{pmatrix}\begin{pmatrix} x \\ y \end{pmatrix} = \begin{pmatrix} -16 \\ -30 \end{pmatrix}$ (ii) $-\frac{1}{2}\begin{pmatrix} -4 & 2 \\ -5 & 3 \end{pmatrix}$ (iii) $x = -2, y = 5$

24. $x=1, y=2$ **25.** $x=-2, y=3$ **26.** $x=4, y=2$

27. $x=-2, y=-5$ **28.** $x=5, y=-6$ **29.** $x=3, y=\sqrt{2}$

Exercise 3.4 ▼

1. $\begin{pmatrix} 32 & 0 \\ 0 & 243 \end{pmatrix}$ **2.** $\begin{pmatrix} 1 & 0 \\ 0 & 64 \end{pmatrix}$ **3.** $\begin{pmatrix} -2187 & 0 \\ 0 & 128 \end{pmatrix}$ **4.** $\begin{pmatrix} 1 & 0 \\ 0 & 65536 \end{pmatrix}$

5. (i) $\begin{pmatrix} 1 & 0 \\ 0 & 4 \end{pmatrix}$ **(ii)** $\begin{pmatrix} 1 & 0 \\ 0 & 8 \end{pmatrix}$ **(iii)** $\begin{pmatrix} 1 & 0 \\ 0 & 32 \end{pmatrix}$ **6.** $\begin{pmatrix} 1 & 0 \\ 0 & -2 \end{pmatrix}$

7. $5\begin{pmatrix} 3 & 0 \\ 0 & 4 \end{pmatrix}$ **8.** $\begin{pmatrix} -1 & 0 \\ 0 & 1024 \end{pmatrix}$ **9.** $\begin{pmatrix} 1296 & 0 \\ 0 & 1 \end{pmatrix}$ **10.** $\begin{pmatrix} -2 & 2 \\ 2 & 1 \end{pmatrix}$

11. $\begin{pmatrix} 4 & 3 \\ 3 & -4 \end{pmatrix}$ **12. (i)** $\dfrac{1}{2}\begin{pmatrix} 3 & 1 \\ -1 & -1 \end{pmatrix}$ **(ii)** $\begin{pmatrix} 1 & -1 \\ -1 & -3 \end{pmatrix}$ **(iii)** $\begin{pmatrix} 1 & 0 \\ 0 & -1 \end{pmatrix}$ **(iv)** $\begin{pmatrix} 1 & 0 \\ 0 & -1 \end{pmatrix}$

13. (i) $\begin{pmatrix} 1 & 2 \\ 1 & 1 \end{pmatrix}$ **(ii)** $\begin{pmatrix} 1 & 2 \\ -1 & -1 \end{pmatrix}$ **(iii)** $\begin{pmatrix} -1 & 0 \\ 0 & 1 \end{pmatrix}; \begin{pmatrix} 3 & 4 \\ -2 & -3 \end{pmatrix}; \begin{pmatrix} 1 & 0 \\ 0 & 1 \end{pmatrix}$

14. (i) $\dfrac{1}{3}\begin{pmatrix} 2 & 1 \\ -1 & -2 \end{pmatrix}$ **(ii)** $\begin{pmatrix} 1 & 0 \\ 0 & -2 \end{pmatrix}$ **(iii)** $\begin{pmatrix} 1 & 0 \\ 0 & -128 \end{pmatrix}; \begin{pmatrix} 44 & 86 \\ -86 & -171 \end{pmatrix}$

15. (i) $\dfrac{1}{2}\begin{pmatrix} 1 & 1 \\ 1 & -1 \end{pmatrix}$ **(ii)** $\begin{pmatrix} 1 & 0 \\ 0 & -3 \end{pmatrix}$ **(iii)** $\begin{pmatrix} 1 & 0 \\ 0 & 81 \end{pmatrix}; \begin{pmatrix} 41 & -40 \\ -40 & 41 \end{pmatrix}$

16. (i) $-\dfrac{1}{4}\begin{pmatrix} 1 & -1 \\ -5 & 1 \end{pmatrix}$ **(ii)** $\begin{pmatrix} 1 & 0 \\ 0 & -3 \end{pmatrix}$ **(iii)** $\begin{pmatrix} -304 & 61 \\ -305 & 62 \end{pmatrix}$

17. $a=-2, b=-1; \begin{pmatrix} -3 & 0 \\ 0 & 2 \end{pmatrix}; \begin{pmatrix} -69 & -399 \\ 266 & 862 \end{pmatrix}$

Exercise 4.1 ▼

1. (i) $\overrightarrow{ed}$ **(ii)** $\overrightarrow{af}$ **(iii)** $\overrightarrow{bc}$ **(iv)** $\overrightarrow{ea}$ **(v)** $\overrightarrow{ec}$ **(vi)** $\overrightarrow{ef}$ **(vii)** $2\overrightarrow{ab}$ or $2\overrightarrow{ed}$

2. (i) $\overrightarrow{xz}$ **(ii)** $\overrightarrow{xg}$ or $\overrightarrow{gz}$ **(iii)** $\overrightarrow{xz}$ **(iv)** $\overrightarrow{yz}$ or $\overrightarrow{xw}$

3. (i) $\overrightarrow{su}$ or $\overrightarrow{tv}$ **(ii)** $\overrightarrow{sr}$ or $\overrightarrow{tu}$ **(iii)** $\overrightarrow{sv}$

4. (i) $\overrightarrow{ab}$ or $\overrightarrow{by}$ or $\overrightarrow{xd}$ or $\overrightarrow{dc}$ **(ii)** $\overrightarrow{ay}$ or $\overrightarrow{xc}$ **(iii)** $\overrightarrow{xb}$ or $\overrightarrow{dy}$ **(iv)** $\overrightarrow{xz}$ or $\overrightarrow{zy}$ **(v)** $\overrightarrow{xc}$ or $\overrightarrow{ay}$
　(vi) $\overrightarrow{xc}$ or $\overrightarrow{ay}$ **(vii)** $\overrightarrow{dc}$ or $\overrightarrow{xd}$ or $\overrightarrow{ab}$ or $\overrightarrow{by}$

5. (i) $\overrightarrow{ae}$ **(ii)** $\overrightarrow{bd}$ or $\overrightarrow{cf}$ **(iii)** $\overrightarrow{be}$ or $\overrightarrow{af}$ **(iv)** $\overrightarrow{bc}$ or $\overrightarrow{ce}$ or $\overrightarrow{ad}$ or $\overrightarrow{df}$

6. $2\overrightarrow{u}+\overrightarrow{v}$ **7. (i)** $\overrightarrow{a}+\overrightarrow{b}$ **(ii)** $\frac{1}{2}\overrightarrow{a}+\frac{1}{2}\overrightarrow{b}$ **(iii)** $\frac{1}{2}\overrightarrow{a}-\frac{1}{2}\overrightarrow{b}$ **(iv)** $\frac{1}{2}\overrightarrow{a}$
　(v) $\frac{1}{2}\overrightarrow{a}+\frac{1}{2}\overrightarrow{b}$ **(vi)** $\overrightarrow{b}$ **(viii)** $2\overrightarrow{a}+3\overrightarrow{b}$

Exercise 4.2 ▼

1. (i) $3\overrightarrow{ab}$ **(ii)** $\frac{2}{3}\overrightarrow{ac}$; $k=-2$ **2.** $\frac{3}{7}\overrightarrow{p}+\frac{4}{7}\overrightarrow{q}$ **3. (i)** $\overrightarrow{a}$

(ii) (a) $\overrightarrow{a}+\overrightarrow{c}$ **(b)** $\frac{1}{2}\overrightarrow{a}+\frac{1}{2}\overrightarrow{c}$ **(c)** $\overrightarrow{a}+\frac{1}{2}\overrightarrow{c}$ **(iii)** $\frac{1}{2}\overrightarrow{c}$ **4. (i)** $\frac{1}{2}\overrightarrow{q}$ **(ii)** $\frac{1}{2}\overrightarrow{p}+\frac{1}{2}\overrightarrow{r}$ **(iii)** $-\frac{1}{2}\overrightarrow{p}+\overrightarrow{q}-\frac{1}{2}\overrightarrow{r}$

5. (i) $\overrightarrow{p}+\overrightarrow{r}$ **(ii)** $\frac{1}{2}\overrightarrow{p}+\overrightarrow{r}$ **(iii)** $\overrightarrow{p}+\frac{2}{3}\overrightarrow{r}$ **(iv)** $-\frac{1}{2}\overrightarrow{p}+\frac{1}{3}\overrightarrow{r}$

6. (i) $\frac{1}{3}\overrightarrow{p}+\frac{2}{3}\overrightarrow{q}$ **(ii)** $-\frac{1}{6}\overrightarrow{p}+\frac{2}{3}\overrightarrow{q}$ **7. (i) (a)** $\frac{1}{2}\overrightarrow{q}$ **(b)** $\frac{1}{2}\overrightarrow{q}-\frac{3}{8}\overrightarrow{p}$ **(ii)** $k=\frac{3}{8}$

8. (i) $\frac{1}{3}\overrightarrow{p}+\frac{1}{3}\overrightarrow{r}$ **(ii)** 3 **9. (i)** $-\frac{3}{5}\overrightarrow{a}-\overrightarrow{c}$ **(ii)** $h=-\frac{1}{5}$, $k=-1$

10. (i) $\frac{1}{2}\overrightarrow{p}$ **(ii) (a)** $\overrightarrow{r}+\frac{1}{2}\overrightarrow{p}$ **(b)** $\frac{2}{3}\overrightarrow{r}-\frac{1}{3}\overrightarrow{p}$

12. $\dfrac{m}{m+n}\overrightarrow{a}$ **(ii)** $\dfrac{m}{m+n}\overrightarrow{b}$ **(iii)** $\overrightarrow{b}-\overrightarrow{a} \parallel \dfrac{m}{m+n}(\overrightarrow{b}-\overrightarrow{a})$

Exercise 4.3 ▼

1. (i) $\frac{2}{3}\overrightarrow{a}$ **(ii) (a)** $\frac{1}{2}\overrightarrow{a}+\frac{1}{2}\overrightarrow{b}$ **(b)** $\frac{2}{3}\overrightarrow{a}-\overrightarrow{b}$ **(iii)** $x=\frac{4}{5}$, $y=\frac{3}{5}$

(iv) (a) $4:5$ **(b)** $3:2$

2. (i) $\frac{1}{2}\overrightarrow{a}+\overrightarrow{c}$ **(ii)** $-\overrightarrow{a}+\frac{1}{2}\overrightarrow{c}$ **(iii)** $h=\frac{4}{5}$ and $k=\frac{3}{5}$ **(iv) (a)** $4:1$ **(b)** $3:5$

3. (i) $\frac{1}{5}\overrightarrow{a}+\frac{4}{5}\overrightarrow{b}$ **(ii)** $-\overrightarrow{a}+\frac{1}{4}\overrightarrow{b}$ **(iii)** $h=\frac{5}{17}$, $k=\frac{16}{17}$

4. (i) $\frac{1}{5}\overrightarrow{a}+\overrightarrow{c}$ **(ii)** $\frac{1}{5}k\overrightarrow{a}+k\overrightarrow{c}$ **(iv)** $k=\frac{5}{6}$ and $t=\frac{1}{6}$

5. (i) $\overrightarrow{b}-\overrightarrow{c}$ **(ii)** $\frac{3}{4}\overrightarrow{b}+\frac{1}{4}\overrightarrow{c}$ **(iii)** $\frac{5}{3}\overrightarrow{c}-\overrightarrow{b}$ **(iv)** $m=\frac{4}{9}$, $n=\frac{2}{3}$

Exercise 4.4 ▼

1. (i) $15\overrightarrow{i}-9\overrightarrow{j}$ **(ii)** $2\overrightarrow{i}-4\overrightarrow{j}$ **(iii)** $3\overrightarrow{i}+\overrightarrow{j}$ **(iv)** $-4\overrightarrow{i}-3\overrightarrow{j}$ **(v)** $-6\overrightarrow{i}+5\overrightarrow{j}$

(vi) $-8\overrightarrow{i}-3\overrightarrow{j}$ **(vii)** $16\overrightarrow{i}-11\overrightarrow{j}$ **(viii)** $16\overrightarrow{i}-10\overrightarrow{j}$ **(ix)** $10\overrightarrow{i}-2\overrightarrow{j}$ **(x)** $4\overrightarrow{i}-\overrightarrow{j}$

2. $\overrightarrow{i}$; $-3\overrightarrow{i}-4\overrightarrow{j}$ **3.** $5\overrightarrow{i}-\overrightarrow{j}$ **4.** $2\overrightarrow{i}-4\overrightarrow{j}$ **5.** $-3\overrightarrow{i}+5\overrightarrow{j}$

6. $\overrightarrow{p}=3\overrightarrow{i}-3\overrightarrow{j}$; $\overrightarrow{q}=\overrightarrow{i}-\overrightarrow{j}$ **7.** $\overrightarrow{x}=-2\overrightarrow{j}$; $\overrightarrow{y}=5\overrightarrow{i}-\overrightarrow{j}$ **8.** $-\overrightarrow{i}-4\overrightarrow{j}$

9. $6\overrightarrow{i}$ **10.** $\frac{1}{4}\overrightarrow{a}+\frac{3}{4}\overrightarrow{b}$; $5\overrightarrow{i}+6\overrightarrow{j}$ **11.** $a=-2$, $b=3$ **12.** $p=5$, $q=2$

13. $h=2$, $k=-3$ **14.** $k=5$, $t=-2$ **15.** $p=2$, $q=-3$ **16.** $h=3$, $k=5$

17. $\overrightarrow{p}=7\overrightarrow{i}+6\overrightarrow{j}$, $\overrightarrow{q}=6\overrightarrow{i}+8\overrightarrow{j}$; $h=-2$, $k=3$ **18.** 3 **19. (i)** $-2\overrightarrow{i}+5\overrightarrow{j}$ **(ii)** $a=2$

Exercise 4.5 ▼

1. 5   **2.** 13   **3.** 17   **4.** 29   **5.** $\sqrt{13}$ **6.** $\sqrt{17}$ **7.** $\sqrt{29}$ **8.** $\sqrt{41}$

9. $\sqrt{20}$ or $2\sqrt{5}$ **10.** $\sqrt{26}$ **11.** $\sqrt{41}$ **12.** $\sqrt{13}$ **13.** (i) $-4\vec{i}-2\vec{j}$

15. ± 3 **16.** ± 5 **17.** ± 7 **18.** $-4, 8$ **19.** $-3, 7$ **20.** $\frac{8}{17}\vec{i}+\frac{15}{17}\vec{j}$

21. $-\frac{5}{\sqrt{29}}\vec{i}+\frac{2}{\sqrt{29}}\vec{j}$ **22.** $\frac{4}{5}\vec{i}-\frac{3}{5}\vec{j}$ **24.** $h=5, k=\frac{15}{4}$

25. (i) $\sqrt{20}$ or $2\sqrt{5}$ (ii) $\sqrt{32}$ or $4\sqrt{2}$

Exercise 4.6 ▼

1. 23   **2.** -6 **3.** 13   **4.** 48   **5.** 30   **6.** 0   **7.** 20   **8.** -32 **9.** 4   **10.** 2

11. 4   **13.** (i) (a) $6\vec{i}-4\vec{j}$ (b) $-2\vec{i}-6\vec{j}$ (ii) (a) 3 (b) 12 (c) 18

14. $4\vec{i}-4\vec{j};$ (i) -28 **15.** 10   **16.** 45°   **17.** 135°   **18.** 60°

19. 42.3°   **21.** 90°   **22.** 63°   **25.** 12   **26.** 8   **27.** (i) 10   (ii) 8   (iii) -2

28. 1   **29.** -3 **30.** (i) $\vec{r}=2\vec{i}-3\vec{j}, \ \vec{s}=3\vec{i}+2\vec{j}$ (ii) (a) 90°   (b) 135°

31. (ii) (a) $\frac{4}{5}$ (b) 16   **32.** (i) 45°   (ii) $\vec{i}+3\vec{j}, \ 3\vec{i}-\vec{j}$ **33.** $-\frac{1}{3}$, 3

34. $|\vec{a}|^2$ **36.** (i) 0   (ii) $|\vec{a}|^2+|\vec{b}|^2$ **37.** (ii) (a) 81   (b) 49   (c) 9   (d) 7

39. $\vec{b}-\vec{a}$ **40.** (i) (a) $\vec{a}-\vec{b}$ (b) $\vec{b}-\vec{a}$

Exercise 4.7 ▼

1. $-3\vec{i}+4\vec{j}$ **2.** $-5\vec{i}+2\vec{j}$ **3.** $2\vec{i}+4\vec{j}$ **4.** $5\vec{i}+6\vec{j}$ **5.** $3\vec{i}-2\vec{j}$ **6.** $\vec{i}-7\vec{j}$

7. $-4\vec{i}-3\vec{j}$ **8.** $-7\vec{i}-2\vec{j}$ **9.** $-15\vec{i}+8\vec{j}$ **10.** $-2\vec{i}+5\vec{j}$

11. $\vec{p}=-3\vec{i}-5\vec{j}, \ \vec{q}=-7\vec{i}-4\vec{j}$; yes   **12.** (i) $\vec{p}^{\perp}=-5\vec{i}-12\vec{j}, \ \vec{q}^{\perp}=-3\vec{i}+4\vec{j}$

(ii) 13; 5   (iii) $\sqrt{2}$ **13.** $t=8, k=4$ **14.** $m=-\frac{1}{4}, m=-\frac{15}{2}$ **15.** $h=3, k=-2$

16. $-5, 1$ **17.** $(6\vec{i}+15\vec{j})+(10\vec{i}-4\vec{j})$ **18.** $(-12\vec{i}-8\vec{j})+(-4\vec{i}+6\vec{j})$

19. $\frac{-2}{\sqrt{13}}\vec{i}+\frac{3}{\sqrt{13}}\vec{j}$ **20.** $\frac{5}{13}\vec{i}-\frac{12}{13}\vec{j}; -\frac{5}{13}\vec{i}+\frac{12}{13}\vec{j}$ **21.** $-\frac{15}{17}\vec{i}+\frac{8}{17}\vec{j}$

22. $-\frac{1}{2}$ **24.** (i) true   (ii) false   (iii) true

25. (i) $\vec{q}=-\vec{i}+5\vec{j}$; $\vec{r}=-6\vec{i}+4\vec{j}$ (ii) 45°   **26.** $(2-2t)\vec{i}+(2+2t)\vec{j}$

1. 30　**2.** 24　**3.** 18　**4.** 42　**5. (i)** 120　**(ii)** 120　**(iii)** 60　**(iv)** 20　**6.** 720

7. 720; **(i)** 120 **(ii)** 24 **(iii)** 240 **(iv)** 48 **(v)** 6 **(vi)** 2　**8.** 720　**9. (i)** 120 **(ii)** 48 **(iii)** 72

10. (i) 40,320　**(ii)** 4,320　**(iii)** 36,000　**11. (i)** 720　**(ii)** 24　**(iii)** 240　**(iv)** 480

12. 360　**13.** 4,536　**14.** 7,800　**15.** 1,263,600　**16. (i)** 48　**(ii)** 100

17. (i) 1,296　**(ii)** 180　**(iii)** 216　**(iv)** 24　**18.** 12　**19.** 60　**20. (i)** 108　**(ii)** 36

21. (i) 85　**(ii)** 34　**22.** 60　**23.** 648; **(i)** 200　**(ii)** 308

1. 10　**2.** 56　**3.** 126　**4.** 1　**5.** 190　**6.** 4,060　**7.** 35

8. 1,365; 1,001; 66　**9. (i)** 210　**(ii)** 84　**(iii)** 126　**(iv)** 70

10. (i) 35　**(ii)** 20　**(iii)** 15　**(iv)** 10　**(v)** 10　**11. (i)** 56　**(ii)** 21　**(iii)** 50

12. (a) (i) 66　**(ii)** 220　**(b) (i)** 495　**(ii)** 45　**(iii)** 450　**13.** 22　**14.** 13,860

15. 270　**16. (i)** 126　**(ii)** 15　**(iii)** 111　**17.** 126; 105　**18.** 6,300

19. 100　**20.** 148　**21.** 180　**22. (i)** 40　**(ii)** 74　**23.** 281　**24.** 245

25. (i) 84　**(ii)** 28　**(iii)** 80　**(iv)** 50

1. (i) $\frac{1}{3}$　**(ii)** $\frac{5}{12}$　**(iii)** $\frac{1}{12}$　**(iv)** $\frac{1}{6}$　**2. (i)** $\frac{1}{8}$　**(ii)** $\frac{1}{4}$　**(iii)** $\frac{1}{2}$

3. (i) $\frac{1}{2}$　**(ii)** $\frac{1}{5}$　**(iii)** $\frac{1}{5}$　**(iv)** $\frac{1}{10}$　**(v)** $\frac{7}{10}$　**(vi)** $\frac{1}{6}$　**(vii)** $\frac{1}{3}$

4. (i) $\frac{1}{52}$　**(ii)** $\frac{1}{2}$　**(iii)** $\frac{1}{4}$　**(iv)** $\frac{1}{13}$　**(v)** $\frac{3}{13}$　**(vi)** $\frac{3}{26}$　**(vii)** $\frac{5}{13}$　**(viii)** $\frac{12}{13}$　**(ix)** 0

5. 20　**6.** 200　**7.** $\frac{2}{5}$; 4　**8.** $\frac{2}{3}$　**9.** $\frac{3}{10}$　**10.** $\frac{2}{3}$

11. (i) $\frac{2}{5}$　**(ii)** $\frac{3}{5}$　**(iii)** $\frac{3}{10}$　**(iv)** $\frac{2}{5}$　**(v)** $\frac{2}{3}$　**(vi)** $\frac{1}{5}$

12. (i) $\frac{2}{5}$　**(ii)** $\frac{3}{5}$　**(iii)** $\frac{3}{20}$　**(iv)** $\frac{1}{2}$　**(v)** $\frac{1}{20}$　**(vi)** $\frac{1}{8}$　**(vii)** $\frac{2}{3}$

13. (i) $\frac{3}{20}$　**(ii)** $\frac{1}{5}$　**(iii)** $\frac{3}{10}$　**(iv)** $\frac{1}{2}$　**14. (i)** $\frac{1}{4}$　**(ii)** $\frac{1}{2}$　**(iii)** $\frac{3}{8}$　**(iv)** $\frac{5}{8}$

15. (i) 36　**(ii) (a)** $\frac{5}{18}$　**(b)** $\frac{1}{6}$　**(c)** $\frac{1}{12}$　**16. (i)** $\frac{3}{4}$　**(ii)** $\frac{5}{12}$　**(iii)** $\frac{7}{36}$

17. (i) $\frac{1}{12}$　**(ii)** $\frac{7}{12}$　**(iii)** $\frac{1}{4}$　**18.** 20　**(i)** $\frac{1}{5}$　**(ii)** $\frac{1}{5}$　**(iii)** $\frac{3}{10}$

19. (i) $\frac{1}{10}$　**(ii)** $\frac{1}{5}$　**(iii)** $\frac{3}{5}$

1. (i) $\frac{1}{2}$ (ii) $\frac{1}{2}$ (iii) $\frac{5}{6}$ **2.** (i) $\frac{1}{2}$ (ii) $\frac{1}{3}$ (iii) $\frac{2}{3}$ (iv) $\frac{1}{3}$

3. (i) $\frac{1}{3}$ (ii) $\frac{1}{5}$ (iii) $\frac{7}{15}$ (iv) $\frac{8}{15}$ **4.** (i) $\frac{1}{9}$ (ii) $\frac{2}{9}$ (iii) $\frac{4}{9}$ (iv) $\frac{2}{3}$ (v) $\frac{1}{3}$

5. (i) $\frac{1}{3}$ (ii) $\frac{2}{3}$ (iii) $\frac{3}{4}$ (iv) $\frac{1}{4}$ **6.** (i) $\frac{7}{20}$ (ii) $\frac{11}{20}$ (iii) $\frac{3}{4}$ (iv) $\frac{17}{20}$

7. (i) $\frac{1}{2}$ (ii) $\frac{3}{7}$ (iii) $\frac{5}{7}$ (iv) $\frac{1}{6}$ (v) $\frac{5}{21}$ (vi) $\frac{1}{3}$ (vii) $\frac{2}{3}$

8. (i) $\frac{1}{2}$ (ii) $\frac{7}{13}$ (iii) $\frac{4}{13}$ (iv) $\frac{9}{13}$ **9.** (i) $\frac{5}{18}$ (ii) $\frac{11}{36}$ **10.** (i) $\frac{5}{8}$ (ii) $\frac{3}{8}$ (iii) $\frac{3}{4}$ (iv) $\frac{1}{4}$

11. (i) $\frac{1}{2}$ (ii) $\frac{1}{4}$ (iii) $\frac{2}{3}$ (iv) $\frac{3}{4}$ (v) $\frac{2}{3}$ (vi) $\frac{1}{3}$

1. $\frac{1}{36}$ **2.** (i) $\frac{1}{12}$ (ii) $\frac{1}{4}$ (iii) $\frac{1}{3}$ (iv) $\frac{1}{6}$ **3.** (i) $\frac{1}{4}$ (ii) $\frac{1}{25}$ (iii) $\frac{1}{5}$ **4.** $\frac{1}{12}$

5. (i) $\frac{1}{24}$ (ii) $\frac{1}{8}$ (iii) $\frac{1}{4}$ (iv) $\frac{5}{24}$ **6.** (i) $\frac{1}{36}$ (ii) $\frac{1}{4}$ **7.** (i) $\frac{1}{8}$ (ii) $\frac{3}{8}$

8. (i) $\frac{5}{33}$ (ii) $\frac{2}{11}$ (iii) $\frac{19}{66}$ **9.** (i) $\frac{4}{9}$ (ii) $\frac{16}{33}$ **10.** (i) $\frac{3}{44}$ (ii) $\frac{3}{11}$

11. (i) $\frac{7}{25}$ (ii) $\frac{6}{25}$ **12.** (i) $\frac{16}{81}$ (ii) $\frac{4}{9}$ (iii) $\frac{1}{9}$ **13.** (i) $\frac{2}{19}$ (ii) $\frac{17}{19}$

15. $\frac{3}{5}$ **16.** (i) $\frac{8}{27}$ (ii) $\frac{19}{27}$ **17.** (i) $\frac{1}{20}$ (ii) $\frac{9}{20}$ (iii) $\frac{1}{2}$

18. (i) $\frac{1}{4}$ (ii) $\frac{37}{64}$ **19.** (i) $\frac{1}{4}$ (ii) $\frac{2}{25}$ (iii) $\frac{12}{25}$ **20.** $\frac{1}{6}$; $\frac{1}{6}$ **21.** $\frac{17}{72}$

22. (i) $\frac{1}{8}$ (ii) $\frac{3}{16}$ (iii) $\frac{1}{16}$ **23.** (i) $\frac{5}{126}$ (ii) $\frac{10}{21}$ **24.** $\frac{7}{15}$ **25.** $\frac{3}{5}$

26. (i) 126 (ii) $\frac{5}{18}$ **27.** (i) 120 (ii) 24 (iii) $\frac{1}{5}$ **28.** (i) 36 (ii) $\frac{5}{6}$ **29.** $\frac{17}{42}$

30. (i) $\frac{3}{8}$ (ii) $\frac{1}{14}$ (iii) $\frac{13}{14}$ (iv) $\frac{5}{28}$ **31.** $\frac{59}{90}$ **32.** (i) $\frac{7}{25}$ (ii) $\frac{3}{10}$

33. (i) $\frac{1}{7}$ (ii) $\frac{6}{7}$ (iii) $\frac{1}{49}$ (iv) $\frac{2}{49}$ (v) $\frac{1}{7}$ (vi) $\frac{6}{7}$

34. (i) $\frac{1}{343}$ (ii) $\frac{1}{49}$ (iii) $\frac{30}{49}$ (iv) $\frac{19}{49}$ (v) $\frac{108}{343}$

35. (i) $\frac{1}{1728}$ (ii) $\frac{1}{144}$ (iii) $\frac{55}{72}$ (iv) $\frac{17}{72}$ **36.** (i) $\dfrac{6}{x+16}$ (ii) 4 (iii) $\frac{33}{95}$

37. (i) $\dfrac{x^2-x}{x^2+11x+30}$ (ii) 3 (iii) $\frac{1}{2}$ **38.** (i) $\dfrac{x^2-x}{x^2+17x+72}$ (ii) (a) 6 (b) 15 (c) $\frac{74}{105}$

39. (i) $\dfrac{x+1}{x+y+5}$ (ii) $\dfrac{x+y}{x+y+5}$; $x=2, y=3$ **40.** $\frac{2}{3}$

Exercise 6.1

1. 4   **2.** 4   **3.** 6.3   **4.** 4.7   **5.** 4.75   **6.** 1   **7.** 3   **8.** 22

9. 47.2 km/h   **10.** 14   **11.** 98   **12.** 4   **13.** 9   **14.** 17   **15.** 3

16. (i) $k+3$ **(ii)** 5   **17. (i)** 7   **(ii)** 9   **18.** $11-x$ **19.** $3\bar{x}+2k$

20. $\dfrac{7w-4v}{3}$

Exercise 6.2

1. 5   **2.** 7   **3.** 105.5   **4.** 17; B; A **5.** S_2; S_1

6. (i) 105.8%   **(ii)** decrease of 0.55%   **7. (i)** 2%   **(ii)** −1%   **(iii)** +1.62%

8. (i) 5 **(ii)** −0.85   **9. (i)** 3 **(ii)** 65.8   **10.** 7

Exercise 6.3

1. 1.87   **2.** 1.63   **3.** 4.24   **4.** 3.87   **5.** 2.65   **6.** 2.73   **7.** 2

8. (a) 10; 2 **(b)** 10; 4   **10. (i)** 15 **(ii)** 4   **11.** 3.02   **12.** 4.02   **13.** 4.36

14. 20.37   **15. (i)** 6 **(ii)** 5

Exercise 6.4

1. $4\bar{x}-3$ **2. (i)** $2-\bar{x}$ **(ii)** $p\bar{x}+q$ **3.** $x=3,\ y=5$ **4.** $2\bar{x}-1$

6. (i) 10   **(ii)** 5   **9. (i) (a)** $p=2q$ **(b)** $\dfrac{24p^2}{5}$ **(ii)** $p=20,\ q=10$

10. (i) (a) $a+3$ **(b)** $\dfrac{3a^2-12a+43}{2}$ **(ii)** $a=1$ or $a=3$ **11. (i)** $a+2$ **(ii)** $a=3$

12. (i) $y=6-x$ **(ii)** $\dfrac{2x^2-12x+46}{10}$ **(iii)** $x=4,\ y=2$

13. (i) (a) $a+2$ **(b)** $\dfrac{8a^2-20a+18}{5}$ **(ii)** 5   **14. (i)** $q=10-p$ **(ii)** $p=6,\ q=4$

15. 2   **16. (i)** $\dfrac{a+b}{2}$ **18. (i)** 3

1. 8, 11, 17, 29   **2.** 1, 26, 524   **3.** (i) $x^2 - 7x + 10 = 0$; $x = 5$ or $x = 2$ (ii) $4(5)^n - 3(2)^n$ (iii) 12,404

4. 2^{n-1}; 64   **5.** $3(3)^n - 2(-1)^n$ **7.** (i) $5^n - 5$ (ii) 3,120   **8.** (i) $3^n - 2^n$ (ii) 665

9. (i) $4(\frac{1}{2})^n - 2(5)^n$ (ii) $-\frac{499}{2}$ **10.** $4(\frac{3}{2})^n - 2(5)^n$ **11.** $2(\frac{1}{2})^n + 6(\frac{2}{3})^n$; $\frac{19}{6}$

12. (i) $3l(3)^n + 2m(2)^n$; $9l(3)^n + 4m(2)^n$ **13.** (i) $1 + \sqrt{2}$, $1 - \sqrt{2}$ (ii) $(1 + \sqrt{2})^n + (1 - \sqrt{2})^n$

14. $(3 + \sqrt{5})^n + (3 - \sqrt{5})^n$ **15.** $\sqrt{2}(3 + \sqrt{2})^n - \sqrt{2}(3 - \sqrt{2})^n$

16. (i) $k = 5$ **17.** (i) $p = -8$; $q = 15$ (ii) $h = 2$; $k = -1$ **18.** 3; $2(\frac{1}{2})^n + 3^n$

19. (i) $\dfrac{1 + \sqrt{5}}{2}$, $\dfrac{1 - \sqrt{5}}{2}$ (ii) (a) 1, 1, 2, 3, 5, 8, 13, 21   **20.** $p = -7$; $q = 12$; $4^n - 3^n$

1. 5, 8   **2.** (i) −2, 1   (ii) $a = 2$, $b = 1$ (iii) 15

3. (i) 6, 14, $n^2 + 7n + 6$ (ii) $p = 2$; $q = 6$ (iii) 6

4. (i) $a = 3$, $b = 4$ (ii) 4   **5.** 3, 5, $2(2)^n + 1$ **11.** 5, 12; 2

17. (i) $a = 3$, $b = 4$, $c = -10$ (ii) 54

1. 48   **2.** 33   **3.** 91   **4.** 70   **5.** −44   **6.** 43   **7.** (i) −22 (ii) $-\frac{23}{60}$

8. (i) 7 (ii) 40   **9.** (i) 18 (ii) 42   **10.** $\frac{23}{12}$ **11.** $2n + 1$ **12.** $2n - 6$

13. $4n - 1$ **14.** (i) $\dfrac{(n-1)(n)}{2}$ (ii) n (iii) 20

15. (i) 2^{n-1} (ii) 2^{n-1} (iii) 512 (iv) 16   **16.** $2^n + 2n - 1$; 271

1. 2, 7, 12   **2.** (i) 79   (ii) 210

3. (i) (a) $2n + 1$ (b) $n^2 + 2n$ (ii) (a) 81 (b) 440   (iii) 94   (iv) 8

4. (i) 3   (ii) (a) $3n + 1$ (b) $\dfrac{n}{2}(3n + 5)$ (iii) (a) 73 (b) 1,000

5. (i) 10; 6   (ii) (a) $6n + 4$ (b) $3n^2 + 7n$ (iii) (a) 64 (b) 370

6. (i) 15; 5   (ii) (a) $5n + 10$ (b) $\dfrac{5n}{2}(n + 5)$ (iii) (a) 35 (b) 260   (iv) 6

7 (i) 7; −3   (ii) (a) $10 - 3n$ (b) $\dfrac{n}{2}(17 - 3n)$ (iii) (a) −50 (b) −430

8. 5; 1 **9. (i)** 4; 3 **(ii) (a)** 31 **(b)** 175 **10.** 2, 18

11. $a = 8, b = 18$ **12.** $p = 10, q = 17, r = 24$ **13.** $A_1 = 10, A_2 = 7, A_3 = 1, A_4 = -5$

14. $45°, 75°, 105°, 135°$ **15.** 20 **16.** 2,920

17. (i) 4 **(ii)** 3 **(iii)** -3 **(iv)** $\frac{1}{3}$ **(v)** 0, 4 **(vi)** $-2, 1$

18. $x = 0$ and $y = -10$; 5, 0, -5, -10 or $x = 3$ and $y = -7$; 17, 9, 1, -7

20. (i) 740 **(ii)** $4n - 5$ **(iii)** 75 **(iv)** 7 **21. (i)** $p = 6, q = -13$ **(ii)** $a = 3, b = -10$

22. (i) 2,600 **(ii)** 5,370 **23.** 1 **24.** 7 **25.** 3, 8, 13 or 13, 8, 3 **26.** 3.5, 8.5

27. 4, 7, 10, 13, 16 **28.** $x = \tan^{-1}\frac{3}{4}$; $d = \frac{2}{5}$, $a = \frac{4}{5}$

29. (i) $\ln x, \ln 2x, \ln 4x$ **(ii)** $u_n - u_{n-1} = \ln 2$ (a constant)

Exercise 7.4 ▼

1. (i) (a) $2(3)^{n-1}$ **(b)** $3^n - 1$ **(ii) (a)** 4,374 **(b)** 6,560

2. (i) (a) $64(-\frac{1}{2})^{n-1}$ **(b)** $\frac{128}{3}[1 - (-\frac{1}{2})^n]$ **(ii) (a)** $-\frac{1}{8}$ **(b)** $\frac{341}{8}$

3. $5(2)^{n-1}$ **4.** $4(3)^{n-1}$ **5.** $27(\frac{2}{3})^{n-1}$ **6.** $50(-\frac{2}{5})^{n-1}$ **7.** $(2a)^{n-1}$

8. $\dfrac{5}{a}\left(\dfrac{2}{a}\right)^{n-1}$ **12. (i)** $3(2)^{n-1}$ **13.** $6(2^n - 1)$ **14.** $18[1 - (\frac{2}{3})^n]$

15. $\frac{189}{4}[1 - (-\frac{1}{3})^n]$ **16.** $54[1 - (\frac{2}{3})^n]$; 6 **17.** 7 **18. (i)** 12 **(ii)** $12(\frac{1}{2})^{n-1}$

19. 6 cm, 9 cm **20.** 6 **21.** 2 **22.** 3 **23.** -3, 10 **24.** $-2, \frac{7}{2}$ **25.** $\frac{3}{2}$, 3

26. (i) 3, -2 **(ii)** 4, 2, 1, $\frac{1}{2}$ or $-1, -3, -9, -27$ **27.** $a = 3, b = \frac{3}{2}$

28. (i) -3 **(ii)** -7 **(iii)** $-7(-3)^{n-1}$ **(iv)** $\frac{7}{4}[(-3)^n - 1]$ **29. (i)** $\frac{4}{9}(3)^{n-1}$ **(ii)** $485\frac{7}{9}$

30. $r = \frac{6}{5}$, $a = 20\frac{5}{6}$ **31. (i)** 6 **(ii)** $\frac{1}{2}, 2$ **(iii)** 3, 6, 12 or 12, 6, 3

32. 1, 3, 9, 27 or 9, 3, 1, $\frac{1}{3}$ **33.** $a = 2, b = 4$ **34.** $p = 4, q = 16$ or $p = -5, q = 25$

35. $d = 2, r = 3$ **36.** 4

Exercise 7.5 ▼

1. 2 **2.** 3 **3.** $\frac{25}{4}$ **4.** 20 **5.** 2 **6.** $\frac{9}{7}$ **7.** $\frac{2}{15}$

8. $\dfrac{1}{1-x}$ **9.** $\dfrac{6}{3-a}$ **10. (i)** $\frac{3}{2}$ **(ii)** 6 **(iii)** 1 **11.** $\frac{5}{9}$ **12.** $\frac{4}{9}$

13. $\frac{20}{9}$ **14.** $\frac{8}{11}$ **15.** $\frac{5}{18}$ **16.** $\frac{11}{90}$ **17.** $\frac{11}{6}$ **18.** 12 **19.** $-\frac{1}{2}$

20. $\frac{5}{6}$ **21.** $\frac{4}{5}$ **22. (i)** $\frac{1}{4}; \frac{1}{3}$ **(ii)** $\frac{1}{2}; \frac{1}{3}$ **(iii)** 2; $\frac{9}{2}$

23. (i) $a-2$ (ii) $\frac{5}{2}$ (iii) $1<a<3$ **24.** (i) (a) $\dfrac{1}{1-x}$ (b) x^2-x (ii) $-5,6$

25. (i) $(1-r)(1+r)$ (ii) $\frac{1}{3}$ **26.** 18, 6, 2 or 9, 6, 4   **27.** $a=3,\ r=-\frac{1}{2}$

1. (i) $\dfrac{1-x^n}{1-x}$ (ii) $S_n=\dfrac{1-x^n}{(1-x)^2}-\dfrac{nx^n}{1-x}$; $\displaystyle\lim_{n\to\infty}S_n=\dfrac{1}{(1-x)^2}$; $\dfrac{25}{16}$ (iii) $\dfrac{1}{(1-x^2)^2}$

2. (i) $\dfrac{2x}{1-x}+\dfrac{x^2(1-x^{n-1})}{(1-x)^2}-\dfrac{(n+1)x^{n+1}}{1-x}$ (ii) $\dfrac{x(2-x)}{(1-x)^2}$ (iii) 3

3. (ii) $\dfrac{3-x}{(1-x)^2}$; 6 **4.** $\dfrac{2}{1-x}+\dfrac{3x(1-x^{n-1})}{(1-x)^2}-\dfrac{(3n-1)x^n}{1-x}$; $\dfrac{2+x}{(1-x)^2}$; $x=\dfrac{1}{4}$

5. $\frac{20}{9}$ **6.** 85   **7** (i) $n\,2^{n+1}$ (ii) 9,216

8. $1.1,\ 2.2,\ 3.2^2,\ 4.2^3$ or 1, 4, 12, 32; 1,793   **10.** $\frac{3}{4}$

1. 2   **2.** $\frac{4}{3}$ **3.** $\frac{2}{3}$ **4.** $\frac{4}{5}$ **5.** $\frac{3}{7}$ **6.** 0   **7.** 1   **8.** $\frac{1}{5}$

9. $\frac{3}{4}$ **10.** $\frac{1}{2}$ **11.** $\frac{3}{2}$ **12.** $\frac{4}{5}$ **13.** 5   **14.** $\frac{1}{3}$ **15.** 2   **16.** 0

17. $\sqrt{2}$ **18.** $\frac{\sqrt{3}}{2}$ **19.** (i) (a) $2n-1$ (b) n^2 (ii) $\frac{1}{2}$

2. (ii) $\dfrac{1}{2}-\dfrac{1}{n+2}$ or $\dfrac{n}{2(n+2)}$ (iii) $\frac{1}{2}$ **3.** (ii) $\dfrac{1}{3}-\dfrac{1}{n+3}$ or $\dfrac{n}{3(n+3)}$ (iii) $\frac{1}{3}$ (iv) $\frac{8}{25}$ (v) 39

4. (i) 1 (ii) 24   **5.** $A=\frac{1}{3},\ B=-\frac{1}{3}$

6. $A=\frac{1}{2},\ B=\frac{1}{2}$ (i) $\dfrac{5}{12}-\dfrac{1}{2(n+2)}-\dfrac{1}{2(n+3)}$ (ii) (a) $\frac{14}{45}$ (b) $\frac{5}{12}$

7. $A=\frac{1}{2},\ B=-\frac{1}{2}$ (i) $\dfrac{3}{4}-\dfrac{1}{2(n+1)}-\dfrac{1}{2(n+2)}$ (ii) $\frac{3}{4}$

8. (i) $\dfrac{1}{6}-\dfrac{1}{2(2n+3)}$ or $\dfrac{2n}{6(2n+3)}$ (ii) $\frac{1}{6}$ (iii) 29

9. (i) (a) $2n-1$ (b) $2n+1$ (ii) (a) $u_r=\dfrac{1}{(2r-1)(2r+1)}$ (b) $\dfrac{1}{2}-\dfrac{1}{2(2n+1)}$ or $\dfrac{n}{2n+1}$
     (c) $\frac{1}{2}$ (d) $\frac{100}{201}$

10. (iii) $1-\dfrac{1}{\sqrt{n+1}}$ or $\dfrac{\sqrt{n+1}-1}{\sqrt{n+1}}$ (iv) $\frac{8}{9}$ (v) 1

11. $\ln(n+1)$; 4.0   **12.** $1-\dfrac{1}{(n+1)!}$ or $\dfrac{(n+1)!-1}{(n+1)!}$

6. (i) 480 **(ii)** 5,950   **7.** $a = 2, b = 1$; 1,620   **8. (i)** $4r^2 - 4r + 1$ **(iii)** 3,990

9. (i) $n + 5$ **(ii)** 5,550   **10. (i)** $n^2 - 4n + 16$ **(ii)** 2,723   **11.** 8,780

12. 1,104   **13.** 8,616   **14.** 1,671   **15. (i)** $\dfrac{n}{6}(4n^2 + 15n + 17)$ **(ii)** 945

16. $a = 2, b = 5, c = -3$; 1,654   **17.** 1,540

1. $y = 10 - x$; 25; $x = 5, y = 5$ **2.** 18   **3.** $x = 6$; 144 m^2 **4.** $2\frac{1}{2}$ revs/sec

5. 200 km   **6.** $h = 12 - x$; 256 cm^3 **7.** $l = 12$ cm, $w = 4$ cm, $h = 6$ cm

8. $y = \dfrac{162}{x}$; 36 m   **9. (i)** $y = \dfrac{96}{x}$ **(ii) (a)** $(x - 4)(y - 6)$ **(b)** $120 - 6x - \dfrac{384}{x^2}$ **(c)** 8 cm by 12 cm

10. 2 cm; 144 cm^3 **11. (i)** $\dfrac{12 - 2r}{r}$ **(iii)** $A = 9$ cm^2, $\theta = 2$ radians

12. (i) $\dfrac{48 - r^2}{r}$ **(ii)** $r = 4$ cm, $h = 8$ cm **(iii)** 128π cm^3

13. (i) $\dfrac{300 - r^2}{2r}$ **(iii)** $r = h = 10$ cm; 1000π cm^3

14. (i) $h = \dfrac{1000}{\pi r^2}$ **(ii)** $A = 2\pi rh + 8r^2$ **(iii)** $A = \dfrac{2000}{r} + 8r^2$ **(iv)** $r = 5$ cm, $h = \dfrac{40}{\pi}$ cm, cost $= 18c$

16. $x = 1, A = 27$ square units   **17. (i)** $\sqrt{x^2 + \dfrac{16}{x^2}}$ **(ii)** $x = 2$ **(iii)** $2\sqrt{2}$ **18.** $\dfrac{c^2}{4m}$

19. (i) $r^2 = 300 - h^2$ **(ii) (a)** $h = 10$ cm **(b)** $r = 10\sqrt{2}$ cm   **20.** $128\sqrt{3}\pi$ cm^3

21. (i) $9 - h^2$ **(ii)** $\sqrt{6}$

23. (i) $155 - x$ **(ii)** $\sqrt{x^2 + 3600}$ **(iii)** $\dfrac{155 - x}{260} + \dfrac{\sqrt{x^2 + 3600}}{100}$; $x = 25$; 69 seconds

24. (i) $10t$ m; $20t$ m **(ii)** $|10t - 100|$ m; $|20t - 300|$ m **(iv)** 14 seconds **25.** $\dfrac{256\pi}{9}$ cm^3

1. $e^x(x - 1) + c$ **2.** $x \sin x + \cos x + c$ **3.** $(2x - 1)e^x + c$

4. $\frac{1}{3}e^{3x}(x - \frac{1}{3}) + c$ **5.** $\frac{1}{2}x \sin 2x + \frac{1}{4}\cos 2x + c$ **6.** $\frac{1}{2}x^2(\ln 2x - \frac{1}{2}) + c$

7. $\frac{1}{4}x^4(\ln x - \frac{1}{4}) + c$ **8.** $-3e^{-x}(x + 1) + c$ **9.** $-\dfrac{1}{x}(1 + \ln x) + c$

10. e **11.** π **12.** $\frac{1}{4}(e^2+1)$ **13.** $\frac{1}{4}$ **14.** $1-\dfrac{2}{e}$ **15.** $\dfrac{\pi-2}{8}$

16. $x^2\sin x+2x\cos x-2\sin x+c$ **17.** $\frac{1}{2}e^{2x}(x^2-x+\frac{1}{2})+c$

18. $-x^2e^{-x}-2xe^{-x}-2e^{-x}+c$ **19.** $\pi-2$ **20.** $e-2$ **21.** $\frac{1}{4}(e^2-1)$

22. $\frac{1}{2}e^x(\cos x+\sin x)+c$; $\frac{1}{2}(e^{\pi/2}-1)$ **23.** $-\frac{1}{2}e^x(\cos x+\sin x)+c$ **24.** $\frac{1}{5}e^{2x}(2\cos x+\sin x)+c$

25. $\frac{1}{5}e^x(2\sin 2x+\cos 2x)+c$ **26.** $\frac{1}{5}(2e^\pi+1)$ **27.** $\frac{1}{4}(e^{-\pi}+1)$ **28.** $\frac{1}{10}(e^{\pi/6}+3)$

29. $\dfrac{\pi+2}{2}$ **30.** $\dfrac{\pi}{4}-\dfrac{1}{2}\ln 2$ **31.** $\dfrac{\pi-2}{2}$

Exercise 8.3 ▼

1. Divergent   **2.** Convergent   **3.** Convergent   **4.** Divergent

5. Convergent   **6.** Divergent   **7.** Convergent   **8.** Convergent

9. Convergent   **10.** Divergent   **11.** Convergent   **12.** Convergent

15. $-\frac{1}{3}<x<\frac{1}{3}$ **16.** $-2<x<2$ **17.** $-1<x<1$

18. $1<x<3$ **19.** $-\frac{3}{2}<x<\frac{3}{2}$ **20.** $-1<x<1$

23. (i) $-4<x<4$ **(ii)** $x<-4$ or $x>4$

Exercise 8.4 ▼

1. (i) $1+x+\dfrac{x^2}{2!}+\dfrac{x^3}{3!}$; $u_n=\dfrac{x^n}{n!}$; by the Ratio Test, convergent for all $x\in\mathbf{R}$.

    (ii) $x-\dfrac{x^2}{2}+\dfrac{x^3}{3}-\dfrac{x^4}{4}$; $u_n=\dfrac{(-1)^{n+1}x^n}{n}$; by the Ratio Test, convergent for $-1<x<1$, $x\in\mathbf{R}$.

    (iii) $x-\dfrac{x^3}{3!}+\dfrac{x^5}{5!}-\dfrac{x^7}{7!}$; $u_n=\dfrac{(-1)^{n+1}x^{2n-1}}{(2n-1)!}$; by the Ratio Test, convergent for all $x\in\mathbf{R}$.

    (iv) $1-\dfrac{x^2}{2!}+\dfrac{x^4}{4!}-\dfrac{x^6}{6!}$; $u_n=\dfrac{(-1)^n x^{2n}}{(2n)!}$; by the Ratio Test, convergent for all $x\in\mathbf{R}$.

2. $1-x+\dfrac{x^2}{2!}-\dfrac{x^3}{3!}$ **3.** $1+2x+2x^2+\frac{4}{3}x^3$ **4.** $1-2x+2x^2-\frac{4}{3}x^3$

5. $1+x^2+\frac{1}{2}x^4+\frac{1}{6}x^6$ **6.** $1+\frac{1}{2}x+\frac{1}{8}x^2+\frac{1}{48}x^3$ **7.** $1+3x+\frac{5}{2}x^2+\frac{7}{6}x^3+\frac{3}{8}x^4$

8. $1+2x+x^2-\frac{2}{3}x^3$ **9.** $-x-\dfrac{x^2}{2}-\dfrac{x^3}{3}-\dfrac{x^4}{4}$ **10.** $2x-2x^2+\frac{8}{3}x^3-4x^4$

11. $-3x-\frac{9}{2}x^2-9x^3-\frac{81}{4}x^4$ **12.** $5x+\frac{5}{2}x^2+\frac{35}{3}x^3+\frac{65}{4}x^4$ **13.** $2x-\frac{4}{3}x^3+\frac{4}{15}x^5-\frac{32}{1,260}x^7$

14. $1 - \frac{9}{2}x^2 + \frac{81}{24}x^4 - \frac{729}{720}x^6$ **15.** $1 + 2x - \frac{9}{2}x^2 - \frac{4}{3}x^3$ **16.** $3 - x + \frac{9}{2}x^2 - \frac{1}{6}x^3$

17. 1.221 **18.** 4.964 **19.** 0.095 **20.** 0.574 **21.** 0.199 **22.** 0.070

23. (i) $x - \dfrac{x^2}{2} + \dfrac{x^3}{3} - \dfrac{x^4}{4}$ **(ii)** $-2x - 2x^2 - \frac{8}{3}x^3 - 4x^4$ **(iii)** 0.01 **(iv)** -0.02 **(vi)** $\frac{1}{5}$ or 0.2 **(vii)** 0.69

24. $a = 2,\ b = 3,\ c = \frac{5}{2}$ **25.** $a = 1,\ b = 2$ **26.** 1

Exercise 8.5 ▼

1. (i) $1 - x + x^2 - x^3$ **(ii) (a)** $1 + x + x^2 + x^3$ **(b)** $1 + 2x + 4x^2 + 8x^3$ **(c)** $1 - x^2 + x^4 - x^6$

     (iii) $(-1)^n x^n$ (starting at $n = 0$) or $(-1)^{n+1}x^{n-1}$ (starting at $n = 1$)

2. (i) $1 - 2x + 3x^2 - 4x^3$; $(-1)^n(n+1)x^n$ (starting at $n = 0$) or $(-1)^{n+1}nx^{n-1}$ (starting at $n = 1$)

     (ii) $-1 < x < 1$ **(iii)** $1 - 2x^2 + 3x^4 - 4x^6$

3. (i) $1 - \frac{1}{2}x - \frac{1}{8}x^2 - \frac{1}{16}x^3$ **(ii)** $1 - \frac{1}{2}x - \frac{1}{8}x^2 - \frac{1}{16}x^3$; 9.95

4. (i) $1 - \frac{1}{2}x + \frac{3}{8}x^2 - \frac{5}{16}x^3$ **(ii)** $1 + \frac{1}{2}x + \frac{3}{8}x^2 + \frac{5}{16}x^3$; 1.005

     (iii) $1 + x + \frac{3}{2}x^2 + \frac{5}{2}x^3$; 1.03 **(iv)** $1 - \frac{1}{2}x - \frac{1}{8}x^2$ **(v)** $1 + x + \frac{1}{2}x^2$; 3.315

5. $1 - \frac{1}{3}x + \frac{2}{9}x^2$; $\frac{277}{576}$

6. (i) $1 - 2x + 3x^2 - 4x^3$ **(ii)** $1 + 6x + 27x^2 + 108x^3$

     (iii) $1 - 3x^2 + 6x^4 - 10x^6$ **(iv)** $1 - x - x^2 - \frac{5}{3}x^3$

Exercise 8.6 ▼

2. (i) $\frac{2}{3}$ **(ii)** $\frac{1}{7}$ **3.** $\frac{3}{10}$ **4. (i)** $a = \frac{4}{7}$; $b = \frac{3}{11}$ **(ii)** $\dfrac{\pi}{4}$ **6.** $\frac{1}{11}$

7. (i) $\dfrac{(-1)^n x^{2n+1}}{2n+1}$ **(ii)** $\frac{304}{105}$ **8. (ii)** $\frac{2}{3} - \frac{8}{81} + \frac{32}{1215}$; $\frac{1}{5} - \frac{1}{375} + \frac{1}{15,625}$; 3.17

9. (ii) (a) $\frac{2}{5} - \frac{8}{375} + \frac{32}{15,625}$ **(b)** $\frac{3}{7} - \frac{9}{343} + \frac{243}{84,035}$; 3.1438

10. (ii) $4\left[\left[\frac{1}{2} + \frac{1}{3}\right] - \frac{1}{3}\left[\left(\frac{1}{2}\right)^3 + \left(\frac{1}{3}\right)^3\right] - \frac{1}{5}\left[\left(\frac{1}{2}\right)^5 + \left(\frac{1}{3}\right)^5\right] - \frac{1}{7}\left[\left(\frac{1}{2}\right)^7 + \left(\frac{1}{3}\right)^7\right] + \ldots \right]$

     (iii) $u_n = 4\left[\dfrac{(-1)^{n+1}}{2n-1}\left[\left(\frac{1}{2}\right)^{2n-1} + \left(\frac{1}{3}\right)^{2n-1}\right] \right]$ **(iv)** 3.1409

2. $\begin{pmatrix} 9 & -10 \\ -2 & 17 \end{pmatrix}$ **3.** $\begin{pmatrix} 1 & 0 \\ -10 & 7 \end{pmatrix}$ **4. (i)** $\begin{pmatrix} 3 & 2 \\ 1 & 1 \end{pmatrix}$ **(ii)** $\begin{pmatrix} 7 & 5 \\ 12 & 9 \end{pmatrix}$ **5. (i)** $\frac{3}{5} + \frac{4}{5}i$ **(ii)** 1

7. $a = -10, b = -5$ **8.** $k = \pm 24$ **9. (i)** $1 - 2i$ **10.** $-2 - 3i; p = 4, q = 13$

11. $2\left(\cos\dfrac{2\pi}{3} + i\sin\dfrac{2\pi}{3}\right)$ **12.** $\lambda = 1$ or $\lambda = 4$ **13.** $-\frac{3}{25}$ **14.** $p = \frac{1}{3}, q = \frac{-2\sqrt{2}}{3}; 1$

15. $-2 - 2\sqrt{3}i$; **(i)** 2 **(ii)** -2 **16.** $-1 + 2i$ **17.** $\begin{pmatrix} 5i & -6 \\ 1 & i \end{pmatrix}$

19. (i) $-\dfrac{1}{5}\begin{pmatrix} 1 & -6 \\ -1 & 1 \end{pmatrix}$ **(ii)** $\begin{pmatrix} 4 & -6 \\ 1 & -3 \end{pmatrix}$ **20.** 0 **21.** $x = 6$ **22.** $\begin{pmatrix} 10 & 12 \\ 18 & 20 \end{pmatrix}$

23. (i) $\begin{pmatrix} 1 & 0 \\ 0 & 1 \end{pmatrix}$ **(ii)** $\begin{pmatrix} 1 & 0 \\ 0 & 1 \end{pmatrix}$ **24.** -1 **25.** $\sqrt{3}$ **26.** $k = \pm 2$

27. $2x^2 + 10xy + 8y^2$ **28. (i)** 17 **(ii)** 4 **29.** 4 **30.** $x = -2$ or $x = \frac{9}{5}$

1. $l = 1, m = -1$ **2.** $i, 1 + i$ **3. (i)** i, i **(ii)** $4 - i, -4 + i$ **4.** $\begin{pmatrix} 24 & 1 \\ 6 & -1 \end{pmatrix}; \begin{pmatrix} 6 & 0 \\ 0 & 1 \end{pmatrix}$

5. 1 **6. (i)** $z^2 - 6z + 10 = 0$ **(ii) (a)** $k = 8$ **(b)** $3 - i, 2$ **7.** $\begin{pmatrix} 4 & 0 \\ 0 & 25 \end{pmatrix}, \begin{pmatrix} 8 & 0 \\ 0 & 125 \end{pmatrix}, \begin{pmatrix} 2^{50} & 0 \\ 0 & 5^{50} \end{pmatrix}$

8. (i) $1 - i$ **(ii)** $\sqrt{2}$ **(iii)** $a = -2, b = 2$ **9. (i)** $h = -9, k = 33$ **(ii)** $2 + 3i, 5$

10. $8\sqrt{3}$ **11.** $\begin{pmatrix} 19 & -7 \\ 29 & -11 \end{pmatrix}$ **12.** $\begin{pmatrix} 0 & 0 \\ 0 & 0 \end{pmatrix}$ **13.** $\begin{pmatrix} 8 & 5 \\ 3 & 2 \end{pmatrix}\begin{pmatrix} x \\ y \end{pmatrix} = \begin{pmatrix} 19 \\ 17 \end{pmatrix}; x = 3, y = -1$

14. $\lambda = 9, u = -20$ **15.** $a = 4, b = 5$ **16. (i)** $-1 + i$ **(ii)** $\frac{3}{10} + \frac{9}{10}i$

17. $x = 4, y = -3$ **18.** $1 + i, 1 - 2i$ **19.** $\begin{pmatrix} 3 & -7 \\ 2 & -3 \end{pmatrix}\begin{pmatrix} x \\ y \end{pmatrix} = \begin{pmatrix} 6 \\ -1 \end{pmatrix}; x = -5, y = -3$

21. (i) $p = -1, q = 5$ **(ii)** $2 - 3i$ **22.** $\begin{pmatrix} 3 & -5 \\ 5 & 8 \end{pmatrix}; p = -2, q = -9, r = 13, s = 34$

23. $\begin{pmatrix} 1 & 0 \\ 0 & 1 \end{pmatrix}$ **24.** $\dfrac{1}{2x}\begin{pmatrix} y+2 & -x \\ -y & x \end{pmatrix}; x = 2, y = 3$ **26.** $3 + 2i, -3 + 2i$

27. $\sqrt{3} - 2i, -\sqrt{3} - 2i$ **28.** $3 + i, \sqrt{10}$ **29.** 1 **30.** $\frac{1}{2}$

32. (i) -4 **(ii)** $2 - 3i, 2 + i$ **33. (i)** 5 **(ii)** $-\frac{1}{4}$ **34. (ii)** $a = -14; 2, 2 - \sqrt{3}i$

35. $\begin{pmatrix} 1 & 0 \\ 0 & 1 \end{pmatrix}; \begin{pmatrix} k & 1+k \\ 1-k & -k \end{pmatrix}; \begin{pmatrix} 2 & 0 \\ 0 & -1 \end{pmatrix}; \begin{pmatrix} 1024 & 0 \\ 0 & 1 \end{pmatrix}$ **36.** $\begin{pmatrix} 6 & 2 \\ 2 & 17 \end{pmatrix}; x = 2, y = 1$

37. $\cos 2\theta + i \sin 2\theta$　　**38. (i)** $\begin{pmatrix} 1 & -\sqrt{3} \\ \sqrt{3} & 1 \end{pmatrix}\begin{pmatrix} x \\ y \end{pmatrix} = \begin{pmatrix} -2 \\ 2\sqrt{3} \end{pmatrix}$　**(ii)** $\frac{1}{4}\begin{pmatrix} 1 & \sqrt{3} \\ -\sqrt{3} & 1 \end{pmatrix}$; $x = 1,\ y = \sqrt{3}$

39. (i) $2 + 0i,\ 5 + \sqrt{3}i,\ 5 - \sqrt{3}i$　　**(ii)** all sides are $\sqrt{12}$ in length

40. (i) $a = -10,\ b = 29$　　**(ii)** $0 + i,\ 5 + 2i,\ 5 - 2i$

Exercise 1R.C ▾

1. true, false, false　　**2. (ii)** $2^9(1 - \sqrt{3}i)$　　**3. (i)** $0 + 6i$　**(ii)** $\sqrt{2}\left(\cos\dfrac{\pi}{4} + i \sin\dfrac{\pi}{4}\right)$; $-32 + 32i$

4. $\begin{pmatrix} 4 & 3 \\ 3 & -4 \end{pmatrix}$; $\begin{pmatrix} 100 & 75 \\ 75 & -100 \end{pmatrix}$　　**5.** $z_1 = 2 + i,\ z_2 = -1 + 3i$　　**7. (i)** $\pm(1 - 2i)$　**(ii)** $2 - i,\ 1 + i$

9. 64　　**10. (i) (a)** $8\left(\cos\dfrac{3\pi}{2} + i \sin\dfrac{3\pi}{2}\right)$　　**(b)** $8\left(\cos\left(\dfrac{3\pi}{2} + 2n\pi\right) + i \sin\left(\dfrac{3\pi}{2} + 2n\pi\right)\right)$

(ii) $2i,\ -\sqrt{3} - i,\ \sqrt{3} - i$　**(iii)** $3i,\ -\sqrt{3},\ \sqrt{3}$　　**11. (i) (a)** $-32i$　**(b)** 2^{12}　**(ii)** $\left(\cos\dfrac{5\pi}{3} + i \sin\dfrac{5\pi}{3}\right),\ 1 + 0i$

12. (i) $\lambda_1 = -1,\ \lambda_2 = 1$　**(ii)** $\begin{pmatrix} -1 & 0 \\ 0 & 1 \end{pmatrix}$　**(iii)** $\begin{pmatrix} 1 & 0 \\ 0 & 1 \end{pmatrix}$　　**13. (i)** $\lambda = 3$　**(ii)** $\left(\cos\dfrac{3\pi}{2} + i \sin\dfrac{3\pi}{2}\right)$; 1

14. $1 - i,\ -1 + i;\ 2 + i,\ 1 + 2i$　　**15.** $4,\ -4,\ -1 - i$

17. (i) $1 + 2i,\ 1 - \frac{1}{2}i$　**(ii)** $1,\ -1,\ \frac{1}{2} + \frac{\sqrt{3}}{2}i,\ -\frac{1}{2} + \frac{\sqrt{3}}{2}i,\ \frac{1}{2} - \frac{\sqrt{3}}{2}i,\ -\frac{1}{2} - \frac{\sqrt{3}}{2}i$

18. $-5 + i,\ 5 - i;\ 2 + i,\ -3 + 2i$　　**19. (i)** 4　**(ii)** $\pm 2,\ \pm(2 - i)$

20. (i) $\cos 0 + i \sin 0$　**(ii)** $1,\ -1,\ i,\ -i$　**(iii)** 4　　**22. (i)** $-2 + 2\sqrt{3}i$　**(ii)** $\begin{pmatrix} 190 & 126 \\ -189 & -125 \end{pmatrix}$

23. $1 - i \tan(\frac{1}{2}\theta)$　　**24.** $\begin{pmatrix} 3 & 2 \\ -1 & -1 \end{pmatrix}$　**(i)** $a = 4,\ b = 2$　**(ii)** $\begin{pmatrix} 94 & 62 \\ -93 & -61 \end{pmatrix}$

25. $\begin{pmatrix} \frac{3}{5} & \frac{4}{5} \\ \frac{4}{5} & -\frac{3}{5} \end{pmatrix}$　**26.** $\dfrac{4\tan\theta - 4\tan^3\theta}{1 - 6\tan^2\theta + \tan^4\theta}$　**27. (i)** $t = 2,\ s = 1$　or　$t = -2,\ s = -1$　**(ii)** $3 + i,\ 1 - 3i$

28. $a = 4,\ b = -1$　or　$a = -4,\ b = 1;\ -1;\ \frac{1}{2} - \frac{5}{2}i$　　**29. (i)** $w_1 = \sqrt{3} + i,\ w_2 = -\sqrt{3} + i$

　(ii) $w_1^{20} = 2^{19}(-1 - \sqrt{3}i),\ w_2^{20} = 2^{19}(-1 + \sqrt{3}i)$　**30. (i)** $\frac{1}{2} + \frac{\sqrt{3}}{2}i$　**(ii)** $\cos\dfrac{\pi}{3} + i \sin\dfrac{\pi}{3};\ n = 3$

31. (i) $-\frac{\sqrt{3}}{2} + \frac{1}{2}i$　**(ii)** $n = 6$　　**32 (i)** $27\left(\cos\dfrac{3\pi}{2} + i \sin\dfrac{3\pi}{2}\right)$　**(ii)** $3i,\ 3\left(-\frac{\sqrt{3}}{2} - \frac{1}{2}i\right),\ 3\left(\frac{\sqrt{3}}{2} - \frac{1}{2}i\right)$

33. $p = 1 + \sqrt{3}i,\ q = 1 - \sqrt{3}i$　　**34. (i)** $\cos\dfrac{5\pi}{3} + i \sin\dfrac{5\pi}{3}$　**(ii)** $\cos\left(\dfrac{5\pi}{3} + 2n\pi\right) + i \sin\left(\dfrac{5\pi}{3} + 2n\pi\right);\ \pm i$

35. (i) $4\left(\cos\dfrac{5\pi}{3} + i \sin\dfrac{5\pi}{3}\right)$　**(ii)** $0 - 8i,\ 0 + 8i$　**36.** $4\left(\cos\dfrac{\pi}{2} + i \sin\dfrac{\pi}{2}\right);\ -4\sqrt{2} + 4\sqrt{2}i,\ 4\sqrt{2} - 4\sqrt{2}i$

37. $\cos\dfrac{\pi}{3} + i \sin\dfrac{\pi}{3};\ \pm\left(\frac{\sqrt{3}}{2} + \frac{1}{2}i\right)$　　**40. (i)** $1,\ -\frac{1}{2} + \frac{\sqrt{3}}{2}i,\ -\frac{1}{2} - \frac{\sqrt{3}}{2}i$　**(iv) (a)** 1　**(b)** 32

1. 4   **2.** 1 or 11   **3. (i)** $\frac{5}{6}$ **(ii)** $-\frac{5}{3}$ or $\frac{5}{2}$ **4.** $\frac{1}{2}, -1$

5. 0, 1, 0, 1; 100   **6. (i)** 3 **(ii)** $\frac{4}{5}$ **7.** 2 or $\frac{9}{2}$ **8. (i)** $2x$ **(ii)** $\dfrac{2x+1}{2x-2}$

9. $-\frac{1}{2} < x < \frac{1}{2}$; $\dfrac{1}{1-2x}$ **10.** $\frac{1}{3}$ **11.** $\frac{25}{99}$ **12.** $\frac{11}{9}$ **13.** $\frac{43}{18}$

14. $3^{12} - 1$ or 531,440   **15. (i)** u_{13} **(ii)** 312 **(iii)** 25   **16. (i)** -1 **(ii)** 16

17. (i) -3 **(ii)** -7 **18.** $6\left[1 - \left(\frac{1}{2}\right)^n\right]$ **19.** $3 - \dfrac{1}{3^{n-1}}$ or $3 - 3^{1-n}$; $n = 5$

20. 4 or 9   **21. (i)** 400 **(ii)** 4,095   **22. (i)** 7 **(ii)** 10 **(iii)** 12

23. 1, 2, 0, 2, 4, 0   **25.** $\frac{1}{4} + \frac{1}{2\sqrt{2}}$ **26.** $x = -24, y = -64$

1. (i) $a = 4, d = 5$ **(ii) (a)** $5n - 1$ **(b)** $\frac{n}{2}(5n + 3)$ **2. (i)** $\frac{3}{2}$; 3 **(ii)** 21

7. (iii) 9,837   **8. (i)** $7 - 6n$ **(ii)** -83 **(iii)** 8

9. (i) $a = -4d$ **(ii)** $p = 22, q = 1$ **10. (ii)** 18; 36

11. (i) $(1 + r)(1 - r + r^2)$ **(ii)** 4, 12, 36, 108; 108, 36, 12, 4

12. (i) (a) $\dfrac{x}{1-x}$ **(b)** $\dfrac{x}{1-2x}$ **(ii)** $x = \frac{3}{8}$ **(iii)** $x < \frac{1}{2}$ **13. (i)** 4, 9, 16 **(ii)** $(n+1)^2$

14. (i) $p = 2, q = -3$ **(ii) (a)** $3n - 1$ **(b)** $\frac{n}{2}(3n + 1)$ **(iii) (a)** 29 **(b)** 155

15. 105   **16.** $x = 5, y = -1$ **17.** $a = 0, b = 2; a = 7, b = 9$ **20.** $m = \frac{3}{2}, n = \frac{25}{4}$

21. $-8, -3, 2; 2, -3, -8$ **22.** $p = -7$ **23. (i)** $-\frac{1}{2}$ **(ii)** 18

24. (i) $\frac{n}{2}(3n + 7)$ **(ii)** $\dfrac{n}{n+1}$ **25. (ii)** $\dfrac{3}{2} - \dfrac{1}{n+1} - \dfrac{1}{n+2}$ **(iii)** $\frac{3}{2}$

26. (ii) $\dfrac{1}{3} - \dfrac{1}{k+3}$ or $\dfrac{k}{3k+9}; \dfrac{1}{3}$ **27. (ii)** $\sqrt{n+1} - 1$ **(iii)** 4 **(iv)** 120

28. €1,600, €2,400, €3,600, €5,400, €8,100

29. (i) 2, 8, 18, 32 **(ii)** $4n + 2$ **(iii)** 6; 4   **30. (i)** $(p+1)(q+2r)$ **(ii)** $\frac{n}{2}(n+1)(a+2b)$

31. $-1, 3, -5, 7, -9, 11; 20$ **32.** 14   **33.** $2n(n+1)^2$; 17,640   **34.** 310   **35. (i)** $n+1$ **(ii)** 90

36. (ii) $n^2 + n + 1$ **37.** 8   **38.** 10

1. $a = -\frac{1}{2}, b = -32$ or $a = 16, b = 1$ **4. (i)** $n^2 - 2n + 4$ **(ii)** 8,645

5. (ii) $\frac{1}{2}$ **(iii)** 50 **6. (ii)** 4 **(iii)** 24 **7. (i)** 1 **(ii)** $a = 4, b = 9, c = -1$

8. (ii) n **(iv)** n^3 **9.** $\frac{7}{2}$ or 3.5 **10.** $\frac{32}{3}, 9, \frac{22}{3}$ **11.** 2, 5, 8

12. (i) $-6x + 8y$ or $-2(3x - 4y)$ **(ii)** $2x - y$ **(iii)** $8x + 36y$ or $4(2x + 9y); 2(n-4)x + (9-n)y$

13. (i) $a = 5, b = -2, c = 3$ **(ii)** 6,078 **14. (i)** $\dfrac{1 - x^n}{1 - x}$

16. (ii) $\frac{9}{16}$ **17. (ii)** $a^n r^{\frac{n}{2}}(n-1)$ **18. (i)** $u_n = \dfrac{1}{2(n+2)} - \dfrac{1}{2(n+4)}$ **(ii)** $\frac{7}{24}$

19. (i) $(n+1)2^{n-1}$ **(ii)** $n2^n$ **(iii)** 10,240 **20. (i) (a)** $2n - 1$ **(b)** $(2n-1)^2$ or $4n^2 - 4n + 1$

(iii) 969 **21. (i)** $\frac{n}{2}(n+1); 2,600$ **(ii)** $\frac{1}{\sqrt{2}}$ **22. (ii)** $2^{21} - 22$ **(iii)** 7

23. $\cos x, -\sin x, -\cos x, \sin x; \frac{1}{2}$ **24. (i)** 2^{r-1} **(ii)** 2^{r-1} **(iii)** $2^r - 1$

25. $\frac{1}{3}; \frac{3}{2}; n = 6$ **27.** $\frac{5}{2}$ or 2.5 **29. (i)** 1, 4, -1, 2, 1

30. $S_{25} = \dfrac{(1+x)^{25} - 1}{x}$; coefficient of $x^2 = \dbinom{25}{3}; p = 25, q = 3$ **31.** $p = 4, q = \frac{1}{2}$

32. $\frac{50}{81}(10^n - 1) - \frac{5}{9}n$

1. $x^2 + y^2 + 6x - 14y - 231 = 0$ **2. (i)** (3, 2) **(ii)** $x^2 + y^2 - 6x - 4y - 27 = 0$

3. $x^2 + y^2 - 8x + 6y + 23 = 0$ **4.** $\frac{7}{9}$ **5.** $4x + 3y - 45 = 0$

6. Centre = (−5, 0); radius = $2\sqrt{2}$ **7.** $p(-2, 0), q(8, 0)$ **8.** $x^2 + y^2 - 8x + 4y + 11 = 0$

9. $4x^2 + 4y^2 - 40x + 24y + 133 = 0$ **10.** $4\sqrt{5}$ **11.** $p(3, 0); k = 9$ **12.** $k = -2$ or $k = 4$

13. $\sqrt{21}$ **14. (ii)** no **15.** $k = 12$ **16.** $x^2 + y^2 = 4$ **17.** 3 **18.** $k = \pm 3$ **19.** $k = 12$

1. (ii) $3x + 4y = 0$ **(iii)** (8, −6), (−8, 6) **2. (ii)** $x^2 + y^2 + 2x + 6y - 40 = 0$

3. (i) $p(-13, 4), q(11, 12)$ **(ii)** yes **4.** $\sqrt{5}$ **5.** (2, −1) **6.** $x^2 + y^2 - 6x - 4y + 9 = 0; x = 1, x = 5$

7. $c = -2$ or $c = -12$ **8.** $k = \frac{2}{11}$ or $k = 2$ **9. (i)** $(5k, -3)$ **(ii)** 2 **(iii)** $d = -53$

10. $k = 3; x^2 + y^2 - 6x + 12y + 20 = 0$ **11.** $x^2 + y^2 - 4x - 10y + 4 = 0$ **12.** $x^2 + y^2 + 4x - 6y - 12 = 0$

13. $4\sqrt{5}$ **14.** $x + y - 1 = 0; x - y + 3 = 0$ **16. (i)** (2, 3), 5 **(ii)** $3x + 4y - 43 = 0$

(iii) $x^2 + y^2 - 16x - 22y + 160 = 0$ **17.** $x^2 + y^2 - 5x = 0; x^2 + y^2 - 11x + 8y + 40 = 0; 3x - 4y - 45 = 0$

19. $(4, 4)$ **20. (i)** $(3, -2), 5$ **(ii)** 36 **21.** $x = 0$

22. (i) $(3, -2), 2\sqrt{5}$ **(ii)** $x^2 + y^2 + 10x - 4y + 9 = 0$; $x^2 + y^2 + 10x - 4y - 151 = 0$

23. (i) $x^2 + y^2 - 26x - 6y + 97 = 0$ **(ii)** $12x + 5y - 54 = 0$ **24. (ii)** $x^2 + y^2 - 4x - 2y - 59 = 0$

25. $x^2 + y^2 + 10x - 6y - 30 = 0$; $x^2 + y^2 + 10x - 6y + 30 = 0$ **26.** $k < 10$

27. (i) $(1, 2)$; 5 **(ii)** $2x - y + 5 = 0$ **(iii)** $4\sqrt{5}$ **28.** $x^2 + y^2 - 6x + 10y + 30 = 0$; $(3, -5), 2$

29. $x^2 + y^2 + 2x - 4y - 20 = 0$; $(-1, 2), 5$ **30.** $x^2 + y^2 + 4x + 10y + 4 = 0$

31. $x^2 + y^2 + 6x - 4y - 3 = 0$ **32.** $x^2 + y^2 - 4x - 14y + 28 = 0$ **33.** $k = -25$ or $k = 48$

Exercise 3R.C ▼

2. $4\sqrt{2}$ **3.** $x^2 + y^2 - 2ax + 6ay - 6a^2 = 0$ **4.** $k = 15$ or $k = -35$ **5.** 7

6. (i) $g = -\frac{9}{2}, f = -\frac{5}{2}, c = 24$ **(ii)** $(6, 2)$ **7.** $x^2 + y^2 - 8x - 10y + 16 = 0$

8. (i) 6 **(ii)** $d = -29$ or $d = 1$ **9. (ii)** $x^2 + y^2 - 7x - 5y + 6 = 0$ **11. (ii)** $x - 2y - 5 = 0$, $x + 2y - 5 = 0$

12. $3x - y - 2 = 0$, $3x - y - 12 = 0$ **13.** $x + y - 6 = 0$, $7x - y - 50 = 0$

14. (i) 5 **(ii)** $L: y = 0$, $M: 4x + 3y + 16 = 0$ **15.** $L: 2x - y - 6 = 0$, $M: 2x - 11y - 26 = 0$

16. (i) $L: x - 3y + 9 = 0$, $M: 3x - y - 5 = 0$ **(ii)** $(-6, 1), (0, 3); (2, 1), (0, 5)$

17. (i) $p(3, 2), q(-5, -2)$; $r_1 = 1, r_2 = 3$ **18.** $(\frac{12}{5}, \frac{9}{5})$ **19. (i) (a)** $c = 0$ **(b)** $g^2 = c$ **(c)** $f^2 = c$

   (ii) $x^2 + y^2 - 6x - 8y + 9 = 0$ **(iii)** $x^2 + y^2 - 2x - 6y + 9 = 0$; $x^2 + y^2 - 10x + 2y + 1 = 0$

20. (i) $(4, -2)$; $5\sqrt{5}$ **(ii)** $x^2 + y^2 - 24x - 8y + 35 = 0$; $x^2 + y^2 + 8x + 16y - 45 = 0$

21. (i) $(1, -2)$ **(ii)** $x^2 + y^2 + 8y - 9 = 0$; $x^2 + y^2 - 4x - 21 = 0$

22. $x^2 + y^2 - 2x + 2y - 18 = 0$; $x^2 + y^2 + 10x - 10y + 30 = 0$

23. $x^2 + y^2 + 2x - 8y + 4 = 0$; $x^2 + y^2 - 6x + 4y = 0$

24. $x^2 + y^2 - 2x - 24 = 0$; $x^2 + y^2 - 4x - 14y + 28 = 0$

25. $x^2 + y^2 - 4x - 10y + 19 = 0$; $x^2 + y^2 + 4x - 2y - 5 = 0$ **26.** $x^2 + y^2 - 3y = 0$

27. $x^2 + y^2 - 6x - 6y + 9 = 0$; $x^2 + y^2 - 30x - 30y + 225 = 0$

Exercise 4R.A ▼

1. $\sqrt{8}$ or $2\sqrt{2}$ **2. (i)** $\vec{a} + \vec{c}$ **(ii)** $\frac{1}{2}\vec{a} + \vec{c}$ **3.** $\vec{i} + 4\vec{j}$ **4.** $0\vec{i} + 8\vec{j}$

5. $13\vec{i} - 3\vec{j}$ **6.** $k = 5, t = -2; 9$ **7.** $2\vec{i} - 8\vec{j}$ **9.** $k = -\frac{1}{2}$ or $k = 2$

10. $k = -14$ **11. (i)** ± 15 **(ii)** ± 5 **12.** $k = 2$ or $k = -4$ **13.** $m = 3, n = -4$

14. $t = 3$ **15. (i)** $\frac{2}{3}\vec{a}$ **(ii)** $\frac{2}{5}\vec{a} - \frac{2}{5}\vec{b}$ **(iii)** $\frac{2}{5}\vec{a} + \frac{3}{5}\vec{b}$

16. $\vec{p} = 7\vec{i} + 6\vec{j},\ \vec{q} = 6\vec{i} + 8\vec{j};\ h = -2,\ k = 3$ **17.** $-\frac{20}{29}\vec{i} + \frac{21}{29}\vec{j}$

18. $-\frac{4}{5}\vec{i} + \frac{3}{5}\vec{j}$ or $\frac{4}{5}\vec{i} - \frac{3}{5}\vec{j}$ **19.** 12   **20.** $k = -2$ or $k = 4$

Exercise 4R.B ▼

1. (i) $-2\vec{i} + 5\vec{j}$ **(ii)** $a = 2;\ \vec{p} = 0\vec{i} + 7\vec{j};\ \sqrt{8}$ or $2\sqrt{2}$

2. (i) (a) $-\vec{i} - 3\vec{j}$ **(b)** $-4\vec{i} - 2\vec{j}$ **(iii)** $\frac{\pi}{4}$ or 45°   **3.** $\frac{\pi}{2}$ or 90°

5. (i) $k = -3$ **(ii)** $11\vec{i} + 3\vec{j}$ **(iii)** 72°   **6. (i)** $\vec{q} = -5\vec{i} - \vec{j};\ \vec{r} = -4\vec{i} - 6\vec{j}$ **(ii)** $\frac{\pi}{4}$ or 45°

7. (i) $\vec{m} = 7\vec{i} - \vec{j};\ \vec{n} = 4\vec{i} + 3\vec{j}$ **(ii)** $\frac{\pi}{4}$ or 45°   **8.** $k = -4$ or $k = 1$

9. (i) $k = -6$ **(ii)** $t = -1$ or $t = 9$ **10.** $k = 3$

11. (i) $\vec{r} = \frac{1}{3}\vec{p} + \frac{2}{3}\vec{q}$ **(ii)** $\vec{r} = 3\vec{i} + \vec{j}$ **12. (i)** $\vec{r} = 9\vec{i} + 9\vec{j}$ **(ii)** $\vec{s} = 7\vec{i} - 3\vec{j}$ **(iii)** $x = 1$ or $x = 13$

13. $(1 - t)\vec{a} + t\vec{b}$ **14. (i)** $\vec{p} = 4\vec{i} - 5\vec{j}$ **(ii)** $10\vec{i} - 13\vec{j}$ **15. (i)** $\frac{1}{2}\vec{a} + \frac{1}{2}\vec{b}$ **(ii)** $\frac{1}{3}\vec{x} + \frac{1}{3}\vec{y} + \frac{1}{3}\vec{z}$

17. (i) $2:3$ **(ii)** $\vec{p} = \frac{1}{4}\vec{a} + \frac{3}{4}\vec{b};\ \vec{r} = \frac{1}{10}\vec{a} + \frac{3}{10}\vec{b}$ **18. (i)** true   **(ii)** true

19. (i) true **(ii)** false **(iii)** true **(iv)** false   **20.** $k = 6$ **21.** $\vec{b} = -7\vec{i} + 6\vec{j}$ or $\vec{b} = 9\vec{i} + 2\vec{j}$

22. $\lambda = -\frac{3}{4}$ **23.** $\vec{q} = 2\vec{i} - \frac{3}{2}\vec{j}$ or $\vec{q} = -2\vec{i} + \frac{3}{2}\vec{j}$

Exercise 4R.C ▼

1. (i) $-3\vec{i} - 4\vec{j};\ 7\vec{i} + \vec{j};\ -4\vec{i} + 3\vec{j}$ **(iii)** $\frac{\pi}{4}$ or 45°

2. (i) $6\vec{i} + 2\vec{j},\ 2\vec{i} - 4\vec{j}$ **(ii)** $2\sqrt{10},\ 2\sqrt{5}$ **(iv)** $\frac{5}{17}$

3. (i) $\vec{p} = \vec{i} - 3\vec{j},\ \vec{q} = 4\vec{i} - 2\vec{j}$ **(ii)** $2\vec{i} - \vec{j}$ **(iii)** $-\frac{7}{4}$

4. $\frac{19}{5}$ **5.** $\vec{b} = \vec{i} + 3\vec{j},\ \vec{c} = 3\vec{i} - \vec{j}$ **6. (i)** 5; 13   **(ii)** $\vec{r} = -\frac{7}{9}\vec{i} + \frac{56}{9}\vec{j}$ **(iii)** $k = 65$

7. (i) $\vec{a}$ **(ii) (a)** $\vec{a} + \vec{c}$ **(b)** $\frac{3}{4}\vec{a} + \frac{3}{4}\vec{c}$ **(c)** $-\frac{1}{4}\vec{a} + \frac{3}{4}\vec{c}$ **(iii)** $h = \frac{4}{3},\ k = \frac{2}{3}$ **(iv)** $1:2$

8. (i) (a) $\vec{r} - \vec{p}$ **(b)** $\frac{1}{5}\vec{p} - \frac{1}{5}\vec{r}$ **(c)** $\frac{1}{5}\vec{p} + \frac{4}{5}\vec{r}$ **(ii) (a)** $(h - 1)\vec{p} + \vec{r}$ **(b)** $\frac{5}{4}$

9. (i) $\frac{3}{4}\vec{a} + \frac{1}{4}\vec{b}$ **(ii)** $\frac{2}{3}\vec{a} - \vec{b}$ **(iii)** $m = \frac{8}{11},\ n = \frac{9}{11}$

10. (i) (a) $\vec{p} - \vec{r}$ **(b)** $\frac{1}{4}\vec{r} - \frac{1}{4}\vec{p}$ **(c)** $\frac{3}{4}\vec{p} + \frac{1}{4}\vec{r}$ **(ii)** $(\frac{3}{4}h - 2)\vec{p} + \frac{1}{4}hr;\ 2:3$

11. (i) $(\frac{1}{2} + h)\vec{m} - \frac{1}{2}\vec{n}$ **(ii)** $\frac{1}{2}km - \frac{3}{10}kn;\ h = \frac{1}{3},\ k = \frac{5}{3}$

12. (i) $\vec{p} = \frac{3}{4}\vec{b} + \frac{1}{4}\vec{a},\ \vec{q} = \frac{1}{2}\vec{b}$ **(ii)** $x = \frac{4}{7},\ y = \frac{6}{7}$ **13. (i)** $3x - 5y + 12$

14. $\vec{r} = \dfrac{n}{m+n}\vec{p} + \dfrac{m}{m+n}\vec{q}$ **16. (i)** $\vec{a} = 4\vec{i} + 2\vec{j}$ **(ii)** $\vec{b} = 4\vec{i} + 4\vec{j}$

18. (ii) (a) 169   **(b)** 121   **(c)** 13   **(d)** 11   **19. (i)** 13   **(ii)** 9

24. $(3 - 2t)\vec{i} + (3 + 2t)\vec{j}$

Exercise 5R.A ▼

1. 340 each; B **2.** 8   **3.** 4   **5. (i)** $\bar{x} = 13$ **(ii)** $\sigma = 8.54$ **6.** $2p + k$ **7.** $\dfrac{9q - 4p}{5}$

8. (i) 3,125   **(ii)** 72   **(iii)** 1,250   **(iv)** 24   **9.** 72; 24   **10. (i)** 10,000   **(ii)** 9,000

11. (i) 360   **(ii)** 24   **12. (i)** 5,040   **(ii)** 720   **(iii)** 4,320   **13.** 48   **14. (i)** 120   **(ii)** 60   **15.** 39

16. (i) 35   **(ii)** 20   **17. (i)** 20   **(ii)** 6   **18. (i)** 45   **(ii)** 120   **(iii)** 210   **(iv)** 28   **(v)** 182

19. 35; 13   **20.** 252; 196   **21.** 65   **22. (i)** 35   **(ii)** 70   **(iii)** 120   **23. (i)** $\frac{5}{36}$ **(ii)** $\frac{21}{36}$

24. (i) $\frac{3}{5}$ **(ii)** $\frac{7}{20}$ **(iii)** $\frac{11}{20}$ **(iv)** $\frac{2}{3}$ **(v)** $\frac{7}{8}$ **25.** 5   **26.** $\frac{88}{16,575}$ **27. (i)** $\frac{1}{18}$ **(ii)** $\frac{1}{6}$

28. $\frac{7}{15}$ **29. (i)** $\frac{9}{64}$ **(ii)** $\frac{17}{32}$ **30.** $\frac{1}{3}$ **31.** $\frac{18}{125}$

Exercise 5R.B ▼

1. (i) 105.72   **(ii)** 0.54   **2.** $x = 8, y = 24$ **3.** $a - b = 4;\ 3a - 5b = 4;\ a = 8, b = 4$

4. (i) 720   **(ii)** 48   **(iii)** 240   **(iv)** 480   **(v)** 144   **5.** 80   **6. (i)** 648   **(ii)** 200   **(iii)** 602

7. (i) 30   **(ii)** 18   **(iii)** 8   **(iv)** $\frac{5}{9}$ **8.** 1,316   **9.** 462   **(i)** 21   **(ii)** 210   **(iii)** 91   **(iv)** 441

10. (i) 715   **(ii)** 315   **(iii)** 470   **11.** 110   **12. (i)** $\frac{1}{12}$ **(ii)** $\frac{5}{12}$ **(iii)** $\frac{7}{12}$

13. (i) $\frac{1}{6}$ **(ii)** $\frac{19}{36}$ **(iii)** $\frac{5}{18}$ **14. (i)** $\frac{1}{5}$ **(ii)** $\frac{1}{10}$ **(iii)** $\frac{3}{10}$

15. (i) $\frac{25}{144}$ **(ii)** $\frac{25}{72}$ **(iii)** $\frac{5}{48}$ **(iv)** $\frac{5}{18}$ **16. (i)** $\frac{16}{81}$ **(ii)** $\frac{1}{6}$ **17. (i)** $\frac{11}{57}$ **(ii)** $\frac{46}{57}$

18. (i) $\frac{4}{9}$ **(ii)** $\frac{5}{9}$ **(iii)** $\frac{4}{9}$ **19. (i)** $\frac{27}{55}$ **(ii)** $\frac{3}{13}$ **(iii)** $\frac{10}{13}$

20. (i) $\frac{1}{22,100}$ **(ii)** $\frac{1}{5,525}$ **(iii)** $\frac{13}{68}$ **(iv)** $\frac{4}{17}$ **21. (i)** $\frac{1}{7}$ **(ii)** $\frac{1}{49}$

22. (i) (a) $\frac{2}{5}$ **(b)** $\frac{7}{10}$ **(ii) (a)** $\frac{7}{10}$ **(b)** $\frac{1}{4}$ **(iii)** $\frac{44}{125}$ **23. (i)** $\frac{1}{13}$ **(ii)** $\frac{36}{65}$ **(iii)** $\frac{16}{65}$

24. $\frac{3}{5}$ **25.** $4(\frac{1}{2})^n - 2(5)^n$ **26. (i)** $3(3)^n - 5$ **27.** $2(\frac{29}{4})^n - 2(-1)^n$

28. (i) $\frac{2}{3}(\frac{1}{2})^n - \frac{3}{5}(\frac{1}{6})^n$ **(ii)** $\frac{29}{360}$ **29.** $\sqrt{7}(1 + \sqrt{7})^n - \sqrt{7}(1 - \sqrt{7})^n$

30. $2(2 + \sqrt{3})^n + 2(2 - \sqrt{3})^n$ **31.** $\sqrt{3}(4 + \sqrt{5})^n - \sqrt{3}(4 - \sqrt{5})^n$ **32.** $\dfrac{1}{\sqrt{6}}(1 + 3\sqrt{6})^n - \dfrac{1}{\sqrt{6}}(1 - 3\sqrt{6})^n$

33. 11; $4(\frac{1}{2})^n - 2(5)^n$ **34.** $h = -8, k = 15;\ p = 11, q = -2$

35. (i) −2   **(ii)** $5(1 + \sqrt{3})^n - 5(1 - \sqrt{3})^n$ **36.** $p = 5, q = 6$ **39. (i)** $x = 3$ **(ii)** $\sigma = \sqrt{\dfrac{12}{13}}$

40. $k = 9$ **41.** $\bar{x} = 3;\ x = 8$

1. 200   **2. (i)** $\frac{11}{25}$ **(ii)** $\frac{1}{23}$ **3. (i)** $\frac{16}{81}$ **(ii)** $\frac{1}{6}$ **4. (i)** 2,112 **(ii)** 90 **(iii)** $\frac{7}{370}$

5. (i) $\frac{3}{10}$ **(ii)** $\frac{1}{12}$ **(iii)** $\frac{11}{12}$ **(iv)** $\frac{1}{8}$ **6. (i)** $\frac{27}{55}$ **(ii)** $\frac{3}{13}$ **(iii)** $\frac{10}{13}$

7. (i) $\frac{2}{27}$ **(ii)** $\frac{4}{135}$ **(iii)** $\frac{4}{675}$ **8.** $\frac{7}{100}$ **9. (i)** 24 **(ii)** $\frac{2}{5}$ **(iii)** $\frac{68}{375}$

10. $\dfrac{m}{m+n} = \dfrac{3}{7}$; $m = 15$, $n = 20$ **11. (i)** $\frac{216}{343}$ **(ii)** $\frac{8}{343}$ **(iii)** $\frac{1}{49}$ **(iv)** $\frac{30}{49}$ **(v)** $\frac{19}{49}$

12. (i) $\frac{11}{46}$ **(ii)** $\frac{216}{343}$ **13. (i)** $\frac{5}{6}$ **(ii)** $\frac{5}{108}$ **14.** $\frac{5}{6}$

15. (i) $\dfrac{x(x-1)}{(x+6)(x+5)}$ **(ii)** 14 **(iii)** $\frac{15}{91}$ **16.** 4   **17. (i)** $\frac{5}{16}$ **(ii)** $\frac{13}{16}$

18. (i) $k+2$ **(ii)** $k=5$ **19. (i)** $k+3$ **(ii)** $k=5$ or $k=7$ **20. (i)** $b = 17 - a$ **(ii)** $a = 7, b = 10$

21. (i) $y = 17 - x$ **(ii)** $\sqrt{\dfrac{2x^2 - 34x + 194}{5}}$; $x = y = \frac{17}{2}$ **22. (i)** $\sqrt{\dfrac{(a-\bar{x})^2 - (b-\bar{x})^2}{2}}$ **(ii)** $\dfrac{a-b}{2}$

23. (i) $\bar{x} = \dfrac{a+b+c}{3}$ **24. (i)** $\bar{x} = \dfrac{p+q+r}{3}$ **(iii)** $r = 7$ **25.** $\sigma = 1$

26. (i) $b = \frac{4}{3}a$ **(ii)** $\sigma = \dfrac{\sqrt{74}a}{10}$ **(iii)** $-5 < a < 5$ **30. (i)** $1 - 3k$ **(ii)** 0.3

31. $\frac{4}{5}$ **32.** $\frac{1}{2}$ **33. (i)** $\frac{23}{45}$ **(ii)** $\frac{6}{625}$ **34. (i)** $\frac{31}{70}$ **(ii)** $\frac{901}{1680}$ **35. (i)** $\frac{5}{144}$ **(ii)** $\frac{7}{12}$

36. (i) $\frac{1}{10}$ **(ii)** $\frac{2}{5}$; $\frac{1}{10}$ **37. (i)** $\frac{1}{21}$ **(ii)** $\frac{1}{3}$

38. (i) $u_{n+2} = u_{n+1} + u_n$ **(ii)** $u_n = \frac{1}{\sqrt{5}}\left(\frac{1}{2} + \frac{\sqrt{5}}{2}\right)^n - \frac{1}{\sqrt{5}}\left(\frac{1}{2} - \frac{\sqrt{5}}{2}\right)^n$

39. $u_{n+2} = \dfrac{u_{n+1} + u_n}{2}$; A **40. (i)** $2\left(\frac{1}{2}\right)^n + 3\left(\frac{1}{3}\right)^n$ **(ii)** $4\left[1 - \left(\frac{1}{2}\right)^{n+1}\right] + \frac{9}{2}\left[1 - \left(\frac{1}{3}\right)^{n+1}\right]$ **(iii)** $\frac{17}{2}$

43. $\frac{1}{3}\sqrt{2x^2 - 2x + 2}$

2. $xe^x - e^x + c$ **3.** $1 + x + \dfrac{x^2}{2!} + \dfrac{x^3}{3!} + \dfrac{x^4}{4!}$; 2.7083   **4.** $\frac{1}{2}x^2 \ln x - \frac{1}{4}x^2 + c$

6. $x \sin x + \cos x + c$ **8.** $\frac{1}{2}xe^{2x} - \frac{1}{4}e^{2x} + c$ **10.** $-xe^{-x} - e^{-x} + c$

11. $-\frac{1}{5}xe^{-5x} - \frac{1}{25}e^{-5x} + c$ **12.** $\frac{1}{4}$ **14. (i)** $-3 < x < 3$ **(ii)** $x < -3$ or $x > 3$;

for $x = \pm 3$ the Ratio Test fails.   **15.** 180   **16.** 32

17. (i) $\dfrac{18 - 3y}{2}$ **(ii)** $36y - 6y^2$ **(iii)** $x = \frac{9}{2}, y = 3$ **19.** $\dfrac{(-1)^n n!}{x^{n+1}}$ **21.** $a = -1, e^{-x}$

2. (ii) $100x - \frac{4}{3}x^3$ **(iii)** $x = 5$, $V = 333\frac{1}{3}$ cm^3 **3. (i)** $x - \frac{x^3}{3!} + \frac{x^5}{5!} - \frac{x^7}{7!}$; **(ii)** $\frac{(-1)^{n-1}x^{2n-1}}{(2n-1)!}$

4. $\frac{1}{2}(e^\pi + 1)$ **5.** 5 cm; 2250 cm^3 **6. (i)** $1 + x + \frac{x^2}{2!} + \frac{x^3}{3!}$

(ii) (a) $1 - x + \frac{x^2}{2!} - \frac{x^3}{3!}$ **(b)** $1 + 2x + 2x^2 + \frac{4}{3}x^3$ **(c)** $1 - 2x + 2x^2 - \frac{4}{3}x^3$

(d) $1 + 4x + 6x^2 + \frac{16}{3}x^3$ **(iii) (a)** $\frac{x^2}{2!} + \frac{x^3}{3!} + \frac{x^4}{4!}$ **(b)** $2x + \frac{2}{3!}x^3 + \frac{2}{5!}x^5$

(c) $x + \frac{4}{3!}x^3 + \frac{16}{5!}x^5$ **(iv)** 2   **7.** $\frac{\pi^2}{4} - 2$ or $\frac{\pi^2 - 8}{4}$

8. $\frac{2000\sqrt{3}\pi}{27}$ cm^3 **9. (i)** $1 - \frac{x^2}{2!} + \frac{x^4}{4!} - \frac{x^6}{6!}$ **(ii) (a)** $1 - 2x^2 + \frac{2}{3}x^4 - \frac{4}{45}x^6$

(b) $9x - 18x^3 + 6x^5 - \frac{4}{5}x^7$ **(iii)** $\frac{(-1)^n x^{2n}}{(2n)!}$

10. (i) $\theta = \frac{8 - 2r}{r}$ **(iii)** 4 m^2 **11.** 6 cm by 2 cm by 3 cm

12. (i) $A = 2\pi r^2 + \frac{1024\pi}{r}$ **(ii)** $r = 8$ cm, $h = 8$ cm   **13.** 50 cm^2

14. (i) $\frac{1}{2}e^{-x}(\sin x - \cos x) + c$ **(ii)** $\frac{1}{2}$ **15. (i)** $\frac{1}{5}e^{2x}(2\cos x + \sin x) + c$ **(ii)** $n = 5$

16. (i) $x - \frac{x^2}{2} + \frac{x^3}{3} - \frac{x^4}{4}$ **(ii)** $-3x - \frac{9}{2}x^2 - 9x^3 - \frac{81}{4}x^4$ **(iii)** $-2x - 5x^2 - \frac{26}{3}x^3$

---

1. $-\frac{11}{2} < x < -\frac{1}{2}$ **2.** $2(3 - e)$ **3. (i)** $\frac{1}{5}$ **(ii)** $x - \frac{x^2}{2} + \frac{x^3}{3} - \frac{x^4}{4} + \frac{x^5}{5}$

(iii) $-x - \frac{x^2}{2} - \frac{x^3}{3} - \frac{x^4}{4} - \frac{x^5}{5}$; $2x + \frac{2}{3}x^3 + \frac{2}{5}x^5$; 0.41

4. (i) $h = \frac{V}{\pi r^2}$ **(iii)** $1 : 2$ **5. (i)** $a\left(\frac{\pi}{2}, 0\right)$ **(ii)** $\frac{\pi}{4}$

6. (i) $1 + 2x + 3x^2 + 4x^3$ **(ii)** nx^{n-1} **(iii)** $-1 < x < 1$ **7.** 15 cm

8. (i) $\frac{100 - 2r}{r}$ **(iii)** 25 cm   **(iv)** 2   **(v)** 625 cm^2 **9. (i) (a)** $1 + \frac{x}{2} - \frac{x^2}{8} + \frac{x^3}{16}$;

(b) $-1 < x < 1$ **(ii)** $1 - x - \frac{x^2}{2} - \frac{x^3}{2}$; 0.98995   **(iii)** 3.2

10. (i) $\bar{C} = \frac{1}{4}q + 3 + \frac{400}{q}$ **(ii)** 40   **11.** 54 square units

12. (i) $1 + x + \dfrac{x^2}{2!} + \dfrac{x^3}{3!}$ **(ii)** $1 - 2x + 2x^2 - \frac{4}{3}x^3$ **(iii)** $a = 2,\ b = -3,\ c = 10$

13. 65   **14. (i)** $\frac{1}{2} - \frac{1}{24} + \frac{1}{160} - \frac{1}{896}$ **(ii)** $4[\frac{1}{2} - \frac{1}{24} + \frac{1}{160} - \frac{1}{896} + \frac{1}{3} - \frac{1}{81} + \frac{1}{1215} - \frac{1}{15,309}]$; 3.1409

15. (i) $r = \dfrac{1,600\pi}{x}$ **(iii)** 160π m   **16. (i)** $\frac{1}{2}(8 - x)(x - 2)^2$ **(ii)** $x = 6$ **(iii)** 16 square units

17. (i) (a) $1 + x + \dfrac{x^2}{2!}$ **(b)** $x - \dfrac{x^3}{3!} + \dfrac{x^5}{5!}$ **(c)** $-x - \dfrac{x^2}{2} - \dfrac{x^3}{3}$

  (ii) $a = 1,\ b = -\frac{1}{6}$ **(iii)** $x + x^2 + \dfrac{x^3}{3}$; $\dfrac{11}{12}$ **18. (i)** $\frac{1}{4}e^{2x}(2x - 1) + c$ **(ii)** $A_1 = \dfrac{2 - e}{4e}$; $A_2 = \dfrac{1}{4}$

19. (i) $mx - y + (m + 2) = 0$ **(ii)** $p\left(\dfrac{-m - 2}{m}, 0\right)$, $q(0,\ m + 2)$ **(iv)** 4

20. $5 \times 10 = 50$ square units   **21. (i)** $\sqrt{x^2 + \dfrac{81}{x^2}}$ **(ii)** $x = 3$ **(iii)** $3\sqrt{2}$

22. $1,\ m,\ m(m - 1),\ m(m - 1)(m - 2)$; $1 + mx + \dfrac{m(m - 1)}{2!}x^2 + \dfrac{m(m - 1)(m - 2)}{3!}x^3$;

  $u_{r+1} = \binom{m}{r}x^r$ or $u_{r+1} = \dfrac{m(m - 1)(m - 2)\ldots(m - r + 1)}{r!}x^r$; convergent for $-1 < x < 1$

23. (i) $h = \frac{4}{3}R$ **(ii)** $288\pi\,\text{cm}^3$ **24. (i)** $h = \dfrac{45 - 3r^2}{2r}$ **(ii)** $r = h = 3$ m

25. (i) $y = \pm\sqrt{r^2 - x^2}$ **26.** $r = \sqrt{\frac{2}{3}a}$; $H = \frac{4}{\sqrt{3}}a$ **27.** 6 m

28. (i) $\dfrac{x}{5}$ km; $\dfrac{x}{10}$ km   **(ii)** $\sqrt{\left(\dfrac{x}{5}\right)^2 + \left(4 - \dfrac{x}{10}\right)^2}$ **(iii)** 8 minutes

30. (i) (a) $\pi r^2 h + \frac{2}{3}\pi r^3$ **(b)** $2\pi rh + 3\pi r^2$ **(iii)** $1 : 1$

31. $h = \dfrac{44 - 11r}{4}$; $\dfrac{704}{27}\,\pi\,\text{cm}^3$